An Introduction
to Probability Theory
and Its Applications

An Introduction
to Probability Theory
and Its Applications

WILLIAM FELLER

Eugene Higgins Professor of Mathematics
Princeton University

VOLUME I

THIRD EDITION

John Wiley & Sons, Inc.
New York · London · Sydney

To

O. E. Neugebauer:

o et praesidium et dulce decus meum

Preface to the Third Edition

WHEN THIS BOOK WAS FIRST CONCEIVED (MORE THAN 25 YEARS AGO) few mathematicians outside the Soviet Union recognized probability as a legitimate branch of mathematics. Applications were limited in scope, and the treatment of individual problems often led to incredible complications. Under these circumstances the book could not be written for an existing audience, or to satisfy conscious needs. The hope was rather to attract attention to little-known aspects of probability, to forge links between various parts, to develop unified methods, and to point to potential applications. Because of a growing interest in probability, the book found unexpectedly many users outside mathematical disciplines. Its widespread use was understandable as long as its point of view was new and its material was not otherwise available. But the popularity seems to persist even now, when the contents of most chapters are available in specialized works streamlined for particular needs. For this reason the character of the book remains unchanged in the new edition. I hope that it will continue to serve a variety of needs and, in particular, that it will continue to find readers who read it merely for enjoyment and enlightenment.

Throughout the years I was the grateful recipient of many communications from users, and these led to various improvements. Many sections were rewritten to facilitate study. Reading is also improved by a better typeface and the superior editing job by Mrs. H. McDougal: although a professional editor she has preserved a feeling for the requirements of readers and reason.

The greatest change is in chapter III. This chapter was introduced only in the second edition, which was in fact motivated principally by the unexpected discovery that its enticing material could be treated by elementary methods. But this treatment still depended on combinatorial artifices which have now been replaced by simpler and more natural probabilistic arguments. In essence this chapter is new.

Most conspicuous among other additions are the new sections on branching processes, on Markov chains, and on the De Moivre-Laplace theorem. Chapter XIII has been rearranged, and throughout the book there appear minor changes as well as new examples and problems.

I regret the misleading nature of the author index, but I felt obliged to state explicitly whenever an idea or example could be traced to a particular source. Unfortunately this means that quotations usually refer to an incidental remark, and are rarely indicative of the nature of the paper quoted. Furthermore, many examples and problems were inspired by reading non-mathematical papers in which related situations are dealt with by different methods. (That newer texts now quote these non-mathematical papers as containing my examples shows how fast probability has developed, but also indicates the limited usefulness of quotations.) Lack of space as well as of competence precluded more adequate historical indications of how probability has changed from the semi-mysterious discussions of the 'twenties to its present flourishing state.

For a number of years I have been privileged to work with students and younger colleagues to whose help and inspiration I owe much. Much credit for this is due to the support by the U.S. Army Research Office for work in probability at Princeton University. My particular thanks are due to Jay Goldman for a thoughtful memorandum about his teaching experiences, and to Loren Pitt for devoted help with the proofs.

WILLIAM FELLER

July, 1967

Preface to the First Edition

IT WAS THE AUTHOR'S ORIGINAL INTENTION TO WRITE A BOOK ON analytical methods in probability theory in which the latter was to be treated as a topic in pure mathematics. Such a treatment would have been more uniform and hence more satisfactory from an aesthetic point of view; it would also have been more appealing to pure mathematicians. However, the generous support by the Office of Naval Research of work in probability theory at Cornell University led the author to a more ambitious and less thankful undertaking of satisfying heterogeneous needs.

It is the purpose of this book to treat probability theory as a self-contained mathematical subject rigorously, avoiding non-mathematical concepts. At the same time, the book tries to describe the empirical background and to develop a feeling for the great variety of practical applications. This purpose is served by many special problems, numerical estimates, and examples which interrupt the main flow of the text. They are clearly set apart in print and are treated in a more picturesque language and with less formality. A number of special topics have been included in order to exhibit the power of general methods and to increase the usefulness of the book to specialists in various fields. To facilitate reading, detours from the main path are indicated by stars. The knowledge of starred sections is not assumed in the remainder.

A serious attempt has been made to unify methods. The specialist will find many simplifications of existing proofs and also new results. In particular, the theory of recurrent events has been developed for the purpose of this book. It leads to a new treatment of Markov chains which permits simplification even in the finite case.

The examples are accompanied by about 340 problems mostly with complete solutions. Some of them are simple exercises, but most of them serve as additional illustrative material to the text or contain various complements. One purpose of the examples and problems is to develop the reader's intuition and art of probabilistic formulation. Several previously treated examples show that apparently difficult problems may become almost trite once they are formulated in a natural way and put into the proper context.

There is a tendency in teaching to reduce probability problems to pure analysis as soon as possible and to forget the specific characteristics of probability theory itself. Such treatments are based on a poorly defined notion of random variables usually introduced at the outset. This book goes to the other extreme and dwells on the notion of sample space, without which random variables remain an artifice.

In order to present the true background unhampered by measurability questions and other purely analytic difficulties this volume is restricted to *discrete sample spaces*. This restriction is severe, but should be welcome to non-mathematical users. It permits the inclusion of special topics which are not easily accessible in the literature. At the same time, this arrangement makes it possible to begin in an elementary way and yet to include a fairly exhaustive treatment of such advanced topics as random walks and Markov chains. The general theory of random variables and their distributions, limit theorems, diffusion theory, etc., is deferred to a succeeding volume.

This book would not have been written without the support of the Office of Naval Research. One consequence of this support was a fairly regular personal contact with J. L. Doob, whose constant criticism and encouragement were invaluable. To him go my foremost thanks. The next thanks for help are due to John Riordan, who followed the manuscript through two versions. Numerous corrections and improvements were suggested by my wife who read both the manuscript and proof.

The author is also indebted to K. L. Chung, M. Donsker, and S. Goldberg, who read the manuscript and corrected various mistakes; the solutions to the majority of the problems were prepared by S. Goldberg. Finally, thanks are due to Kathryn Hollenbach for patient and expert typing help; to E. Elyash, W. Hoffman, and J. R. Kinney for help in proofreading.

WILLIAM FELLER

Cornell University
January 1950

Note on the Use of the Book

THE EXPOSITION CONTAINS MANY SIDE EXCURSIONS AND DOES NOT ALWAYS progress from the easy to the difficult; comparatively technical sections appear at the beginning and easy sections in chapters XV and XVII. Inexperienced readers should not attempt to follow many side lines, lest they lose sight of the forest for too many trees. Introductory remarks to the chapters and stars at the beginnings of sections should facilitate orientation and the choice of omissions. The unstarred sections form a self-contained whole in which the starred sections are not used.

A first introduction to the basic notions of probability is contained in chapters I, V, VI, IX; beginners should cover these with as few digressions as possible. Chapter II is designed to develop the student's technique and probabilistic intuition; some experience in its contents is desirable, but it is not necessary to cover the chapter systematically: it may prove more profitable to return to the elementary illustrations as occasion arises at later stages. For the purposes of a first introduction, the elementary theory of continuous distributions requires little supplementary explanation. (The elementary chapters of volume 2 now provide a suitable text.)

From chapter IX an introductory course may proceed directly to chapter XI, considering generating functions as an example of more general transforms. Chapter XI should be followed by some applications in chapters XIII (recurrent events) or XII (chain reactions, infinitely divisible distributions). Without generating functions it is possible to turn in one of the following directions: limit theorems and fluctuation theory (chapters VIII, X, III); stochastic processes (chapter XVII); random walks (chapter III and the main part of XIV). These chapters are almost independent of each other. The Markov chains of chapter XV depend conceptually on recurrent events, but they may be studied independently if the reader is willing to accept without proof the basic ergodic theorem.

Chapter III stands by itself. Its contents are appealing in their own right, but the chapter is also highly illustrative for new insights and new methods in probability theory. The results concerning fluctuations in coin tossing show that widely held beliefs about the law of large numbers are fallacious. They are so amazing and so at variance with common intuition that even sophisticated colleagues doubted that coins actually misbehave as theory predicts. The record of a simulated experiment is therefore included in section 6. The chapter treats only the simple coin-tossing game, but the results are representative of a fairly general situation.

The sign ▶ is used to indicate the end of a proof or of a collection of examples.

It is hoped that the extensive index will facilitate coordination between the several parts.

Contents

---

* Starred sections are not required for the understanding of the sequel and should be omitted at first reading.

The Nature
of Probability Theory

1. THE BACKGROUND

Probability is a mathematical discipline with aims akin to those, for example, of geometry or analytical mechanics. In each field we must carefully distinguish three aspects of the theory: (*a*) the formal logical content, (*b*) the intuitive background, (*c*) the applications. The character, and the charm, of the whole structure cannot be appreciated without considering all three aspects in their proper relation.

(a) Formal Logical Content

Axiomatically, mathematics is concerned solely with relations among undefined things. This aspect is well illustrated by the game of chess. It is impossible to "define" chess otherwise than by stating a set of rules. The conventional shape of the pieces may be described to some extent, but it will not always be obvious which piece is intended for "king." The chessboard and the pieces are helpful, but they can be dispensed with. The essential thing is to know how the pieces move and act. It is meaningless to talk about the "definition" or the "true nature" of a pawn or a king. Similarly, geometry does not care what a point and a straight line "really are." They remain undefined notions, and the axioms of geometry specify the relations among them: two points determine a line, etc. These are the rules, and there is nothing sacred about them. Different forms of geometry are based on different sets of axioms, and the logical structure of non-Euclidean geometries is independent of their relation to reality. Physicists have studied the motion of bodies under laws of attraction different from Newton's, and such studies are meaningful even if Newton's law of attraction is accepted as true in nature.

(b) Intuitive Background

In contrast to chess, the axioms of geometry and of mechanics have an intuitive background. In fact, geometrical intuition is so strong that it is prone to run ahead of logical reasoning. The extent to which logic, intuition, and physical experience are interdependent is a problem into which we need not enter. It is certain that intuition can be trained and developed. The bewildered novice in chess moves cautiously, recalling individual rules, whereas the experienced player absorbs a complicated situation at a glance and is unable to account rationally for his intuition. In like manner mathematical intuition grows with experience, and it is possible to develop a natural feeling for concepts such as four-dimensional space.

Even the collective intuition of mankind appears to progress. Newton's notions of a field of force and of action at a distance and Maxwell's concept of electromagnetic waves were at first decried as "unthinkable" and "contrary to intuition." Modern technology and radio in the homes have popularized these notions to such an extent that they form part of the ordinary vocabulary. Similarly, the modern student has no appreciation of the modes of thinking, the prejudices, and other difficulties against which the theory of probability had to struggle when it was new. Nowadays newspapers report on samples of public opinion, and the magic of statistics embraces all phases of life to the extent that young girls watch the statistics of their chances to get married. Thus everyone has acquired a feeling for the meaning of statements such as "the chances are three in five." Vague as it is, this intuition serves as background and guide for the first step. It will be developed as the theory progresses and acquaintance is made with more sophisticated applications.

(c) Applications

The concepts of geometry and mechanics are in practice identified with certain physical objects, but the process is so flexible and variable that no general rules can be given. The notion of a rigid body is fundamental and useful, even though no physical object is rigid. Whether a given body can be treated as if it were rigid depends on the circumstances and the desired degree of approximation. Rubber is certainly not rigid, but in discussing the motion of automobiles on ice textbooks usually treat the rubber tires as rigid bodies. Depending on the purpose of the theory, we disregard the atomic structure of matter and treat the sun now as a ball of continuous matter, now as a single mass point.

In applications, the abstract mathematical models serve as tools, and different models can describe the same empirical situation. *The manner in which mathematical theories are applied does not depend on preconceived ideas; it is a purposeful technique depending on, and changing with, experi-ence.* A philosophical analysis of such techniques is a legitimate study, but is is not within the realm of mathematics, physics, or statistics. The philosophy of the foundations of probability must be divorced from mathematics and statistics, exactly as the discussion of our intuitive space concept is now divorced from geometry.

2. PROCEDURE

The history of probability (and of mathematics in general) shows a stimulating interplay of theory and applications; theoretical progress opens new fields of applications, and in turn applications lead to new problems and fruitful research. The theory of probability is now applied in many diverse fields, and the flexibility of a general theory is required to provide appropriate tools for so great a variety of needs. We must therefore withstand the temptation (and the pressure) to build the theory, its terminology, and its arsenal too close to one particular sphere of interest. We wish instead to develop a mathematical theory in the way which has proved so successful in geometry and mechanics.

We shall start from the simplest experiences, such as tossing a coin or throwing dice, where all statements have an obvious intuitive meaning. This intuition will be translated into an abstract model to be generalized gradually and by degrees. Illustrative examples will be provided to explain the empirical background of the several models and to develop the reader's intuition, but the theory itself will be of a mathematical character. We shall no more attempt to explain the "true meaning" of probability than the modern physicist dwells on the "real meaning" of mass and energy or the geometer discusses the nature of a point. Instead, we shall prove theorems and show how they are applied.

Historically, the original purpose of the theory of probability was to describe the exceedingly narrow domain of experience connected with games of chance, and the main effort was directed to the calculation of certain probabilities. In the opening chapters we too shall calculate a few typical probabilities, but it should be borne in mind that numerical probabilities are not the principal object of the theory. Its aim is to discover general laws and to construct satisfactory theoretical models. Probabilities play for us the same role as masses in mechanics. The motion of the planetary system can be discussed without knowledge of the individual masses and without contemplating methods for their actual measurements. Even models for non-existent planetary systems may be the object of a profitable and illuminating study. Similarly, practical and *useful probability models may refer to non-observable worlds.* For example, billions of dollars have been invested in automatic telephone exchanges. These are based on simple probability models in which various possible systems are compared. The theoretically best system is built and the others will never exist. In insurance, probability theory is used to calculate the probability of ruin; that is, the theory is used to avoid certain undesirable situations, and consequently it applies to situations that are not actually observed. Probability theory would be effective and useful even if not a single numerical value were accessible.

3. "STATISTICAL" PROBABILITY

The success of the modern mathematical theory of probability is bought at a price: the theory is limited to one particular aspect of "chance." The intuitive notion of probability is connected with inductive reasoning and with judgments such as "Paul is probably a happy man," "Probably this book will be a failure," "Fermat's conjecture is probably false." Judgments of this sort are of interest to the philosopher and the logician, and they are a legitimate object of a mathematical theory.[1] It must be understood, however, that we are concerned not with modes of inductive reasoning but with something that might be called physical or *statistical probability*. In a rough way we may characterize this concept by saying that our probabilities do not refer to judgments but to possible outcomes of a *conceptual experiment*. Before we speak of probabilities, we must agree on an idealized model of a particular conceptual experiment such as tossing a coin, sampling kangaroos on the moon, observing a particle under diffusion, counting the number of telephone calls. At the outset we must agree on the possible outcomes of this experiment (our *sample space*) and the probabilities associated with them. This is analogous to the procedure in mechanics where fictitious models involving two, three, or seventeen mass points are introduced, these points being devoid of individual properties. Similarly, in analyzing the coin tossing game we are not concerned with the accidental circumstances of an actual experiment: the object of our theory is sequences (or arrangements) of symbols such as "head, head, tail, head, ..." There is no place in our system for speculations concerning the probability that the sun will rise tomorrow. Before speaking of it we should have to agree on an (idealized) model which would presumably run along the lines "out of infinitely many worlds

---

[1] B. O. Koopman, *The axioms and algebra of intuitive probability*, Ann. of Math. (2), vol. 41 (1940), pp. 269–292, and *The bases of probability*, Bull. Amer. Math. Soc., vol. 46 (1940), pp. 763–774.

For a modern text based on subjective probabilities see L. J. Savage, *The foundations of statistics*, New York (John Wiley) 1954.

one is selected at random. . . ." Little imagination is required to construct such a model, but it appears both uninteresting and meaningless.

The astronomer speaks of measuring the temperature at the center of the sun or of travel to Sirius. These operations seem impossible, and yet it is not senseless to contemplate them. By the same token, we shall not worry whether or not our conceptual experiments can be performed; we shall analyze abstract models. In the back of our minds we keep an intuitive interpretation of probability which gains operational meaning in certain applications. We *imagine* the experiment performed a great many times. An event with probability 0.6 should be expected, in the long run, to occur sixty times out of a hundred. This description is deliberately vague but supplies a picturesque intuitive background sufficient for the more elementary applications. As the theory proceeds and grows more elaborate, the operational meaning and the intuitive picture will become more concrete.

4. SUMMARY

We shall be concerned with theoretical models in which probabilities enter as free parameters in much the same way as masses in mechanics. They are applied in many and variable ways. The technique of applications and the intuition develop with the theory.

This is the standard procedure accepted and fruitful in other mathematical disciplines. No alternative has been devised which could conceivably fill the manifold needs and requirements of *all* branches of the growing entity called probability theory and its applications.

We may fairly lament that intuitive probability is insufficient for scientific purposes, but it is a historical fact. In example I, (6.*b*), we shall discuss random distributions of particles in compartments. The appropriate, or "natural," probability distribution seemed perfectly clear to everyone and has been accepted without hesitation by physicists. It turned out, however, that physical particles are not trained in human common sense, and the "natural" (or Boltzmann) distribution has to be given up for the Einstein-Bose distribution in some cases, for the Fermi-Dirac distribution in others. No intuitive argument has been offered why photons should behave differently from protons and why they do not obey the "a priori" laws. *If* a justification could now be found, it would only show that intuition develops with theory. At any rate, even for applications freedom and flexibility are essential, and it would be pernicious to fetter the theory to fixed poles.

It has also been claimed that the modern theory of probability is too abstract and too general to be useful. This is the battle cry once raised by practical-minded people against Maxwell's field theory. The argument could be countered by pointing to the unexpected new applications opened by the abstract theory of stochastic processes, or to the new insights offered by the modern fluctuation theory which once more belies intuition and is leading to a revision of practical attitudes. However, the discussion is useless; it is too easy to condemn. Only yesterday the practical things of today were decried as impractical, and the theories which will be practical tomorrow will always be branded as valueless games by the practical men of today.

5. HISTORICAL NOTE

The statistical, or empirical, attitude toward probability has been developed mainly by R. A. Fisher and R. von Mises. The notion of sample space[2] comes from von Mises. This notion made it possible to build up a strictly mathematical theory of probability based on measure theory. Such an approach emerged gradually in the 'twenties under the influence of many authors. An axiomatic treatment representing the modern development was given by A. Kolmogorov.[3] We shall follow this line, but the term axiom appears too solemn inasmuch as the present volume deals only with the simple case of discrete probabilities.

---

[2] The German word is *Merkmalraum* (label space). von Mises' basic treatise *Wahrscheinlichkeitsrechnung* appeared in 1931. A modernized version (edited and complemented by Hilda Geiringer) appeared in 1964 under the title *Mathematical theory of probability and statistics*, New York (Academic Press). von Mises' philosophical ideas are best known from his earlier booklet of 1928, revised by H. Geiringer: *Probability, statistics and truth*, London (Macmillan), 1957.

[3] A. Kolmogoroff, *Grundbegriffe der Wahrscheinlichkeitsrechnung*, Berlin (Springer) 1933. An English translation (by N. Morrison) appeared in 1956: *Foundations of the theory of probability*, New York (Chelsea).

CHAPTER I

The Sample Space

1. THE EMPIRICAL BACKGROUND

The mathematical theory of probability gains practical value and an intuitive meaning in connection with real or conceptual experiments such as tossing a coin once, tossing a coin 100 times, throwing three dice, arranging a deck of cards, matching two decks of cards, playing roulette, observing the life span of a radioactive atom or a person, selecting a random sample of people and observing the number of left-handers in it, crossing two species of plants and observing the phenotypes of the offspring; or with phenomena such as the sex of a newborn baby, the number of busy trunklines in a telephone exchange, the number of calls on a telephone, random noise in an electrical communication system, routine quality control of a production process, frequency of accidents, the number of double stars in a region of the skies, the position of a particle under diffusion. All these descriptions are rather vague, and, in order to render the theory meaningful, we have to agree on what we mean by *possible results of the experiment or observation in question.*

When a coin is tossed, it does not necessarily fall heads or tails; it can roll away or stand on its edge. Nevertheless, we shall agree to regard "head" and "tail" as the only possible outcomes of the experiment. This convention simplifies the theory without affecting its applicability. Idealizations of this type are standard practice. It is impossible to measure the life span of an atom or a person without some error, but for theoretical purposes it is expedient to imagine that these quantities are exact numbers. The question then arises as to which numbers can actually represent the life span of a person. Is there a maximal age beyond which life is impossible, or is any age conceivable? We hesitate to admit that man can grow 1000 years old, and yet current actuarial practice admits no bounds to the possible duration of life. According to formulas on which modern mortality tables are based, the proportion of men surviving 1000 years is of the

7

order of magnitude of one in $10^{10^{36}}$—a number with 10^{27} billions of zeros. This statement does not make sense from a biological or sociological point of view, but considered exclusively from a statistical standpoint it certainly does not contradict any experience. There are fewer than 10^{10} people born in a century. To test the contention statistically, more than $10^{10^{35}}$ centuries would be required, which is considerably more than $10^{10^{34}}$ lifetimes of the earth. Obviously, such extremely small probabilities are compatible with our notion of impossibility. Their use may appear utterly absurd, but it does no harm and is convenient in simplifying many formulas. Moreover, if we were seriously to discard the possibility of living 1000 years, we should have to accept the existence of maximum age, and the assumption that it should be possible to live x years and impossible to live x years and two seconds is as unappealing as the idea of unlimited life.

Any theory necessarily involves idealization, and our first idealization concerns the possible outcomes of an "experiment" or "observation." If we want to construct an abstract model, we must at the outset reach a decision about what consitutes a possible outcome of the (idealized) experiment.

For uniform terminology, the results of experiments or observations will be called *events*. Thus we shall speak of the event that of five coins tossed more than three fell heads. Similarly, the "experiment" of distributing the cards in bridge[1] may result in the "event" that North has two aces. The composition of a sample ("two left-handers in a sample of 85") and the result of a measurement ("temperature 120°," "seven trunklines busy") will each be called an event.

We shall distinguish between *compound* (or decomposable) and *simple* (or indecomposable) *events*. For example, saying that a throw with two dice resulted in "sum six" amounts to saying that it resulted in "(1, 5) or (2, 4) or (3, 3) or (4, 2) or (5, 1)," and this enumeration decomposes the event "sum six" into five simple events. Similarly, the event "two odd faces" admits of the decomposition "(1, 1) or (1, 3) or . . . or (5, 5)" into nine simple events. Note that if a throw results in (3, 3), then *the same throw* results also in the events "sum six" and "two odd faces"; these events are not mutually exclusive and hence may occur simultaneously.

---

[1] *Definition of bridge and poker.* A deck of bridge cards consists of 52 cards arranged in four suits of thirteen each. There are thirteen face values (2, 3, . . . , 10, jack, queen, king, ace) in each suit. The four suits are called spades, clubs, hearts, diamonds. The last two are red, the first two black. Cards of the same face value are called of the same kind. For our purposes, playing bridge means distributing the cards to four players, to be called North, South, East, and West (or N, S, E, W, for short) so that each receives thirteen cards. Playing poker, by definition, means selecting five cards out of the pack.

As a second example consider the age of a person. Every particular value x represents a *simple* event, whereas the statement that a person is in his fifties describes the compound event that x lies between 50 and 60. In this way every compound event can be decomposed into simple events, that is to say, a compound event is an *aggregate of certain simple events*.

If we want to speak about "experiments" or "observations" in a theoretical way and without ambiguity, we must first agree on the simple events representing the thinkable outcomes; *they define the idealized experiment*. In other words: The term simple (or indecomposable) event remains undefined in the same way as the terms point and line remain undefined in geometry. Following a general usage in mathematics *the simple events will be called sample points*, or *points* for short. By definition, *every indecomposable result of the* (*idealized*) *experiment is represented by one, and only one, sample point*. The aggregate of all sample points will be called the *sample space*. All events connected with a given (idealized) experiment can be described as aggregates of sample points.

Before formalizing these basic conventions, we proceed to discuss a few typical examples which will play a role further on.

2. EXAMPLES

(*a*) *Distribution of the three balls in three cells.* Table 1 describes all possible outcomes of the "experiment" of placing three balls into three cells.

Each of these arrangements represents a simple event, that is, a sample point. The event A "one cell is multiply occupied" is realized in the arrangements numbered 1–21, and we express this by saying that the event A is the aggregate of the sample points 1–21. Similarly, the event B "first cell is not empty" is the aggregate of the sample points 1, 4–15, 22–27.

TABLE 1

1. $\{abc \mid - \mid - \}$	10. $\{a \quad \mid bc \mid - \}$	19. $\{ - \mid a \quad \mid bc\}$
2. $\{ - \mid abc \mid - \}$	11. $\{ b \mid a\ c \mid - \}$	20. $\{ - \mid b \mid a\ c\}$
3. $\{ - \mid - \mid abc\}$	12. $\{ c \mid ab \mid - \}$	21. $\{ - \mid c \mid ab \}$
4. $\{ab \mid c \mid - \}$	13. $\{a \quad \mid - \mid bc\}$	22. $\{a \mid b \mid c\}$
5. $\{a\ c \mid b \mid - \}$	14. $\{ b \mid - \mid a\ c\}$	23. $\{a \mid c \mid b \}$
6. $\{ bc \mid a \mid - \}$	15. $\{ c \mid - \mid ab \}$	24. $\{ b \mid a \mid c\}$
7. $\{ab \mid - \mid c\}$	16. $\{ - \mid ab \mid c\}$	25. $\{ b \mid c \mid a \}$
8. $\{a\ c \mid - \mid b \}$	17. $\{ - \mid a\ c \mid b \}$	26. $\{ c \mid a \mid b \}$
9. $\{ bc \mid - \mid a \}$	18. $\{ - \mid bc \mid a \}$	27. $\{ c \mid b \mid a \}$.

The event C defined by "both A and B occur" is the aggregate of the thirteen sample points 1, 4–15. In this particular example it so happens that each of the 27 points belongs to either A or B (or to both); therefore the event "either A or B or both occur" is the entire sample space and occurs with absolute certainty. The event D defined by "A does not occur" consists of the points 22–27 and can be described by the condition that no cell remains empty. The event "first cell empty and no cell multiply occupied" is impossible (does not occur) since no sample point satisfies these specifications.

(b) *Random placement of r balls in n cells.* The more general case of r balls in n cells can be studied in the same manner, except that the number of possible arrangements increases rapidly with r and n. For $r = 3$ balls in $n = 4$ cells, the sample space contains already 81 points, and for $r = n = 10$ there are 10^{10} sample points; a complete tabulation would require some hundred thousand big volumes.

We use this example to illustrate the important fact that the nature of the sample points is irrelevant for our theory. To us the sample space (together with the probability distribution defined in it) *defines* the idealized experiment. We use the picturesque language of balls and cells, but the same sample space admits of a great variety of different practical interpretations. To clarify this point, and also for further reference, *we list here a number of situations in which the intuitive background varies; all are, however, abstractly equivalent to the scheme of placing r balls into n cells, in the sense that the outcomes differ only in their verbal description.* The appropriate assignment of probabilities is not the same in all cases and will be discussed later on.

(b,1). *Birthdays.* The possible configurations of the birthdays of r people correspond to the different arrangements of r balls in $n = 365$ cells (assuming the year to have 365 days).

(b,2). *Accidents.* Classifying r accidents according to the weekdays when they occurred is equivalent to placing r balls into $n = 7$ cells.

(b,3). *In firing* at n targets, the hits correspond to balls, the targets to cells.

(b,4). *Sampling.* Let a group of r people be classified according to, say, age or profession. The classes play the role of our cells, the people that of balls.

(b,5). *Irradiation in biology.* When the cells in the retina of the eye are exposed to light, the light particles play the role of balls, and the actual cells are the "cells" of our model. Similarly, in the study of the genetic effect of irradiation, the chromosomes correspond to the cells of our model and α-particles to the balls.

(b,6). In *cosmic ray experiments* the particles reaching Geiger counters represent balls, and the counters function as cells.

(b,7). An *elevator* starts with r passengers and stops at n floors. The different arrangements of discharging the passengers are replicas of the different distributions of r balls in n cells.

(b,8). *Dice.* The possible outcomes of a throw with r dice correspond to placing r balls into $n = 6$ cells. When *tossing a coin* we are in effect dealing with only $n = 2$ cells.

(b,9). *Random digits.* The possible orderings of a sequence of r digits correspond to the distribution of r balls (= places) into ten cells called $0, 1, \ldots, 9$.

(b,10). The *sex distribution* of r persons. Here we have $n = 2$ cells and r balls.

(b,11). *Coupon collecting.* The different kinds of coupons represent the cells; the coupons collected represent the balls.

(b,12). *Aces in bridge.* The four players represent four cells, and we have $r = 4$ balls.

(b,13). *Gene distributions.* Each descendant of an individual (person, plant, or animal) inherits from the progenitor certain genes. If a particular gene can appear in n forms $A_1, \ldots, A_n$, then the descendants may be classified according to the type of the gene. The descendants correspond to the balls, the genotypes $A_1, \ldots, A_n$ to the cells.

(b,14). *Chemistry.* Suppose that a long-chain polymer reacts with oxygen. An individual chain may react with $0, 1, 2, \ldots$ oxygen molecules. Here the reacting oxygen molecules play the role of balls and the polymer chains the role of cells into which the balls are put.

(b,15). *Theory of photographic emulsions.* A photographic plate is covered with grains sensitive to light quanta: a grain reacts if it is hit by a certain number, r, of quanta. For the theory of black-white contrast we must know how many cells are likely to be hit by the r quanta. We have here an occupancy problem where the grains correspond to cells, and the light quanta to balls. (Actually the situation is more complicated since a plate usually contains grains of different sensitivity.)

(b,16). *Misprints.* The possible distributions of r misprints in the n pages of a book correspond to all the different distributions of r balls in n cells, provided r is smaller than the number of letters per page.

(c) *The case of indistinguishable balls.* Let us return to example (a) and suppose that the three balls are not distinguishable. This means that we no longer distinguish between three arrangements such as 4, 5, 6, and thus table 1 reduces to Table 2. The latter *defines* the sample space of the ideal experiment which we call *"placing three indistinguishable balls into three cells,"* and a similar procedure applies to the case of r balls in n cells.

TABLE 2

1. $\{*** \mid - \mid - \}$	6. $\{ * \mid ** \mid - \}$
2. $\{ - \mid *** \mid - \}$	7. $\{ * \mid - \mid ** \}$
3. $\{ - \mid - \mid ***\}$	8. $\{ - \mid ** \mid * \}$
4. $\{** \mid * \mid - \}$	9. $\{ - \mid * \mid ** \}$
5. $\{** \mid - \mid * \}$	10. $\{ * \mid * \mid * \}$.

Whether or not actual balls are in practice distinguishable is irrelevant for our theory. Even if they are, we may decide to treat them as indistinguishable. The aces in bridge [example $(b,12)$] or the people in an elevator [example $(b,7)$] certainly are distinguishable, and yet it is often preferable to treat them as indistinguishable. The dice of example $(b,8)$ may be colored to make them distinguishable, but whether in discussing a particular problem we use the model of distinguishable or indistinguishable balls is purely a matter of purpose and convenience. The nature of a concrete problem may dictate the choice, but under any circumstances our theory begins only after the appropriate model has been chosen, that is, after the sample space has been defined.

In the scheme above we have considered indistinguishable balls, but table 2 still refers to a first, second, third cell, and their order is essential. We can go a step further and assume that even the cells are indistinguishable (for example, the cell may be chosen at random without regard to its contents). With both balls and cells indistinguishable, only three different arrangements are possible, namely $\{*** \mid - \mid - \}$, $\{** \mid * \mid - \}$, $\{ * \mid * \mid * \}$.

(*d*) *Sampling.* Suppose that a sample of 100 people is taken in order to estimate how many people smoke. The only property of the sample of interest in this connection is the number x of smokers; this may be an integer between 0 and 100. In this case we may agree that our sample space consists of the 101 "points" $0, 1, \ldots, 100$. Every particular sample or observation is completely described by stating the corresponding point x. An example of a compound event is the result that "the majority of the people sampled are smokers." This means that the experiment resulted in one of the fifty simple events $51, 52, \ldots, 100$, but it is not stated in which. Similarly, every property of the sample can be described in enumerating the corresponding cases or sample points. For uniform terminology we speak of events rather than properties of the sample. Mathematically, an event is simply the aggregate of the corresponding sample points.

(e) *Sampling (continued).* Suppose now that the 100 people in our sample are classified not only as smokers or non-smokers but also as males or females. The sample may now be characterized by a quadruple (M_s, F_s, M_n, F_n) of integers giving in order the number of male and female smokers, male and female non-smokers. For sample points we take the quadruples of integers lying between 0 and 100 and adding to 100. There are 176,851 such quadruples, and they constitute the sample space (cf. II, 5). The event "relatively more males than females smoke" means that in our sample the ratio M_s/M_n is greater than F_s/F_n. The point (73, 2, 8, 17) has this property, but (0, 1, 50, 49) has not. Our event can be described in principle by enumerating all quadruples with the desired property.

(f) *Coin tossing.* For the experiment of tossing a coin three times, the sample space consists of eight points which may conveniently be represented by *HHH, HHT, HTH, THH, HTT, THT, TTH, TTT.* The event *A,* "two or more heads," is the aggregate of the first four points. The event *B,* "just one tail," means either *HHT,* or *HTH,* or *THH*; we say that *B* contains these three points.

(g) *Ages of a couple.* An insurance company is interested in the age distribution of couples. Let *x* stand for the age of the husband, *y* for the age of the wife. Each observation results in a number-pair (x, y). For the sample space we take the first quadrant of the *x,y*-plane so that each point $x > 0$, $y > 0$ is a sample point. The event *A,* "husband is older than 40," is represented by all points to the right of the line $x = 40$; the event *B,* "husband is older than wife," is represented by the angular region between the *x*-axis and the bisector $y = x$, that is to say, by the aggregate of points with $x > y$; the event *C,* "wife is older than 40," is represented by the points above the line $y = 40$. A geometric representation of the joint age distributions of two couples requires a four-dimensional space.

(h) *Phase space.* In statistical mechanics, each possible "state" of a system is called a "point in phase space." This is only a difference in terminology. The phase space is simply our sample space; its points are our sample points.

3. THE SAMPLE SPACE. EVENTS

It should be clear from the preceding that we shall never speak of probabilities except in relation to a given sample space (or, physically, in relation to a certain conceptual experiment). *We start with the notion of a sample space and its points; from now on they will be considered given. They are the primitive and undefined notions of the theory* precisely as the notions of "points" and "straight line" remain undefined in an axiomatic treatment of Euclidean geometry. The nature of the sample points does not enter our theory. The sample space provides a model of an ideal experiment in the sense that, by definition, *every thinkable outcome of the experiment is completely described by one, and only one, sample point.* It is meaningful to talk about an event *A* only when it is clear for *every* outcome of the experiment whether the event *A* has or has not occurred. The collection of all those sample points representing outcomes where *A* has occurred completely describes the event. Conversely, any given aggregate *A* containing one or more sample points can be called an event; this event does, or does not, occur according as the outcome of the experiment is, or is not, represented by a point of the aggregate *A*. We therefore define the word *event to mean the same as an aggregate of sample points.* We shall say that an *event A consists of* (*or contains*) *certain points,* namely those representing outcomes of the ideal experiment in which *A* occurs.

Example. In the sample space of example (2.*a*) consider the event *U* consisting of the points number 1, 7, 13. This is a formal and straightforward definition, but *U* can be described in many equivalent ways. For example, *U* may be defined as the event that the following three conditions are satisfied: (1) the second cell is empty, (2) the ball *a* is in the first cell, (3) the ball *b* does not appear after *c*. Each of these conditions itself describes an event. The event U_1 defined by the condition (1) alone consists of points 1, 3, 7–9, 13–15. The event U_2 defined by (2) consists of points 1, 4, 5, 7, 8, 10, 13, 22, 23; and the event U_3 defined by (3) contains the points 1–4, 6, 7, 9–11, 13, 14, 16, 18–20, 22, 24, 25. The event *U* can also be described as the *simultaneous realization* of all three events U_1, U_2, U_3.   ▶

The terms "sample point" and "event" have an intuitive appeal, but they refer to the notions of point and point set common to all parts of mathematics.

We have seen in the preceding example and in (2.*a*) that new events can be defined in terms of two or more given events. With these examples in mind we now proceed to introduce the notation of the formal *algebra of events* (that is, algebra of point sets).

4. RELATIONS AMONG EVENTS

We shall now suppose that an arbitrary, but fixed, sample space $\mathfrak{S}$ is given. We use capitals to denote *events,* that is, sets of sample points. The fact that a point *x* is contained in the event *A* is denoted by $x \in A$.

Thus $x \in \mathfrak{S}$ for every point x. We write $A = B$ only if the two events consist of exactly the same points.

In general, events will be defined by certain conditions on their points, and it is convenient to have a symbol to express the fact that no point satisfies a specified set of conditions. The next definition serves this purpose.

Definition 1. *We shall use the notation* $A = 0$ *to express that the event* A *contains no sample points* (*is impossible*). The zero must be interpreted in a symbolic sense and not as the numeral.

To every event A there corresponds another event defined by the condition "A does not occur." It contains all points not contained in A.

Definition 2. *The event consisting of all points not contained in the event* A *will be called the complementary event* (*or negation*) *of* A *and will be denoted by* A'. *In particular,* $\mathfrak{S}' = 0$.

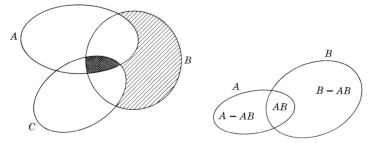

Figures 1 and 2. Illustrating relations among events. In Figure 1 the domain within heavy boundaries is the union $A \cup B \cup C$. The triangular (*heavily shaded*) domain is the intersection ABC. The moon-shaped (*lightly shaded*) domain is the intersection of B with the complement of $A \cup C$.

With any two events A and B we can associate two new events defined by the conditions "*both* A *and* B *occur*" and "*either* A *or* B *or both occur*." These events will be denoted by AB and $A \cup B$, respectively. The event AB contains all sample points which are common to A and B. If A and B exclude each other, then there are no points common to A and B and the event AB is impossible; analytically, this situation is described by the equation

(4.1) $$AB = 0$$

which should be read "A and B are *mutually exclusive*." The event AB' means that both A and B' occur or, in other words, that A but not B occurs. Similarly, $A'B'$ means that neither A nor B occurs. The event $A \cup B$ means that at least one of the events A and B occurs;

it contains all sample points except those that belong neither to A nor to B.

In the theory of probability we can describe the event AB as the simultaneous occurrence of A and B. In standard mathematical terminology AB is called the (logical) intersection of A and B. Similarly, $A \cup B$ is the union of A and B. Our notion carries over to the case of events $A, B, C, D, \ldots$.

Definition 3. *To every collection $A, B, C, \ldots$ of events we define two new events as follows. The aggregate of the sample points which belong to all the given sets will be denoted by $ABC \ldots$ and called the intersection[2] (or simultaneous realization) of $A, B, C, \ldots$. The aggregate of sample points which belong to at least one of the given sets will be denoted by $A \cup B \cup C \ldots$ and called the union (or realization of at least one) of the given events. The events $A, B, C, \ldots$ are mutually exclusive if no two have a point in common, that is, if $AB = 0$, $AC = 0, \ldots$, $BC = 0, \ldots$.*

We still require a symbol to express the statement that A cannot occur without B occurring, that is, that the occurrence of A implies the occurrence of B. This means that every point of A is contained in B. Think of intuitive analogies like the aggregate of all mothers, which forms a part of the aggregate of all women: All mothers are women but not all women are mothers.

Definition 4. *The symbols $A \subset B$ and $B \supset A$ are equivalent and signify that every point of A is contained in B; they are read, respectively, "A implies B" and "B is implied by A". If this is the case, we shall also write $B - A$ instead of BA' to denote the event that B but not A occurs.*

The event $B - A$ contains all those points which are in B but not in A. With this notation we can write $A' = \mathfrak{S} - A$ and $A - A = 0$.

Examples. *(a)* If A and B are mutually exclusive, then the occurrence of A implies the non-occurrence of B and vice versa. Thus $AB = 0$ means the same as $A \subset B'$ and as $B \subset A'$.

(b) The event $A - AB$ means the occurrence of A but not of both A and B. Thus $A - AB = AB'$.

(c) In the example (2.g), the event AB means that the husband is older than 40 *and* older than his wife; AB' means that he is older than

---

[2] The standard mathematical notation for the intersection of two or more sets is $A \cap B$ or $A \cap B \cap C$, etc. This notation is more suitable for certain specific purposes (see IV, 1 of volume 2). At present we use the notation AB, ABC, etc., since it is less clumsy in print.

40 but *not* older than his wife. AB is represented by the infinite trapezoidal region between the x-axis and the lines $x = 40$ and $y = x$, and the event AB' is represented by the angular domain between the lines $x = 40$ and $y = x$, the latter boundary included. The event AC means that both husband and wife are older than 40. The event $A \cup C$ means that at least one of them is older than 40, and $A \cup B$ means that the husband is either older than 40 or, if not that, at least older than his wife (in official language, "husband's age exceeds 40 years or wife's age, whichever is smaller").

(*d*) In example (2.*a*) let E_i be the event that the cell number i is empty (here $i = 1, 2, 3$). Similarly, let S_i, D_i, T_i, respectively, denote the event that the cell number i is occupied simply, doubly, or triply. Then $E_1 E_2 = T_3$, and $S_1 S_2 \subset S_3$, and $D_1 D_2 = 0$. Note also that $T_1 \subset E_2$, etc. The event $D_1 \cup D_2 \cup D_3$ is defined by the condition that there exist at least one doubly occupied cell.

(*e*) *Bridge* (cf. footnote 1). Let A, B, C, D be the events, respectively, that North, South, East, West have at least one ace. It is clear that at least one player has an ace, so that one or more of the four events must occur. Hence $A \cup B \cup C \cup D = \mathfrak{S}$ is the whole sample space. The event $ABCD$ occurs if, and only if, each player has an ace. The event "West has all four aces" means that none of the three events A, B, C has occurred; this is the same as the simultaneous occurrence of A' and B' and C' or the event $A'B'C'$.

(*f*) In the example (2.*g*) we have $BC \subset A$: in words, "if husband is older than wife (B) and wife is older than 40 (C), then husband is older that 40 (A)." How can the event $A - BC$ be described in words? ▶

5. DISCRETE SAMPLE SPACES

The simplest sample spaces are those containing only a finite number, n, of points. If n is fairly small (as in the case of tossing a few coins), it is easy to visualize the space. The space of distributions of cards in bridge is more complicated, but we may imagine each sample point represented on a chip and may then consider the collection of these chips as representing the sample space. An event A (like "North has two aces") is represented by a certain set of chips, the complement A' by the remaining ones. It takes only one step from here to imagine a bowl with infinitely many chips or a sample space with an infinite sequence of points $E_1, E_2, E_3, \ldots$.

Examples. (*a*) Let us toss a coin as often as necessary to turn up one head. The points of the sample space are then $E_1 = H$, $E_2 = TH$, $E_3 = TTH$, $E_4 = TTTH$, etc. We may or may not consider as thinkable the possibility that H never appears. If we do, this possibility should be represented by a point E_0.

(b) Three players a, b, c take turns at a game, such as chess, according to the following rules. At the start a and b play while c is out. The loser is replaced by c and at the second trial the winner plays against c while the loser is out. The game continues in this way until a player wins twice in succession, thus becoming the winner of the game. For simplicity we disregard the possibility of ties at the individual trials. The possible outcomes of our game are then indicated by the following scheme:

(*) $\quad$ *aa, acc, acbb, acbaa, acbacc, acbacbb, acbacbaa, . . .*

$\quad$ *bb, bcc, bcaa, bcabb, bcabcc, bcabcaa, bcabcabb, ...*

In addition, it is thinkable that no player ever wins twice in succession, in which case the play continues indefinitely according to one of the patterns

(**) $\qquad$ *acbacbacbacb . . . , $\qquad$ bcabcabcabca . . . .*

The sample space corresponding to our ideal "experiment" is defined by (*) and (**) and is infinite. It is clear that the sample points can be arranged in a simple sequence by taking first the two points (**) and continuing with the points of (*) in the order *aa, bb, acc, bcc, ...* [See problems 5–6, example V,(2.a), and problem 5 of XV,14.] ▶

Definition. *A sample space is called discrete if it contains only finitely many points or infinitely many points which can be arranged into a simple sequence $E_1, E_2, ...$*

Not every sample space is discrete. It is a known theorem (due to G. Cantor) that the sample space consisting of all positive numbers is not discrete. We are here confronted with a distinction familiar in mechanics. There it is usual first to consider discrete mass points with each individual point carrying a finite mass, and then to pass to the notion of a continuous mass distribution, where each individual point has zero mass. In the first case, the mass of a system is obtained simply by adding the masses of the individual points; in the second case, masses are computed by integration over mass densities. Quite similarly, the probabilities of events in discrete sample spaces are obtained by mere additions, whereas in other spaces integrations are necessary. Except for the technical tools required, there is no essential difference between the two cases. In order to present actual probability considerations unhampered by technical difficulties, we shall take up only discrete sample spaces. It will be seen that even this special case leads to many interesting and important results.

In this volume we shall consider only discrete sample spaces.

6. PROBABILITIES IN DISCRETE SAMPLE SPACES: PREPARATIONS

Probabilities are numbers of the same nature as distances in geometry or masses in mechanics. The theory assumes that they are given but need assume nothing about their actual numerical values or how they are measured in practice. Some of the most important applications are of a qualitative nature and independent of numerical values. In the relatively few instances where numerical values for probabilities are required, the procedures vary as widely as do the methods of determining distances. There is little in common in the practices of the carpenter, the practical surveyor, the pilot, and the astronomer when they measure distances. In our context, we may consider the diffusion constant, which is a notion of the theory of probability. To find its numerical value, physical considerations relating it to other theories are required; a direct measurement is impossible. By contrast, mortality tables are constructed from rather crude observations. In most actual applications the determination of probabilities, or the comparison of theory and observation, requires rather sophisticated statistical methods, which in turn are based on a refined probability theory. In other words, the intuitive meaning of probability is clear, but only as the theory proceeds shall we be able to see how it is applied. All possible "definitions" of probability fall far short of the actual practice.

When tossing a "good" coin we do not hesitate to associate probability $\frac{1}{2}$ with either head or tail. This amounts to saying that when a coin is tossed n times all 2^n possible results have the same probability. From a theoretical standpoint, this is a *convention*. Frequently, it has been contended that this convention is logically unavoidable and the only possible one. Yet there have been philosophers and statisticians defying the convention and starting from contradictory assumptions (uniformity or non-uniformity in nature). It has also been claimed that the probabilities $\frac{1}{2}$ are due to experience. As a matter of fact, whenever refined statistical methods have been used to check on actual coin tossing, the result has been invariably that head and tail are *not* equally likely. And yet we stick to our model of an "ideal" coin, even though no good coins exist. We preserve the model not merely for its logical simplicity, but essentially for its usefulness and applicability. In many applications it is sufficiently accurate to describe reality. More important is the empirical fact that departures from our scheme are always coupled with phenomena such as an eccentric position of the center of gravity. In this way our idealized model can be extremely useful even if it never applies exactly. For example, in modern statistical quality control based on Shewhart's methods, idealized probability models are used to discover "assignable causes" for flagrant departures from these models and thus to remove impending machine troubles and process irregularities at an early stage.

Similar remarks apply to other cases. The number of possible distributions of cards in bridge is almost 10^{30}. Usually we agree to consider them as equally probable. For a check of this convention more than 10^{30} experiments would be required—thousands of billions of years if every living person played one game every second, day and night. However, consequences of the assumption can be verified experimentally, for example, by observing the frequency of multiple aces in the hands at bridge. It turns out that for crude purposes the idealized model describes experience sufficiently well, provided the card shuffling is done better than is usual. It is more important that the idealized scheme, when it does not apply, permits the discovery of "assignable causes" for the discrepancies, for example, the reconstruction of the mode of shuffling. These are examples of limited importance, but they indicate the usefulness of assumed models. More interesting cases will appear only as the theory proceeds.

Examples. (*a*) *Distinguishable balls.* In example (2.*a*) it appears natural to assume that all sample points are *equally probable*, that is, that *each sample point has probability* $\frac{1}{27}$. We can start from this *definition* and investigate its consequences. Whether or not our model will come reasonably close to actual experience will depend on the type of phenomena to which it is applied. In some applications the assumption of equal probabilities is imposed by physical considerations; in others it is introduced to serve as the simplest model for a general orientation, even though it quite obviously represents only a crude first approximation [e.g., consider the examples (2.*b*,1), birthdays; (2.*b*,7), elevator problem; or (2.*b*,11) coupon collecting].

(*b*) *Indistinguishable balls: Bose-Einstein statistics.* We now turn to the example (2.*c*) of three indistinguishable balls in three cells. It is possible to argue that the actual physical experiment is unaffected by our failure to distinguish between the balls; physically there remain 27 different possibilities, even though only ten different forms are disinguishable. This consideration leads us to attribute the following probabilities to the ten points of table 2.

Point number:	1	2	3	4	5	6	7	8	9	10
Probability:	$\frac{1}{27}$	$\frac{1}{27}$	$\frac{1}{27}$	$\frac{1}{9}$	$\frac{1}{9}$	$\frac{1}{9}$	$\frac{1}{9}$	$\frac{1}{9}$	$\frac{1}{9}$	$\frac{2}{9}$.

It must be admitted that for most applications listed in example (2.*b*) this argument appears sound and the assignment of probabilities reasonable. Historically, our argument was accepted for a long time without question and served in statistical mechanics as the basis for the derivation of the *Maxwell-Boltzmann statistics* for the distribution of r balls in n cells. The greater was the surprise when Bose and Einstein showed that certain particles are subject to the *Bose-Einstein* statistics (for details see II,5). In our case with $r = n = 3$, this model attributes *probability* $\frac{1}{10}$ *to each of the ten sample points.*

This example shows that different assignments of probabilities are compatible with the same sample space and illustrates the intricate

TABLE 3

Trials number	Number of heads										Total
0– 1,000	54	46	53	55	46	54	41	48	51	53	501
– 2,000	48	46	40	53	49	49	48	54	53	45	485
– 3,000	43	52	58	51	51	50	52	50	53	49	509
– 4,000	58	60	54	55	50	48	47	57	52	55	536
– 5,000	48	51	51	49	44	52	50	46	53	41	485
– 6,000	49	50	45	52	52	48	47	47	47	51	488
– 7,000	45	47	41	51	49	59	50	55	53	50	500
– 8,000	53	52	46	52	44	51	48	51	46	54	497
– 9,000	45	47	46	52	47	48	59	57	45	48	494
–10,000	47	41	51	48	59	51	52	55	39	41	484

interrelation between theory and experience. In particular, it teaches us not to rely too much on a priori arguments and to be prepared to accept new and unforeseen schemes.

(*c*) *Coin tossing.* A frequency interpretation of the postulate of equal probabilities requires records of actual experiments. Now in reality every coin is biased, and it is possible to devise physical experiments which come much closer to the ideal model of coin tossing than real coins ever do. To give an idea of the fluctuations to be expected, we give the record of such a simulated experiment corresponding to 10,000 trials with a coin.[3] Table 3 contains the number of occurrences of "heads" in a series of 100 experiments each corresponding to a sequence of 100 trials with a coin. The grand total is 4979. Looking at these figures the reader is probably left with a vague feeling of: So what? The truth is that a more advanced

---

[3] The table actually records the frequency of even digits in a section of *A million random digits with 100,000 normal deviates*, by The RAND Corporation, Glencoe, Illinois (The Free Press), 1955.

theory is necessary to judge to what extent such empirical data agree with our abstract model. (Incidentally, we shall return to this material in III,6.) ▶

7. THE BASIC DEFINITIONS AND RULES

Fundamental Convention. *Given a discrete sample space* $\mathfrak{S}$ *with sample points* $E_1, E_2, \ldots$, *we shall assume that with each point* E_j *there is associated a number, called the probability of* E_j *and denoted by* $\mathbf{P}\{E_j\}$. *It is to be non-negative and such that*

(7.1)
$$\mathbf{P}\{E_1\} + \mathbf{P}\{E_2\} + \cdots = 1.$$

Note that we do not exclude the possibility that a point has probability zero. This convention may appear artificial but is necessary to avoid complications. In discrete sample spaces probability zero is in practice interpreted as an impossibility, and any sample point known to have probability zero can, with impunity, be eliminated from the sample space. However, frequently the numerical values of the probabilities are not known in advance, and involved considerations are required to decide whether or not a certain sample point has positive probability.

Definition. *The probability* $\mathbf{P}\{A\}$ *of any event* A *is the sum of the probabilities of all sample points in it.*

By (7.1) the probability of the entire sample space $\mathfrak{S}$ is unity, or $\mathbf{P}\{\mathfrak{S}\} = 1$. It follows that for any event A

(7.2)
$$0 \leq \mathbf{P}\{A\} \leq 1.$$

Consider now two arbitrary events A_1 and A_2. To compute the probability $\mathbf{P}\{A_1 \cup A_2\}$ that either A_1 or A_2 or both occur, we have to add the probabilities of all sample points contained either in A_1 or in A_2, but each point is to be counted only once. We have, therefore,

(7.3)
$$\mathbf{P}\{A_1 \cup A_2\} \leq \mathbf{P}\{A_1\} + \mathbf{P}\{A_2\}.$$

Now, if E is any point contained both in A_1 and in A_2, then $\mathbf{P}\{E\}$ occurs twice in the right-hand member but only once in the left-hand member. Therefore, the right side exceeds the left side by the amount $\mathbf{P}\{A_1 A_2\}$, and we have the simple but important

Theorem. *For any two events* A_1 *and* A_2 *the probability that either* A_1 *or* A_2 *or both occur is given by*

(7.4)
$$\mathbf{P}\{A_1 \cup A_2\} = \mathbf{P}\{A_1\} + \mathbf{P}\{A_2\} - \mathbf{P}\{A_1 A_2\}.$$

If $A_1A_2 = 0$, that is, if A_1 and A_2 are mutually exclusive, then (7.4) reduces to

(7.5) $$\mathbf{P}\{A_1 \cup A_2\} = \mathbf{P}\{A_1\} + \mathbf{P}\{A_2\}.$$

Example. A coin is tossed twice. For sample space we take the four points HH, HT, TH, TT, and associate with each probability $\frac{1}{4}$. Let A_1 and A_2 be, respectively, the events "head at first and second trial." Then A_1 consists of HH and HT, and A_2 of TH and HH. Furthermore $A = A_1 \cup A_2$ contains the three points HH, HT, and TH, whereas A_1A_2 consists of the single point HH. Thus

$$\mathbf{P}\{A_1 \cup A_2\} = \tfrac{1}{2} + \tfrac{1}{2} - \tfrac{1}{4} = \tfrac{3}{4}. \qquad \blacktriangleright$$

The probability $\mathbf{P}\{A_1 \cup A_2 \cup \cdots \cup A_n\}$ of the realization of at least one among n events can be computed by a formula analogous to (7.4), derived in IV,1. Here we note only that the argument leading to (7.3) applies to any number of terms. Thus *for arbitrary events $A_1, A_2, \ldots$ the inequality*

(7.6) $$\mathbf{P}\{A_1 \cup A_2 \cup \cdots\} \le \mathbf{P}\{A_1\} + \mathbf{P}\{A_2\} + \cdots$$

holds. In the special case where the events $A_1, A_2, \ldots$ are mutually exclusive, we have

(7.7) $$\mathbf{P}\{A_1 \cup A_2 \cup \cdots\} = \mathbf{P}\{A_1\} + \mathbf{P}\{A_2\} + \cdots$$

Occasionally (7.6) is referred to as *Boole's inequality*.

We shall first investigate the simple special case where the sample space has a finite number, N, of points each having probability $1/N$. In this case, the probability of any event A equals the number of points in A divided by N. In the older literature, the points of the sample space were called "cases," and the points of A "favorable" cases (favorable for A). *If* all points have the same probability, then the probability of an event A is the ratio of the number of favorable cases to the total number of cases. Unfortunately, this statement has been much abused to provide a "definition" of probability. It is often contended that in *every* finite sample space probabilities of all points are equal. This is not so. For a single throw of an untrue coin, the sample space still contains only the two points, head and tail, but they may have arbitrary probabilities p and q, with $p + q = 1$. A newborn baby is a boy or girl, but in applications we have to admit that the two possibilities are not equally likely. A further counterexample is provided by (6.b). The usefulness of sample spaces in which all sample points have the same probability is restricted almost entirely to the study of games of chance and to combinatorial analysis.

8. PROBLEMS FOR SOLUTION

1. Among the digits 1, 2, 3, 4, 5 first one is chosen, and then a second selection is made among the remaining four digits. Assume that all twenty possible results have the same probability. Find the probability that an odd digit will be selected (a) the first time, (b) the second time, (c) both times.

2. In the sample space of example (2.a) attach equal probabilities to all 27 points. Using the notation of example (4.d), verify formula (7.4) for the two events $A_1 = S_1$ and $A_2 = S_2$. How many points does $S_1 S_2$ contain?

3. Consider the 24 possible arrangements (permutations) of the symbols 1234 and attach to each probability $\frac{1}{24}$. Let A_i be the event that the digit i appears at its natural place (where $i = 1, 2, 3, 4$). Verify formula (7.4).

4. A coin is tossed until for the first time the same result appears twice in succession. To every possible outcome requiring n tosses attribute probability $1/2^{n-1}$. Describe the sample space. Find the probability of the following events: (a) the experiment ends before the sixth toss, (b) an *even* number of tosses is required.

5. In the sample space of example (5.b) let us attribute to each point of (∗) containing exactly k letters probability $1/2^k$. (In other words, aa and bb carry probability $\frac{1}{4}$, acb has probability $\frac{1}{8}$, etc.) (a) Show that the probabilities of the points of (∗) add up to unity, whence the two points (∗∗) receive probability zero. (b) Show that the probability that a wins is $\frac{5}{14}$. The probability of b winning is the same, and c has probability $\frac{2}{7}$ of winning. (c) The probability that no decision is reached at or before the kth turn (game) is $1/2^{k-1}$.

6. Modify example (5.b) to take account of the possibility of ties at the individual games. Describe the appropriate sample space. How would you define probabilities?

7. In problem 3 show that $A_1 A_2 A_3 \subset A_4$ and $A_1 A_2 A_3' \subset A_4'$.

8. Using the notations of example (4.d) show that (a) $S_1 S_2 D_3 = 0$; (b) $S_1 D_2 \subset E_3$; (c) $E_3 - D_2 S_1 \supset S_2 D_1$.

9. Two dice are thrown. Let A be the event that the sum of the faces is odd, B the event of at least one ace. Describe the events AB, $A \cup B$, AB'. Find their probabilities assuming that all 36 sample points have equal probabilities.

10. In example (2.g), discuss the meaning of the following events:
(a) ABC,   (b) $A - AB$,   (c) $AB'C$.

11. In example (2.g), verify that $AC' \subset B$.

12. *Bridge* (cf. footnote 1). For $k = 1, 2, 3, 4$ let N_k be the event that North has at least k aces. Let S_k, E_k, W_k be the analogous events for South, East, West. Discuss the number x of aces in West's possession in the events
(a) W_1',   (b) $N_2 S_2$,   (c) $N_1' S_1' E_1'$,   (d) $W_2 - W_3$,
(e) $N_1 S_1 E_1 W_1$,   (f) $N_3 W_1$,   (g) $(N_2 \cup S_2) E_2$.

13. In the preceding problem verify that
(a) $S_3 \subset S_2$,   (b) $S_3 W_2 = 0$,   (c) $N_2 S_1 E_1 W_1 = 0$,
(d) $N_2 S_2 \subset W_1'$,   (e) $(N_2 \cup S_2) W_3 = 0$,   (f) $W_4 = N_1' S_1' E_1'$.

14. Verify the following relations.[4]

(a) $(A \cup B)' = A'B'.$

(b) $(A \cup B) - B = A - AB = AB'.$

(c) $AA = A \cup A = A.$

(d) $(A - AB) \cup B = A \cup B.$

(e) $(A \cup B) - AB = AB' \cup A'B.$

(f) $A' \cup B' = (AB)'.$

(g) $(A \cup B)C = AC \cup BC.$

15. Find simple expressions for

(a) $(A \cup B)(A \cup B')$, (b) $(A \cup B)(A' \cup B)(A \cup B')$, (c) $(A \cup B)(B \cup C)$.

16. State which of the following relations are correct and which incorrect:

(a) $(A \cup B) - C = A \cup (B - C).$

(b) $ABC = AB(C \cup B).$

(c) $A \cup B \cup C = A \cup (B - AB) \cup (C - AC).$

(d) $A \cup B = (A - AB) \cup B.$

(e) $AB \cup BC \cup CA \supset ABC.$

(f) $(AB \cup BC \cup CA) \subset (A \cup B \cup C).$

(g) $(A \cup B) - A = B.$

(h) $AB'C \subset A \cup B.$

(i) $(A \cup B \cup C)' = A'B'C'.$

(j) $(A \cup B)'C = A'C \cup B'C.$

(k) $(A \cup B)'C = A'B'C.$

(l) $(A \cup B)'C = C - C(A \cup B).$

17. Let A, B, C be three arbitrary events. Find expressions for the events that of A, B, C:

(a) Only A occurs.

(b) Both A and B, but not C, occur.

(c) All three events occur.

(d) At least one occurs.

(e) At least two occur.

(f) One and no more occurs.

(g) Two and no more occur.

(h) None occurs.

(i) Not more than two occur.

18. The union $A \cup B$ of two events can be expressed as the union of two mutually exclusive events, thus: $A \cup B = A \cup (B - AB)$. Express in a similar way the union of three events A, B, C.

19. Using the result of problem 18 prove that

$$\mathbf{P}\{A \cup B \cup C\} =$$

$$= \mathbf{P}\{A\} + \mathbf{P}\{B\} + \mathbf{P}\{C\} - \mathbf{P}\{AB\} - \mathbf{P}\{AC\} - \mathbf{P}\{BC\} + \mathbf{P}\{ABC\}$$

[This is a special case of IV, (1.5).]

---

[4] Notice that $(A \cup B)'$ denotes the complement of $A \cup B$, which is not the same as $A' \cup B'$. Similarly, $(AB)'$ is not the same as $A'B'$.

CHAPTER II

Elements
of Combinatorial Analysis

This chapter explains the basic notions of combinatorial analysis and develops the corresponding probabilistic background; the last part describes some simple analytic techniques. Not much combinatorial analysis is required for the further study of this book, and readers without special interest in it should pass as soon as possible to chapter V, where the main theoretical thread of chapter I is taken up again. It may be best to read the individual sections of the present chapter in conjunction with related topics in later chapters.

In the study of simple games of chance, sampling procedures, occupancy and order problems, etc., we are usually dealing with finite sample spaces in which the same probability is attributed to all points. To compute the probability of an event A we have then to divide the number of sample points in A ("favorable cases") by the total number of sample points ("possible cases"). This is facilitated by a systematic use of a few rules which we shall now proceed to review. Simplicity and economy of thought can be achieved by adhering to a few standard tools, and we shall follow this procedure instead of describing the shortest computational method in each special case.[1]

1. PRELIMINARIES

Pairs. *With m elements $a_1, \ldots, a_m$ and n elements $b_1, \ldots, b_n$, it is possible to form mn pairs (a_j, b_k) containing one element from each group.*

---

[1] The interested reader will find many topics of elementary combinatorial analysis treated in the classical textbook, *Choice and chance*, by W. A. Whitworth, fifth edition, London, 1901, reprinted by G. E. Stechert, New York, 1942. The companion volume by the same author, *DCC exercises*, reprinted New York, 1945, contains 700 problems with complete solutions.

Proof. Arrange the pairs in a rectangular array in the form of a multiplication table with m rows and n columns so that (a_j, b_k) stands at the intersection of the jth row and kth column. Then each pair appears once and only once, and the assertion becomes obvious. ▶

Examples. (a) *Bridge cards* (cf. footnote 1 to chapter I). As sets of elements take the four suits and the thirteen face values, respectively. Each card is defined by its suit and its face value, and there exist $4 \cdot 13 = 52$ such combinations, or cards.

(b) *"Seven-way lamps."* Some floor lamps so advertised contain 3 ordinary bulbs and also an indirect lighting fixture which can be operated on three levels but need not be used at all. Each of these four possibilities can be combined with 0, 1, 2, or 3 bulbs. Hence there are $4 \cdot 4 = 16$ possible combinations of which one, namely (0, 0), means that no bulb is on. There remain fifteen (not seven) ways of operating the lamps. ▶

Multiplets. *Given n_1 elements $a_1, \ldots, a_{n_1}$ and n_2 elements $b_1, \ldots, b_{n_2}$, etc., up to n_r elements $x_1, \ldots, x_{n_r}$; it is possible to form $n_1 n_2 \cdots n_r$ ordered r-tuplets $(a_{j_1}, b_{j_2} \ldots, x_{j_r})$ containing one element of each kind.*

Proof. If $r = 2$, the assertion reduces to the first rule. If $r = 3$, take the pair (a_i, b_j) as element of a new kind. There are $n_1 n_2$ such pairs and n_3 elements c_k. Each triple (a_i, b_j, c_k) is itself a pair consisting of (a_i, b_j) and an element c_k; the number of triplets is therefore $n_1 n_2 n_3$. Proceeding by induction, the assertion follows for every r. ▶

Many applications are based on the following reformulation of the last theorem: *r successive selections (decisions) with exactly n_k choices possible at the kth step can produce a total of $n_1 \cdot n_2 \cdots n_r$ different results.*

Examples. (c) *Multiple classifications.* Suppose that people are classified according to sex, marital status, and profession. The various categories play the role of elements. If there are 17 professions, then we have $2 \cdot 2 \cdot 17 = 68$ classes in all.

(d) In an agricultural experiment three different treatments are to be tested (for example, the application of a fertilizer, a spray, and temperature). If these treatments can be applied on r_1, r_2, and r_3 levels or concentrations, respectively, then there exist a total of $r_1 r_2 r_3$ combinations, or ways of treatment.

(e) *"Placing balls into cells"* amounts to choosing one cell for each ball. With r balls we have r independent choices, and therefore *r balls can be placed into n cells in n^r different ways.* It will be recalled from example I,(2.b) that a great variety of conceptual experiments are abstractly equivalent to that of placing balls into cells. For example, considering the faces of a die as "cells," the last proposition implies that the experiment of throwing a die r times has 6^r possible outcomes, of which 5^r satisfy the condition that no ace turns up. Assuming that all outcomes are equally probable, the event "no ace in r throws" has therefore probability $(\frac{5}{6})^r$. We might expect naively that in six throws "an ace should turn up," but the probability of this event is only $1 - (\frac{5}{6})^6$ or less than $\frac{2}{3}$. [Cf. example (3.b).]

(f) *Display of flags.*[2] For a more sophisticated example suppose that r flags of different colors are to be displayed on n poles in a row. In how many ways can this be done? We disregard, of course, the absolute position of the flags on the poles and the practical limitations on the number of flags on a pole. We assume only that the flags on each pole are in a definite order from top to bottom.

The display can be planned by making r successive decisions for the individual flags. For the first flag we choose one among the n poles. This pole is thereby divided into two segments, and hence there are now $n + 1$ choices possible for the position of the second flag. In like manner it is seen that $n + 2$ choices are possible for the third flag, and so on. It follows that $n(n + 1)(n + 2) \cdots (n + r - 1)$ *different displays are possible.*
▶

2. ORDERED SAMPLES

Consider the set or "population" of n elements $a_1, a_2, \ldots, a_n$. Any ordered arrangement $a_{j_1}, a_{j_2}, \ldots, a_{j_r}$ of r symbols is called *an ordered sample of size* r drawn from our population. For an intuitive picture we can imagine that the elements are selected one by one. Two procedures are then possible. First, *sampling with replacement;* here each selection is made from the entire population, so that the same element can be drawn more than once. The samples are then arrangements in which repetitions are permitted. Second, *sampling without replacement;* here an element once chosen is removed from the population, so that the sample becomes an arrangement without repetitions. Obviously, in this case, the sample size r cannot exceed the population size n.

In sampling with replacement each of the r elements can be chosen in n ways: the number of possible samples is therefore n^r, as can be seen from the last theorem with $n_1 = n_2 = \cdots = n$. In sampling without replacement we have n possible choices for the first element, but only

---

[2] H. M. Finucan, *A teaching sequence for* ^nH_r, The Math. Gazette, vol. 48 (1964), pp. 440–441.

$n - 1$ for the second, $n - 2$ for the third, etc., and so there are $n(n-1) \cdots$ $(n-r+1)$ choices in all. Products of this type appear so often that it is convenient to introduce the notation[3]

$$(2.1) \qquad (n)_r = n(n-1) \cdots (n-r+1).$$

Clearly $(n)_r = 0$ for integers $r > n$. We have thus the following

Theorem. *For a population of n elements and a prescribed sample size r, there exist n^r different samples with replacement and $(n)_r$ samples without replacement.*

We note the special case where $r = n$. In sampling without replacement a sample of size n includes the whole population and represents a reordering (or *permutation*) of its elements. Accordingly, n elements $a_1, \ldots, a_n$ can be ordered in $(n)_n = n \cdot (n-1) \cdots 2 \cdot 1$ different ways. Instead of $(n)_n$ we write $n!$, which is the more usual notation. We see that our theorem has the following

Corollary. *The number of different orderings of n elements is*

$$(2.2) \qquad n! = n(n-1) \cdots 2 \cdot 1.$$

Examples. (*a*) Three persons A, B, and C form an ordered sample from the human population. Their birthdays are a sample from the population of calendar days; their ages are a sample of three numbers.

(*b*) If by "ten-letter word" is meant a (possibly meaningless) sequence of ten letters, then such a word represents a sample from the population of 26 letters. Since repetitions are permitted there are 26^{10} such words. On the other hand, in a printing press letters exist not only conceptually but also physically in the form of type. For simplicity let us assume that exactly 1,000 pieces of type are available for each letter. To set up a word in type the printer has to choose ten pieces of type, and here repetitions are excluded. A word can therefore be set up in $(26,000)_{10}$ different ways. This number is practically the same as $26,000^{10}$ and exceeds 10^{44}.

(*c*) Mr. and Mrs. Smith form a sample of size two drawn from the human population; at the same time, they form a sample of size one drawn from the population of all couples. The example shows that the sample size is defined only in relation to a given population. Tossing a coin r times is one way of obtaining a sample of size r drawn from the

---

[3] The notation $(n)_r$ is not standard but will be used consistently in this book *even when n is not an integer.*

population of the two letters H and T. The same arrangement of r letters H and T is a single sample point in the space corresponding to the experiment of tossing a coin r times.

(d) *Concerning ordering and sampling in practice.* When the smoking habits of a population are investigated by sampling one feels intuitively that the order within the sample should be irrelevant, and the beginner is therefore prone to think of samples as not being ordered. But conclusions from a sample are possible only on the basis of certain probabilistic assumptions, and for these it is necessary to have an appropriate model for the conceptual experiment of obtaining a sample. Now such an experiment obviously involves choices that can be distinguished from each other, meaning choices that are labeled in some way. For theoretical purposes it is simplest to use the integers as labels, and this amounts to ordering the sample. Other procedures may be preferable in practice, but even the reference to the "third guy interviewed by Jones on Tuesday" constitutes a labeling. In other words, even though the order within the samples may be ultimately disregarded, the conceptual experiment involves ordered samples, and we shall now see that this affects the appropriate assignment of probabilities.   ►

Drawing in succession r elements from a population of size n is an experiment whose possible outcomes are samples of size r. Their number is n^r or $(n)_r$, depending on whether or not replacement is used. In either case, our conceptual experiment is described by a sample space in which each individual point represents a sample of size r.

So far we have not spoken of probabilities associated with our samples. Usually we shall assign equal probabilities to all of them and then speak of random samples. The word "random" is not well defined, but when applied to samples or selections it has a unqiue meaning. The term *random choice* is meant to imply that all outcomes are equally probable. Similarly, whenever we speak of *random samples of fixed size r, the adjective random is to imply that all possible samples have the same probability*, namely, n^{-r} in sampling with replacement and $1/(n)_r$ in sampling without replacement, n denoting the size of the population from which the sample is drawn. If n is large and r relatively small, the ratio $(n)_r/n^r$ is near unity. This leads us to expect that, for large populations and relatively small samples, the two ways of sampling are practically equivalent (cf. problems 11.1, 11.2, and problem 35 of VI, 10).

We have introduced a practical terminology but have made no statements about the applicability of our model of random sampling to reality. Tossing coins, throwing dice, and similar activities may be interpreted as experiments in practical random sampling with replacements, and our probabilities are numerically close to frequencies observed in long-run experiments, even though perfectly balanced coins or dice do not exist. Random sampling without replacement is typified by successive drawings of cards from a shuffled deck (provided shuffling is done much better than is usual). In sampling human populations the statistician encounters considerable and often unpredictable difficulties, and bitter experience has shown that it is difficult to obtain even a crude image of randomness.

Exercise. In sampling without replacement the probability for any fixed element of the population to be included in a random sample of size r is

$$1 - \frac{(n-1)_r}{(n)_r} = 1 - \frac{n-r}{n} = \frac{r}{n} .$$

In sampling with replacement the corresponding probability is $1 - (1-1/n)^r$.

3. EXAMPLES

The examples of this section represent special cases of the following problem. A random sample of size r with replacement is taken from a population of n elements. We seek the probability of the event that in the sample no element appears twice, that is, that our sample could have been obtained also by sampling without replacement. The last theorem shows that there exist n^r different samples in all, of which $(n)_r$ satisfy the stipulated condition. Assuming that all arrangements have equal probability, we conclude that *the probability of no repetition in our sample is*

$$(3.1) \qquad p = \frac{(n)_r}{n^r} = \frac{n(n-1)\cdots(n-r+1)}{n^r} .$$

The following concrete interpretations of this formula will reveal surprising features.

(*a*) *Random sampling numbers.* Let the population consist of the ten digits $0, 1, \ldots, 9$. Every succession of five digits represents a sample of size $r = 5$, and we assume that each such arrangement has probability 10^{-5}. By (3.1), *the probability that five consecutive random digits are all different is* $p = (10)_5 10^{-5} = 0.3024$.

We expect intuitively that in large mathematical tables having many decimal places the last five digits will have many properties of randomness. (In ordinary logarithmic and many other tables the tabular difference is nearly constant, and the last digit therefore varies regularly.) As an experiment, sixteen-place tables were selected and the entries were counted whose last five digits are all different. In the first twelve batches of a hundred entries each, the number of entries with five different digits varied as follows: 30, 27, 30, 34, 26, 32, 37, 36, 26, 31, 36, 32. Small-sample theory shows that the magnitude of the fluctuations is well within the expected limits. The average frequency is 0.3142, which is rather close to the theoretical probability, 0.3024 [cf. example VII, (4.g)].

Consider next the number $e = 2.71828 \ldots$. The first 800 decimals[4] form 160 groups of five digits each, which we arrange in sixteen batches of ten each. In these sixteen batches the numbers of groups in which all five digits are different are as follows:

$$3, \ 1, \ 3, \ 4, \ 4, \ 1, \ 4, \ 4, \ 4, \ 2, \ 3, \ 1, \ 5, \ 4, \ 6, \ 3.$$

The frequencies again oscillate around the value 0.3024, and small-sample theory confirms that the magnitude of the fluctuations is not larger than should be expected. The overall frequency of our event in the 160 groups is $\frac{52}{160} = 0.325$, which is reasonably close to $p = 0.3024$.

(b) *If* n *balls are randomly placed into* n *cells, the probability that each cell will be occupied equals* $n!/n^n$. It is surprisingly small: For $n = 7$ it is only $0.00612 \ldots$. This means that *if in a city seven accidents occur each week, then* (assuming that all possible distributions are equally likely) *practically all weeks will contain days with two or more accidents, and on the average only one week out of* 165 *will show a uniform distribution of one accident per day.* This example reveals an unexpected characteristic of pure randomness. (All possible configurations of seven balls in seven cells are exhibited in table 1, section 5. The probability that two or more cells remain empty is about 0.87.) For $n = 6$ the probability $n! \, n^{-n}$ equals $0.01543 \ldots$. This shows how extremely improbable it is that in six throws with a perfect die *all* faces turn up. [The probability that a particular face does not turn up is about $\frac{1}{3}$; cf. example (1.e).]

(c) *Elevator.* An elevator starts with $r = 7$ passengers and stops at $n = 10$ floors. What is the probability p that no two passengers leave at the same floor? To render the question precise, we assume that all arrangements of discharging the passengers have the same probability (which is a crude approximation). Then

$$p = 10^{-7}(10)_7 = (10 \cdot 9 \cdot 8 \cdot 7 \cdot 6 \cdot 5 \cdot 4)10^{-7} = 0.06048.$$

When the event was once observed, the occurrence was deemed remarkable

[4] For farther-going results obtained by modern computers see R. G. Stoneham, *A study of 60,000 digits of the transcendental e*, Amer. Math. Monthly, vol. 72 (1965), pp. 483–500 and R. K. Pathria, *A statistical study of the first 10,000 digits of* π, Mathematics of Computation, vol. 16 (1962), pp. 188–197.

and odds of 1000 to 1 were offered against a repetition. (Cf. the *answer* to problem 10.43.)

(*d*) *Birthdays.* The birthdays of r people form a sample of size r from the population of all days in the year. The years are not of equal length, and we know that the birth rates are not quite constant throughout the year. However, in a first approximation, we may take a random selection of people as equivalent to random selection of birthdays and consider the year as consisting of 365 days.

With these conventions we can interpret equation (3.1) to the effect *that the probability that all r birthdays are different equals*[5]

$$(3.2) \qquad p = \frac{(365)_r}{365^r} = \left(1 - \frac{1}{365}\right)\left(1 - \frac{2}{365}\right)\cdots\left(1 - \frac{r-1}{365}\right).$$

Again the numerical consequences are astounding. Thus for $r = 23$ people we have $p < \frac{1}{2}$, that is, *for 23 people the probability that at least two people have a common birthday exceeds $\frac{1}{2}$.*

Formula (3.2) looks forbidding, but it is easy to derive good numerical approximations to p. If r is small, we can neglect all cross products and have in first approximation[6]

$$(3.3) \qquad p \approx 1 - \frac{1 + 2 + \cdots + (r-1)}{365} = 1 - \frac{r(r-1)}{730}.$$

For $r = 10$ the correct value is $p = 0.883\ldots$ whereas (3.3) gives the approximation 0.877.

For larger r we obtain a much better approximation by passing to logarithms. For small positive x we have $\log(1-x) \approx -x$, and thus from (3.2)

$$(3.4) \qquad \log p \approx -\frac{1 + 2 + \cdots + (r-1)}{365} = -\frac{r(r-1)}{730}.$$

For $r = 30$ this leads to the approximation 0.3037 whereas the correct value is $p = 0.294$. For $r \leq 40$ the error in (3.4) is less than 0.08. (For a continuation see section 7. See also answer to problem 10.44.)

---

[5] Cf. R. von Mises, *Ueber Aufteilungs- und Besetzungs-Wahrscheinlichkeiten*, Revue de la Faculté des Sciences de l'Université d'Istanbul, N. S. vol. 4 (1938–1939), pp. 145–163.

[6] The sign $\approx$ signifies that the equality is only approximate. Products of the form (3.2) occur frequently, and the described method of approximation is of wide use.

4. SUBPOPULATIONS AND PARTITIONS

As before, we use the term *population of size* n to denote an aggregate of n elements *without regard to their order*. Two populations are considered different only if one contains an element not contained in the other.

Consider a subpopulation of size r of a given population consisting of n elements. An arbitrary numbering of the elements of the subpopulation changes it into an ordered sample of size r and, conversely, every such sample can be obtained in this way. Since r elements can be numbered in $r!$ different ways, it follows that there are exactly $r!$ times as many samples as there are subpopulations of size r. The number of subpopulations of size r is therefore given by $(n)_r/r!$. Expressions of this kind are known as *binomial coefficients*, and the standard notation for them is

$$(4.1) \qquad \binom{n}{r} = \frac{(n)_r}{r!} = \frac{n(n-1)\cdots(n-r+1)}{1 \cdot 2 \cdots (r-1) \cdot r}.$$

We have now proved

Theorem 1. *A population of* n *elements possesses* $\binom{n}{r}$ *different subpopulations of size* $r \leq n$.

In other words, a subset of r elements can be chosen in $\binom{n}{r}$ different ways. Such a subset is uniquely determined by the $n - r$ elements *not* belonging to it, and these form a subpopulation of size $n - r$. It follows that there are exactly as many subpopulations of size r as there are subpopulations of size $n - r$, and hence for $1 \leq r \leq n$ we must have

$$(4.2) \qquad \binom{n}{r} = \binom{n}{n-r}.$$

To prove equation (4.2) directly we observe that an alternative way of writing the binomial coefficient (4.1) is

$$(4.3) \qquad \binom{n}{r} = \frac{n!}{r!\,(n-r)!}.$$

[This follows on multiplying numerator and denominator of (4.1) by $(n-r)!$.] Note that the left side in equation (4.2) is not defined for $r = 0$, but the right side is. In order to make equation (4.2) valid for all integers r such that $0 \leq r \leq n$, *we now define*

$$(4.4) \qquad \binom{n}{0} = 1, \qquad 0! = 1,$$

and $(n)_0 = 1$.

Examples. (*a*) *Bridge and poker* (cf. footnote 1 of chapter I). The order of the cards in a hand is conventionally disregarded, and hence there exist $\binom{52}{13} = 635{,}013{,}559{,}600$ different hands at bridge, and $\binom{52}{5} = 2{,}598{,}960$ hands at poker. Let us calculate the probability, x, that a hand at poker contains five different face values. These face values can be chosen in $\binom{13}{5}$ ways, and corresponding to each card we are free to choose one of the four suits. It follows that $x = 4^5 \cdot \binom{13}{5} \Big/ \binom{52}{5}$, which is approximately 0.5071. For bridge the probability of thirteen different face values is $4^{13} \Big/ \binom{52}{13}$ or, approximately, 0.0001057.

(*b*) Each of the 50 states has two senators. We consider the events that in a committee of 50 senators chosen at random: (1) a given state is represented, (2) all states are represented.

In the first case it is better to calculate the probability q of the complementary event, namely, that the given state is *not* represented. There are 100 senators, and 98 not from the given state. Hence,

$$q = \binom{98}{50} \Big/ \binom{100}{50} = \frac{50 \cdot 49}{100 \cdot 99} = 0.24747\ldots.$$

Next, the theorem of section 2 shows that a committee including one senator from each state can be chosen in 2^{50} different ways. The probability that *all* states are included in the committee is, therefore, $p = 2^{50} \Big/ \binom{100}{50}$. Using Stirling's formula (cf. section 9), it can be shown that $p \approx \sqrt{2\pi} \cdot 5 \cdot 2^{-50} \approx 4.126 \cdot 10^{-14}$.

(*c*) *An occupancy problem.* Consider once more a random distribution of r balls n cells (i.e., each of the n^r possible arrangements has probability n^{-r}). To find the *probability*, p_k, *that a specified cell contains exactly* k *balls* $(k = 0, 1, \ldots, r)$ we note that the k balls can be chosen in $\binom{r}{k}$ ways, and the remaining $r - k$ balls can be placed into the remaining $n - 1$ cells in $(n-1)^{r-k}$ ways. It follows that

$$(4.5) \qquad p_k = \binom{r}{k} \cdot \frac{1}{n^r} \cdot (n-1)^{r-k} = \binom{r}{k} \cdot \frac{1}{n^k} \cdot \left(1 - \frac{1}{n}\right)^{r-k}.$$

This is a special case of the so-called *binomial distribution* which will be taken up in chapter VI. Numerical values will be found in table 3 of chapter IV. ▶

The distinction between distinguishable and indistinguishable elements has similarities to the relationship between a subpopulation and the corresponding ordered samples. Deleting all subscripts in an arrangement (or grouping) of r elements $a_1, \ldots, a_r$ yields an arrangement of r indistinguishable letters. Conversely, an arbitrary numbering of the r letters in an arrangement of the latter kind produces an arrangement of the letters $a_1, \ldots, a_r$. This procedure yields exactly r new arrangements provided, of course, that any interchange of a_i and a_k counts as re-arrangement. The following examples show how this principle can be applied and extended to situations in which the elements a_k are only partially identified.

Examples. (*d*) *Flags of one or two colors.* In example (1.*f*) it was shown that r flags can be displayed on n poles in $N = n(n+1) \cdots (n+r-1)$ different ways. We now consider the same problem for flags of one color (considered indistinguishable). Numbering the flags of such a display yields exactly $r!$ displays of r distinguishable flags and *hence r flags of the same color can be displayed in $N/r!$ ways.*

Suppose next that p among the flags are red (and indistinguishable) and q are blue (where $p + q = r$). It is easily seen that every display of r numbered flags can be obtained by numbering the red flags from 1 to p and the blue flags from $p + 1$ to $p + q$. It follows that the number of different displays is now $N/(p! \, q!)$.

(*e*) *Orderings involving two kinds of elements.* Let us consider the number of sequences of length $p + q$ consisting of p alphas and q betas. Numbering the alphas from 1 to p and the betas from $p + 1$ to $p + q$ yields an ordered sequence of $p + q$ distinguishable elements. There are $(p+q)!$ such sequences, and exactly $p! \, q!$ among them correspond to the same ordering of alphas and betas. Accordingly, *p alphas and q betas can be arranged in exactly*

$$\frac{(p+q)!}{p! \, q!} = \binom{p+q}{p} = \binom{p+q}{q}$$

distinguishable ways.

The same result follows directly from theorem 1 and the fact that all orderings of p alphas and q betas can be obtained by choosing p among $p + q$ available places and assigning them to the alphas.

(*f*) The number of shortest polygonal paths (with horizontal and vertical segments) joining two diagonally opposite vertices of a chessboard equals $\binom{16}{8} = 12{,}870$.   ▶

Theorem 2. *Let* $r_1, \ldots, r_k$ *be integers such that*

(4.6) $r_1 + r_2 + \cdots + r_k = n,$ $r_i \geq 0.$

The number of ways in which a population of n *elements can be divided into* k *ordered parts (partitioned into* k *subpopulations) of which the first contains* r_1 *elements, the second* r_2 *elements, etc., is*

(4.7) $$\frac{n!}{r_1! \, r_2! \cdots r_k!}.$$

[The numbers (4.7) are called *multinomial coefficients.*]

Note that the order of the subpopulations is essential in the sense that $(r_1 = 2, r_2 = 3)$ and $(r_1 = 3, r_2 = 2)$ represent different partitions; however, no attention is paid to the order within the groups. Note also that $0! = 1$ so that the vanishing r_i in no way affect formula (4.7). Since it is permitted that $r_i = 0$, the n elements are divided into k *or fewer* subpopulations. The case $r_i > 0$ of partitions into *exactly* k classes is treated in problem 11.7.

Proof. A repeated use of (4.3) will show that the number (4.7) may be rewritten in the form

(4.8) $\dbinom{n}{r_1}\dbinom{n-r_1}{r_2}\dbinom{n-r_1-r_2}{r_3} \cdots \dbinom{n-r_1-\cdots-r_{k-2}}{r_{k-1}}$

On the other hand, in order to effect the desired partition, we have first to select r_1 elements out of the given n; of the remaining $n - r_1$ elements we select a second group of size r_2, etc. After forming the $(k-1)$st group there remain $n - r_1 - r_2 - \cdots - r_{k-1} = r_k$ elements, and these form the last group. We conclude that (4.8) indeed represents the number of ways in which the operation can be performed.   ▶

Examples. (*g*) *Bridge.* At a bridge table the 52 cards are partitioned into four equal groups and therefore the number of different situations is $52! \cdot (13!)^{-4} = (5.36\ldots) \cdot 10^{28}$. Let us now calculate the probability that each player has an ace. The four aces can be ordered in $4! = 24$ ways, and each order represents one possibility of giving one ace to each player. The remaining 48 cards can be distributed in $(48!)(12!)^{-4}$ ways. Hence the required probability is $24 \cdot 48! \cdot (13)^4/52! = 0.105 \ldots.$

(*h*) *Dice.* A throw of twelve dice can result in 6^{12} different outcomes, to all of which we attribute equal probabilities. The event that each face appears twice can occur in as many ways as twelve dice can be arranged in six groups of two each. Hence the probability of the event is $12!/(2^6 \cdot 6^{12}) = 0.003438 \ldots.$

*5. APPLICATION TO OCCUPANCY PROBLEMS

The examples of chapter I, 2, indicate the wide applicability of the model of placing randomly r balls into n cells. In many situations it is necessary to treat the balls as *indistinguishable*. For example, in statistical studies of the distribution of accidents among weekdays, or of birthdays among calendar days, one is interested only in the number of occurrences, and not in the individuals involved. Again, throwing r dice is equivalent to a placement of r balls into $n = 6$ cells. Although it would be possible to keep track of the r individual results, one prefers usually to specify only the numbers of aces, twos, etc. In such situations we may still suppose the balls numbered, but we focus our attention on events that are independent of the numbering. Such an event is completely described by its *occupancy numbers* $r_1, r_2, \ldots, r_n$, where r_k stands for the number of balls in the kth cell. Every n-tuple of integers satisfying

$$(5.1) \qquad\qquad r_1 + r_2 + \cdots + r_n = r, \qquad\qquad r_k \geq 0$$

describes a possible configuration of occupancy numbers. *With indistinguishable balls two distributions are distinguishable only if the corresponding n-tuples* $(r_1, \ldots, r_n)$ *are not identical.* We now prove that:

(*i*) *The number of distinguishable distributions* [*i.e. the number of different solutions of equation* (5.1)] *is*[7]

$$(5.2) \qquad\qquad A_{r,n} = \binom{n+r-1}{r} = \binom{n+r-1}{n-1}.$$

(*ii*) *The number of distinguishable distributions in which no cell remains empty is* $\binom{r-1}{n-1}$.

Proof. We represent the balls by stars and indicate the n cells by the n spaces between $n + 1$ bars. Thus $| *** | * | | | | **** |$ is used as a symbol for a distribution of $r = 8$ balls in $n = 6$ cells with occupancy numbers 3, 1, 0, 0, 0, 4. Such a symbol necessarily starts and ends with a bar, but the remaining $n - 1$ bars and r stars can appear in an arbitrary order. In this way it becomes apparent that the number of distinguishable distributions equals the number of ways of selecting r places out of $n + r - 1$, namely $A_{r,n}$.

---

* The material of this section is useful and illuminating but will not be used explicitly in the sequel.

[7] The special case $r = 100$, $n = 4$ has been used in example I, (2.*e*).

The condition that no cell be empty imposes the restriction that no two bars be adjacent. The r stars leave $r - 1$ spaces of which $n - 1$ are to be occupied by bars: thus we have $\binom{r-1}{n-1}$ choices and the lemma is is proved.   ▶

Examples. (a) There are $\binom{r+5}{5}$ distinguishable results of a throw with r indistinguishable dice.

(b) *Partial derivatives.* The partial derivatives of order r of an analytic function $f(x_1, \ldots, x_n)$ of n variables do not depend on the order of differentiation but only on the number of times that each variable appears. Thus each variable corresponds to a cell, and hence *there exist* $\binom{n+r-1}{r}$ *different partial derivatives of rth order.* A function of three variables has fifteen derivatives of fourth order and 21 derivatives of fifth order.   ▶

Consider now n fixed integers satisfying (5.1). The number of placements of r balls in n cells resulting in the occupancy numbers $r_1, \ldots, r_n$ is given by theorem 4.2. Assuming that all n^r possible placements are equally probable, *the probability to obtain the given occupancy numbers* $r_1, \ldots, r_n$ *equals*

$$(5.3) \qquad \frac{r!}{r_1! \, r_2! \cdots r_n!} \, n^{-r}.$$

This assignment of probabilities was used in all applications mentioned so far, and it used to be taken for granted that it is inherent to the intuitive notion of randomness. No alternative assignment has ever been suggested on probabilistic or intuitive grounds. It is therefore of considerable methodological interest that *experience* compelled physicists to replace the distribution (5.3) by others which originally came as a shock to intuition. This will be discussed in the next subsection. [In physics (5.3) is known as the *Maxwell-Boltzmann* distribution.]

In various connections it is necessary to go a step farther and to consider the cells themselves as indistinguishable; this amounts to disregarding the order among the occupancy numbers. The following example is intended to explain a routine method of problems arising in this way.

Example. (c) *Configurations of* $r = 7$ *balls in* $n = 7$ *cells.* (The cells may be interpreted as days of the week, the balls as calls, letters, accidents, etc.) For the sake of definiteness let us consider the distributions with occupancy numbers 2, 2, 1, 1, 1, 0, 0 *appearing in an arbitrary order.* These seven occupancy numbers induce a partition of the *seven cells* into three subpopulations (categories) consisting, respectively, of the two doubly occupied, the three simply occupied, and the two empty cells. Such a partition into three groups of size 2, 3, and 2 can be effected in $7! \div (2! \cdot 3! \cdot 2!)$

ways. To each particular assignment of our occupancy numbers to the seven cells there correspond $7! \div (2! \cdot 2! \cdot 1! \cdot 1! \cdot 1! \cdot 0! \cdot 0!) = 7! \div (2! \cdot 2!)$ different distributions of the $r = 7$ balls into the seven cells. Accordingly, *the total number of distributions such that the occupancy numbers coincide with* 2, 2, 1, 1, 1, 0, 0 *in some order is*

$$(5.4) \qquad \frac{7!}{2!\,3!\,2!} \times \frac{7!}{2!\,2!}.$$

It will be noticed that this result has been derived by a *double application of* (4.7), namely to balls and to cells. The same result can be derived and rewritten in many ways,

TABLE 1

RANDOM DISTRIBUTIONS OF 7 BALLS IN 7 CELLS

Occupancy numbers	Number of arrangements equals $7! \times 7!$ divided by	Probability (number of arrangements divided by 7^7)
1, 1, 1, 1, 1, 1, 1	$7! \times 1!$	0.006 120
2, 1, 1, 1, 1, 1, 0	$5! \times 2!$	0.128 518
2, 2, 1, 1, 1, 0, 0	$2!\,3!\,2! \times 2!\,2!$	0.321 295
2, 2, 2, 1, 0, 0, 0	$3!\,3! \times 2!\,2!\,2!$	0.107 098
3, 1, 1, 1, 1, 0, 0	$4!\,2! \times 3!$	0.107 098
3, 2, 1, 1, 0, 0, 0	$2!\,3! \times 3!\,2!$	0.214 197
3, 2, 2, 0, 0, 0, 0	$2!\,4! \times 3!\,2!\,2!$	0.026 775
3, 3, 1, 0, 0, 0, 0	$2!\,4! \times 3!\,3!$	0.017 850
4, 1, 1, 1, 0, 0, 0	$3!\,3! \times 4!$	0.035 699
4, 2, 1, 0, 0, 0, 0	$4! \times 4!\,2!$	0.026 775
4, 3, 0, 0, 0, 0, 0	$5! \times 4!\,3!$	0.001 785
5, 1, 1, 0, 0, 0, 0	$2!\,4! \times 5!$	0.005 355
5, 2, 0, 0, 0, 0, 0	$5! \times 5!\,2!$	0.001 071
6, 1, 0, 0, 0, 0, 0	$5! \times 6!$	0.000 357
7, 0, 0, 0, 0, 0, 0	$6! \times 7!$	0.000 008

but the present method provides the simplest routine technique for a great variety of problems. (Cf. problems 43–45 of section 10.) Table 1 contains the analogue to (5.4) and the probabilities for all possible configurations of occupancy numbers in the case $r = n = 7$. ▶

(a) Bose-Einstein and Fermi-Dirac statistics

Consider a mechanical system of r indistinguishable particles. In statistical mechanics it is usual to subdivide the phase space into a large number, n, of small regions or cells so that each particle is assigned to one cell. In this way the state of the entire system is described in terms of a random distribution of the r particles in n cells. Offhand it would seem that (at least with an appropriate definition of the n cells) all n^r arrangements should have equal probabilities. If this is true, the physicist speaks of *Maxwell-Boltzmann statistics* (the term "statistics" is here used in a sense peculiar to physics). Numerous attempts have been made to prove that physical particles behave to accordance with Maxwell-Boltzmann statistics, but modern theory has shown beyond doubt that this statistics *does not apply to any known particles;* in no case are all n^r arrangements approximately equally probable. Two different probability models have been introduced, and each describes satisfactorily the behavior of one type of particle. The justification of either model depends on its success. Neither claims universality, and it is possible that some day a third model may be introduced for certain kinds of particles.

Remember that we are here concerned only with *indistinguishable* particles. We have r particles and n cells. *By Bose-Einstein statistics we mean that only distinguishable arrangements are considered and that each is assigned probability* $1/A_{r,n}$ with $A_{r,n}$ defined in (5.2). It is shown in statistical mechanics that this assumption holds true for photons, nuclei, and atoms containing an even number of elementary particles.[8] To describe other particles a third possible assignment of probabilities must be introduced. *Fermi-Dirac statistics* is based on these hypotheses: (1) *it is impossible for two or more particles to be in the same cell,* and (2) *all distinguishable arrangements satisfying the first condition have equal probabilities.* The first hypothesis requires that $r \leq n$. An arrangement is then completely described by stating which of the n cells contain a particle; and since there are r particles, the corresponding cells can be chosen in $\binom{n}{r}$ ways. Hence, with *Fermi-Dirac statistics there are in all* $\binom{n}{r}$ *possible arrangements, each having probability* $\binom{n}{r}^{-1}$. This model applies to electrons, neutrons, and protons. We have here an instructive example of the impossibility of selecting or justifying probability models by *a priori* arguments. In fact, no pure reasoning could tell that photons and protons would not obey the same probability laws. (Essential differences between Maxwell-Boltzmann and Bose-Einstein statistics are discussed in section 11, problems 14–19.)

To sum up: *the probability that cells number* $1, 2, \ldots, n$ *contain* $r_1, r_2, \ldots, r_n$ *balls, respectively (where* $r_1 + \cdots + r_n = r$*) is given by* (5.3) *under Maxwell-Boltzmann statistics; it is given by* $1/A_{r,n}$ *under Bose-Einstein statistics; and it equals* $\binom{n}{r}^{-1}$ *under Fermi-Dirac statistics provided each* r_j *equals* 0 *or* 1.

---

[8] Cf. H. Margenau and G. M. Murphy, *The mathematics of physics and chemistry*, New York (Van Nostrand), 1943, Chapter 12.

Examples. (*a*) Let $n = 5$, $r = 3$. The arrangement $(* \mid - \mid * \mid * \mid -)$ has probability $\frac{6}{125}$, $\frac{1}{35}$, or $\frac{1}{10}$, according to whether Maxwell-Boltzmann, Bose-Einstein, or Fermi-Dirac statistics is used. See also example I, (6.*b*).

(*b*) *Misprints.* A book contains n symbols (letters), of which r are misprinted. The distribution of misprints corresponds to a distribution of r balls in n cells with no cell containing more than one ball. It is therefore reasonable to suppose that, approximately, *the misprints obey the Fermi-Dirac statistics.* (Cf. problem 10.38.)   ▶

(b) Application to Runs

In any ordered sequence of elements of two kinds, each maximal subsequence of elements of like kind is called *a run*. For example, the sequence $\alpha\alpha\alpha\beta\alpha\alpha\beta\beta\beta\alpha$ opens with an alpha run of length 3; it is followed by runs of length 1, 2, 3, 1, respectively. The alpha and beta runs alternate so that the total number of runs is always one plus the number of *unlike neighbors* in the given sequence.

Examples of applications. The theory of runs is applied in statistics in many ways, but its principal uses are connected with tests of randomness or tests of homogeneity.

(*a*) In *testing randomness*, the problem is to decide whether a given observation is attributable to chance or whether a search for assignable causes is indicated. As a simple example suppose that an observation[9] yielded the following arrangement of empty and occupied seats along a lunch counter: *EOEEOEEEOEEEOEOE*. Note that no two occupied seats are adjacent. Can this be due to chance? With five occupied and eleven empty seats it is impossible to get more than eleven runs, and this number was actually observed. It will be shown later that if all arrangements were equally probable the probability of eleven runs would be 0.0578 . . . . This small probability to some extent confirms the hunch that the separations observed were intentional. This suspicion cannot be proved by statistical methods, but further evidence could be collected from continued observation. If the lunch counter were frequented by families, there would be a tendency for occupants to cluster together, and this would lead to relatively small numbers of runs. Similarly counting runs of boys and girls in a classroom might disclose the mixing to be better or worse than random. Improbable arrangements give clues to assignable causes; *an excess of runs points to intentional mixing, a paucity of runs to intentional clustering.* It is true that these conclusions are never foolproof, but efficient statistical techniques have been developed which in actual practice minimize the risk of incorrect conclusions.

The theory of runs is also useful in industrial quality control as introduced by Shewhart. As washers are produced, they will vary in thickness. Long runs of thick washers may suggest imperfections in the production process and lead to the removal of the causes; thus oncoming trouble may be forestalled and greater homogeneity of product achieved.

In biological field experiments successions of healthy and diseased plants are counted,

---

[9] F. S. Swed and C. Eisenhart, *Tables for testing randomness of grouping in a sequence of alternatives*, Ann. Math. Statist., vol. 14 (1943), pp. 66–87.

and long runs are suggestive of contagion. The meteorologist watches successions of dry and wet months[10] to discover clues to a tendency of the weather to persist.

(*b*) To understand a typical problem of *homogeneity*, suppose that two drugs have been applied to two sets of patients, or that we are interested in comparing the efficiency of two treatments (medical, agricultural, or industrial). In practice, we shall have two sets of observations, say, $\alpha_1, \alpha_2, \ldots, \alpha_a$ and $\beta_1, \beta_2, \ldots, \beta_b$ corresponding to the two treatments or representing a certain characteristic (such as weight) of the elements of two populations. The alphas and betas are *numbers* which we imagine ordered in increasing order of magnitude: $\alpha_1 \le \alpha_2 \le \cdots \le \alpha_a$ and $\beta_1 \le \beta_2 \le \cdots \le \beta_b$. We now pool the two sets into one sequence ordered according to magnitude. An extreme case is that all alphas precede all betas, and this may be taken as indicative of a significant difference between the two treatments or populations. On the other hand, if the two treatments are identical, the alphas and betas should appear more or less in random order. Wald and Wolfowitz[11] have shown that the theory of runs can be often advantageously applied to discover small systematic differences. (An illustrative example, but treated by a different method, will be found in III, 1.*b*.)   ▶

Many problems concerning runs can be solved in an exceedingly simple manner. Given a indistinguishable alphas and b indistinguishable betas, we know from example (4.*e*) that there are $\binom{a+b}{a}$ distinguishable orderings. If there are n_1 alpha runs, the number of beta runs is necessarily one of the numbers $n_1 \pm 1$ or n_1. Arranging the a alphas in n_1 runs is equivalent to arranging them into n_1 cells, none of which is empty. By the last lemma this can be done in $\binom{a-1}{n_1-1}$ distinguishable ways. It follows, for example, that there are $\binom{a-1}{n_1-1}\binom{b-1}{n_1}$ arrangements with n_1 alpha runs and n_1+1 beta runs (continued in problems 20–25 of section 11).

(*c*) In physics, the theory of runs is used in the study of cooperative phenomena. In Ising's theory of one-dimensional lattices the energy depends on the number of unlike neighbors, that is, the number of runs.   ▶

6. THE HYPERGEOMETRIC DISTRIBUTION

Many combinatorial problems can be reduced to the following form. In a population of n elements n_1 are red and $n_2 = n - n_1$ are black. A group of r elements is chosen at random. We seek the probability q_k that the group so chosen will contain exactly k red elements. Here k can be any integer between zero and n_1 or r, whichever is smaller. To find q_k, we note that the chosen group contains k red and $r - k$

---

[10] W. G. Cochran, *An extension of Gold's method of examining the apparent persistence of one type of weather*, Quarterly Journal of the Royal Meteorological Society, vol. 64, No. 277 (1938), pp. 631–634.

[11] A. Wald and J. Wolfowitz, *On a test whether two samples are from the same population*, Ann. Math. Statist., vol. 2 (1940), pp. 147–162.

black elements. The red ones can be chosen in $\binom{n_1}{k}$ different ways and the black ones in $\binom{n-n_1}{r-k}$ ways. Since any choice of k red elements may be combined with any choice of black ones, we find

$$(6.1) \qquad q_k = \frac{\binom{n_1}{k}\binom{n-n_1}{r-k}}{\binom{n}{r}}.$$

The system of probabilities so defined is called the *hypergeometric distribution*.[12] Using (4.3), it is possible to rewrite (6.1) in the form

$$(6.2) \qquad q_k = \frac{\binom{r}{k}\binom{n-r}{n_1-k}}{\binom{n}{n_1}}.$$

Note. The probabilities q_k are defined only for k not exceeding r or n_1, but since $\binom{a}{b} = 0$ whenever $b > a$, formulas (6.1) and (6.2) give $q_k = 0$ if either $k > n_1$ or $k > r$. Accordingly, the definitions (6.1) and (6.2) may be used for all $k \geq 0$, provided the relation $q_k = 0$ is interpreted as impossibility.

Examples. (*a*) *Quality inspection.* In industrial quality control, lots of size n are subjected to sampling inspection. The defective items in the lot play the role of "red" elements. Their number n_1 is, of course, unknown. A sample of size r is taken, and the number k of defective items in it is determined. Formula (6.1) then permits us to draw inferences about the likely magnitude of n_1; this is a typical problem of statistical estimation, but is beyond the scope of the present book.

(*b*) In example (4.*b*), the population consists of $n = 100$ senators of whom $n_1 = 2$ represent the given state (are "red"). A group of $r = 50$ senators is chosen at random. It may include $k = 0, 1,$ or 2 senators from the given state. From (6.2) we find, remembering (4.4),

$$q_0 = q_2 = \frac{50 \cdot 49}{100 \cdot 99} = 0.24747 \ldots , \qquad q_1 = \frac{50}{99} = 0.50505 \ldots .$$

The value q_0 was obtained in a different way in example (4.*b*).

---

[12] The name is explained by the fact that the generating function (cf. chapter XI) of $\{q_k\}$ can be expressed in terms of hypergeometric functions.

(c) *Estimation of the size of an animal population from recapture data.*[13]
Suppose that 1000 fish caught in a lake are marked by red spots and
released. After a while a new catch of 1000 fish is made, and it is found
that 100 among them have red spots. What conclusions can be drawn
concerning the number of fish in the lake? This is a typical problem of
statistical estimation. It would lead us too far to describe the various
methods that a modern statistician might use, but we shall show how the
hypergeometric distribution gives us a clue to the solution of the problem.
We assume naturally that the two catches may be considered as random
samples from the population of all fish in the lake. (In practice this
assumption excludes situations where the two catches are made at one
locality and within a short time.) We also suppose that the number of fish
in the lake does not change between the two catches.

We generalize the problem by admitting arbitrary sample sizes. Let

n = the (unknown) number of fish in the lake.
n_1 = the number of fish in the first catch. They play the role of red balls.
r = the number of fish in the second catch.
k = the number of red fish in the second catch.
$q_k(n)$ = the probability that the second catch contains exactly k red fish.

In this formulation it is rather obvious that $q_k(n)$ is given by (6.1).
In practice n_1, r, and k can be observed, but n is unknown. Notice,
incidentally, that n is a fixed number which in no way depends on chance.
It is, therefore, meaningless to ask for the probability that n is greater
than, say, 6000. We know that $n_1 + r - k$ different fish were caught,
and therefore $n \geq n_1 + r - k$. This is all that can be said with certainty.
In our example we had $n_1 = r = 1000$ and $k = 100$; it is conceivable
that the lake contains only 1900 fish, but starting from this hypothesis, we
are led to the conclusion that an event of a fantastically small probability
has occurred. In fact, assuming that there are $n = 1900$ fish in all, the
probability that two samples of size 1000 each will between them exhaust
the entire population is by (6.1),

$$\binom{1000}{100}\binom{900}{900}\binom{1900}{1000}^{-1} = \frac{(1000!)^2}{100!\,1900!}.$$

---

[13] This example was used in the first edition without knowledge that the method is
widely used in practice. Newer contributions to the literature include N. T. J. Bailey,
On estimating the size of mobile populations from recapture data, Biometrika, vol. 38
(1951), pp. 293–306, and D. G. Chapman, *Some properties of the hypergeometric
distribution with applications to zoological sample censuses,* University of California
Publications in Statistics, vol. 1 (1951), pp. 131–160.

Stirling's formula (cf. section 9) shows this probability to be of the order of magnitude 10^{-430}, and in this situation common sense bids us to reject our hypothesis as unreasonable. A similar reasoning would induce us to reject the hypothesis that n is very large, say, a million. This consideration leads us to seek the particular value of n for which $q_k(n)$ attains its largest value, since for that n our observation would have the greatest probability. For any particular set of observations n_1, r, k, the value of n for which $q_k(n)$ is largest is denoted by $\hat{n}$ and is called the *maximum likelihood estimate* of n. This notion was introduced by R. A. Fisher. To find $\hat{n}$ consider the ratio

$$(6.3) \qquad \frac{q_k(n)}{q_k(n-1)} = \frac{(n-n_1)(n-r)}{(n-n_1-r+k)n} .$$

A simple calculation shows that this ratio is greater than or smaller than unity, according as $nk < n_1 r$ or $nk > n_1 r$. This means that with increasing n the sequence $q_k(n)$ first increases and then decreases; it reaches its maximum when n is the largest integer short of $n_1 r / k$, so that $\hat{n}$ equals about $n_1 r / k$. In our particular example the maximum likelihood estimate of the number of fish is $\hat{n} = 10{,}000$.

The true number n may be larger or smaller, and we may ask for limits within which we may reasonably expect n to lie. For this purpose let us test the hypothesis that n is smaller than 8500. We substitute in (6.1) $n = 8500$, $n_1 = r = 1000$, and calculate the probability that the second sample contains 100 or fewer red fish. This probability is $x = q_0 + q_1 + \cdots + q_{100}$. A direct evaluation is cumbersome, but using the normal approximation of chapter VII, we find easily that $x = 0.04$. Similarly, if $n = 12{,}000$, the probability that the second sample contains 100 or more red fish is about 0.03. These figures would justify a bet that the true number n of fish lies somewhere between 8500 and 12,000. There exist other ways of formulating these conclusions and other methods of estimation, but we do not propose to discuss the details. ▶

From the definition of the probabilities q_k it follows that

$$q_0 + q_1 + q_2 + \cdots = 1.$$

Formula (6.2) therefore implies that for any positive integers n, n_1, r

$$(6.4) \quad \binom{r}{0}\binom{n-r}{n_1} + \binom{r}{1}\binom{n-r}{n_1-1} + \cdots + \binom{r}{n_1}\binom{n-r}{0} = \binom{n}{n_1}.$$

This identity is frequently useful. We have proved it only for positive integers n and r, but it holds true without this restriction for arbitrary positive or negative numbers n and r (it is meaningless if n_1 is not a positive integer). (An indication of two proofs is given in section 12, problems 8 and 9.)

The hypergeometric distribution can easily be generalized to the case where the original population of size n contains several classes of elements. For example, let the population contain three classes of sizes n_1, n_2, and $n - n_1 - n_2$, respectively. If a sample of size r is taken, the probability that it contains k_1 elements of the first, k_2 elements of the second, and $r - k_1 - k_2$ elements of the last class is, by analogy with (6.1),

$$(6.5) \qquad \binom{n_1}{k_1}\binom{n_2}{k_2}\binom{n-n_1-n_2}{r-k_1-k_2}\bigg/\binom{n}{r}.$$

It is, of course, necessary that

$$k_1 \leq n_1, \qquad k_2 \leq n_2, \qquad r - k_1 - k_2 \leq n - n_1 - n_2.$$

Example. (*d*) *Bridge.* The population of 52 cards consists of four classes, each of thirteen elements. The probability that a hand of thirteen cards consists of five spades, four hearts, three diamonds, and one club is

$$\binom{13}{5}\binom{13}{4}\binom{13}{3}\binom{13}{1}\bigg/\binom{52}{13}. \qquad\qquad \blacktriangleright$$

7. EXAMPLES FOR WAITING TIMES

In this section we shall depart from the straight path of combinatorial analysis in order to consider some sample spaces of a novel type to which we are led by a simple variation of our occupancy problems. Consider once more the conceptual "experiment" of placing balls randomly into n cells. This time, however, we do not fix in advance the number r of balls but let the balls be placed one by one as long as necessary for a prescribed situation to arise. Two such possible situations will be discussed explicitly: (i) *The random placing of balls continues until for the first time a ball is placed into a cell already occupied.* The process terminates when the first duplication of this type occurs. (ii) *We fix a cell (say cell number* 1) *and continue the procedure of placing balls as long as this cell remains empty.* The process terminates when a ball is placed into the prescribed cell.

A few interpretations of this model will elucidate the problem.

Examples. (*a*) *Birthdays.* In the birthday example (3.*d*), the $n = 365$ days of the year correspond to cells, and people to balls. Our model (i) now amounts to this: If we select people at random one by one, how many people shall we have to sample in order to find a pair with a common birthday? Model (ii) corresponds to waiting for *my* birthday to turn up in the sample.

(*b*) *Key problem.* A man wants to open his door. He has n keys, of which only one fits the door. For reasons which can only be surmised, he tries the keys at random so that at each try each key has probability n^{-1} of being tried and all possible outcomes involving the same number of trials are equally likely. What is the probability that the man will succeed exactly at the rth trial? This is a special case of model (ii). It is interesting to compare this random search for the key with a more systematic approach (problem 11 of section 10; see also problem 5 in V, 8).

(*c*) In the preceding example we can replace the sampling of keys by a sampling from an arbitrary population, say by the *collecting of coupons*. Again we ask when the first duplication is to be expected and when a prescribed element will show up for the first time.

(*d*) *Coins and dice.* In example I, (5.*a*) a coin is tossed as often as necessary to turn up one head. This is a special case of model (ii) with $n = 2$. When a die is thrown until an ace turns up for the first time, the same question applies with $n = 6$. (Other waiting times are treated in problems 21, 22, and 36 of section 10, and 12 of section 11.) ▶

We begin with the conceptually simpler model (i). It is convenient to use symbols of the form $(j_1, j_2, \ldots, j_r)$ to indicate that the first, second, . . . , rth ball are placed in cells number $j_1, j_2, \ldots, j_r$ and that the process terminates at the rth step. This means that the j_i are integers between 1 and n; furthermore, $j_1, \ldots, j_{r-1}$ are all different, but j_r equals one among them. Every arrangement of this type represents a sample point. For r only the values $2, 3, \ldots, n + 1$ are possible, since a doubly occupied cell cannot appear before the second ball or after the $(n+1)$st ball is placed. The connection of our present problem with the old model of placing a fixed number of balls into the n cells leads us to attribute to each sample point $(j_1, \ldots, j_r)$ involving exactly r balls the probability n^{-r}. We proceed to show that this convention is permissible (i.e., that our probabilities add to unity) and that it leads to reasonable results.

For a fixed r the aggregate of all sample points $(j_1, \ldots, j_r)$ represents *the event that the process terminates at the rth step.* According to (2.1) the numbers $j_1, \ldots, j_{r-1}$ can be chosen in $(n)_{r-1}$ different ways; for j_r we have the choice of the $r - 1$ numbers $j_1, \ldots, j_{r-1}$. It follows that *the probability of the process terminating at the rth step is*

$$(7.1) \qquad q_r = \frac{(n)_{r-1} \cdot (r-1)}{n^r} = \left(1 - \frac{1}{n}\right) \cdots \left(1 - \frac{r-2}{n}\right) \cdot \frac{r-1}{n},$$

with $q_1 = 0$ and $q_2 = 1/n$. The probability that the process lasts for more *than r steps is* $p_r = 1 - (q_1 + q_2 + \cdots + q_r)$ *or* $p_1 = 1$ *and*

$$(7.2) \qquad p_r = \frac{(n)_r}{n^r} = \left(1 - \frac{1}{n}\right) \cdots \left(1 - \frac{r-1}{n}\right)$$

as can be seen by simple induction. In particular, $p_{n+1} = 0$ and $q_1 + \cdots + q_{n+1} = 1$, as is proper. Furthermore, when $n = 365$, formula (7.2) reduces to (3.2), and in general our new model leads to the same quantitative results as the previous model involving a fixed number of balls.

The model (ii) differs from (i) in that it depends on *an infinite sample space*. The sequences $(j_1, \ldots, j_r)$ are now subjected to the condition that the numbers $j_1, \ldots, j_{r-1}$ are different from a prescribed number $a \leq n$, but $j_r = a$. Moreover, there is no a priori reason why the process should ever terminate. For a fixed r we attribute again to each sample point of the form $(j_1, \ldots, j_r)$ probability n^{-r}. For $j_1, \ldots, j_{r-1}$ we have $n - 1$ choices each, and for j_r no choice at all. For *the probability that the process terminates at the rth step* we get therefore

$$(7.3) \qquad q_r^* = \left(\frac{n-1}{n}\right)^{r-1} \cdot \frac{1}{n}, \qquad r = 1, 2, \ldots .$$

Summing this geometric series we find $q_1^* + q_2^* + \cdots = 1$. Thus the probabilities add to unity, and there is no necessity of introducing a sample point to represent the possibility that no ball will ever be placed into the prescribed cell number a. For *the probability*

$$p_r^* = 1 - (q_1^* + \cdots + q_r^*)$$

that the process lasts for more than r steps we get

$$(7.4) \qquad p_r^* = \left(1 - \frac{1}{n}\right)^r, \qquad r = 1, 2, \ldots$$

as was to be expected.

The medians for the distributions $\{p_r\}$ and $\{p_r^*\}$ are defined as those values of r for which p_r and p_r^* come closest to $\frac{1}{2}$; it is about as likely that the process continues beyond the median as that it stops before. [In the *birthday* example (3.d) the median is $r = 23$.] To calculate the median for $\{p_r\}$ we pass to logarithms as we did in (3.4). When r is small as compared to n, we see that $-\log p_r$ is close to $r^2/2n$. It follows that *the median to* $\{p_r\}$ is close to $\sqrt{n \cdot 2 \cdot \log 2}$ or approximately $\frac{6}{5}\sqrt{n}$. It is interesting that the median increases with the square root of the population size. By contrast, *the median for* $\{p_r^*\}$ *is close to* $n \cdot \log 2$

or $0.7n$ and increases linearly with n. The probability of the waiting time in model (ii) to exceed n is $(1-n^{-1})^n$ or, approximately, $e^{-1} = 0.36788\ldots$.

8. BINOMIAL COEFFICIENTS

We have used binomial coefficients $\binom{n}{r}$ only when n is a positive integer, but it is very convenient to extend their definition. The number $(x)_r$ introduced in equation (2.1), namely

$$(8.1) \qquad (x)_r = x(x-1)\cdots(x-r+1)$$

is well defined for all real x provided only that r is a positive integer. For $r = 0$ we put $(x)_0 = 1$. Then

$$(8.2) \qquad \binom{x}{r} = \frac{(x)_r}{r!} = \frac{x(x-1)\cdots(x-r+1)}{r!}$$

defines the binomial coefficients for all values of x *and all positive integers* r. *For* $r = 0$ *we put, as in* (4.4), $\binom{x}{0} = 1$ *and* $0! = 1$. *For negative integers* r *we define*

$$(8.3) \qquad \binom{x}{r} = 0, \qquad\qquad r < 0.$$

We shall never use the symbol $\binom{x}{r}$ *if* r *is not an integer.*

It is easily verified that with this definition we have, for example,

$$(8.4) \qquad \binom{-1}{r} = (-1)^r \qquad \binom{-2}{r} = (-1)^r(r+1).$$

Three important properties will be used in the sequel. First, for *any positive integer* n

$$(8.5) \qquad \binom{n}{r} = 0 \qquad \text{if either} \quad r > n \quad \text{or} \quad r < 0.$$

Second, *for any number* x *and any integer* r

$$(8.6) \qquad \binom{x}{r-1} + \binom{x}{r} = \binom{x+1}{r}.$$

These relations are easily verified from the definition. The proof of the next relation can be found in calculus textbooks: *for any number* a *and all values* $-1 < t < 1$, *we have Newton's binomial formula*

(8.7) $$(1+t)^a = 1 + \binom{a}{1}t + \binom{a}{2}t^2 + \binom{a}{3}t^3 + \cdots.$$

If a is a positive integer, all terms to the right containing powers higher than t^a vanish automatically and the formula is correct for all t. If a is not a positive integer, the right side represents an *infinite* series.

Using (8.4), we see that for $a = -1$ the expansion (8.7) reduces to the *geometric series*

(8.8) $$\frac{1}{1+t} = 1 - t + t^2 - t^3 + t^4 - + \cdots.$$

Integrating (8.8), we obtain another formula which will be useful in the sequel, namely, the *Taylor expansion of the natural logarithm*

(8.9) $$\log(1+t) = t - \tfrac{1}{2}t^2 + \tfrac{1}{3}t^3 - \tfrac{1}{4}t^4 + \cdots.$$

Two alternative forms for (8.9) are frequently used. Replacing t by $-t$ we get

(8.10) $$\log \frac{1}{1-t} = t + \tfrac{1}{2}t^2 + \tfrac{1}{3}t^3 + \tfrac{1}{4}t^4 + \cdots.$$

Adding the last two formulas we find

(8.11) $$\tfrac{1}{2} \log \frac{1+t}{1-t} = t + \tfrac{1}{3}t^3 + \tfrac{1}{5}t^5 + \cdots.$$

All these expansions are valid only for $-1 < t < 1$.

Section 12 contains many useful relations derived from (8.7). Here we mention only that when $a = n$ is an integer and $t = 1$, then (8.7) reduces to

(8.12) $$\binom{n}{0} + \binom{n}{1} + \binom{n}{2} + \cdots + \binom{n}{n} = 2^n.$$

This formula admits of a simple combinatorial interpretation: The left side represents the number of ways in which a population of n elements can be divided into two subpopulations if the size of the first group is permitted to be any number $k = 0, 1, \ldots, n$. On the other hand, such a division can be effected directly by deciding for each element whether it is to belong to the first or second group. [A similar argument shows that the multinomial coefficients (4.7) add to k^n.]

9. STIRLING'S FORMULA

An important tool of analytical probability theory is contained in a classical theorem[14] known as

Stirling's formula:

$$(9.1) \qquad n! \sim \sqrt{2\pi}\, n^{n+\frac{1}{2}} e^{-n}$$

where the sign $\sim$ is used to indicate that the ratio of the two sides tends to unity as $n \to \infty$.

This formula is invaluable for many theoretical purposes and can be used also to obtain excellent numerical approximations. It is true that the difference of the two sides in (9.1) increases over all bounds, but it is the percentage error which really matters. It decreases steadily, and Stirling's approximation is remarkably accurate even for small n. In fact, the right side of (9.1) approximates 1! by 0.9221 and 2! by 1.919 and $5! = 120$ by 118.019. The percentage errors are 8 and 4 and 2, respectively. For $10! = 3,628,800$ the approximation is 3,598,600 with an error of 0.8 per cent. For 100! the error is only 0.08 per cent.

Proof of Stirling's formula. Our first problem is to derive some sort of estimate for

$$(9.2) \qquad \log n! = \log 1 + \log 2 + \cdots + \log n.$$

Since $\log x$ is a monotone function of x we have

$$(9.3) \qquad \int_{k-1}^{k} \log x\, dx < \log k < \int_{k}^{k+1} \log x\, dx.$$

Summing over $k = 1, \ldots, n$ we get

$$(9.4) \qquad \int_{0}^{n} \log x\, dx < \log n! < \int_{1}^{n+1} \log x\, dx$$

or

$$(9.5) \qquad n \log n - n < \log n! < (n+1) \log (n+1) - n.$$

This double inequality suggests comparing $\log n!$ with some quantity close to the arithmetic mean of the extreme members. The simplest such

---

[14] James Stirling, *Methodus differentialis*, 1730.

quantity is $(n+\frac{1}{2}) \log n - n$, and accordingly we proceed to estimate the difference[15]

$$(9.6) \qquad d_n = \log n! - (n+\frac{1}{2}) \log n + n.$$

Note that

$$(9.7) \qquad d_n - d_{n+1} = (n+\frac{1}{2}) \log \frac{n+1}{n} - 1.$$

But

$$(9.8) \qquad \frac{n+1}{n} = \frac{1 + \dfrac{1}{2n+1}}{1 - \dfrac{1}{2n+1}},$$

and using the expansion (8.11) we get

$$(9.9) \qquad d_n - d_{n+1} = \frac{1}{3(2n+1)^2} + \frac{1}{5(2n+1)^4} + \cdots.$$

By comparison of the right side with a geometric series with ratio $(2n+1)^{-2}$ one sees that

$$(9.10) \quad 0 < d_n - d_{n+1} < \frac{1}{3[(2n+1)^2 - 1]} = \frac{1}{12n} - \frac{1}{12(n+1)}.$$

From (9.9) we conclude that the sequence $\{d_n\}$ is decreasing, while (9.10) shows that the sequence $\{d_n - (12n)^{-1}\}$ is increasing. It follows that a finite limit

$$(9.11) \qquad C = \lim d_n$$

exists. But in view of (9.6) the relation $d_n \to C$ is equivalent to

$$(9.12) \qquad n! \sim e^C \cdot n^{n+\frac{1}{2}} e^{-n}.$$

This is Stirling's formula, except that the constant C is not yet specified. That $e^C = \sqrt{2\pi}$ will be proved in VII, 2. The proof is elementary and independent of the material in chapters IV–VI; it is postponed to chapter VII because it is naturally connected with the normal approximation theorem.[16]

---

[15] The following elegant argument and the inequality (9.14) are due to H. E. Robbins, Amer. Math. Monthly, vol. 62 (1955), pp. 26–29.

[16] The usual proof that $e^C = \sqrt{2\pi}$ relies on the formula of Wallis. For a simple direct proof see W. Feller, Amer. Math. Monthly (1967).

Refinements. The inequality (9.10) has a companion inequality in the reverse direction. Indeed, from (9.9) it is obvious that

$$(9.13) \qquad d_n - d_{n+1} > \frac{1}{3(2n+1)^2} > \frac{1}{12n+1} - \frac{1}{12(n+1)+1}.$$

It follows that the sequence $\{d_n - (12n+1)^{-1}\}$ decreases. Since $\{d_n - (12n)^{-1}\}$ increases this implies the double inequality

$$(9.14) \qquad C + \frac{1}{12n+1} < d_n < C + \frac{1}{12n}.$$

Substituting into (9.6), and anticipating that $e^C = \sqrt{2\pi}$, we get

$$(9.15) \qquad \sqrt{2\pi}\, n^{n+\frac{1}{2}} e^{-n} \cdot e^{(12n+1)^{-1}} < n! < \sqrt{2\pi}\, n^{n+\frac{1}{2}} e^{-n} \cdot e^{(12n)^{-1}}$$

This double inequality supplements Stirling's formula in a remarkable manner. The ratio of the extreme members is close to $1 - (12n^2)^{-1}$, and hence *the right-hand member in (9.15) overestimates n!, but with an error of less than $9n^{-2}$ per cent.* In reality the error is much smaller;[17] for $n = 2$ the right side in (9.15) yields 2.0007, for $n = 5$ we get 120.01.

PROBLEMS FOR SOLUTION

Note: Sections 11 and 12 contain problems of a different character and diverse complements to the text.

10. EXERCISES AND EXAMPLES

Note: *Assume in each case that all arrangements have the same probability.*

1. How many different sets of initials can be formed if every person has one surname and (*a*) exactly two given names, (*b*) at most two given names, (*c*) at most three given names?

2. Letters in the Morse code are formed by a succession of dashes and dots with repetitions permitted. How many letters is it possible to form with ten symbols or less?

3. Each domino piece is marked by two numbers. The pieces are symmetrical so that the number-pair is not ordered. How many different pieces can be made using the numbers $1, 2, \ldots, n$?

4. The numbers $1, 2, \ldots, n$ are arranged in random order. Find the probability that the digits (*a*) 1 and 2, (*b*) 1, 2, and 3, appear as neighbors in the order named.

---

[17] Starting from (9.9) it is possible to show that $d_n = C + (12n)^{-1} - (360n^3)^{-1} + \cdots$ where the dots indicate terms dominated by a multiple of n^{-4}.

5. *A* throws six dice and wins if he scores at least one ace. *B* throws twelve dice and wins if he scores at least two aces. Who has the greater probability to win?[18]

Hint: Calculate the probabilities to lose.

6. (*a*) Find the probability that among three random digits there appear exactly 1, 2, or 3 different ones. (*b*) Do the same for four random digits.

7. Find the probabilities p_r that in a sample of *r* random digits no two are equal. Estimate the numerical value of p_{10}, using Stirling's formula.

8. What is the probability that among *k* random digits (*a*) 0 does not appear; (*b*) 1 does not appear; (*c*) neither 0 nor 1 appears; (*d*) at least one of the two digits 0 and 1 does not appear? Let *A* and *B* represent the events in (*a*) and (*b*). Express the other events in terms of *A* and *B*.

9. If *n* balls are placed at random into *n* cells, find the probability that exactly one cell remains empty.

10. At a parking lot there are twelve places arranged in a row. A man observed that there were eight cars parked, and that the four empty places were adjacent to each other (formed *one* run). Given that there are four empty places, is this arrangement surprising (indicative of non-randomness)?

11. A man is given *n* keys of which only one fits his door. He tries them successively (sampling without replacement). This procedure may require 1, 2, ..., *n* trials. Show that each of these *n* outcomes has probability n^{-1}.

12. Suppose that each of *n* sticks is broken into one long and one short part. The 2*n* parts are arranged into *n* pairs from which new sticks are formed. Find the probability (*a*) that the parts will be joined in the original order, (*b*) that all long parts are paired with short parts.[19]

13. *Testing a statistical hypothesis.* A Cornell professor got a ticket twelve times for illegal overnight parking. All twelve tickets were given either Tuesdays or Thursdays. Find the probability of this event. (Was his renting a garage only for Tuesdays and Thursdays justified?)

14. *Continuation.* Of twelve police tickets none was given on Sunday. Is this evidence that no tickets are given on Sundays?

15. A box contains ninety good and ten defective screws. If ten screws are used, what is the probability that none is defective?

16. From the population of five symbols *a*, *b*, *c*, *d*, *e*, a sample of size 25 is taken. Find the probability that the sample will contain five symbols of each

---

[18] This paraphrases a question addressed in 1693 to I. Newton by the famous Samuel Pepys. Newton answered that "an easy computation" shows *A* to be at an advantage. On prodding he later submitted the calculations, but he was unable to convince Pepys. For a short documented account see E. D. Schell, *Samuel Pepys, Isaac Newton, and probability*, The Amer. Statistician, vol. 14 (1960), pp. 27–30. There reference is made to *Private correspondence and miscellaneous papers of Samuel Pepys*, London (G. Bell and Sons), 1926.

[19] When cells are exposed to harmful radiation, some chromosomes break and play the role of our "sticks." The "long" side is the one containing the so-called centromere. If two "long" or two "short" parts unite, the cell dies. See D. G. Catcheside, *The effect of X-ray dosage upon the frequency of induced structural changes in the chromosomes of* Drosophila Melanogaster, Journal of Genetics, vol. 36 (1938), pp. 307–320.

kind. Check the result in tables of random numbers,[20] identifying the digits 0 and 1 with a, the digits 2 and 3 with b, etc.

17. If n men, among whom are A and B, stand in a row, what is the probability that there will be exactly r men between A and B? If they stand in a ring instead of in a row, show that the probability is independent of r and hence $1/(n-1)$. (In the circular arrangement consider only the arc leading from A to B in the positive direction.)

18. What is the probability that two throws with three dice each will show the same configuration if (a) the dice are distinguishable, (b) they are not?

19. Show that it is more probable to get at least one ace with four dice than at least one double ace in 24 throws of two dice. The answer is known as de Méré's paradox.[21]

20. From a population of n elements a sample of size r is taken. Find the probability that none of N prescribed elements will be included in the sample, assuming the sampling to be (a) without, (b) with replacement. Compare the numerical values for the two methods when (i) $n = 100$, $r = N = 3$, and (ii) $n = 100$, $r = N = 10$.

21. *Spread of rumors.* In a town of $n + 1$ inhabitants, a person tells a rumor to a second person, who in turn repeats it to a third person, etc. At each step the recipient of the rumor is chosen at random from the n people available. Find the probability that the rumor will be told r times without: (a) returning to the originator, (b) being repeated to any person. Do the same problem when at each step the rumor is told by one person to a gathering of N randomly chosen people. (The first question is the special case $N = 1$.)

22. *Chain letters.* In a population of $n + 1$ people a man, the "progenitor," sends out letters to two distinct persons, the "first generation." These repeat the performance and, generally, for each letter received the recipient sends out two letters to two persons chosen at random without regard to the past development. Find the probability that the generations number $1, 2, \ldots, r$ will not include the progenitor. Find the median of the distribution, supposing n to be large.

23. *A family problem.* In a certain family four girls take turns at washing dishes. Out of a total of four breakages, three were caused by the youngest girl, and she was thereafter called clumsy. Was she justified in attributing the frequency of her breakages to chance? Discuss the connection with random placements of balls.

24. What is the probability that (a) the birthdays of twelve people will fall in twelve different calendar months (assume equal probabilities for the twelve months), (b) the birthdays of six people will fall in exactly two calendar months?

---

[20] They are occasionally miraculously obliging: see J. A. Greenwood and E. E. Stuart, *Review of Dr. Feller's critique*, Journal for Parapsychology, vol. 4 (1940), pp. 298–319, in particular p. 306.

[21] An often repeated story asserts that the problem arose at the gambling table and that in 1654 de Méré proposed it to Pascal. This incident is supposed to have greatly stimulated the development of probability theory. The problem was in fact treated by Cardano (1501–1576). See O. Ore, *Pascal and the invention of probability theory*, Amer. Math. Monthly, vol. 67 (1960), pp. 409–419, and *Cardano, the gambling scholar*, Princeton (Princeton Univ. Press), 1953.

25. Given thirty people, find the probability that among the twelve months there are six containing two birthdays and six containing three.

26. A closet contains n pairs of shoes. If $2r$ shoes are chosen at random (with $2r < n$), what is the probability that there will be (a) no complete pair, (b) exactly one complete pair, (c) exactly two complete pairs among them?

27. A car is parked among N cars in a row, not at either end. On his return the owner finds that exactly r of the N places are still occupied. What is the probability that both neighboring places are empty?

28. A group of $2N$ boys and $2N$ girls is divided into two equal groups. Find the probability p that each group will be equally divided into boys and girls. Estimate p, using Stirling's formula.

29. In bridge, prove that the probability p of West's receiving exactly k aces is the same as the probability that an arbitrary hand of thirteen cards contains exactly k aces. (This is intuitively clear. Note, however, that the two probabilities refer to two different experiments, since in the second case thirteen cards are chosen at random and in the first case all 52 are distributed.)

30. The probability that in a bridge game East receives m and South n spades is the same as the probability that of two hands of thirteen cards each, drawn at random from a deck of bridge cards, the first contains m and the second n spades.

31. What is the probability that the bridge hands of North and South together contain exactly k aces, where $k = 0, 1, 2, 3, 4$?

32. Let a, b, c, d be four non-negative integers such that $a + b + c + d = 13$. Find the probability $p(a, b, c, d)$ that in a bridge game the players North, East, South, West have a, b, c, d spades, respectively. Formulate a scheme of placing red and black balls into cells that contains the problem as a special case.

33. Using the result of problem 32, find the probability that some player receives a, another b, a third c, and the last d spades if (a) $a = 5$, $b = 4$, $c = 3$, $d = 1$; (b) $a = b = c = 4$, $d = 1$; (c) $a = b = 4$, $c = 3$, $d = 2$. Note that the three cases are essentially different.

34. Let a, b, c, d be integers with $a + b + c + d = 13$. Find the probability $q(a, b, c, d)$ that a hand at bridge will consist of a spades, b hearts, c diamonds, and d clubs and show that the problem does *not* reduce to one of placing, at random, thirteen balls into four cells. Why?

35. *Distribution of aces among r bridge cards.* Calculate the probabilities $p_0(r), p_1(r), \ldots, p_4(r)$ that among r bridge cards drawn at random there are $0, 1, \ldots, 4$ aces, respectively. Verify that $p_0(r) = p_4(52 - r)$.

36. *Continuation: waiting times.* If the cards are drawn one by one, find the probabilities $f_1(r), \ldots, f_4(r)$ that the first, $\ldots$, fourth ace turns up at the rth trial. *Guess* at the *medians* of the waiting times for the first, $\ldots$, fourth ace and then calculate them.

37. Find the probability that each of two hands contains exactly k aces if the two hands are composed of r bridge cards each, and are drawn (a) from the same deck, (b) from two decks. Show that when $r = 13$ the probability in part (a) is the probability that two preassigned bridge players receive exactly k aces each.

38. *Misprints.* Each page of a book contains N symbols, possibly misprints. The book contains $n = 500$ pages and $r = 50$ misprints. Show that

(a) the probability that pages number $1, 2, \ldots, n$ contain, respectively, r_1, $r_2, \ldots, r_n$ misprints equals

$$\binom{N}{r_1}\binom{N}{r_2}\cdots\binom{N}{r_n}\bigg/\binom{nN}{r}\ ;$$

(b) for large N this probability may be approximated by (5.3). Conclude that *the r misprints are distributed in the n pages approximately in accordance with a random distribution of r balls in n cells.* (*Note.* The distribution of the r misprints among the N available places follows the Fermi-Dirac statistics. Our assertion may be restated as a general limiting property of Fermi-Dirac statistics. Cf. section 5.*a*.)

Note: *The following problems refer to the material of section 5.*

39. If r_1 indistinguishable things of one kind and r_2 indistinguishable things of a second kind are placed into n cells, find the number of distinguishable arrangements.

40. If r_1 dice and r_2 coins are thrown, how many results can be distinguished?

41. In how many different distinguishable ways can r_1 white, r_2 black, and r_3 red balls be arranged?

42. Find the probability that in a random arrangement of 52 bridge cards no two aces are adjacent.

43. *Elevator.* In the example (3.*c*) the elevator starts with seven passengers and stops at ten floors. The various arrangements of discharge may be denoted by symbols like (3, 2, 2), to be interpreted as the event that three passengers leave together at a certain floor, two other passengers at another floor, and the last two at still another floor. Find the probabilities of the fifteen possible arrangements ranging from (7) to (1, 1, 1, 1, 1, 1, 1).

44. *Birthdays.* Find the probabilities for the various configurations of the birthdays of 22 people.

45. Find the probability for a *poker* hand to be a (a) royal flush (ten, jack, queen, king, ace in a single suit); (b) four of a kind (four cards of equal face values); (c) full house (one pair and one triple of cards with equal face values); (d) straight (five cards in sequence regardless of suit); (e) three of a kind (three equal face values plus two extra cards); (f) two pairs (two pairs of equal face values plus one other card); (g) one pair (one pair of equal face values plus three different cards).

11. PROBLEMS AND COMPLEMENTS OF A THEORETICAL CHARACTER

1. A population of n elements includes np red ones and nq black ones $(p + q = 1)$. A random sample of size r is taken with replacement. Show that the probability of its including exactly k red elements is

(11.1) $$\binom{r}{k} p^k q^{r-k}.$$

2. *A limit theorem for the hypergeometric distribution.* If n is large and $n_1/n = p$, then the probability q_k given by (6.1) and (6.2) is close to (11.1). More precisely,

$$(11.2) \quad \binom{r}{k}\left(p - \frac{k}{n}\right)^k\left(q - \frac{r-k}{n}\right)^{r-k} < q_k < \binom{r}{k}p^k q^{r-k}\left(1 - \frac{r}{n}\right)^{-r}.$$

A comparison of this and the preceding problem shows: *For large populations there is practically no difference between sampling with and without replacement.*

3. A random sample of size r *without replacement* is taken from a population of n elements. The probability u_r that N given elements will all be included in the sample is

$$(11.3) \qquad\qquad u_r = \binom{n-N}{r-N}\bigg/\binom{n}{r}.$$

[The corresponding formula for sampling *with replacement* is given by (11.10) and cannot be derived by a direct argument. For an alternative form of (11.3) cf. problem 9 of IV, 6.]

4. *Limiting form.* If $n \to \infty$ and $r \to \infty$ so that $r/n \to p$, then $u_r \to p^N$ (cf. problem 13).

Note:[22] *Problems 5–13 refer to the classical occupancy problem (Boltzmann-Maxwell statistics): That is, r balls are distributed among n cells and each of the n^r possible distributions has probability n^{-r}.*

5. The probability p_k that a given cell contains exactly k balls is given by the binomial distribution (4.5). The most probable number is the integer v such that $(r-n+1)/n < v \leq (r+1)/n$. (In other words, it is asserted that $p_0 < p_1 < \cdots < p_{v-1} \leq p_v > p_{v+1} > \cdots > p_r$; cf. problem 15.)

6. *Limiting form.* If $n \to \infty$ and $r \to \infty$ so that the average number $\lambda = r/n$ of balls per cell remains constant, then

$$(11.4) \qquad\qquad p_k \to e^{-\lambda}\lambda^k/k!.$$

(This is the *Poisson distribution,* discussed in chapter VI; for the corresponding limit theorem for Bose-Einstein statistics see problem 16.)

7. Let $A(r, n)$ be the number of distributions leaving *none of the n cells empty.* Show by a combinatorial argument that

$$(11.5) \qquad\qquad A(r, n+1) = \sum_{k=1}^{r}\binom{r}{k}A(r-k, n).$$

---

[22] Problems 5–19 play a role in quantum statistics, the theory of photographic plates, G-M counters, etc. The formulas are therefore frequently discussed and discovered in the physical literature, usually without a realization of their classical and essentially elementary character. Probably all the problems occur (although in modified form) in the book by Whitworth quoted at the opening of this chapter.

Conclude that

$$(11.6) \qquad A(r, n) = \sum_{v=0}^{n} (-1)^v \binom{n}{v} (n-v)^r.$$

Hint: Use induction; assume (11.6) to hold and express $A(r-k, n)$ in (11.5) accordingly. Change the order of summation and use the binomial formula to express $A(r, n+1)$ as the difference of two simple sums. Replace in the second sum $v + 1$ by a new index of summation and use (8.6).

Note: *Formula (11.6) provides a theoretical solution to an old problem but obviously it would be a thankless task to use it for the calculation of the probability x, say, that in a village of $r = 1900$ people every day of the year is a birthday. In IV,2 we shall derive (11.6) by another method and shall obtain a simple approximation formula (showing, e.g., that $x = 0.135$, approximately).*

8. Show that *the number of distributions leaving exactly m cells empty is*

$$(11.7) \quad E_m(r, n) = \binom{n}{m} A(r, n-m) = \binom{n}{m} \sum_{v=0}^{n-m} (-1)^v \binom{n-m}{v} (n-m-v)^r.$$

9. Show without using the preceding results that *the probability*

$$p_m(r, n) = n^{-r} E_m(r, n)$$

of finding exactly m cells empty satisfies

$$(11.8) \qquad p_m(r+1, n) = p_m(r, n) \frac{n-m}{n} + p_{m+1}(r, n) \frac{m+1}{n}.$$

10. Using the results of problems 7 and 8, show by direct calculation that (11.8) holds. Show that this method provides *a new derivation (by induction on r)* of (11.6).

11. From problem 8 conclude that *the probability $x_m(r, n)$ of finding m or more cells empty equals*

$$(11.9) \qquad \binom{n}{m} \sum_{v=0}^{n-m} (-1)^v \binom{n-m}{v} \left(1 - \frac{m+v}{n}\right)^r \frac{m}{m+v}.$$

(For $m \geq n$ this expression reduces to zero, as is proper.)

Hint: Evaluate $\qquad x_m(r, n) - p_m(r, n).$

12. *The probability that each of N given cells is occupied is*

$$(11.10) \qquad u(r, n) = n^{-r} \sum_{k=0}^{r} \binom{r}{k} A(k, N)(n-N)^{r-k}$$

Conclude that

$$(11.11) \qquad u(r, n) = \sum_{v=0}^{N} (-1)^v \binom{N}{v} \left(1 - \frac{v}{n}\right)^r.$$

[Use the binomial theorem. For $N = n$ we have $u(r, n) = n^{-r}A(r, n)$. Note that (11.11) is the analogue of (11.3) for *sampling with replacement*.[23] For an alternative derivation see problem 8 of IV, 6.]

13. *Limiting form.* For the passage to the limit described in problem 4 one has $u(r, n) \to (1 - e^{-p})^N$.

Note: *In problems 14–19, r and n have the same meaning as above, but we assume that the balls are indistinguishable and that all distinguishable arrangements have equal probabilities (Bose-Einstein statistics).*

14. The probability that a given cell contains exactly k balls is

$$(11.12) \qquad q_k = \binom{n+r-k-2}{r-k} \bigg/ \binom{n+r-1}{r}.$$

15. Show that when $n > 2$ zero is the most probable number of balls in any specified cell, or more precisely, $q_0 > q_1 > \cdots$ (cf. problem 5).

16. *Limit theorem.* Let $n \to \infty$ and $r \to \infty$, so that the average number of particles per cell, r/n, tends to λ. Then

$$(11.13) \qquad q_k \to \frac{\lambda^k}{(1+\lambda)^{k+1}}.$$

(The right side is known as the *geometric distribution*.)

17. The probability that exactly m cells remain empty is

$$(11.14) \qquad p_m = \binom{n}{m}\binom{r-1}{n-m-1} \bigg/ \binom{n+r-1}{r}.$$

18. The probability that group of m prescribed cells contains a total of exactly j balls is

$$(11.15) \qquad q_j(m) = \binom{m+j-1}{m-1}\binom{n-m+r-j-1}{r-j} \bigg/ \binom{n+r-1}{r}.$$

---

[23] Note that $u(r, n)$ may be interpreted as the probability that the *waiting time* up to the moment when the Nth element joins the sample is less than r. The result may be applied to *random sampling digits:* here $u(r, 10) - u(r-1, 10)$ is the probability that a sequence of r elements must be observed to include the complete set of all ten digits. This can be used as a test of randomness. R. E. Greenwood [*Coupon collector's test for random digits,* Mathematical Tables and Other Aids to Computation, vol. 9 (1955), pp. 1–5] tabulated the distribution and compared it to actual counts for the corresponding waiting times for the first 2035 decimals of π and the first 2486 decimals of e. The median of the waiting time for a complete set of all ten digits is 27. The probability that this waiting time exceeds 50 is greater than 0.05, and the probability of the waiting time exceeding 75 is about 0.0037.

19. Limiting form. For the passage to the limit of problem 4 we have

(11.16) $$q_j(m) \to \binom{m+j-1}{m-1} \frac{p^j}{(1+p)^{m+j}}.$$

(The right side is a special case of the *negative binomial distribution* to be introduced in VI, 8.)

Theorems on Runs. *In problems 20–25 we consider arrangements of r_1 alphas and r_2 betas and assume that all arrangements are equally probable* [*see example (4.e)*]. *This group of problems refers to section 5b.*

20. The probability that the arrangement contains exactly k runs of either kind is

(11.17) $$P_{2v} = 2 \binom{r_1-1}{v-1}\binom{r_2-1}{v-1} \Big/ \binom{r_1+r_2}{r_1}$$

when $k = 2v$ is even, and

(11.18) $$P_{2v+1} = \left\{ \binom{r_1-1}{v}\binom{r_2-1}{v-1} + \binom{r_1-1}{v-1}\binom{r_2-1}{v} \right\} \Big/ \binom{r_1+r_2}{r_1}$$

when $k = 2v + 1$ is odd.

21. *Continuation.* Conclude that the most probable number of runs is an integer k such that $\dfrac{2r_1r_2}{r_1+r_2} < k < \dfrac{2r_1r_2}{r_1+r_2} + 3$. (*Hint:* Consider the ratios P_{2v+2}/P_{2v} and P_{2v+1}/P_{2v-1}.)

22. The probability that the arrangement starts with an alpha run of length $v \geq 0$ is $(r_1)_v r_2/(r_1+r_2)_{v+1}$. (*Hint:* Choose the v alphas and the beta which must follow it.) What does the theorem imply for $v = 0$?

23. The probability of having exactly k runs of alphas is

(11.19) $$\pi_k = \binom{r_1-1}{k-1}\binom{r_2+1}{k} \Big/ \binom{r_1+r_2}{r_1}.$$

Hint: This follows easily from the second part of the lemma of section 5. Alternatively (11.19) may be derived from (11.17) and (11.18), but this procedure is more laborious.

24. The probability that the nth alpha is preceded by exactly m betas is

(11.20) $$\binom{r_1+r_2-n-m}{r_2-m}\binom{m+n-1}{m} \Big/ \binom{r_1+r_2}{r_1}.$$

25. The probability for the alphas to be arranged in k runs of which k_1 are of length 1, k_2 of length 2, ..., k_v of length v (with $k_1 + \cdots + k_v = k$) is

(11.21) $$\frac{k!}{k_1!\,k_2!\cdots k_v!}\binom{r_2+1}{k} \Big/ \binom{r_1+r_2}{r_1}.$$

12. PROBLEMS AND IDENTITIES INVOLVING BINOMIAL COEFFICIENTS

1. For integral $n \geq 2$

$$1 - \binom{n}{1} + \binom{n}{2} - + \cdots = 0$$

$$\binom{n}{1} + 2\binom{n}{2} + 3\binom{n}{3} + \cdots = n2^{n-1}$$

(12.1)

$$\binom{n}{1} - 2\binom{n}{2} + 3\binom{n}{3} - + \cdots = 0,$$

$$2 \cdot 1\binom{n}{2} + 3 \cdot 2\binom{n}{3} + 4 \cdot 3\binom{n}{4} + \cdots = n(n-1)2^{n-2}$$

Hint: Use the binomial formula.

2. Prove that for positive integers n, k

(12.2) $$\binom{n}{0}\binom{n}{k} - \binom{n}{1}\binom{n-1}{k-1} + \binom{n}{2}\binom{n-2}{k-2} \cdots \pm \binom{n}{k}\binom{n-k}{0} = 0.$$

More generally[24]

(12.3) $$\sum \binom{n}{v}\binom{n-v}{k-v} t^v = \binom{n}{k} (1+t)^k.$$

3. For any $a > 0$

(12.4) $$\binom{-a}{k} = (-1)^k \binom{a+k-1}{k}.$$

If a is an integer, this can be proved also by repeated differentiation of the geometric series $\sum x^k = (1-x)^{-1}$.

4. Prove that

(12.5) $$\binom{2n}{n} 2^{-2n} = (-1)^n \binom{-\frac{1}{2}}{n},$$

$$\frac{1}{n}\binom{2n-2}{n-1} 2^{-2n+1} = (-1)^{n-1} \binom{\frac{1}{2}}{n}.$$

5. For integral non-negative n and r and all real a

(12.6) $$\sum_{v=0}^{n} \binom{a-v}{r} = \binom{a+1}{r+1} - \binom{a-n}{r+1}.$$

Hint: Use (8.6). The special case $n = a$ is frequently used.

---

[24] The reader is reminded of the convention (8.5): *if v runs through all integers, only finitely many terms in the sum in (12.3) are different from zero.*

6. For arbitrary a and integral $n \geq 0$

(12.7)
$$\sum_{\nu=0}^{n} (-1)^{\nu} \binom{a}{\nu} = (-1)^{n} \binom{a-1}{n}.$$

Hint: Use (8.6).

7. For positive integers r, k

(12.8)
$$\sum_{\nu=0}^{r} \binom{\nu+k-1}{k-1} = \binom{r+k}{k}.$$

(a) Prove this using (8.6). (b) Show that (12.8) is a special case of (12.7). (c) Show by an inductive argument that (12.8) leads to a new proof of the first part of the lemma of section 5. (d) Show that (12.8) is equivalent to

(12.8a)
$$\sum_{j=0}^{n} \binom{j}{m} = \binom{n+1}{m+1}.$$

8. In section 6 we remarked that the terms of the hypergeometric distribution should add to unity. This amounts to saying that for any positive integers a, b, n,

(12.9)
$$\binom{a}{0}\binom{b}{n} + \binom{a}{1}\binom{b}{n-1} + \cdots + \binom{a}{n}\binom{b}{0} = \binom{a+b}{n}.$$

Prove this by induction. *Hint:* Prove first that equation (12.9) holds for $a = 1$ and all b.

9. *Continuation.* By a comparison of the coefficients of t^n on both sides of

(12.10)
$$(1+t)^a(1+t)^b = (1+t)^{a+b}$$

prove more generally that (12.9) is true for arbitrary numbers a, b (and integral n).

10. Using (12.9), prove that

(12.11)
$$\binom{n}{0}^2 + \binom{n}{1}^2 + \binom{n}{2}^2 + \cdots + \binom{n}{n}^2 = \binom{2n}{n}.$$

11. Using (12.11), prove that

(12.12)
$$\sum_{\nu=0}^{n} \frac{(2n)!}{(\nu!)^2(n-\nu)!^2} = \binom{2n}{n}^2.$$

12. Prove that for integers $0 < a < b$

(12.13)
$$\sum_{k=1}^{a} (-1)^{a-k} \binom{a}{k}\binom{b+k}{b+1} = \binom{b}{a-1}.$$

Hint: Using (12.4) show that (12.11) is a special case of (12.9). Alternatively, compare the coefficients of t^{a-1} in $(1-t)^a(1-t)^{-b-2} = (1-t)^{a-b-2}$.

13. By specialization derive from (12.9) the identities

$$(12.14) \qquad \binom{a}{k} - \binom{a}{k-1} + - \cdots \mp \binom{a}{1} \pm 1 = \binom{a-1}{k}$$

and

$$(12.15) \qquad \sum_{v} (-1)^v \binom{a}{v} \binom{n-v}{r} = \binom{n-a}{n-r},$$

valid if k, n, and r are positive integers. *Hint:* Use (12.4).

14. Using (12.9), prove that[25] for arbitrary a, b and integral k

$$(12.16) \qquad \sum_{j=0}^{k} \binom{a+k-j-1}{k-j} \binom{b+j-1}{j} = \binom{a+b+k-1}{k}.$$

Hint: Apply (12.4) back and forth. Alternatively, use (12.10) with changed signs of the exponents.

Note the important special cases $b = 1, 2$.

15. Referring to the problems of section 11, notice that (11.12), (11.14), (11.15), and (11.16) define probabilities. In each the quantities should therefore add to unity. Show that this is implied, respectively, by (12.8), (12.9), (12.16), and the binomial theorem.

16. From the definition of $A(r, n)$ in problem 7 of section 11 it follows that $A(r, n) = 0$ if $r < n$ and $A(n, n) = n!$. In other words

$$(12.17) \qquad \sum_{k=0}^{n} (-1)^{n-k} \binom{n}{k} k^r = \begin{array}{ll} 0 & \text{if } r < n \\ n! & \text{if } r = n. \end{array}$$

(a) Prove (12.17) directly by reduction from n to $n-1$. (b) Next prove (12.17) by considering the rth derivative of $(1-e^t)^n$ at $t = 0$. (c) Generalize (12.17) by starting from (11.11) instead of (11.6).

17. If $0 \leq N \leq n$ prove by induction that for each integer $r \geq 0$

$$(12.18) \qquad \sum_{v=0}^{N} (-1)^v \binom{N}{v} (n-v)_r = \binom{n-N}{r-N} r!.$$

(Note that the right-hand member vanishes when $r < N$ and when $r > n$.) Verify (12.18) by considering the rth derivative of $t^{n-N}(t-1)^N$ at $t = 1$.

18. Prove by induction (using the binomial theorem)

$$(12.19) \qquad \binom{n}{1}\frac{1}{1} - \binom{n}{2}\frac{1}{2} + \cdots + (-1)^{n-1} \binom{n}{n}\frac{1}{n} = 1 + \frac{1}{2} + \frac{1}{3} + \cdots + \frac{1}{n}.$$

Verify (12.19) by integrating the identity $\sum_{0}^{n-1} (1-t)^v = \{1 - (1-t)^n\}t^{-1}$.

---

[25] For a more elegant proof see problem 15 of IX, 9.

19. Show that for any positive integer m

$$(12.20) \qquad (x+y+z)^m = \sum \frac{m!}{a!\,b!\,c!}\, x^a y^b z^c$$

where the summation extends over all non-negative integers a, b, c, such that $a + b + c = m$.

20. Show that $\Gamma(a+1) = a\Gamma(a)$ for all $a > 0$, whence

$$(12.21) \qquad \binom{-a}{k} = (-1)^k \frac{\Gamma(a+k)}{k!\,\Gamma(a)}\,.$$

21. Prove that for any positive integers a and b

$$(12.22) \qquad \frac{(a+1)(a+2)\cdots(a+n)}{(b+1)(b+2)\cdots(b+n)} \sim \frac{b!}{a!}\, n^{a-b}.$$

22. The *gamma function* is defined by

$$(12.23) \qquad \Gamma(x) = \int_0^\infty t^{x-1} e^{-t}\, dt$$

where $x > 0$. Show that $\Gamma(x) \sim \sqrt{2\pi}\, e^{-x} x^{x-\frac{1}{2}}$. [Notice that if $x = n$ is an integer, $\Gamma(n) = (n-1)!$.]

23. Let a and r be arbitrary positive numbers and n a positive integer. Show that

$$(12.24) \qquad a(a+r)(a+2r)\cdots(a+nr) \sim Cr^{n+1}n^{n+\frac{1}{2}+a/r}.$$

$$\left[\text{The constant } C \text{ is equal to } \frac{\sqrt{2\pi}}{\Gamma(a/r)}. \right]$$

24. Using the results of the preceding problem, show that

$$(12.25) \qquad \frac{a(a+r)(a+2r)\cdots(a+nr)}{b(b+r)(b+2r)\cdots(b+nr)} \sim \frac{\Gamma(b/r)}{\Gamma(a/r)}\, n^{(a-b)/r}.$$

25. From (8.10) conclude

$$(12.26) \qquad e^{-t/(1-t)} < 1 - t = e^{-t}, \qquad\qquad 0 < t < 1.$$

CHAPTER III*

Fluctuations in Coin Tossing
and Random Walks

This chapter digresses from our main topic, which is taken up again only in chapter V. Its material has traditionally served as a first orientation and guide to more advanced theories. Simple methods will soon lead us to results of far-reaching theoretical and practical importance. We shall encounter theoretical conclusions which not only are unexpected but actually come as a shock to intuition and common sense. They will reveal that commonly accepted notions concerning chance fluctuations are without foundation and that the implications of the law of large numbers are widely misconstrued. For example, in various applications it is assumed that observations on an individual coin-tossing game during a long time interval will yield the same statistical characteristics as the observation of the results of a huge number of independent games at one given instant. This is not so. Indeed, using a currently popular jargon we reach the conclusion that in a population of normal coins the majority is necessarily maladjusted. [For empirical illustrations see section 6 and example (4.b).]

Until recently the material of this chapter used to be treated by analytic methods and, consequently, the results appeared rather deep. The elementary method[1] used in the sequel is therefore a good example of the newly discovered power of combinatorial methods. The results are fairly representative of a wider class of fluctuation phenomena[2] to be discussed

---

* This chapter may be omitted or read in conjunction with the following chapters. Reference to its contents will be made in chapters X (laws of large numbers), XI (first-passage times), XIII (recurrent events), and XIV (random walks), but the contents will not be used explicitly in the sequel.

[1] The discovery of the possibility of an elementary approach was the principal motivation for the second edition of this book (1957). The present version is new and greatly improved since it avoids various combinatorial tricks.

[2] See footnote 12.

in volume 2. All results will be derived anew, independently, by different methods. This chapter will therefore serve primarily readers who are not in a hurry to proceed with the systematic theory, or readers interested in the spirit of probability theory without wanting to specialize in it. For other readers a comparison of methods should prove instructive and interesting. Accordingly, *the present chapter should be read at the reader's discretion independently of, or parallel to, the remainder of the book*.

1. GENERAL ORIENTATION.
THE REFLECTION PRINCIPLE

From a formal point of view we shall be concerned with arrangements of finitely many plus ones and minus ones. Consider $n = p + q$ symbols $\epsilon_1, \ldots, \epsilon_n$, each standing either for $+1$ or for -1; suppose that there are p plus ones and q minus ones. The partial sum $s_k = \epsilon_1 + \cdots + \epsilon_k$ represents the difference between the number of pluses and minuses occurring at the first k places. Then

$$(1.1) \qquad s_k - s_{k-1} = \epsilon_k = \pm 1, \qquad s_0 = 0, \qquad s_n = p - q,$$

where $k = 1, 2, \ldots, n$.

We shall use a geometric terminology and refer to rectangular coordinates t, x; for definiteness we imagine the t-axis is horizontal, the x-axis vertical. The arrangement $(\epsilon_1, \ldots, \epsilon_n)$ will be represented by a polygonal line whose kth side has slope ϵ_k and whose kth vertex has ordinate s_k. Such lines will be called paths.

Definition. *Let $n > 0$ and x be integers. A path $(s_1, s_2, \ldots, s_n)$ from the origin to the point (n, x) is a polygonal line whose vertices have abscissas $0, 1, \ldots, n$ and ordinates $s_0, s_1, \ldots, s_n$ satisfying (1.1) with $s_n = x$.*

We shall refer to n as the *length* of the path. There are 2^n paths of length n. If p among the ϵ_k are positive and q are negative, then

$$(1.2) \qquad\qquad n = p + q, \qquad x = p - q.$$

A path from the origin to an arbitrary point (n, x) exists only if n and x are of the form (1.2). In this case the p places for the positive ϵ_k can be chosen from the $n = p + q$ available places in

$$(1.3) \qquad\qquad N_{n,x} = \binom{p+q}{p} = \binom{p+q}{q}$$

different ways. For convenience we *define $N_{n,x} = 0$ whenever n and x*

are not of the form (1.2). With this convention *there exist exactly* $N_{n,x}$ *different paths from the origin to an arbitrary point* (n, x).

Before turning to the principal topic of this chapter, namely the theory of random walks, we illustrate possible applications of our scheme.

Examples.   (*a*) *The ballot theorem.* The following amusing proposition was proved in 1878 by W. A. Whitworth, and again in 1887 by J. Bertrand.

Suppose that, in a ballot, candidate P scores p votes and candidate Q scores q votes, where $p > q$. The probability that throughout the counting there are always more votes for P than for Q equals $(p-q)/(p+q)$.

Similar problems of arrangements have attracted the attention of students of combinatorial analysis under the name of ballot problems. The recent renaissance of combinatorial methods has increased their popularity, and it is now realized that a great many important problems may be reformulated as variants of some generalized ballot problem.[3]

Figure 1. Illustrating positive paths. The figure shows also that there are exactly as many strictly positive paths from the origin to the point $(2n, 0)$ as there are nonnegative paths from the origin to $(2n-2, 0)$.

The whole voting record may be represented by a path of length $p + q$ in which $\epsilon_k = +1$ if the kth vote is for P; conversely, every path from the origin to the point $(p + q, p - q)$ can be interpreted as a record of a voting with the given totals p and q. Clearly s_k is the number of votes by which P leads, or trails, just after the kth vote is cast. The candidate P leads throughout the voting if, and only if, $s_1 > 0, \ldots, s_n > 0$, that is, if all vertices lie strictly above the t-axis. (The path from 0 to N_1 in figure 1 is of this type.) The ballot theorem assumes tacitly that all admissible paths are equally probable. The assertion then reduces to the theorem proved at the end of this section as an immediate consequence of the reflection lemma.

(*b*) *Galton's rank order test.*[4] Suppose that a quantity (such as the height

---

[3] A survey of the history and the literature may be found in *Some aspects of the random sequence*, by D. E. Barton and C. L. Mallows [Ann. Math. Statist., vol. 36 (1965), pp. 236–260]. These authors discuss also various applications. The most recent generalization with many applications in queuing theory is due to L. Takacs.

[4] J. L. Hodges, Biometrika, vol. 42 (1955), pp. 261–262.

of plants) is measured on each of r treated subjects, and also on each of r control subjects. Denote the measurements by $a_1, \ldots, a_r$ and $b_1, \ldots, b_r$, respectively. To fix ideas, suppose that each group is arranged in decreasing order: $a_1 > a_2 > \cdots$ and $b_1 > b_2 > \ldots$. (To avoid trivialities we assume that no two observations are equal.) Let us now combine the two sequences into one sequence of $n = 2r$ numbers arranged in decreasing order. For an extremely successful treatment all the a's should precede the b's, whereas a completely ineffectual treatment should result in a random placement of a's and b's. Thus the efficiency of the treatment can be judged by the number of different a's that precede the b of the same rank, that is, by the number of subscripts k for which $a_k > b_k$. This idea was first used in 1876 by F. Galton for data referred to him by Charles Darwin. In this case r equaled 15 and the a's were ahead 13 times. Without knowledge of the actual probabilities Galton concluded that the treatment *was* effective. But, assuming perfect randomness, the probability that the a's lead 13 times or more equals $\frac{3}{16}$. This means that in three out of sixteen cases a perfectly ineffectual treatment would appear as good or better than the treatment classified as effective by Galton. This shows that a quantitative analysis may be a valuable supplement to our rather shaky intuition.

For an interpretation in terms of paths write $\epsilon_k = +1$ or -1 according as the kth term of the combined sequence is an a or a b. The resulting path of length $2r$ joins the origin to the point $(2r, 0)$ of the t-axis. The event $a_k > b_k$ occurs if, and only if, s_{2k-1} contains at least k plus ones, that is, if $s_{2k-1} > 0$. This entails $s_{2k} \geq 0$, and so the $(2k-1)$st and the $2k$th sides are above the t-axis. It follows that the inequality $a_k > b_k$ holds ν times if, and only if, 2ν sides lie above the t-axis. In section 9 we shall prove the unexpected result that the probability for this is $1/(r+1)$, irrespective of ν. (For related tests based on the theory of runs see II, 5.b.)

(c) *Tests of the Kolmogorov-Smirnov type.* Suppose that we observe two populations of the same biological species (animals or plants) living at different places, or that we wish to compare the outputs of two similar machines. For definiteness let us consider just one measurable characteristic such as height, weight, or thickness, and suppose that for each of the two populations we are given a sample of r observations, say $a_1, \ldots, a_r$ and $b_1, \ldots, b_r$. The question is roughly whether these data are consistent with the hypothesis that the two populations are statistically identical. In this form the problem is vague, but for our purposes it is not necessary to discuss its more precise formulation in modern statistical theory. It suffices to say that the tests are based on a comparison of the two empirical distributions. For every t denote by $A(t)$ the fraction k/n of subscripts i for which $a_i \leq t$. The function so defined over the real axis is the *empirical distribution* of the a's. The empirical distribution B is defined in like manner. A refined mathematical theory originated by N. V. Smirnov (1939) derives the probability distribution of the maximum of the discrepancies $|A(t) - B(t)|$ and of other quantities which can be used for testing the stated hypothesis. The theory is rather intricate, but was greatly simplified and made more intuitive by B. V. Gnedenko who had the lucky idea to connect it with the geometric theory of paths. As in the preceding example we associate with the two samples a path of length $2r$ leading from the origin to the point $(2r, 0)$. To say that the two populations are statistically indistinguishable amounts to saying that ideally the sampling experiment makes all possible paths equally probable. Now it is easily seen that $|A(t) - B(t)| > \xi$ for some t if, and only if, $|s_k| > \xi r$ for some k. The probability of this event is simply the probability that a path of length $2r$ leading from the origin to the point $(0, 2r)$ is not constrained to the interval between $\pm\xi r$. This probability has been known for a long time because it is connected with the ruin problem in random walks and with the physical problem of diffusion with absorbing barriers. (See problem 3.)

This example is beyond the scope of the present volume, but it illustrates how random walks can be applied to problems of an entirely different nature.

(*d*) *The ideal coin-tossing game and its relation to stochastic processes.* A path of length n can be interpreted as the record of an ideal experiment consisting of n successive tosses of a coin. If $+1$ stands for heads, then s_k equals the (positive or negative) excess of the accumulated number of heads over tails at the conclusion of the kth trial. The classical description introduces the fictitious gambler Peter who at each trial wins or loses a unit amount. The sequence $s_1, s_2, \ldots, s_n$ then represents Peter's successive cumulative gains. It will be seen presently that they are subject to chance fluctuations of a totally unexpected character.

The picturesque language of gambling should not detract from the general importance of the coin-tossing model. In fact, the model may serve as a first approximation to many more complicated chance-dependent processes in physics, economics, and learning theory. Quantities such as the energy of a physical particle, the wealth of an individual, or the accumulated learning of a rat are supposed to vary in consequence of successive collisions or random impulses of some sort. For purposes of a first orientation one assumes that the individual changes are of the same magnitude, and that their sign is regulated by a coin-tossing game. Refined models take into account that the changes and their probabilities vary from trial to trial, but even the simple coin-tossing model leads to surprising, indeed to shocking, results. They are of practical importance because they show that, contrary to generally accepted views, the laws governing a prolonged series of individual observations will show patterns and averages far removed from those derived for a whole population. In other words, currently popular psychological tests would lead one to say that in a population of "normal" coins most individual coins are "maladjusted."

It turns out that the chance fluctuations in coin tossing are typical for more general chance processes with cumulative effects. Anyhow, it stands to reason that if even the simple coin-tossing game leads to paradoxical results that contradict our intuition, the latter cannot serve as a reliable guide in more complicated situations.   ◄

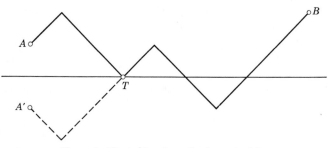

Figure 2. Illustrating the reflection principle.

It is as surprising as it is pleasing that most important conclusions can be drawn from the following simple lemma.

Let $A = (a, \alpha)$ and $B = (b, \beta)$ be integral points in the positive quadrant: $b > a \geq 0$, $\alpha > 0$, $\beta > 0$. By reflection of A on the t-axis is meant the point $A' = (a, -\alpha)$. (See figure 2.) A path from A to B is defined in the obvious manner.

Lemma.[5]   (*Reflection principle.*) *The number of paths from A to B which touch or cross the x-axis equals the number of all paths from A' to B.*

Proof. Consider a path $(s_a = \alpha, s_{a+1}, \ldots, s_b = \beta)$ from A to B having one or more vertices on the t-axis. Let t be the abscissa of the first such vertex (see figure 2); that is, choose t so that $s_a > 0, \ldots, s_{t-1} > 0$, $s_t = 0$. Then $(-s_a, -s_{a+1}, \ldots, -s_{t-1}, s_t = 0, s_{t+1}, s_{t+2}, \ldots, s_b)$ is a

---

[5] The reflection principle is used frequently in various disguises, but without the geometrical interpretation it appears as an ingenious but incomprehensible trick. The probabilistic literature attributes it to D. André (1887). It appears in connection with the difference equations for random walks in XIV, 9. These are related to some partial differential equations where the reflection principle is a familiar tool called *method of images*. It is generally attributed to Maxwell and Lord Kelvin. For the use of repeated reflections see problems 2 and 3.

path leading from A' to B and having $T = (t, 0)$ as its first vertex on the t-axis. The sections AT and $A'T$ being reflections of each other, there exists a one-to-one correspondence between all paths from A' to B and such paths from A to B that have a vertex on the x-axis. This proves the lemma.   ▶

As an immediate consequence we prove the result discussed in example (a). It will serve as starting point for the whole theory of this chapter.

The ballot theorem. *Let n and x be positive integers. There are exactly $\dfrac{x}{n} N_{n,x}$ paths $(s_1, \ldots, s_n = x)$ from the origin to the point (n, x) such that $s_1 > 0, \ldots, s_n > 0$.*

Proof. Clearly there exist exactly as many admissible paths as there are paths from the point $(1, 1)$ to (n, x) which neither touch or cross the t-axis. By the last lemma the number of such paths equals

$$N_{n-1,x-1} - N_{n-1,x+1} = \binom{p+q-1}{p-1} - \binom{p+q-1}{p}$$

with p and q defined in (1.2). A trite calculation shows that the right side equals $N_{n,x}(p-q)/(p+q)$, as asserted.   ▶

2. RANDOM WALKS: BASIC NOTIONS AND NOTATIONS

The ideal coin-tossing game will now be described in the terminology of random walks which has greater intuitive appeal and is better suited for generalizations. As explained in the preceding example, when a path $(s_1, \ldots, s_\rho)$ is taken as record of ρ successive coin tossings the partial sums $s_1, \ldots, s_\rho$ represent the successive cumulative gains. For the geometric description it is convenient to pretend that the tossings are performed at a uniform rate so that the nth trial occurs at epoch[6] n. The successive partial sums $s_1, \ldots, s_n$ will be marked as points on the vertical x-axis; they will be called the positions of a "particle" performing a random walk. Note that the particle moves in unit steps, up or down, on a

---

[6] Following J. Riordan, the word *epoch* is used to denote *points* on the time axis because some contexts use the alternative terms (such as moment, time, point) in different meanings. Whenever used mathematically, the word time will refer to an interval or duration. A physical experiment may take some time, but our ideal trials are timeless and occur at epochs.

line. A path represents the record of such a movement. For example, the path from O to N in figure 1 stands for a random walk of six steps terminating by a return to the origin.

Each path of length ρ can be interpreted as the outcome of a random walk experiment; there are 2^ρ such paths, and we attribute probability $2^{-\rho}$ to each. (Different assignments will be introduced in chapter XIV. To distinguish it from others the present random walk is called *symmetric*.)

We have now completed the definition of the sample space and of the probabilities in it, but the dependence on the unspecified number ρ is disturbing. To see its role consider the event that the path passes through the point $(2, 2)$. The first two steps must be positive, and there are $2^{\rho-2}$ paths with this property. As could be expected, the probability of our event therefore equals $\frac{1}{4}$ regardless of the value of ρ. More generally, for any $k \leq \rho$ it is possible to prescribe arbitrarily the first k steps, and exactly $2^{\rho-k}$ paths will satisfy these k conditions. It follows that *an event determined by the first $k \leq \rho$ steps has a probability independent of ρ*. In practice, therefore, the number ρ plays no role provided it is sufficiently large. In other words, any path of length n can be taken as the initial section of a very long path, and there is no need to specify the latter length. Conceptually and formally it is most satisfactory to consider unending sequences of trials, but this would require the use of non-denumerable sample spaces. In the sequel it is therefore understood that the length ρ of the paths constituting the sample space is larger than the number of steps occurring in our formulas. Except for this we shall be permitted, and glad, to forget about ρ.

To conform with the notations to be used later on in the general theory we shall denote the individual steps generically by $X_1, X_2, \ldots$ and the positions of the particle by $S_1, S_2, \ldots$. Thus

$$(2.1) \qquad S_n = X_1 + \cdots + X_n, \qquad S_0 = 0.$$

From any particular path one can read off the corresponding values of $X_1, X_2, \ldots$; that is, the X_k are functions of the path.[7] For example, for the path of figure 1 clearly $X_1 = X_2 = X_4 = 1$ and $X_3 = X_5 = = X_6 = -1$.

We shall generally describe all events by stating the appropriate conditions on the sums S_k. Thus the event "at epoch n the particle is at the point r" will be denoted by $\{S_n = r\}$. For its probability we write $p_{n,r}$. (For smoother language we shall describe this event as a "visit" to r at

---

[7] In the terminology to be introduced in chapter IX the X_k are random variables.

epoch n.) The number $N_{n,r}$ of paths from the origin to the point (n, r) is given by (1.3), and hence

$$(2.2) \qquad p_{n,r} = \mathbf{P}\{\mathbf{S}_n = r\} = \binom{n}{\dfrac{n+r}{2}} 2^{-n},$$

where it is understood that the binomial coefficient is to be interpreted as zero unless $(n+r)/2$ is an integer between 0 and n, inclusive.

A *return to the origin* occurs at epoch k if $\mathbf{S}_k = 0$. Here k is necessarily even, and for $k = 2\nu$ the probability of a return to the origin equals $p_{2\nu,0}$. Because of the frequent occurrence of this probability we denote it by $u_{2\nu}$. Thus

$$(2.3) \qquad u_{2\nu} = \binom{2\nu}{\nu} 2^{-2\nu}.$$

When the binomial coefficient is expressed in terms of factorials, Stirling's formula II, (9.1) shows directly that

$$(2.4) \qquad u_{2\nu} \sim \frac{1}{\sqrt{\pi\nu}}$$

where the sign $\sim$ indicates that the ratio of the two sides tends to 1 as $\nu \to \infty$; the right side serves as excellent approximation[8] to $u_{2\nu}$ even for moderate values of ν.

Among the returns to the origin the *first return* commands special attention. A first return occurs at epoch 2ν if

$$(2.5) \qquad \mathbf{S}_1 \neq 0, \ldots, \mathbf{S}_{2\nu-1} \neq 0, \quad but \quad \mathbf{S}_{2\nu} = 0.$$

The probability for this event will be denoted by $f_{2\nu}$. By definition $f_0 = 0$.

The probabilities f_{2n} and u_{2n} are related in a noteworthy manner. A visit to the origin at epoch $2n$ may be the first return, or else the first return occurs at an epoch $2k < 2n$ and is followed by a renewed return $2n - 2k$ time units later. The probability of the latter contingency is $f_{2k}u_{2n-2k}$ because there are $2^{2k}f_{2k}$ paths of length $2k$ ending with a first return, and $2^{2n-2k}u_{2n-2k}$ paths from the point $(2k, 0)$ to $(2n, 0)$. It follows that

$$(2.6) \qquad u_{2n} = f_2 u_{2n-2} + f_4 u_{2n-4} + \cdots + f_{2n}u_0, \qquad n \geq 1.$$

(See problem 5.)

---

[8] For the true value $u_{10} = 0.2461$ we get the approximation 0.2523; for $u_{20} = 0.1762$ the approximation is 0.1784. The per cent error decreases roughly in inverse proportion to ν.

The normal approximation. Formula (2.2) gives no direct clue as to the range within which S_n is likely to fall. An answer to this question is furnished by an approximation formula which represents a special case of the central limit theorem and will be proved[9] in VII, 2.

The probability that $a < S_n < b$ is obtained by summing probabilities $p_{n,r}$ over all r between a and b. For the evaluation it suffices to know the probabilities for all inequalities of the form $S_n > a$. Such probabilities can be estimated from the fact that for all x as $n \to \infty$

$$(2.7) \qquad P\{S_n > x\sqrt{n}\} \to 1 - \mathfrak{N}(x) = \frac{1}{\sqrt{2\pi}} \int_x^\infty e^{-\frac{1}{2}t^2}\, dt$$

where $\mathfrak{N}$ stands for the normal distribution function defined in VII, 1. Its nature is of no particular interest for our present purposes. The circumstance that the limit exists shows the important fact that for large n the ratios $S_n/\sqrt{n}$ are governed approximately by the same probabilities and so the same approximation can be used for all large n.

The accompanying table gives a good idea of the probable range of S_n. More and better values will be found in table 1 of chapter VII.

TABLE 1

x	0.5	1.0	1.5	2.0	2.5	3.0
$P\{S_n > x\sqrt{n}\}$	0.309	0.159	0.067	0.023	0.006	0.001

3. THE MAIN LEMMA

As we saw, the probability of a return to the origin at epoch 2ν equals the quantity $u_{2\nu}$ of (2.3). As the theory of fluctuations in random walks began to take shape it came as a surprise that almost all formulas involved this probability. One reason for this is furnished by the following simple lemma, which has a mild surprise value of its own and provides the key to the deeper theorems of the next section.

Lemma 1.[10] *The probability that no return to the origin occurs up to and including epoch $2n$ is the same as the probability that a return occurs at epoch $2n$. In symbols,*

$$(3.1) \qquad P\{S_1 \neq 0, \ldots, S_{2n} \neq 0\} = P\{S_{2n} = 0\} = u_{2n}.$$

---

[9] The special case required in the sequel is treated *separately* in VII, 2 without reference to the general binomial distribution. The proof is simple and can be inserted at this place.

[10] This lemma is obvious from the form of the generating function $\Sigma f_{2k} s^{2k}$ [see XI, (3.6)] and has been noted for its curiosity value. The discovery of its significance is recent. For a geometric proof see problem 7.

Here, of course, $n > 0$. When the event on the left occurs either all the S_j are positive, or all are negative. The two contingencies being equally probable we can restate (3.1) in the form

(3.2) $$P\{S_1 > 0, \ldots, S_{2n} > 0\} = \tfrac{1}{2}u_{2n}.$$

Proof. Considering all the possible values of S_{2n} it is clear that

(3.3) $$P\{S_1 > 0, \ldots, S_{2n} > 0\} = \sum_{r=1}^{\infty} P\{S_1 > 0, \ldots, S_{2n-1} > 0, S_{2n} = 2r\}$$

(where all terms with $r > n$ vanish). By the ballot theorem the number of paths satisfying the condition indicated on the right side equals $N_{2n-1,2r-1} - N_{2n-1,2r+1}$, and so the rth term of the sum equals

$$\tfrac{1}{2}(p_{2n-1,2r-1} - p_{2n-1,2r+1}).$$

The negative part of the rth term cancels against the positive part of the $(r+1)$st term with the result that the sum in (3.3) reduces to $\tfrac{1}{2}p_{2n-1,1}$. It is easily verified that $p_{2n-1,1} = u_{2n}$ and this concludes the proof. ▶

The lemma can be restated in several ways; for example,

(3.4) $$P\{S_1 \geq 0, \ldots, S_{2n} \geq 0\} = u_{2n}.$$

Indeed, a path of length $2n$ with all vertices strictly above the x-axis passes through the point $(1, 1)$. Taking this point as new origin we obtain a path of length $2n - 1$ with all vertices above or on the new x-axis. It follows that

(3.5) $$P\{S_1 > 0, \ldots, S_{2n} > 0\} = \tfrac{1}{2}P\{S_1 \geq 0, \ldots, S_{2n-1} \geq 0\}.$$

But S_{2n-1} is an odd number, and hence $S_{2n-1} \geq 0$ implies that also $S_{2n} \geq 0$. The probability on the right in (3.5) is therefore the same as (3.4) and hence (3.4) is true. (See problem 8.)

Lemma 1 leads directly to an explicit expression for the probability distribution for the first return to the origin. Saying that a first return occurs at epoch $2n$ amounts to saying that the conditions

$$S_1 \neq 0, \ldots, S_{2k} \neq 0$$

are satisfied for $k = n - 1$, but not for $k = n$. In view of (3.1) this means that

(3.6) $$f_{2n} = u_{2n-2} - u_{2n}, \qquad n = 1, 2, \ldots.$$

A trite calculation reduces this expression to

$$(3.7) \qquad\qquad f_{2n} = \frac{1}{2n-1}\, u_{2n}.$$

We have thus proved

Lemma 2. *The probability that the first return to the origin occurs at epoch 2n is given by* (3.6) *or* (3.7).

It follows from (3.6) that $f_2 + f_4 + \cdots = 1$. In the coin-tossing terminology this means that an ultimate equalization of the fortunes becomes practically certain if the game is prolonged sufficiently long. This was to be anticipated on intuitive grounds, except that the great number of trials necessary to achieve practical certainty comes as a surprise. For example, the probability that no equalization occurs in 100 tosses is about 0.08.

4. LAST VISIT AND LONG LEADS

We are now prepared for a closer analysis of the nature of chance fluctuations in random walks. The results are startling. According to widespread beliefs a so-called law of averages should ensure that in a long coin-tossing game each player will be on the winning side for about half the time, and that the lead will pass not infrequently from one player to the other. Imagine then a huge sample of records of ideal coin-tossing games, each consisting of exactly $2n$ trials. We pick one at random and observe the epoch of the last tie (in other words, the number of the last trial at which the accumulated numbers of heads and tails were equal). This number is even, and we denote it by $2k$ (so that $0 \le k \le n$). Frequent changes of the lead would imply that k is likely to be relatively close to n, but this is not so. Indeed, the next theorem reveals the amazing fact that the distribution of k is symmetric in the sense that any value k has exactly the same probability as $n - k$. This symmetry implies in particular that the inequalities $k > n/2$ and $k < n/2$ are equally likely.[11] *With probability $\frac{1}{2}$ no equalization occurred in the second half of the game, regardless of the length of the game.* Furthermore, the probabilities near the end points are *greatest*; the most probable values for k are the extremes 0 and n. These results show that intuition leads to an erroneous picture of the probable effects of chance fluctuations. A few numerical results may be illuminating.

---

[11] The symmetry of the distribution for k was found empirically by computers and verified theoretically without knowledge of the exact distribution (4.1). See D. Blackwell, P. Dewel, and D. Freedman, Ann. Math. Statist., vol. 35 (1964), p. 1344.

Examples. (*a*) Suppose that a great many coin-tossing games are conducted simultaneously at the rate of one per second, day and night, for a whole year. On the average, in one out of ten games the last equalization will occur before 9 days have passed, and the lead will not change during the following 356 days. In one out of twenty cases the last equalization takes place within $2\frac{1}{4}$ days, and in one out of a hundred cases it occurs within the first 2 hours and 10 minutes.

(*b*) Suppose that in a learning experiment lasting one year a child was consistently lagging except, perhaps, during the initial week. Another child was consistently ahead except, perhaps, during the last week. Would the two children be judged equal? Yet, let a group of 11 children be exposed to a similar learning experiment involving no intelligence but only chance. One among the 11 would appear as leader for all but one week, another as laggard for all but one week.

The exact probabilities for the possible values of k are given by

Theorem 1. (*Arc sine law for last visits.*) *The probability that up to and including epoch* $2n$ *the last visit to the origin occurs at epoch* $2k$ *is given by*

$$(4.1) \qquad\qquad \alpha_{2k,2n} = u_{2k}u_{2n-2k}, \qquad\qquad k = 0, 1, \ldots, n.$$

Proof. We are concerned with paths satisfying the conditions $S_{2k} = 0$ and $S_{2k+1} \neq 0, \ldots, S_{2n} \neq 0$. The first $2k$ vertices can be chosen in $2^{2k}u_{2k}$ different ways. Taking the point $(2k, 0)$ as new origin and using (3.1) we see that the next $(2n-2k)$ vertices can be chosen in $2^{2n-2k}u_{2n-2k}$ ways. Dividing by 2^{2n} we get (4.1). ▶

It follows from the theorem that the numbers (4.1) add to unity. The probability distribution which attaches weight $\alpha_{2k,2n}$ to the point $2k$ will be called *the discrete arc sine distribution of order* n, because the inverse sine function provides excellent numerical approximations. The distribution is symmetric in the sense that $\alpha_{2k,2n} = \alpha_{2n-2k,2n}$. For $n = 2$ the three values are $\frac{3}{8}, \frac{2}{8}, \frac{3}{8}$; for $n = 10$ see table 2. The central term is always smallest.

The main features of the arc sine distributions are best explained by

TABLE 2

DISCRETE ARC SINE DISTRIBUTION OF ORDER 10

	$k = 0$ $k = 10$	$k = 1$ $k = 9$	$k = 2$ $k = 8$	$k = 3$ $k = 7$	$k = 4$ $k = 6$	$k = 5$
$\alpha_{2k,20}$	0.1762	0.0927	0.0736	0.0655	0.0617	0.0606

means of the graph of the function

(4.2) $$f(x) = \frac{1}{\pi\sqrt{x(1-x)}} \qquad 0 < x < 1.$$

Using Stirling's formula it is seen that u_{2n} is close to $1/\sqrt{\pi n}$, except when

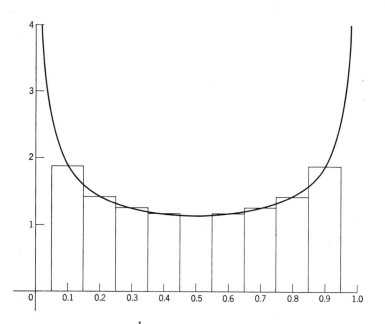

Figure 3. Graph of $f(x) = \dfrac{1}{\pi\sqrt{x(1-x)}}$. The construction explains the approximation (4.3).

n is very small. This yields the approximation

(4.3) $$\alpha_{2k,2n} \approx \frac{1}{n} f(x_k), \qquad \text{where} \quad x_k = \frac{k}{n};$$

the error committed is negligible except when k is extremely close to 0 or n. The right side equals the area of a rectangle with height $f(x_k)$ whose basis is the interval of length $1/n$ centered at x_k (see figure 3). For $0 < p < q < 1$ and large n the sum of the probabilities $\alpha_{2k,2n}$ with $pn < k < qn$ is therefore approximately equal to the area under the graph of f and above the interval $p < x < q$. This remains true also for $p = 0$ and $q = 1$ because the total area under the graph equals unity which is also true of the sum over all $\alpha_{2k,2n}$. Fortunately (4.2) can be integrated explicitly and we conclude that *for fixed* $0 < x < 1$ *and* n *sufficiently large*

(4.4)
$$\sum_{k < xn} \alpha_{2k,2n} \approx \frac{2}{\pi} \arcsin \sqrt{x}$$

approximately. Note that the right side is independent of n which means

TABLE 3

THE CONTINUOUS ARC SINE DISTRIBUTION $A(x) = \dfrac{2}{\pi} \arcsin \sqrt{x}$

x	$A(x)$	x	$A(x)$	x	$A(x)$
0.00	0.000	0.20	0.295	0.40	0.436
0.01	0.064	0.21	0.303	0.41	0.442
0.02	0.090	0.22	0.311	0.42	0.449
0.03	0.111	0.23	0.318	0.43	0.455
0.04	0.128	0.24	0.326	0.44	0.462
0.05	0.144	0.25	0.333	0.45	0.468
0.06	0.158	0.26	0.341	0.46	0.474
0.07	0.171	0.27	0.348	0.47	0.481
0.08	0.183	0.28	0.355	0.48	0.487
0.09	0.194	0.29	0.362	0.49	0.494
				0.50	0.500
0.10	0.205	0.30	0.369		
0.11	0.215	0.31	0.376		
0.12	0.225	0.32	0.383		
0.13	0.235	0.33	0.390		
0.14	0.244	0.34	0.396		
0.15	0.253	0.35	0.403		
0.16	0.262	0.36	0.410		
0.17	0.271	0.37	0.416		
0.18	0.279	0.38	0.423		
0.19	0.287	0.39	0.429		

For $x > \frac{1}{2}$ use $A(1 - x) = A(x)$.

that table 3 suffices for all arc sine distributions of large order. (Actually the approximations are rather good even for relatively small values of n.)

We saw that, contrary to popular notions, it is quite likely that in a long coin-tossing game one of the players remains practically the whole time on the winning side, the other on the losing side. The next theorem elucidates the same phenomenon by an analysis of the fraction of the total time that the particle spends on the positive side. One feels intuitively that this fraction is most likely to be close to $\frac{1}{2}$, but the opposite is true: The possible values close to $\frac{1}{2}$ are least probable, whereas the extremes $k = 0$ and $k = n$ have the greatest probability. The analysis is facilitated by the fortunate circumstance that the theorem again involves the discrete arc sine distribution (4.1) (which will occur twice more in section 8).

Theorem 2. (*Discrete arc sine law for sojourn times.*) *The probability that in the time interval from 0 to $2n$ the particle spends $2k$ time units on the positive side and $2n - 2k$ time units on the negative side equals* $\alpha_{2k,2n}$.

(The total time spent on the positive side is necessarily even.)

Corollary.[12] *If $0 < x < 1$, the probability that xn time units are spent on the positive side and $(1 - x)n$ on the negative side tends to $\dfrac{2}{\pi}$ arc sin $\sqrt{x}$ as $n \to \infty$.*

Examples. (*c*) From table 1 it is seen that the probability that in 20 tossings the lead never passes from one player to the other is about 0.352. The probability that the luckier player leads 16 times or more is about 0.685. (The approximation obtained from the corollary with $x = \frac{4}{5}$ is 0.590.) The probability that each player leads 10 times is only 0.06.

(*d*) Let n be large. With probability 0.20 the particle spends about 97.6 per cent of the time on the same side of the origin. In one out of ten cases the particle spends 99.4 per cent of the time on the same side.

(*e*) In example (*a*) a coin is tossed once per second for a total of 365 days. The accompanying table gives the times t_p such that with the stated

---

[12] Paul Lévy [*Sur certains processus stochastiques homogènes*, Compositia Mathematica, vol. 7 (1939), pp. 283–339] found this arc sine law for Brownian motion and referred to the connection with the coin-tossing game. A general arc sine limit law for the number of positive partial sums in a sequence of mutually independent random variables was proved by P. Erdös and M. Kac, *On the number of positive sums of independent random variables*, Bull. Amer. Math. Soc., vol. 53 (1947), pp. 1011–1020. The wide applicability of the arc sine limit law appeared at that time mysterious. The whole theory was profoundly reshaped when E. Sparre Andersen made the surprising discovery that many facets of the fluctuation theory of sums of independent random variables are of a purely combinatorial nature. [See Mathematica Scandinavica, vol. 1 (1953), pp. 263–285, and vol. 2 (1954), pp. 195–223.] The original proofs were exceedingly complicated, but they opened new avenues of research and are now greatly simplified. Theorem 2 was first proved by K. L. Chung and W. Feller by complicated methods. (See sections XII,5-6 of the first edition of this book.) Theorem 1 is new.

probability p the less fortunate player will be in the lead for a total time less than t_p.

p	t_p	p	t_p
0.9	153.95 days	0.3	19.89 days
0.8	126.10 days	0.2	8.93 days
0.7	99.65 days	0.1	2.24 days
0.6	75.23 days	0.05	13.5 hours
0.5	53.45 days	0.02	2.16 hours
0.4	34.85 days	0.01	32.4 minutes

▶

Proof of Theorem 2. Consider paths of the fixed length $2n$ and denote by $b_{2k,2n}$ the probability that exactly $2k$ sides lie above the t-axis. We have to prove that

(4.5) $$b_{2k,2v} = \alpha_{2k,2v}.$$

Now (3.4) asserts that $b_{2v,2v} = u_{2v}$ and for reasons of symmetry we have also $b_{0,2v} = u_{2v}$. It suffices therefore to prove (4.5) for $1 \leq k \leq v - 1$.

Assume then that exactly $2k$ out of the $2n$ time units are spent on the positive side, and $1 \leq k \leq v - 1$. In this case a first return to the origin must occur at some epoch $2r < 2n$, and two contingencies are possible. First, the $2r$ time units up to the first return may be spent on the positive side. In this case $r \leq k \leq n - 1$, and the section of the path beyond the vertex $(2r, 0)$ has exactly $2k - 2r$ sides above the axis. Obviously the number of such paths equals $\frac{1}{2} \cdot 2^{2r} f_{2r} \cdot 2^{2n-2r} b_{2k-2r,2n-2r}$. The other possibility is that the $2r$ time units up to the first return are spent on the negative side. In this case the section beyond the vertex $(2r, 0)$ has exactly $2k$ sides above the axis, whence $n - r \geq k$. The number of such paths equals $\frac{1}{2} \cdot 2^{2r} f_{2r} \cdot 2^{2n-2r} b_{2k,2n-2r}$. Accordingly, when $1 \leq k \leq n - 1$

(4.6) $$b_{2k,2n} = \frac{1}{2} \sum_{r=1}^{k} f_{2r} b_{2k-2r,2n-2r} + \frac{1}{2} \sum_{r=1}^{n-k} f_{2r} b_{2k,2n-2r}.$$

We now proceed by induction. The assertion (4.5) is trivially true for $v = 1$, and we assume it to be true for $v \leq n - 1$. Then (4.6) reduces to

(4.7) $$b_{2k,2n} = \frac{1}{2} u_{2n-2k} \sum_{r=1}^{k} f_{2r} u_{2k-2r} + \frac{1}{2} u_{2k} \sum_{r=1}^{n-k} f_{2r} u_{2n-2k-2r}.$$

In view of (2.6) the first sum equals u_{2k} while the second equals u_{2n-2k}. Hence (4.5) is true also for $v = n$.

. ▶

[A paradoxical result connected with the arc sine law is contained in problem 4 of XIV,9.]

*5. CHANGES OF SIGN

The theoretical study of chance fluctuations confronts us with many paradoxes. For example, one should expect naively that in a prolonged coin-tossing game the observed number of changes of lead should increase roughly in proportion to the duration of the game. In a game that lasts twice as long, Peter should lead about twice as often. This intuitive reasoning is false. We shall show that, in a sense to be made precise, the number of changes of lead in n trials increases only as $\sqrt{n}$: in $100n$ trials one should expect only 10 times as many changes of lead as in n trials. This proves once more that the waiting times between successive equalizations are likely to be fantastically long.

We revert to random walk terminology. A *change of sign* is said to occur at epoch n if S_{n-1} and S_{n+1} are of opposite signs, that is, if the path crosses the axis. In this case $S_n = 0$, and hence n is necessarily an even (positive) integer.

Theorem 1.[13]   *The probability* $\xi_{r,2n+1}$ *that up to epoch* $2n + 1$ *there occur exactly* r *changes of sign equals* $2p_{2n+1,2r+1}$. *In other words*

$$(5.1) \qquad\qquad \xi_{r,2n+1} = 2P\{S_{2n+1} = 2r + 1\}, \qquad r = 0, 1, \ldots.$$

Proof. We begin by rephrasing the theorem in a more convenient form. If the first step leads to the point $(1, 1)$ we take this point as the origin of a new coordinate system. To a crossing of the horizontal axis in the old system there now corresponds a crossing of the line below the new axis, that is, a crossing of the level -1. An analogous procedure is applicable when $S_1 = -1$, and it is thus seen that the theorem is fully equivalent to the following *proposition*: The probability that up to epoch $2n$ the level -1 is crossed exactly r times equals $2p_{2n+1,2r+1}$.

Consider first the case $r = 0$. To say that the level -1 has not been crossed amounts to saying that the level -2 has not been touched (or crossed). In this case S_{2n} is a non-negative even integer. For $k \geq 0$ we conclude from the basic reflection lemma of section 1 that the number of paths from $(0, 0)$ to $(2n, 2k)$ that do touch the level -2 equals the number of paths to $(2n, 2k + 4)$. The probability to reach the point

---

* This section is not used explicitly in the sequel.
[13] For an analogous theorem for the number of returns to the origin see problems 9-10. For an alternative proof see problem 11.

$(2n, 2k)$ without having touched the level -2 is therefore equal to $p_{2n,2k} - p_{2n,2k+4}$. The probability that the level -2 has not been touched equals the sum of the quantities for $k = 0, 1, 2, \ldots$. Most terms cancel, and we find that our probability equals $p_{2n,0} + p_{2n,2}$. This proves the assertion when $r = 0$ because

$$(5.2) \qquad p_{2n+1,1} = \tfrac{1}{2}(p_{2n,0} + p_{2n,2})$$

as is obvious from the fact that every path through $(2n + 1, 1)$ passes through either $(2n, 0)$ or $(2n, 2)$.

Next let $r = 1$. A path that crosses the level -1 at epoch $2\nu - 1$ may be decomposed into the section from $(0, 0)$ to $(2\nu, -2)$ and a path of length $2n - 2\nu$ starting at $(2\nu, -2)$. To the latter section we apply the result for $r = 0$ but interchanging the roles of plus and minus. We conclude that the number of paths of length $2n - 2\nu$ starting at $(2\nu, -2)$ and not crossing the level -1 equals the number of paths from $(2\nu, -2)$ to $(2n + 1, -3)$. But each path of this kind combines with the initial section to a path from $(0, 0)$ to $(2n + 1, -3)$. It follows that the number of paths of length $2n$ that cross the level -1 exactly once equals the number of paths from the origin to $(2n + 1, -3)$, that is, $2^{2n+1}p_{2n+1,3}$. This proves the assertion for $r = 1$.

The proposition with arbitrary r now follows by induction, the argument used in the second part of the proof requiring no change. (It was presented for the special case $r = 1$ only to avoid extra letters.) ▶

An amazing consequence of the theorem is that *the probability* $\xi_{r,n}$ *of* r *changes of sign in* n *trials decreases with* r:

$$(5.3) \qquad \xi_{0,n} \geq \xi_{1,n} > \xi_{2,n} > \cdots.$$

This means that regardless of the number of tosses, the event that the lead never changes is more probable than any preassigned number of changes.

Examples. (*a*) The probabilities x_r for exactly r changes of sign in 99 trials are as follows:

r	x_r	r	x_r
0	0.1592	7	0.0517
1	0.1529	8	0.0375
2	0.1412	9	0.0260
3	0.1252	10	0.0174
4	0.1066	11	0.0111
5	0.0873	12	0.0068
6	0.0686	13	0.0040

(b) The probability that in 10,000 trials no change of sign occurs is about 0.0160. The probabilities x_r for exactly r changes decrease very slowly; for $r = 10, 20, 30$ the values are $x_r = 0.0156, 0.0146$, and 0.0130. The probability that in 10,000 trials the lead changes at most 10 times is about 0.0174; in other words, one out of six such series will show not more than 10 changes of lead.   ▶

A pleasing property of the identity (5.1) is that it enables us to apply the normal approximation derived in section 2. Suppose that n is large and x a fixed positive number. The probability that fewer than $x\sqrt{n}$ changes of sign occur before epoch n is practically the same as $2\mathbf{P}\{S_n < 2x\sqrt{n}\}$, and according to (2.8) the last probability tends to $\mathfrak{N}(2x) - \frac{1}{2}$ as $n \to \infty$. We have thus

Theorem 2. (*Normal approximation.*) *The probability that fewer than* $x\sqrt{n}$ *changes of sign occur before epoch* n *tends to* $2\mathfrak{N}(2x) - 1$ *as* $n \to \infty$.

It follows that the *median* for the number of changes of sign is about $0.337\sqrt{n}$; this means that for n sufficiently large it is about as likely that there occur fewer than $0.337\sqrt{n}$ changes of sign than that occur more. With probability $\frac{1}{10}$ there will be fewer than $0.0628\sqrt{n}$ changes of sign, etc.[14]

6. AN EXPERIMENTAL ILLUSTRATION

Figure 4 represents the result of a computer experiment simulating 10,000 tosses of a coin; the same material is tabulated in example I, (6.c). The top line contains the graph of the first 550 trials; the next two lines represent the entire record of 10,000 trials the scale in the horizontal direction being changed in the ratio $1:10$. The scale in the vertical direction is the same in the two graphs.

When looking at the graph most people feel surprised by the length of the intervals between successive crossings of the axis. As a matter of fact, the graph represents a rather mild case history and was chosen as the mildest among three available records. A more startling example is obtained by looking at the same graph in the *reverse* direction; that is, reversing the order in which the 10,000 trials actually occurred (see section 8). Theoretically, the series as graphed and the reversed series are equally legitimate as representative of an ideal random walk. The reversed random

---

[14] This approximation gives $\frac{1}{10}$ for the probability of at most 6 equalizations in 10,000 trials. This is an underestimate, the true value being about 0.112.

Figure 4. The record of 10,000 tosses of an ideal coin (described in section 6).

walk has the following characteristics. Starting from the origin

the path stays on the

negative side		*positive side*	
for the first 7804 *steps*		*next* 8 *steps*	
next	2 *steps*	*next* 54 *steps*	
next	30 *steps*	*next* 2 *steps*	
next	48 *steps*	*next* 6 *steps*	
next	2046 *steps*		

Total of 9930 steps   *Total of* 70 steps

Fraction of time: 0.993   *Fraction of time:* 0.007

This *looks* absurd, and yet the probability that in 10,000 tosses of a perfect coin the lead is at one side for more than 9930 trials and at the other for fewer than 70 exceeds $\frac{1}{10}$. In other words, on the average *one record out of ten will look worse than the one just described.* By contrast, the probability of a balance better than in the graph is only 0.072.

The original record of figure 4 contains 78 changes of sign and 64 other returns to the origin. The reversed series shows 8 changes of sign and 6 other returns to the origin. Sampling of expert opinion revealed that even trained statisticians expect much more than 78 changes of sign in 10,000 trials, and nobody counted on the possibility of only 8 changes of sign. Actually the probability of not more than 8 changes of sign exceeds 0.14, whereas the probability of more than 78 changes of sign is about 0.12. As far as the number of changes of sign is concerned the two records stand on a par and, theoretically, neither should cause surprise. If they seem startling, this is due to our faulty intuition and to our having been exposed to too many vague references to a mysterious "law of averages."

7. MAXIMA AND FIRST PASSAGES

Most of our conclusions so far are based on the basic lemma 3.1, which in turn is a simple corollary to the reflection principle. We now turn our attention to other interesting consequences of this principle.

Instead of paths that remain above the x-axis we consider paths that remain below the line $x = r$, that is, paths satisfying the condition

(7.1) $\mathbf{S}_0 < r, \quad \mathbf{S}_1 < r, \ldots, \mathbf{S}_n < r.$

We say in this case that the *maximum* of the path is $< r$. (The maximum is ≥ 0 because $\mathbf{S}_0 = 0$.) Let $A = (n, k)$ be a point with ordinate $k \leq r$. A path from 0 to A touches or crosses the line $x = r$ if it violates the condition (7.1). By the reflection principle the number of such paths equals the number of paths from the origin to the point $A' = (n, 2r - k)$ which is the reflection of A on the line $x = r$. This proves

Lemma 1. *Let $k \geq r$. The probability that a path of length n leads to $A = (n, k)$ and has a maximum $\leq r$ equals* $p_{n,2r-k} = \mathbf{P}\{\mathbf{S}_n = 2r - k\}$.

The probability that the maximum equals r is given by the difference $p_{n,2r-k} - p_{n,2r+2-k}$. Summing over all $k \leq r$ we obtain the probability that an arbitrary path of length n has a maximum exactly equal to r. The sum is telescoping and reduces to $p_{n,r} + p_{n,r+1}$. Now $p_{n,r}$ vanishes unless n and r have the same parity, and in this case $p_{n,r+1} = 0$. We have thus

Theorem 1. *The probability that the maximum of a path of length n equals $r \geq 0$ coincides with the positive member of the pair $p_{n,r}$ and $p_{n,r+1}$.*

For $r = 0$ and even epochs the assertion reduces to

$$(7.2) \qquad \mathbf{P}\{\mathbf{S}_1 \leq 0, \mathbf{S}_2 \leq 0, \ldots, \mathbf{S}_{2n} \leq 0\} = u_{2n}.$$

This, of course, is equivalent to the relation (3.4) which represents one version of the basic lemma. Accordingly, theorem 1 is a generalization of that lemma.

We next come to a notion that plays an important role in the general theory of stochastic processes. A *first passage through the point $r > 0$* is said to take place at epoch n if

$$(7.3) \qquad \mathbf{S}_1 < r, \ldots, \mathbf{S}_{n-1} < r, \qquad \mathbf{S}_n = r.$$

In the present context it would be preferable to speak of a first *visit*, but the term first passage, which originates in the physical literature, is well established; furthermore, the term visit is not applicable to continuous processes.

Obviously a path satisfying (7.3) must pass through $(n - 1, r - 1)$ and its maximum up to epoch $n - 1$ must equal $r - 1$. We saw that the probability for this event equals $p_{n-1,r-1} - p_{n-1,r+1}$, and so we have

Theorem 2. *The probability $\varphi_{r,n}$ that the first passage through r occurs at epoch n is given by*

$$(7.4) \qquad \varphi_{r,n} = \tfrac{1}{2}[p_{n-1,r-1} - p_{n-1,r+1}].$$

A trite calculation shows that

$$(7.5) \qquad \varphi_{r,n} = \frac{r}{n}\binom{n}{\frac{n+r}{2}}2^{-n}$$

[as always, the binomial coefficient is to be interpreted as zero if $(n+r)/2$ is not an integer]. For an alternative derivation see section 8.*b*.

The distribution (7.5) is most interesting when r is large. To obtain the probability that the first passage through r occurs before epoch N we must sum $\varphi_{r,n}$ over all $n \leq N$. It follows from the normal approximation (2.6) that only those terms will contribute significantly to the sum for which r^2/n is neither very large nor very close to 0. For such terms (2.6) provides the approximation

$$(7.6) \qquad\qquad \varphi_{r,n} \sim \sqrt{\frac{2}{\pi}} \frac{r}{\sqrt{n^3}} e^{-r^2/2n}$$

In the summation it must be borne in mind that n must have the same parity as r. The sum is the Riemann sum to an integral, and one is led to

Theorem 3. (*Limit theorem for first passages.*) *For fixed t the probability that the first passage through r occurs before epoch tr^2 tends to*[15]

$$(7.7) \qquad\qquad 2\left[1 - \Re\left(\frac{1}{\sqrt{t}}\right)\right] = \sqrt{\frac{2}{\pi}} \int_{1/\sqrt{t}}^{\infty} e^{-\frac{1}{2}s^2} ds$$

as $r \to \infty$, where $\Re$ is the normal distribution defined in VII,1.

It follows that, roughly speaking, the waiting time for the first passage through r increases with the *square* of r: the probability of a first passage after epoch $\frac{3}{4}r^2$ has a probability close to $\frac{1}{2}$. It follows that there must exist points $k < r$ such that the passage from k to $k + 1$ takes a time longer than it took to go from 0 to k.

The distribution of the first-passage times leads directly to the distribution of the epoch when the particle returns to the origin for the rth time.

Theorem 4.   *The probability that the rth return to the origin occurs at epoch n is given by the quantity $\varphi_{r,n-r}$ of* (7.5).

In words: An rth return at epoch n has the same probability as a first passage through r at epoch $n - r$.

Proof.[16]   Consider a path from the origin to $(n, 0)$ with all sides below the axis and exactly $r - 1$ interior vertices on the axis. For simplicity we shall call such a path representative. (Figure 5 shows such a path with $n = 20$ and $r = 5$.) A representative path consists of r sections with endpoints on the axis, and we may construct 2^r different paths by assigning different signs to the vertices in the several sections (that is, by mirroring sections on the axis). In this way we obtain all paths ending with an rth return, and thus there are exactly 2^r times as many paths ending with an rth return at epoch n as there are representative paths. The theorem may

---

[15] (7.7) defines the so-called positive stable distribution of order $\frac{1}{2}$. For a generalization of theorem 3 see problem 14 of XIV,9.

[16] For a proof in terms of generating functions see XI,(3.17).

be therefore restated as follows: There are exactly as many representative paths of length n as there are paths of length $n - r$ ending with a first passage through r. This is so, because if in a representative path we delete the r sides whose left endpoints are on the axis we get a path of length $n - r$ ending with a first passage through r. This procedure can be reversed by inserting r sides with negative slope starting at the origin and the $r - 1$ vertices marking the first passages through $1, 2, \ldots, r - 1$. (See figure 5.)   ▶

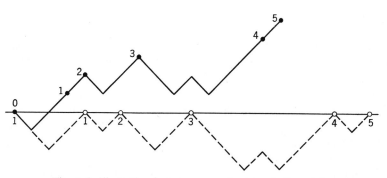

Figure 5. Illustrating first passages and returns to the origin.

It follows that the limit theorem for first returns is also applicable to rth returns as $r \to \infty$: *the probability that the rth return to the origin occurs before epoch tr^2 tends to the quantity* (7.7).

This result reveals another unexpected feature of the chance fluctuations in random walks. In the obvious sense the random walk starts from scratch every time when the particle returns to the origin. The epoch of the rth return is therefore the sum of r waiting times which can be interpreted as "measurements of the same physical quantity under identical conditions." It is generally believed that the average of r such observations is bound to converge to a "true value." But in the present case the sum is practically certain to be of the order of magnitude r^2, and so *the average increases roughly in proportion to r.* A closer analysis reveals that one among the r waiting times is likely to be of the same order of magnitude as the whole sum, namely r^2. In practice such a phenomenon would be attributed to an "experimental error" or be discarded as "outlier." It is difficult to see what one does not expect to see.

8. DUALITY. POSITION OF MAXIMA

Every path corresponds to a finite sequence of plus ones and minus ones, and reversing the order of the terms one obtains a new path. Geometrically the new path is obtained by rotating the given path through 180 degrees about its right endpoint, and taking the latter as origin of a new coordinate system. To every class of paths there corresponds in this way a new class of the same cardinality. If the steps of the original random walk are $X_1, X_2, \ldots, X_n$, then the steps of the new random walk are defined by

$$(8.1) \qquad X_1^* = X_n, \ldots, X_n^* = X_1.$$

The vertices of the new random walk are determined by the partial sums

$$(8.2) \qquad S_k^* = X_1^* + \cdots + X_k^* = S_n - S_{n-k}$$

(whence $S_0^* = 0$ and $S_n^* = S_n$). We shall refer to this as *the dual random walk*. To every event defined for the original random walk there corresponds an event of equal probability in the dual random walk, and in this way almost every probability relation has its dual. This simple method of deriving new relations is more useful than might appear at first sight. Its full power will be seen only in volume 2 in connection with general random walks and queuing theory, but even in the present context we can without effort derive some interesting new results.

To show this we shall review a few pairs of dual events, listing in each case the most noteworthy aspect. In the following list n is considered given and, to simplify language, the endpoint (n, S_n) of the path will be called *terminal point*. It is convenient to start from known events in the dual random walk.

(*a*) *First-passage times.* From (8.2) it is clear that the events defined, respectively, by

$$(8.3) \qquad S_j^* > 0, \qquad\qquad j = 1, 2, \ldots, n,$$

and

$$(8.4) \qquad S_n > S_j, \qquad\qquad j = 0, 1, \ldots, n - 1$$

are dual to each other. The second signifies that the terminal point was not visited before epoch n. We know from (3.2) that the first event has probability $\frac{1}{2} u_{2\nu}$ when $n = 2\nu > 0$ is even; for $n = 2\nu + 1$ the probability is the same because $S_{2\nu}^* > 0$ implies $S_{2\nu+1}^* > 0$. Accordingly, *the probability that a first passage through a positive point takes place at epoch n equals $\frac{1}{2} u_{2\nu}$ where $\nu = \frac{1}{2} n$ or $\nu = \frac{1}{2}(n-1)$.* (This is trivially true also for $n = 1$, but false for $n = 0$.) The duality principle leads us here to an interesting result which is not easy to verify directly.

(*b*) *Continuation.* In the preceding proposition the terminal point was not specified in advance. Prescribing the point r of the first passage means supplementing (8.4) by the condition $\mathbf{S}_n = r$. The dual event consists of the path from the origin to (n, r) with all intermediate vertices above the axis. The number of such paths follows directly from the reflection lemma [with $A = (1, 1)$ and $B = (n, r)$], and we get thus a new proof for (7.4).

(*c*) *Maximum at the terminal point.* A new pair of dual events is defined when the strict inequalities $>$ in (8.3) and (8.4) are changed to $\geq$. The second event occurs whenever the term $\mathbf{S}_n$ is maximal even when this maximum was already attained at some previous epoch.[17] Referring to (3.4) one sees that *the probability of this event equals* $u_{2\nu}$ where $\nu = \frac{1}{2}n$ or $\nu = \frac{1}{2}(n+1)$. It is noteworthy that the probabilities are twice the probabilities found under (*a*).

(*d*) The event that k returns to the origin have taken place is dual to the event that k visits to the terminal point occurred before epoch n. A similar statement applies to changes of sign. (For the probabilities see section 5 and problems 9–10.)

(*e*) *Arc sine law for the first visit to the terminal point.* Consider a randomly chosen path of length $n = 2\nu$. We saw under (*a*) that with probability $\frac{1}{2}u_{2\nu}$ the value $\mathbf{S}_{2\nu}$ is positive and such that no term of the sequence $\mathbf{S}_0, \mathbf{S}_1, \ldots, \mathbf{S}_{2\nu-1}$ equals $\mathbf{S}_{2\nu}$. The same is true for negative $\mathbf{S}_{2\nu}$, and hence the probability that the value $\mathbf{S}_{2\nu}$ is not attained before epoch 2ν equals $u_{2\nu}$; this is also the probability of the event that $\mathbf{S}_{2\nu} = 0$ in which the terminal value is attained already at epoch 0. Consider now more generally the event that the first visit to the terminal point takes place at epoch $2k$ (in other words, we require that $\mathbf{S}_{2k} = \mathbf{S}_{2\nu}$ but $\mathbf{S}_j \neq \mathbf{S}_{2\nu}$ for $j < 2k$). This is the dual to the event that the last visit to the origin took place at epoch $2k$, and we saw in section 4 that such visits are governed by the discrete arc sine distribution. We have thus the unexpected result that *with probability* $\alpha_{2k,2\nu} = u_{2k}u_{2\nu-2k}$ *the first visit to the terminal point* $\mathbf{S}_{2\nu}$ *took place at epoch* $2k$ $(k = 0, 1, \ldots, \nu)$. It follows, in particular, that the epochs $2k$ and $2\nu - 2k$ are equally probable. Furthermore, very early and very late first visits are much more probable than first visits at other times.

(*f*) *Arc sine law for the position of the maxima.* As a last example of the usefulness of the duality principle we show that the results derived under (*a*) and (*c*) yield directly the probability distribution for the epochs at which the sequence $\mathbf{S}_0, \mathbf{S}_1, \ldots, \mathbf{S}_n$ reaches its maximum value. Unfortunately the maximum value can be attained repeatedly, and so we must distinguish

---

[17] In the terminology used in chapter 12 of volume 2 we are considering a *weak ladder point* in contrast to the *strict* ladder points treated under (*a*).

between the first and the last maximum. The results are practically the same, however.

For simplicity let $n = 2\nu$ be even. The *first* maximum occurs at epoch k if

$$(8.5a) \qquad\qquad \mathbf{S}_0 < \mathbf{S}_k, \qquad \ldots, \mathbf{S}_{k-1} < \mathbf{S}_k$$

$$(8.5b) \qquad\qquad \mathbf{S}_{k+1} \leq \mathbf{S}_k, \ldots \qquad , \mathbf{S}_{2\nu} \leq \mathbf{S}_k.$$

Let us write k in the form $k = 2\rho$ or $k = 2\rho + 1$. According to (a) the probability of $(8.5a)$ equals $\frac{1}{2}u_{2\rho}$, except when $\rho = 0$. The event $(8.5b)$ involves only the section of the path following the epoch k and its probability obviously equals the probability that in a path of length $2\nu - k$ all vertices lie below or on the t-axis. It was shown under (c) that this probability equals $u_{2\nu-2\rho}$. Accordingly, *if* $0 < k < 2\nu$ *the probability that in the sequence* $\mathbf{S}_0, \ldots, \mathbf{S}_{2\nu}$ *the first maximum occurs at epochs* $k = 2\rho$ *or* $k = 2\rho + 1$ *is given by* $\frac{1}{2}u_{2\rho}u_{2\nu-2\rho}$. *For* $k = 0$ *and* $k = 2\nu$ *the probabilities are* $u_{2\nu}$ *and* $\frac{1}{2}u_{2\nu}$, *respectively.*

(For the *last* maximum the probabilities for the epochs 0 and 2ν are interchanged; the other probabilities remain unchanged provided k is written in the form $k = 2\rho$ or $k = 2\rho - 1$.)

We see that with a proper pairing of even and odd subscripts the position of the maxima becomes subject to the discrete arc sine distribution. Contrary to intuition the maximal accumulated gain is much more likely to occur towards the very beginning or the very end of a coin-tossing game than somewhere in the middle.

9. AN EQUIDISTRIBUTION THEOREM

We conclude this chapter by proving the theorem mentioned in connection with Galton's rank order test in example $(1.b)$. It is instructive in that it shows how an innocuous variation in conditions can change the character of the result.

It was shown in section 4 that the number of sides lying above the x-axis is governed by the discrete arc sine distribution. We now consider the same problem but restricting our attention to paths leading from the origin to a point of the x-axis. The result is unexpected in itself and because of the striking contrast to the arc sine law.

Theorem. *The number of paths of length* $2n$ *such that* $\mathbf{S}_{2n} = 0$ *and exactly* $2k$ *of its sides lie above the axis is independent of* k *and equal to* $2^{2n}u_{2n}/(n+1) = 2^{2n+1}f_{2n+2}$. *(Here* $k = 0, 1, \ldots, n$.)

Proof. We consider the cases $k = 0$ and $k = n$ separately. The number of paths to $(2n, 0)$ with all sides above the x-axis equals the number of paths from $(1, 1)$ to $(2n, 0)$ which do not touch the line directly below the x-axis. By the reflection principle this number equals

$$(9.1) \qquad \binom{2n-1}{n} - \binom{2n-1}{n+1} = \frac{1}{n+1}\binom{2n}{n}.$$

This proves the assertion for $k = n$ and, by symmetry, also for $k = 0$.

For $1 \leq k \leq n - 1$ we use induction. The theorem is easily verified when $n = 1$, and we assume it correct for all paths of length less than $2n$. Denote by $2r$ the epoch of the first return. There are two possibilities. If the section of the path up to epoch $2r$ is on the positive side we must have $1 \leq r \leq k$ and the second section has exactly $2k - 2r$ sides above the axis. By the induction hypothesis a path satisfying these conditions can be chosen in

$$(9.2) \qquad 2^{2r-1}f_{2r} \cdot \frac{2^{2n-2r}}{n-r+1} u_{2n-2r} = \frac{2^{2n-2}}{r(n-r+1)} u_{2r-2} u_{2n-2r}$$

different ways. On the other hand, if the section up to the first return to the origin is on the negative side, then the terminal section of length $2n - 2r$ contains exactly $2k$ positive sides, and hence in this case $n - r \geq k$. For fixed r the number of paths satisfying these conditions is again given by (9.2). Thus the numbers of paths of the two types are obtained by summing (9.2) over $1 \leq r \leq k$ and $1 \leq r \leq n - k$, respectively. In the second sum change the summation index r to $\rho = n + 1 - r$. Then ρ runs from $k + 1$ to n, and the terms of the sum are identical with (9.2) when r is replaced by ρ. It follows that the number of paths with k positive sides is obtained by summing (9.2) over $1 \leq r \leq n$. Since k does not appear in (9.2) the sum is independent of k as asserted. Since the total number of paths is $2^{2n}u_{2n}$ this determines the number of paths in each category. (For a direct evaluation see problem 13.) ▶

An analogous theorem holds also for the position of the maxima. (See problem 14.)

10. PROBLEMS FOR SOLUTION

1. (a) If $a > 0$ and $b > 0$, the number of paths $(s_1, s_2, \ldots, s_n)$ such that $s_1 > -b, \ldots, s_{n-1} > -b, s_n = a$ equals $N_{n,a} - N_{n,a+2b}$.
(b) If $b > a > 0$ there are $N_{n,a} - N_{n,2b-a}$ paths satisfying the conditions $s_1 < b, \ldots, s_{n-1} < b, s_n = a$.

2. Let $a > c > 0$ and $b > 0$. The number of paths which touch the line $x = a$ and then lead to (n, c) without having touched the line $x = -b$ equals

$N_{n,2a-c} - N_{n,2a+2b+c}$. (Note that this includes paths touching the line $x = -b$ *before* the line $x = a$.)

3. *Repeated reflections.* Let a and b be positive, and $-b < c < a$. The number of paths to the point (n, c) which meet neither the line $x = -b$ nor $x = a$ is given by the series

$$\sum (N_{n,4k(a+b)+c} - N_{n,4k(a+b)+2a-c}),$$

the series extending over all integers k from $-\infty$ to ∞, but having only finitely many non-zero terms.

Hint: Use and extend the method of the preceding problem.

Note. This is connected with the so-called *ruin problem* which arises in gambling when the two players have initial capitals a and b so that the game terminates when the accumulated gain reaches either a or $-b$. For the connection with statistical tests, see example (1.*c*).

(The method of repeated reflections will be used again in problem 17 of XIV,9 and in connection with diffusion theory in volume 2; X,5.)

4. From lemma 3.1 conclude (without calculations) that

$$u_0 u_{2n} + u_2 u_{2n-2} + \cdots + u_{2n} u_0 = 1.$$

5. Show that

$$u_{2n} = (-1)^n \binom{-\frac{1}{2}}{n} \qquad f_{2n} = (-1)^{n-1} \binom{\frac{1}{2}}{n}.$$

Derive the identity of the preceding problem as well as (2.6) from II, (12.9).

6. Prove geometrically that there are exactly as many paths ending at $(2n + 2, 0)$ and having all interior vertices strictly above the axis as there are paths ending at $(2n, 0)$ and having all vertices above or on the axis. Therefore $P\{S_1 \geq 0, \ldots, S_{2n-1} \geq 0, S_{2n} = 0\} = 2f_{2n+2}$.

Hint: Refer to figure 1.

7. Prove lemma 3.1 geometrically by showing that the following construction establishes a one-to-one correspondence between the two classes of paths:

Given a path to $(2n, 0)$ denote its *leftmost* minimum point by $M = (k, m)$. Reflect the section from the origin to M on the vertical line $t = k$ and slide the reflected section to the endpoint $(2n, 0)$. If M is taken as origin of a new coordinate system the new path leads from the origin to $(2n, 2m)$ and has all vertices strictly above or on the axis. (This construction is due to E. Nelson.)

8. Prove formula (3.5) directly by considering the paths that never meet the line $x = -1$.

9. The probability that *before* epoch $2n$ there occur exactly r returns to the origin equals the probability that a return takes place at epoch $2n$ and is preceded by at least r returns. *Hint:* Use lemma 3.1.

10. *Continuation.* Denote by $z_{r,2n}$ the probability that exactly r returns to the origin occur up to and including epoch $2n$. Using the preceding problem show that $z_{r,2n} = p_{r,2n} + p_{r+1,2n} + \cdots$ where $p_{r,2n}$ is the probability that the rth return occurs at epoch $2n$. Using theorem 7.4 conclude that

$$z_{r,2n} = \frac{1}{2^{2n-r}} \cdot \binom{2n-r}{n}.$$

11. *Alternative derivation for the probabilities for the number of changes of sign.* Show that

$$\xi_{r,2n-1} = \frac{1}{2} \sum_{k=1}^{n-1} f_{2k}[\xi_{r-1,2n-1-2k} + \xi_{r,2n-1-2k}].$$

Assuming by induction that (5.1) holds for all epochs prior to $2n-1$ show that this reduces to

$$\xi_{r,2n-1} = \sum_{1}^{n-1} f_{2k} p_{2n,2r}$$

which is the probability of reaching the point $(2n, 2r)$ after a visit to the origin. Using the ballot theorem conclude that (5.1) holds.

12. The probability that $S_{2n} = 0$ and the maximum of $S_1, \ldots, S_{2n-1}$ equals k is the same as $P\{S_{2n} = 2k\}$. Prove this, (a) by reflection, (b) by establishing a one-to-one correspondence between the corresponding paths.

13. In the proof of section 9 it was shown that

$$\sum_{r=1}^{n} \frac{1}{r(n-r+1)} u_{2r-2} u_{2n-2r} = \frac{1}{n+1} u_{2n}.$$

Show that this relation is equivalent to (2.6). *Hint:* Decompose the fraction.

14. Consider a path of length $2n$ with $S_{2n} = 0$. We order the sides in circular order by identifying 0 and $2n$ with the result that the first and the last side become adjacent. Applying a cyclical permutation amounts to viewing the same closed path with (k, S_k) as origin. Show that this preserves maxima, but moves them k steps ahead. Conclude that when all $2n$ cyclical permutations are applied the number of times that a maximum occurs at r is independent of r.

Consider now a randomly chosen path with $S_{2n} = 0$ and pick the place of the maximum if the latter is unique; if there are several maxima, pick one at random. This procedure leads to a number between 0 and $2n - 1$. Show that all possibilities are equally probable.

CHAPTER IV *

Combination of Events

This chapter is concerned with events which are defined in terms of certain other events $A_1, A_2, \ldots, A_N$. For example, in bridge the event A, "at least one player has a complete suit," is the union of the four events A_k, "player number k has a complete suit" ($k = 1, 2, 3, 4$). Of the events A_k one, two, or more can occur simultaneously, and, because of this overlap, the probability of A is not the sum of the four probabilities $\mathbf{P}\{A_k\}$. Given a set of events $A_1, \ldots, A_N$, we shall show how to compute the probabilities that $0, 1, 2, 3, \ldots$ among them occur.[1]

1. UNION OF EVENTS

If A_1 and A_2 are two events, then $A = A_1 \cup A_2$ denotes the event that either A_1 or A_2 or both occur. From I, (7.4) we know that

(1.1) $$\mathbf{P}\{A\} = \mathbf{P}\{A_1\} + \mathbf{P}\{A_2\} - \mathbf{P}\{A_1 A_2\}.$$

We want to generalize this formula to the case of N events $A_1, A_2, \ldots, A_N$; that is, we wish to compute the probability of the event that at least one among the A_k occurs. In symbols this event is

$$A = A_1 \cup A_2 \cup \cdots \cup A_N.$$

For our purpose it is not sufficient to know the probabilities of the individual events A_k, but we must be given complete information concerning all possible overlaps. This means that for every pair (i, j), every triple (i, j, k), etc., we must know the probability of A_i and A_j, or A_i, A_j, and

---

* The material of this chapter will not be used explicitly in the sequel. Only the first theorem is of considerable importance.

[1] For further information see M. Fréchet, *Les probabilités associées a un système d'événements compatibles et dépendants*, Actualités scientifiques et industrielles, nos. 859 and 942, Paris, 1940 and 1943.

A_k, etc., occurring simultaneously. For convenience of notation we shall denote these probabilities by the letter p with appropriate subscripts. Thus

$$(1.2) \qquad p_i = \mathbf{P}\{A_i\}, \qquad p_{ij} = \mathbf{P}\{A_i A_j\}, \qquad p_{ijk} = \mathbf{P}\{A_i A_j A_k\}, \ldots.$$

The order of the subscripts is irrelevant, but for uniqueness we shall always *write the subscripts in increasing order*; thus, we write $p_{3,7,11}$ and not $p_{7,3,11}$. Two subscripts are never equal. For the sum of all p's with r subscripts we shall write S_r, that is, we define

$$(1.3) \qquad S_1 = \sum p_i, \qquad S_2 = \sum p_{ij}, \qquad S_3 = \sum p_{ijk}, \ldots.$$

Here $i < j < k < \cdots \leq N$, so that in the sums each combination appears once and only once; hence S_r has $\binom{N}{r}$ terms. The last sum, S_N, reduces to the single term $p_{1,2,3,\ldots,N}$, which is the probability of the simultaneous realization of all N events. For $N = 2$ we have only the two terms S_1 and S_2, and (1.1) can be written

$$(1.4) \qquad\qquad\qquad \mathbf{P}\{A\} = S_1 - S_2.$$

The generalization to an arbitrary number N of events is given in the following

Theorem. *The probability P_1 of the realization of at least one among the events $A_1, A_2, \ldots, A_N$ is given by*

$$(1.5) \qquad\qquad P_1 = S_1 - S_2 + S_3 - S_4 + - \cdots \pm S_N.$$

Proof. We prove (1.5) by the so-called method of inclusion and exclusion (cf. problem 26). To compute P_1 we should add the probabilities of all sample points which are contained in at least one of the A_i, but each point should be taken only once. To proceed systematically we first take the points which are contained in only one A_i, then those contained in exactly two events A_i, and so forth, and finally the points (if any) contained in all A_i. Now let E be any sample point contained in exactly n among our N events A_i. Without loss of generality we may number the events so that E is contained in $A_1, A_2, \ldots, A_n$ but not contained in $A_{n+1}, A_{n+2}, \ldots, A_N$. Then $\mathbf{P}\{E\}$ appears as a contribution to those $p_i, p_{ij}, p_{ijk}, \ldots$ whose subscripts range from 1 to n. Hence $\mathbf{P}\{E\}$ appears n times as a contribution to S_1, and $\binom{n}{2}$ times as a contribution to S_2, etc. In all, when the right-hand side of (1.5) is expressed in terms of the probabilities of sample points we find $P\{E\}$ with the factor

$$(1.6) \qquad n - \binom{n}{2} + \binom{n}{3} - + \cdots \pm \binom{n}{n}.$$

It remains to show that this number equals 1. This follows at once on comparing (1.6) with the binomial expansion of $(1-1)^n$ [cf. II, (8.7)]. The latter starts with 1, and the terms of (1.6) follow with reversed sign. Hence for every $n \geq 1$ the expression (1.6) equals 1.   ▶

Examples. (a) In a game of bridge let A_i be the event "player number i has a complete suit." Then $p_i = 4 / \binom{52}{13}$; the event that both player i and player j have complete suits can occur in 4·3 ways and has probability $p_{ij} = 12 / \binom{52}{13}\binom{39}{13}$; similarly we find

$$p_{ijk} = 24 / \binom{52}{13}\binom{39}{13}\binom{26}{13}.$$

Finally, $p_{1,2,3,4} = p_{1,2,3}$, since whenever three players have a complete suit so does the fourth. The probability that *some* player has a complete suit is therefore $P_1 = 4p_1 - 6p_{1,2} + 4p_{1,2,3} - p_{1,2,3,4}$. Using Stirling's formula, we see that $P_1 = \frac{1}{4} \cdot 10^{-10}$ approximately. In this particular case P_1 is very nearly the sum of the probabilities of A_i, but this is the exception rather than the rule.

(b) *Matches (coincidences).* The following problem with many variants and a surprising solution goes back to Montmort (1708). It has been generalized by Laplace and many other authors.

Two equivalent decks of N different cards each are put into random order and matched against each other. If a card occupies the same place in both decks, we speak of a *match (coincidence* or *rencontre).* Matches may occur at any of the N places and at several places simultaneously. This experiment may be described in more amusing forms. For example, the two decks may be represented by a set of N letters and their envelopes, and a capricious secretary may perform the random matching. Alternatively we may imagine the hats in a checkroom mixed and distributed at random to the guests. A match occurs if a person gets his own hat. It is instructive to venture guesses as to how the probability of a match depends on N: How does the probability of a match of hats in a diner with 8 guests compare with the corresponding probability at a gathering of 10,000 people? It seems surprising that the probability is practically independent of N and roughly $\frac{2}{3}$. (For less frivolous applications cf. problems 10 and 11.)

The probabilities of having exactly 0, 1, 2, 3, . . . matches will be calculated in section 4. Here we shall derive only the probability P_1 of at least 1 match. For simplicity of expression let us renumber the cards 1, 2, . . . , N in such a way that one deck appears in its natural order, and assume that each permutation of the second deck has probability $1/N!$. Let A_k be the event that a match occurs at the kth place. This means that card number k is at the kth place, and the remaining $N - 1$ cards may be in an arbitrary order. Clearly $p_k = (N-1)!/N! = 1/N$. Similarly, for every combination i, j we have $p_{ij} = (N-2)!/N! = 1/N(N-1)$, etc. The sum S_r contains $\binom{N}{r}$ terms, each of which equals $(N-r)!/N!$. Hence $S_r = 1/r!$, and from (1.5) we find the required probability to be

$$(1.7) \qquad P_1 = 1 - \frac{1}{2!} + \frac{1}{3!} - + \cdots \pm \frac{1}{N!}.$$

Note that $1 - P_1$ represents the first $N + 1$ terms in the expansion

$$(1.8) \qquad e^{-1} = 1 - 1 + \frac{1}{2!} - \frac{1}{3!} + \frac{1}{4!} - + \cdots,$$

and hence

$$(1.9) \qquad P_1 \approx 1 - e^{-1} = 0.63212 \ldots,$$

approximately. The degree of approximation is shown in the following table of correct values of P_1:

$N =$	3	4	5	6	7
$P_1 =$	0.66667	0.62500	0.63333	0.63196	0.63214	▶

2. APPLICATION TO THE CLASSICAL OCCUPANCY PROBLEM

We now return to the problem of a random distribution of r balls in n cells, assuming that each arrangement has probability n^{-r}. We seek the probability $p_m(r, n)$ of finding exactly m cells empty.[2]

Let A_k be the event that cell number k is empty ($k = 1, 2, \ldots, n$). In this event all r balls are placed in the remaining $n - 1$ cells, and this can be done in $(n-1)^r$ different ways. Similarly, there are $(n-2)^r$

---

[2] This probability was derived, by an entirely different method, in problem 8 in II, 11. Compare also the concluding remark in section 3.

arrangements, leaving two preassigned cells empty, etc. Accordingly

$$(2.1) \qquad p_i = \left(1 - \frac{1}{n}\right)^r, \quad p_{ij} = \left(1 - \frac{2}{n}\right)^r, \quad p_{ijk} = \left(1 - \frac{3}{n}\right)^r, \ldots$$

and hence for every $\nu \leq n$

$$(2.2) \qquad S_\nu = \binom{n}{\nu}\left(1 - \frac{\nu}{n}\right)^r.$$

The probability that at least one cell is empty is given by (1.5), and hence we find for the *probability that all cells are occupied*

$$(2.3) \qquad p_0(r, n) = 1 - S_1 + S_2 - + \cdots = \sum_{\nu=0}^{n}(-1)^\nu\binom{n}{\nu}\left(1 - \frac{\nu}{n}\right)^r.$$

Consider now a distribution in which exactly m cells are empty. These m cells can be chosen in $\binom{n}{m}$ ways. The r balls are distributed among the remaining $n - m$ cells so that each of these cells is occupied; the number of such distributions is $(n-m)^r p_0(r, n - m)$. Dividing by n^r we find for the *probability that exactly m cells remain empty*

$$(2.4) \qquad p_m(r, n) = \binom{n}{m}\left(1 - \frac{m}{n}\right)^r p_0(r, n-m) =$$

$$= \binom{n}{m}\sum_{\nu=0}^{n-m}(-1)^\nu\binom{n-m}{\nu}\left(1 - \frac{m + \nu}{n}\right)^r.$$

We have already used the model of r random digits to illustrate the random distribution of r things in $n = 10$ cells. Empty cells correspond in this case to missing digits: if m cells are empty, $10 - m$ different digits appear in the given sequence. Table 1 provides a numerical illustration.

It is clear that a direct numerical evaluation of (2.4) is limited to the case of relatively small n and r. On the other hand, the occupancy problem is of particular interest when n is large. If 10,000 balls are distributed in 1000 cells, is there any chance of finding an empty cell? In a group of 2000 people, is there any chance of finding a day in the year which is not a birthday? Fortunately, questions of this kind can be answered by means of a remarkably simple approximation with an error which tends to zero as $n \to \infty$. This approximation and the argument leading to it are typical of many *limit theorems* in probability.

Our purpose, then, is to discuss the limiting form of the formula (2.4) as $n \to \infty$ and $r \to \infty$. The relation between r and n is, in principle,

TABLE 1

PROBABILITIES $p_m(r, 10)$ ACCORDING TO (2.4)

m	$r = 10$	$r = 18$
0	0.000 363	0.134 673
1	0.016 330	0.385 289
2	0.136 080	0.342 987
3	0.355 622	0.119 425
4	0.345 144	0.016 736
5	0.128 596	0.000 876
6	0.017 189	0.000 014
7	0.000 672	0.000 000
8	0.000 005	0.000 000
9	0.000 000	0.000 000

$p_m(r, 10)$ is the probability that exactly m of the digits $0, 1, \ldots, 9$ will *not* appear in a sequence of r random digits.

arbitrary, but if the average number r/n of balls per cell is excessively large, then we cannot expect any empty cells; in this case $p_0(r, n)$ is near unity and all $p_m(r, n)$ with $m \geq 1$ are small. On the other hand, if r/n tends to zero, then practically all cells must be empty, and in this case $p_m(r, n) \to 0$ for every fixed m. Therefore only the intermediate case is of real interest.

We begin by estimating the quantity S_ν of (2.2). Since

$$(n-\nu)^\nu < (n)_\nu < n^\nu$$

we have

$$(2.5) \qquad n^\nu \left(1 - \frac{\nu}{n}\right)^{\nu+r} < \nu! \, S_\nu < n^\nu \left(1 - \frac{\nu}{n}\right)^r.$$

For $0 < t < 1$ it is clear from the expansion II, (8.10) that $-\log(1-t)$ lies between t and $t/(1-t)$. Therefore

$$(2.6) \qquad \{ne^{-(\nu+r)/(n-\nu)}\}^\nu < \nu! \, S_\nu < \{ne^{-r/n}\}^\nu.$$

Now put for abbreviation

$$(2.7) \qquad ne^{-r/n} = \lambda$$

and suppose that r and n increase in such a way that λ remains constrained to a finite interval $0 < a < \lambda < b$. For each fixed ν the ratio of

TABLE 2

Poisson Approximation (2.11) to the Probabilities of Finding Exactly m Empty Cells When r Balls Are Randomly Distributed in $n = 1000$ Cells

$$p(m; \lambda)$$

r	λ	$m = 0$	$m = 1$	$m = 2$	$m = 3$	$m = 4$	$m = 5$	$m = 6$	$m = 7$	$m = 8$	$m = 9$	$m = 10$	$m = 11$
5000	6.74	0.0012	0.0080	0.0269	0.0604	0.1017	0.1371	0.1540	0.1482	0.1249	0.0935	0.0630	0.0386
5500	4.09	0.0167	0.0685	0.1400	0.1909	0.1951	0.1596	0.1088	0.0636	0.0325	0.0148	0.0060	0.0023
6000	2.48	0.0838	0.2077	0.2575	0.2128	0.1320	0.0655	0.0271	0.0096	0.0030	0.0008	0.0002	
6500	1.50	0.2231	0.3347	0.2510	0.1255	0.0471	0.0141	0.0035	0.0008	0.0001			
7000	0.91	0.4027	0.3661	0.1666	0.0506	0.0115	0.0021	0.0003					
7500	0.55	0.5777	0.3163	0.0873	0.0162	0.0023	0.0003						
8000	0.34	0.7126	0.2406	0.0414	0.0049	0.0004							
8500	0.20	0.8187	0.1637	0.0164	0.0011	0.0001							
9000	0.12	0.8869	0.1064	0.0064	0.0003								

the extreme members in (2.6) then tends to unity, and so

$$(2.8) \qquad 0 \leq \frac{\lambda^v}{v!} - S_v \to 0.$$

This relation holds trivially when $\lambda \to 0$, and hence (2.8) remains true whenever r and n increase in such way that λ remains bounded. Now

$$(2.9) \qquad e^{-\lambda} - p_0(r, n) = \sum_{v=0}^{\infty} (-1)^v \left(\frac{\lambda^v}{v!} - S_v \right)$$

and (2.8) implies that the right side tends to zero. Furthermore, the factor of $p_0(r, n - m)$ in (2.4) may be rewritten as S_m, and we have therefore for each fixed m

$$(2.10) \qquad p_m(r, n) - e^{-\lambda} \frac{\lambda^m}{m!} \to 0.$$

This completes the proof of the

Theorem.[3] *If n and r tend to infinity so that $\lambda = ne^{-r/n}$ remains bounded, then* (2.10) *holds for each fixed m.*

The approximating expressions

$$(2.11) \qquad p(m; \lambda) = e^{-\lambda} \frac{\lambda^m}{m!}$$

define the so-called *Poisson distribution*, which is of great importance and describes a variety of phenomena; it will be studied in chapter VI.

In practice we may use $p(m; \lambda)$ as an approximation whenever n is great. For moderate values of n an estimate of the error is required, but we shall not enter into it.

Examples. (*a*) Table 2 gives the approximate probabilities of finding m cells empty when the number of cells is 1000 and the number of balls varies from 5000 to 9000. For $r = 5000$ the median value of the number of empty cells is six: seven or more empty cells are about as probable as six or fewer. Even with 9000 balls in 1000 cells we have about one chance in nine to find an empty cell.

(*b*) In birthday statistics [example II, (3.*d*)] $n = 365$, and r is the number of people. For $r = 1900$ we find $\lambda = 2$, approximately. *In a village of 1900 people the probabilities $P_{[m]}$ of finding m days of the year*

---

[3] Due (with a different proof) to R. von Mises, *Über Aufteilungs- und Besetzungs-wahrscheinlichkeiten*, Revue de la Faculté des Sciences de l'Université d'Istanbul, N.S., vol. 4 (1939), pp. 145–163.

which are not birthdays are approximately as follows:

$$P_{[0]} = 0.135, \quad P_{[1]} = 0.271, \quad P_{[2]} = 0.271, \quad P_{[3]} = 0.180,$$
$$P_{[4]} = 0.090, \quad P_{[5]} = 0.036, \quad P_{[6]} = 0.012, \quad P_{[7]} = 0.003.$$

(c) When $n \log n + an$ balls are placed into n cells and n is large, the probability of finding all cells occupied is $1 - e^{-a}$. ▶

Instead of empty cells one may consider cells containing exactly k balls. The argument used above for the special case $k = 0$ applies with minor changes. As von Mises has shown, the probability of finding exactly m cells with k-tuple occupancy can again be approximated by the Poisson distribution (2.11), but this time λ must be defined as

$$(2.12) \qquad \lambda = n \frac{e^{-r/n}}{k!} \left(\frac{r}{n}\right)^k.$$

3. THE REALIZATION OF m AMONG N EVENTS

The theorem of section 1 can be strengthened as follows.

Theorem. *For any integer* m *with* $1 \leq m \leq N$ *the probability* $P_{[m]}$ *that exactly* m *among the* N *events* $A_1, \ldots, A_N$ *occur simultaneously is given by*

$$(3.1) \quad P_{[m]} = S_m - \binom{m+1}{m} S_{m+1} + \binom{m+2}{m} S_{m+2} - + \cdots \pm \binom{N}{m} S_N.$$

Note: According to (1.5), the probability $P_{[0]}$ that none among the A_j occurs is

$$(3.2) \qquad P_{[0]} = 1 - P_1 = 1 - S_1 + S_2 - S_3 \pm \cdots \mp S_N.$$

This shows that (3.1) gives the correct value also for $m = 0$ provided we put $S_0 = 1$.

Proof. We proceed as in the proof of (1.5). Let E be an arbitrary sample point, and suppose that it is contained in exactly n among the N events A_j. Then $\mathbf{P}\{E\}$ appears as a contribution to $P_{[m]}$ only if $n = m$. To investigate how $\mathbf{P}\{E\}$ contributes to the right side of (3.1), note that $\mathbf{P}\{E\}$ appears in the sums $S_1, S_2, \ldots, S_n$ but not in S_{n+1}, $\ldots, S_N$. It follows that $\mathbf{P}\{E\}$ does not contribute to the right side in (3.1) if $n < m$. If $n = m$, then $\mathbf{P}\{E\}$ appears in one and only one term of S_m. To complete the proof of the theorem it remains to show that for $n > m$ the contributions of $\mathbf{P}\{E\}$ to the terms $S_m, S_{m+1}, \ldots, S_n$ on the right in (3.1) cancel. Now $\mathbf{P}\{E\}$ appears in S_k with the factor $\binom{n}{k}$, namely the number of k-tuplets that can be formed out of the n events containing the point E. For $n > m$ the total contribution of $\mathbf{P}\{E\}$ to the right side in (3.1) is therefore

$$(3.3) \qquad \binom{n}{m} - \binom{m+1}{m}\binom{n}{m+1} + \binom{m+2}{m}\binom{n}{m+2} - + \cdots.$$

When the binomial coefficients are expressed in terms of factorials, it is seen that this expression reduces to

$$(3.4) \qquad \binom{n}{m}\left\{\binom{n-m}{0} - \binom{n-m}{1} + - \cdots \pm \binom{n-m}{n-m}\right\}.$$

Within the braces we have the binomial expansion of $(1-1)^{n-m}$ so that (3.3) vanishes, as asserted. ▶

The reader is asked to verify that a substitution from formula (2.2) into (3.1) leads *directly* to (2.4).

4. APPLICATION TO MATCHING AND GUESSING

In example (1.*b*) we considered the matching of two decks of cards and found that $S_k = 1/k!$. Substituting into (3.1), we find the following result.

In a random matching of two equivalent decks of N distinct cards the probability $P_{[m]}$ of having exactly m matches is given by

$$P_{[0]} = 1 - 1 + \frac{1}{2!} - \frac{1}{3!} + - \cdots \pm \frac{1}{(N-2)!} \mp \frac{1}{(N-1)!} \pm \frac{1}{N!}$$

$$(4.1) \qquad P_{[1]} = 1 - 1 + \frac{1}{2!} - \frac{1}{3!} + - \cdots \pm \frac{1}{(N-2)!} \mp \frac{1}{(N-1)!}$$

$$P_{[2]} = \frac{1}{2!}\left\{1 - 1 + \frac{1}{2!} - \frac{1}{3!} + - \cdots \pm \frac{1}{(N-3)!} \mp \frac{1}{(N-2)!}\right\}$$

$$P_{[3]} = \frac{1}{3!}\left\{1 - 1 + \frac{1}{2!} - \frac{1}{3!} + - \cdots \pm \frac{1}{(N-3)!}\right\}$$

$$\cdots \cdots \cdots \cdots \cdots \cdots \cdots$$

$$\cdots \cdots \cdots \cdots \cdots \cdots \cdots$$

$$P_{[N-2]} = \frac{1}{(N-2)!}\left\{1 - 1 + \frac{1}{2!}\right\}$$

$$P_{[N-1]} = \frac{1}{(N-1)!}\{1 - 1\} = 0 \qquad P_{[N]} = \frac{1}{N!}.$$

TABLE 3

PROBABILITIES OF m CORRECT GUESSES IN CALLING A DECK OF N DISTINCT CARDS

	$N = 3$		$N = 4$		$N = 5$		$N = 6$		$N = 10$		
	$P_{[m]}$	b_m	$P_{[m]}$	b_m	$P_{[m]}$	b_m	$P_{[m]}$	b_m	$P_{[m]}$	b_m	p_m
0	0.333	0.296	0.375	0.316	0.367	0.328	0.368	0.335	0.36788	0.34868	0.367879
1	0.500	0.444	0.333	0.422	0.375	0.410	0.367	0.402	0.36788	0.38742	0.367879
2	...	0.222	0.250	0.211	0.167	0.205	0.187	0.201	0.18394	0.19371	0.183940
3	0.167	0.037	...	0.047	0.083	0.051	0.056	0.053	0.06131	0.05740	0.061313
4			0.042	0.004	...	0.006	0.021	0.008	0.01534	0.01116	0.015328
5					0.008	0.000	...	0.001	0.00306	0.00149	0.003066
6							0.001	0.000	0.00052	0.00014	0.000511
7									0.00007	0.00001	0.000073
8									0.00001	.....	0.000009
9									.....	.....	0.000001
10									.....	.....	0.000000

The $P_{[m]}$ are given by (4.1), the b_m by (4.4). The last column gives the Poisson limits (4..3)

The last relation is obvious. The vanishing of $P_{[N-1]}$ expresses the impossibility of having $N-1$ matches without having all N cards in the same order.

The braces on the right in (4.1) contain the initial terms of the expansion of e^{-1}. *For large N we have therefore approximately*

$$(4.2) \qquad P_{[m]} \approx \frac{e^{-1}}{m!}$$

In table 3 the columns headed $P_{[m]}$ give the exact values of $P_{[m]}$ for $N = 3, 4, 5, 6, 10$. The last column gives the limiting values

$$(4.3) \qquad p_m = \frac{e^{-1}}{m!}.$$

The approximation of p_m to $P_{[m]}$ is rather good even for moderate values of N.

For the numbers p_m defined by (4.3) we have

$$\sum p_k = e^{-1}\left(1+1+\frac{1}{2!}+\frac{1}{3!}+\cdots\right) = e^{-1}e = 1.$$

Accordingly, the p_k may be interpreted as probabilities. Note that (4.3) represents the special case $\lambda = 1$ of the *Poisson distribution* (2.11).

Example. *Testing guessing abilities.* In wine tasting, psychic experiments, etc., the subject is asked to call an unknown order of N things, say, cards. Any actual insight on the part of the subject will appear as a departure from randomness. To judge the amount of insight we must appraise the probability of turns of good luck. Now chance guesses can be made according to several systems among which we mention three extreme possibilities. (i) The subject sticks to one card and keeps calling it. With this system he is sure to have one, and only one, correct guess in each series; chance fluctuations are eliminated. (ii) The subject calls each card once so that each series of N guesses corresponds to a rearrangement of the deck. If this system is applied without insight, formulas (4.1) should apply. (iii) A third possibility is that N guesses are made absolutely independently of each other. There are N^N possible arrangements. It is true that every person has fixed mental habits and is prone to call certain patterns more frequently than others, but in first approximation we may assume all N^N arrangements to be equally probable. Since m correct and $N - m$ incorrect guesses can be arranged in $\binom{N}{m}(N-1)^{N-m}$ different ways, the probability of exactly m correct guesses is now

$$(4.4) \qquad b_m = \binom{N}{m}\frac{(N-1)^{N-m}}{N^N}.$$

[This is a special case of the binomial distribution and has been derived in example II, (4.c).]

Table 3 gives a comparison of the probabilities of success when guesses are made in accordance with system (ii) or (iii). To judge the merits of the two methods we require the theory of mean values and probable fluctuations. It turns out that the average number of correct chance guesses is one under all systems; the chance fluctuations are somewhat larger under system (ii) than (iii). A glance at table 3 will show that in practice the differences will not be excessive.   ▶

5. MISCELLANY

(a) The Realization of at Least m Events

With the notations of section 3 *the probability P_m that m or more of the events $A_1, \ldots, A_N$ occur simultaneously is given by*

$$(5.1) \qquad P_m = P_{[m]} + P_{[m+1]} + \cdots + P_{[N]}.$$

To find a formula for P_m in terms of S_k it is simplest to proceed by induction, starting with the expression (1.5) for P_1 and using the recurrence relation $P_{m+1} = P_m - P_{[m]}$. We get for $m \geq 1$

$$(5.2) \quad P_m = S_m - \binom{m}{m-1}S_{m+1} +$$
$$+ \binom{m+1}{m-1}S_{m+2} - \binom{m+2}{m-1}S_{m+3} + \cdots \pm \binom{N-1}{m-1}S_N.$$

It is also possible to derive (5.2) directly, using the argument which led to (3.1).

(b) Further Identities

The coefficients S_v can be expressed in terms of either $P_{[k]}$ or P_k as follows

(5.3)
$$S_v = \sum_{k=v}^{N} \binom{k}{v} P_{[k]}$$

and

(5.4)
$$S_v = \sum_{k=v}^{N} \binom{k-1}{v-1} P_k.$$

Indication of proof. For given values of $P_{[m]}$ the equations (3.1) may be taken as linear equations in the unknowns S_v, and we have to prove that (5.3) represents the unique solution. If (5.3) is introduced into the expression (3.1) for $P_{[m]}$, the coefficient of $P_{[k]}$ ($m \leq k \leq N$) to the right is found to be

(5.5)
$$\sum_{v=m}^{k} (-1)^{v-m} \binom{v}{m}\binom{k}{v} = \binom{k}{m} \sum_{v=m}^{k} (-1)^{v-m} \binom{k-m}{v-m}.$$

If $k = m$ this expression reduces to 1. If $k > m$ the sum is the binomial expansion of $(1-1)^{k-m}$ and therefore vanishes. Hence the substitution (5.3) reduces (3.1) to the identity $P_{[m]} = P_{[m]}$. The uniqueness of the solution of (3.1) follows from the fact that each equation introduces only one new unknown, so that the S_v can be computed recursively. The truth of (5.4) can be proved in a similar way.

(c) Bonferroni's Inequalities

A string of inequalities both for $P_{[m]}$ and for P_m can be obtained in the following way. If in either (3.1) or (5.2) only the terms involving $S_m, S_{m+1},$ ..., S_{m+r-1} are retained while the terms involving $S_{m+r}, S_{m+r+1}, \ldots, S_N$ are dropped, then the error (i.e., true value minus approximation) has the sign of the first omitted term [namely, $(-1)^r$], and is smaller in absolute value. Thus, for $r = 1$ and $r = 2$:

(5.6)
$$S_m - (m+1)S_{m+1} \leq P_{[m]} \leq S_m$$

and

(5.7)
$$S_m - mS_{m+1} \leq P_m \leq S_m.$$

Indication of Proof. To prove the statement for (3.1) it must be shown that

(5.8)
$$\sum_{v=t}^{N} (-1)^{v-t} \binom{v}{m} S_v \geq 0,$$

for every t. Now use (5.3) to write the left side as a linear combination of the $P_{[k]}$. For $t \leq k \leq N$ the coefficient of $P_{[k]}$ equals

$$\sum_{v=t}^{k} (-1)^{v-t} \binom{v}{m} \binom{k}{v} = \binom{k}{m} \sum_{v=t}^{k} (-1)^{v-t} \binom{k-m}{v-m}.$$

The last sum equals $\binom{k-m-1}{t-m-1}$ and is therefore positive (problem 13 of II, 12). For further inequalities the reader is referred to Fréchet's monograph cited at the beginning of the chapter.

6. PROBLEMS FOR SOLUTION

Note: *Assume in each case that all possible arrangements have the same probability.*

1. Ten pair of shoes are in a closet. Four shoes are selected at random. Find the probability that there will be at least one pair among the four shoes selected.

2. Five dice are thrown. Find the probability that at least three of them show the same face. (Verify by the methods of II, 5.)

3. Find the probability that in five tossings a coin falls heads at least three times in succession.

4. Solve problem 3 for a head-run of at least length five in ten tossings.

5. Solve problems 3 and 4 for ace runs when a die is used instead of a coin.

6. Two dice are thrown r times. Find the probability p_r that each of the six combinations $(1, 1), \ldots, (6, 6)$ appears at least once.

7. *Quadruples in a bridge hand.* By a quadruple we shall understand four cards of the same face value, so that a bridge hand of thirteen cards may contain 0, 1, 2, or 3 quadruples. Calculate the corresponding probabilities.

8. *Sampling with replacement.* A sample of size r is taken from a population of n people. Find the probability u_r that N given people will all be included in the sample. (This is problem 12 of II, 11.)

9. *Sampling without replacement.* Answer problem 8 for this case and show that 8 holds with $u_r \to p^N$. (This is problem 3 of II, 11, but the present method leads to a formally entirely different result.)

10. In the general expansion of a determinant of order N the number of terms containing one or more diagonal elements is $N! P_1$ defined by (1.7).

11. The number of ways in which 8 rooks can be placed on a chessboard so that none can take another and that none stands on the white diagonal is $8! (1 - P_1)$, where P_1 is defined by (1.7) with $N = 8$.

12. *A sampling (coupon collector's) problem.* A pack of cards consists of s identical series, each containing n cards numbered $1, 2, \ldots, n$. A random sample of $r \geq n$ cards is drawn from the pack without replacement. Calculate the probability u_r that each number is represented in the sample. (Applied to a deck of bridge cards we get for $s = 4$, $n = 13$ the probability that a hand of r cards contains all 13 values; and for $s = 13$, $n = 4$ we get the probability that all four suits are represented.)

13. *Continuation.* Show that as $s \to \infty$ one has $u_r \to p_0(r, n)$ where the latter expression is defined in (2.3). This means that in the limit our sampling becomes random sampling with replacement from the population of the numbers $1, 2, \ldots, n$.

14. *Continuation.* From the result of problem 12 conclude that

$$\sum_{k=0}^{n} (-1)^k \binom{n}{k} (ns - ks)_r = 0$$

if $r < n$ and for $r = n$

$$\sum_{k=0}^{n} (-1)^k \binom{n}{k} (ns - ks)_n = s^n n!.$$

Verify this by evaluating the rth derivative, at $x = 0$, of

$$\frac{1}{(1-x)^{ns-r+1}} \{1 - (1-x)^s\}^n.$$

15. In the sampling problem 12 find the probability that it will take exactly r drawings to get a sample containing all numbers. Pass to the limit as $s \to \infty$.

16. A cell contains N chromosomes, between any two of which an interchange of parts may occur. If r interchanges occur (which can happen in $\binom{N}{2}^r$ distinct ways), find the probability that exactly m chromosomes will be involved.[4]

17. Find the probability that exactly k suits will be missing in a poker hand.

18. Find the probability that a hand of thirteen bridge cards contains the ace-king pairs of exactly k suits.

19. *Multiple matching.* Two similar decks of N distinct cards each are matched simultaneously against a similar target deck. Find the probability u_m of having exactly m double matches. Show that $u_0 \to 1$ as $N \to \infty$ (which implies that $u_m \to 0$ for $m \geq 1$).

20. *Multiple matching.* The procedure of the preceding problem is modified as follows. Out of the $2N$ cards N are chosen at random, and only these N are matched against the target deck. Find the probability of no match. Prove that it tends to $1/e$ as $N \to \infty$.

21. *Multiple matching.* Answer problem 20 if r decks are used instead of two.

22. In the classical occupancy problem, the probability $P_{[m]}(k)$ of finding exactly m cells occupied by exactly k things is

$$P_{[m]}(k) = \frac{(-1)^m n! \, r!}{m! \, n^r} \sum_j (-1)^j \frac{(n-j)^{r-jk}}{(j-m)! \, (n-j)! \, (r-jk)! \, (k!)^j}$$

the summation extending over those $j \geq m$ for which $j \leq n$ and $kj \leq r$.

[4] For $N = 6$ see D. G. Catcheside, D. E. Lea, and J. M. Thoday, *Types of chromosome structural change introduced by the irradiation* of tradescantia *microspores*, Journal of Genetics, vol. 47 (1945–46), pp. 113–149.

23. Prove the last statement of section 2 for the case $k = 1$.

24. Using (3.1), derive the probability of finding exactly m empty cells in the case of Bose-Einstein statistics.

25. Verify that the formula obtained in 24 checks with II, (11.14).

26. Prove (1.5) by induction on N.

CHAPTER V

Conditional Probability.
Stochastic Independence

With this chapter we resume the systematic exposition of the funda-
mentals of probability theory.

1. CONDITIONAL PROBABILITY

The notion of conditional probability is a basic tool of probability
theory, and it is unfortunate that its great simplicity is somewhat obscured
by a singularly clumsy terminology. The following considerations lead in
a natural way to the formal definition.

Preparatory Examples

Suppose a population of N people includes N_A colorblind people and
N_H females. Let the events that a person chosen at random is colorblind
and a female be A and H, respectively. Then (cf. the definition of random choice, II, 2)

(1.1)
$$P\{A\} = \frac{N_A}{N}, \qquad P\{H\} = \frac{N_H}{N}.$$

We may now restrict our attention to the subpopulation consisting of
females. The probability that a person chosen at random from this subpopulation is colorblind equals N_{HA}/N_H, where N_{HA} is the number of
colorblind females. We have here no new notion, but we need a new
notation to designate which particular subpopulation is under investigation. The most widely adopted symbol is $P\{A \mid H\}$; it may be read "the
probability of the event A (colorblindness), assuming the event H (that
the person chosen is female)." In symbols:

(1.2)
$$P\{A \mid H\} = \frac{N_{AH}}{N_H} = \frac{P\{AH\}}{P\{H\}}.$$

114

Obviously every subpopulation may be considered as a population in its own right; we speak of a subpopulation merely for convenience of language to indicate that we have a larger population in the back of our minds. An insurance company may be interested in the frequency of damages of a fixed amount caused by lightning (event A). Presumably this company has several categories of insured objects such as industrial, urban, rural, etc. Studying separately the damages to industrial objects means to study the event A only in conjunction with the event H—"Damage is to an industrial object." Formula (1.2) again applies in an obvious manner. Note, however, that for an insurance company specializing in industrial objects the category H coincides with the whole sample space, and $P\{A \mid H\}$ reduces to $P\{A\}$.

Finally consider the bridge player North. Once the cards are dealt, he knows his hand and is interested only in the distribution of the remaining 39 cards. It is legitimate to introduce the aggregate of all possible distributions of these 39 cards as a new sample space, but it is obviously more convenient to consider them in conjunction with the given distribution of the 13 cards in North's hand (event H) and to speak of the probability of an event A (say South's having two aces) assuming the event H. Formula (1.2) again applies. ▶

By analogy with (1.2) we now introduce the formal

Definition. *Let H be an event with positive probability. For an arbitrary event A we shall write*

(1.3) $$P\{A \mid H\} = \frac{P\{AH\}}{P\{H\}} .$$

The quantity so defined will be called the conditional probability of A on the hypothesis H (or for given H). When all sample points have equal probabilities, $P\{A \mid H\}$ is the ratio N_{AH}/N_H of the number of sample points common to A and H, to the number of points in H.

Conditional probabilities remain undefined when the hypothesis has zero probability. This is of no consequence in the case of discrete sample spaces but is important in the general theory.

Though the symbol $P\{A \mid H\}$ itself is practical, its phrasing in words is so unwieldy that in practice less formal descriptions are used. Thus in our introductory example we referred to the probability that a female is colorblind instead of saying "the conditional probability that a randomly chosen person is colorblind given that this person is a female." Often the phrase "on the hypothesis H" is replaced by "if it is known that H

occurred." In short, our formulas and symbols are unequivocal, but phrasings in words are often informal and must be properly interpreted.

For stylistic clarity probabilities in the original sample space are sometimes called *absolute probabilities* in contradistinction to conditional ones. Strictly speaking, the adjective "absolute" is redundant and will be omitted.

Taking conditional probabilities of various events with respect to a particular hypothesis H amounts to choosing H as a new sample space with probabilities proportional to the original ones; the proportionality factor $\mathbf{P}\{H\}$ is necessary in order to reduce the total probability of the new sample space to unity. This formulation shows that *all general theorems on probabilities are valid also for conditional probabilities with respect to any particular hypothesis H.* For example, the fundamental relation for the probability of the occurrence of either A or B or both takes on the form

$$(1.4) \qquad \mathbf{P}\{A \cup B \mid H\} = \mathbf{P}\{A \mid H\} + \mathbf{P}\{B \mid H\} - \mathbf{P}\{AB \mid H\}.$$

Similarly, all theorems of chapter IV concerning probabilities of the realization of m among N events carry over to conditional probabilities, but we shall not need them.

Formula (1.3) is often used in the form

$$(1.5) \qquad\qquad \mathbf{P}\{AH\} = \mathbf{P}\{A \mid H\} \cdot \mathbf{P}\{H\}.$$

This is the so-called theorem on compound probabilities. To generalize it to three events A, B, C we first take $H = BC$ as hypothesis and then apply (1.5) once more; it follows that

$$(1.6) \qquad\qquad \mathbf{P}\{ABC\} = \mathbf{P}\{A \mid BC\} \cdot \mathbf{P}\{B \mid C\} \cdot \mathbf{P}\{C\}.$$

A further generalization to four or more events is straightforward.

We conclude with a simple formula which is frequently useful. Let $H_1, \ldots, H_n$ be a set of mutually exclusive events of which one necessarily occurs (that is, the union of $H_1, \ldots, H_n$ is the entire sample space). Then any event A can occur only in conjunction with some H_j, or in symbols,

$$(1.7) \qquad\qquad A = AH_1 \cup AH_2 \cup \cdots \cup AH_n.$$

Since the AH_j are mutually exclusive, their probabilities add. Applying (1.5) to $H = H_j$ and adding, we get

$$(1.8) \qquad\qquad \mathbf{P}\{A\} = \sum \mathbf{P}\{A \mid H_j\} \cdot \mathbf{P}\{H_j\}.$$

This formula is useful because an evaluation of the conditional probabilities $\mathbf{P}\{A \mid H_j\}$ is frequently easier than a direct calculation of $\mathbf{P}\{A\}$.

Examples. (*a*) *Sampling without replacement.* From a population of the n elements $1, 2, \ldots, n$ an ordered sample is taken. Let i and j be two different elements. Assuming that i is the first element drawn (event H), what is the probability that the second element is j (event A)? Clearly $\mathbf{P}\{AH\} = 1/n(n-1)$ and $\mathbf{P}\{A \mid H\} = 1/(n-1)$. This expresses the fact that the second choice refers to a population of $n - 1$ elements, each of which has the same probability of being chosen. In fact, the most natural *definition* of random sampling is: "*Whatever the first r choices, at the $(r+1)$st step each of the remaining $n - r$ elements has probability $1/(n-r)$ to be chosen.*" This definition is equivalent to that given in chapter II, but we could not have stated it earlier since it involves the notion of conditional probability.

(*b*) Four balls are placed successively into four cells, all 4^4 arrangements being equally probable. Given that the first two balls are in different cells (event H), what is the probability that one cell contains exactly three balls (event A)? Given H, the event A can occur in two ways, and so $\mathbf{P}\{A \mid H\} = 2 \cdot 4^{-2} = \frac{1}{8}$. (It is easy to verify directly that the events H and AH contain $12 \cdot 4^2$ and $12 \cdot 2$ points, respectively.)

(*c*) *Distribution of sexes.* Consider families with exactly two children. Letting b and g stand for boy and girl, respectively, and the first letter for the older child, we have four possibilities: bb, bg, gb, gg. These are the four sample points, and we associate probability $\frac{1}{4}$ with each. Given that a family has a boy (event H), what is the probability that both children are boys (event A)? The event AH means bb, and H means bb, or bg, or gb. Therefore, $\mathbf{P}\{A \mid H\} = \frac{1}{3}$; in about one-third of the families with the characteristic H we can expect that A also will occur. It is interesting that most people expect the answer to be $\frac{1}{2}$. This is the correct answer to a different question, namely: A boy is chosen at random and found to come from a family with two children; what is the probability that the other child is a boy? The difference may be explained empirically. With our original problem we might refer to a card file of families, with the second to a file of males. In the latter, each family with two boys will be represented twice, and this explains the difference between the two results.

(*d*) *Stratified populations.* Suppose a human population consists of subpopulations or strata $H_1, H_2, \ldots$. These may be races, age groups, professions, etc. Let p_j be the probability that an individual chosen at random belongs to H_j. Saying "q_j is the probability that an individual in H_j is left-handed" is short for "q_j is the conditional probability of the event A (left-handedness) on the hypothesis that an individual belongs to

H_j." The probability that an individual chosen at random is left-handed is $p_1q_1 + p_2q_2 + p_3q_3 + \cdots$, which is a special case of (1.8). Given that an individual is left-handed, the conditional probability of his belonging to stratum H_j is

$$(1.9) \qquad \mathbf{P}\{H_j \mid A\} = \frac{p_jq_j}{p_1q_1 + p_2q_2 + \cdots}. \qquad \blacktriangleright$$

2. PROBABILITIES DEFINED BY CONDITIONAL PROBABILITIES. URN MODELS

In the preceding section we have taken the probabilities in the sample space for granted and merely calculated a few conditional probabilities. In applications, many experiments are described by specifying certain conditional probabilities (although the adjective "conditional" is usually omitted). Theoretically this means that the probabilities in the sample space are to be derived from the given conditional probabilities. It has already been pointed out [example (1.a)] that sampling without replacement is best defined by saying that whatever the result of the r first selections, each of the remaining elements has the same probability of being selected at the $(r+1)$st step. Similarly, in example (1.d) our stratified population is completely described by stating the absolute probabilities p_j of the several strata, and the conditional probability q_j of the characteristic "left-handed" within each stratum. A few more examples will reveal the general scheme more effectively than a direct description could.

Examples. (a) We return to example I,(5.b) in which three players a, b, and c take turns at a game. The scheme (*) on p. 18 describes the points of the sample space, but we have not yet assigned probabilities to them. Suppose now that the game is such that at each trial each of the two partners has probability $\frac{1}{2}$ of winning. This statement does not contain the word "conditional probability" but refers to it nonetheless. For it says that if player a participates in the rth round (event H), his probability of winning that particular round is $\frac{1}{2}$. It follows from (1.5) that the probability of a winning at the first and second try is $\frac{1}{4}$; in symbols, $\mathbf{P}\{aa\} = \frac{1}{4}$. A repeated application of (1.5) shows that $\mathbf{P}\{acc\} = \frac{1}{8}$, $\mathbf{P}\{acbb\} = \frac{1}{16}$, etc.; that is, a sample point of the scheme (*) involving r letters has probability 2^{-r}. This is the assignment of probabilities used in problem 5 in Chapter I,8 but now the description is more intuitive. (Continued in problem 14.)

(b) *Families.* We want to interpret the following statement. "The probability of a family having exactly k children is p_k (where $\sum p_k = 1$). For any family size all sex distributions have equal probabilities." Letting

b stand for boy and g for girl, our sample space consists of the points 0 (no children), b, g, bb, bg, gb, gg, bbb, ... The second assumption in quotation marks can be stated more formally thus: If it is known that the family has exactly n children, each of the 2^n possible sex distributions has conditional probability 2^{-n}. The probability of the hypothesis is p_n, and we see from (1.5) that the absolute probability of any arrangement of n letters b and g is $p_n \cdot 2^{-n}$.

Note that this is an example of a *stratified population*, the families of size j forming the stratum H_j. As an exercise let A stand for the event "the family has boys but no girls." Its probability is obviously $\mathbf{P}\{A\} = = p_1 \cdot 2^{-1} + p_2 \cdot 2^{-2} + \cdots$ which is a special case of (1.8). The hypothesis H_j in this case is "family has j children." We now ask the question: If it is known that a family has no girls, what is the (conditional) probability that it has only one child? Here A is the hypothesis. Let H be the event "only one child." Then AH means "one child and no girl," and

$$(2.1) \quad \mathbf{P}\{H \mid A\} = \frac{\mathbf{P}\{AH\}}{\mathbf{P}\{A\}} = \frac{p_1 2^{-1}}{p_1 2^{-1} + p_2 2^{-2} + p_3 2^{-3} + \cdots},$$

which is a special case of (1.9).

(*c*) *Urn models for aftereffect.* For the sake of definiteness consider an industrial plant liable to accidents. The occurrence of an accident might be pictured as the result of a superhuman game of chance: Fate has in storage an urn containing red and black balls; at regular time intervals a ball is drawn at random, a red ball signifying an accident. If the chance of an accident remains constant in time, the composition of the urn is always the same. But it is conceivable that each accident has an *aftereffect* in that it either increases or decreases the chance of new accidents. This corresponds to an urn whose composition changes according to certain rules that depend on the outcome of the successive drawings. It is easy to invent a variety of such rules to cover various situations, but we shall be content with a discussion of the following[1]

Urn model: An urn contains b black and r red balls. A ball is drawn at random. It is replaced and, moreover, c balls of the color drawn and d balls of the opposite color are added. A new random drawing is made from

---

[1] The idea to use urn models to describe aftereffects (contagious diseases) seems to be due to Polya. His scheme [first introduced in F. Eggenberger and G. Polya, *Über die Statistik verketteter Vorgänge*, Zeitschrift für Angewandte Mathematik and Mechanik, vol. 3 (1923), pp. 279–289] served as a prototype for many models discussed in the literature. The model described in the text and its three special cases were proposed by B. Friedman, *A simple urn model*, Communications on Pure and Applied Mathematics, vol. 2 (1949), pp. 59–70.

the urn (now containing $r + b + c + d$ balls), and this procedure is repeated. Here c and d are arbitrary integers. They may be chosen *negative*, except that in this case the procedure may terminate after finitely many drawings for lack of balls. In particular, choosing $c = -1$ and $d = 0$ we have the model of *random drawings without replacement* which terminates after $r + b$ steps.

To turn our picturesque description into mathematics, note that it specifies conditional probabilities from which certain basic probabilities are to be calculated. A typical point of the sample space corresponding to n drawings may be represented by a sequence of n letters B and R. The event "black at first drawing" (i.e., the aggregate of all sequences starting with B) has probability $b/(b+r)$. If the first ball is black, the (conditional) probability of a black ball at the second drawing is

$$(b+c)/(b+r+c+d).$$

The (absolute) probability of the sequence black, black (i.e., the aggregate of the sample points starting with BB) is therefore, by (1.5),

(2.2)
$$\frac{b}{b+r} \cdot \frac{b+c}{b+r+c+d}.$$

The probability of the sequence black, black, black is (2.2) multiplied by $(b+2c)/(b+r+2c+2d)$, etc. In this way the probabilities of all sample points can be calculated. It is easily verified by induction that the probabilities of all sample points indeed add to unity.

Explicit expressions for the probabilities are not readily obtainable except in the most important and best-known special case, that of

Polya's urn scheme which is characterized by $d = 0$, $c > 0$. Here after each drawing the number of balls of the color drawn increases, whereas the balls of opposite color remain unchanged in number. In effect the drawing of either color increases the probability of the same color at the next drawing, and we have a rough model of phenomena such as *contagious diseases*, where each occurrence increases the probability of further occurrences. The probability that of $n = n_1 + n_2$ drawings the first n_1 ones result in black balls and the remaining n_2 ones in red balls is given by

(2.3)
$$\frac{b(b+c)(b+2c) \cdots (b+n_1 c-c) \cdot r(r+c) \cdots (r+n_2 c-c)}{(b+r)(b+r+c)(b+r+2c) \cdots (b+r+nc-c)}.$$

Consider now any other ordering of n_1 black and n_2 red balls. In calculating the probability that n drawings result in this particular order of colors we encounter the same factors as in (2.3) but rearranged in a new order. It follows that all possible sequences of n_1 black and n_2 red balls have the same probability. The analytical simplicity (and hence the easy applicability) of Polya's urn scheme is due mainly to this characteristic property. To obtain the probability $p_{n_1, n}$ that n drawings result in n_1 black and n_2 red balls in any order we must multiply the quantity (2.3) by $\binom{n}{n_1}$, namely the number of possible orderings. The use of general binomial coefficients permits us to rewrite this probability in either of the following forms:

$$(2.4) \qquad p_{n_1, n} = \frac{\binom{n_1 - 1 + b/c}{n_1}\binom{n_2 - 1 + r/c}{n_2}}{\binom{n - 1 + (b + r)/c}{n}} = \frac{\binom{-b/c}{n_1}\binom{-r/c}{n_2}}{\binom{-(b + r)/c}{n}}.$$

(The discussion of the Polya scheme is continued in problems 18–24. See also problems 9 and 10 of XVII, 10.)

In addition to the Polya scheme our urn model contains another special case of interest, namely the

Ehrenfest model[2] *of heat exchange* between two isolated bodies. In the original description, as used by physicists, the Ehrenfest model envisages two containers I and II and k particles distributed in them. A particle is chosen at random and moved from its container into the other container. This procedure is repeated. What is the distribution of the particles after n steps? To reduce this to an urn model it suffices to call the particles in container I red, the others black. Then at each drawing the ball drawn is replaced by a ball of the opposite color, that is, we have $c = -1$, $d = 1$. It is clear that in this case the process can continue as long as we please (if there are no red balls, a black ball is drawn automatically and replaced by a red one). [We shall discuss the Ehrenfest model in another way in example XV, (2.e).]

The special case $c = 0$, $d > 0$ has been proposed by Friedman as a model of a *safety campaign*. Every time an accident occurs (i.e., a red ball is drawn), the safety campaign is pushed harder; whenever no accident occurs, the campaign slackens and the probability of an accident increases.

(d) *Urn models for stratification. Spurious contagion.* To continue in the vein of the preceding example, suppose that each person is liable to accidents and that their occurrence is determined by random drawings from

---

[2] P. and T. Ehrenfest, *Über zwei bekannte Einwände gegen das Boltzmannsche H-Theorem*, Physikalische Zeitschrift, vol. 8 (1907), pp. 311–314. For a mathematical discussion see M. Kac, *Random walk and the theory of Brownian motion*, Amer. Math. Monthly, vol. 54 (1947), pp. 369–391.

an urn. This time, however, we shall suppose that no aftereffect exists, so that the composition of the urn remains unchanged throughout the process. Now the chance of an accident or proneness to accidents may vary from person to person or from profession to profession, and we imagine that each person (or each profession) has his own urn. In order not to complicate matters unnecessarily, let us suppose that there are just two types of people (two professions) and that their numbers in the total population stand in the ratio $1:5$. We consider then an urn I containing r_1 red and b_1 black balls, and an urn II containing r_2 red and b_2 black balls. The experiment "choose a person at random and observe how many accidents he has during n time units" has the following counterpart: *A die is thrown; if ace appears, choose urn* I, *otherwise urn* II. *In each case n random drawings with replacement are selected from the urn.* Our experiment describes the situation of an insurance company accepting a new subscriber.

By using (1.8) it is seen that the probability of red at the first drawing is

$$(2.5) \qquad \mathbf{P}\{R\} = \frac{1}{6} \cdot \frac{r_1}{b_1 + r_1} + \frac{5}{6} \cdot \frac{r_2}{b_2 + r_2}$$

and the probability of a sequence red, red

$$(2.6) \qquad \mathbf{P}\{RR\} = \frac{1}{6} \cdot \left(\frac{r_1}{b_1 + r_1}\right)^2 + \frac{5}{6} \cdot \left(\frac{r_2}{b_2 + r_2}\right)^2.$$

No mathematical problem is involved in our model, but it has an interesting feature which has caused great confusion in applications. Suppose our insurance company observes that a new subscriber has an accident during the first year, and is interested in the probability of a further accident during the second year. In other words, given that the first drawing resulted in red, we ask for the (conditional) probability of a sequence red, red. This is clearly the ratio $\mathbf{P}\{RR\}/\mathbf{P}\{R\}$ and is *different* from $\mathbf{P}\{R\}$. For the sake of illustration suppose that

$$r_1/(b_1+r_1) = 0.6 \quad \text{and} \quad r_2/(b_2+r_2) = 0.06.$$

The probability of red at any drawing is 0.15, but if the first drawing resulted in red, the chances that the next drawing also results in red are 0.42. Note that our model assumes *no aftereffect* in the total population, and yet the occurrence of an accident for a person chosen at random increases the odds that this same person will have a second accident. This is, however, merely an effect of sampling: The occurrence of an accident has no real effect on the future, but it does serve as an indication that the person involved has a relatively high proneness to accidents. Continued observations enable us for this reason to improve our predictions for the future even though in reality this future is not at all affected by the past.

In the statistical literature it has become customary to use the word *contagion* instead of aftereffect. The *apparent* aftereffect of sampling was at first misinterpreted as an effect of true contagion, and so statisticians now speak of contagion (or contagious probability distributions) in a vague and misleading manner. Take, for example, the ecologist searching for insects in a field. If after an unsuccessful period he finds an insect, it is quite likely that he has finally reached the proximity of a litter, and in this case he may reasonably expect increased success. In other words, in practice every success increases the probability for further success, but once more this is only a side effect of the increased amount of information provided by the sampling. No aftereffect is involved, and it is misleading when the statistician speaks of contagion.

(*e*) The following example is famous and illustrative, but somewhat artificial. Imagine a collection of $N + 1$ urns, each containing a total of N red and white balls; the urn number k contains k red and $N - k$ white balls ($k = 0, 1, 2, \ldots, N$). An urn is chosen at random and n random drawings are made from it, the ball drawn being replaced each time. Suppose that all n balls turn out to be red (event A). We seek the (conditional) probability that the next drawing will also yield a red ball (event B). If the first choice falls on urn number k, then the probability of extracting in succession n red balls is $(k/N)^n$. Hence, by (1.8),

$$(2.7) \qquad \mathbf{P}\{A\} = \frac{1^n + 2^n + \cdots + N^n}{N^n(N+1)}.$$

The event AB means that $n + 1$ drawings yield red balls, and therefore

$$(2.8) \qquad \mathbf{P}\{AB\} = \mathbf{P}\{B\} = \frac{1^{n+1} + 2^{n+1} + \cdots + N^{n+1}}{N^{n+1}(N+1)}.$$

The required probability is $\mathbf{P}\{B \mid A\} = \mathbf{P}\{B\}/\mathbf{P}\{A\}$.

When N is large the numerator in (2.7) differs relatively little from the area between the x-axis and the graph of x^n between 0 and N. We have then approximately

$$(2.9) \qquad \mathbf{P}\{A\} \approx \frac{1}{N^n(N+1)} \int_0^N x^n \, dx = \frac{N}{N+1} \cdot \frac{1}{n+1} \approx \frac{1}{n+1}.$$

A similar calculation applies to (2.8) and we conclude that for large N approximately

$$(2.10) \qquad \mathbf{P}\{B \mid A\} \approx \frac{n+1}{n+2}.$$

This result can be interpreted roughly as follows: If all compositions of an urn are equally probable, and if n trials yielded red balls, the probability of a red ball at the next trial is $(n+1)/(n+2)$. This is the so-called law of succession of Laplace (1812).

Before the ascendance of the modern theory, the notion of equal probabilities was often used as synonymous for "no advance knowledge." Laplace himself has illustrated the use of (2.10) by computing the probability that the sun will rise tomorrow, given that it has risen daily for 5000 years or $n = 1,826,213$ days. It is said that Laplace was ready to bet 1,826,214 to 1 in favor of regular habits of the sun, and we should be in a position to better the odds since regular service has followed for another century. A historical study would be necessary to appreciate what Laplace had in mind and to understand his intentions. His successors, however, used similar arguments in routine work and recommended methods of this kind to physicists and engineers in cases where the formulas have no operational meaning. We should have to reject the method even if, for sake of argument, we were to concede that our universe was chosen at random from a collection in which all conceivable possibilities were equally likely. In fact, it pretends to judge the chances of the sun's rising tomorrow from the *assumed* risings in the past. But the assumed rising of the sun on February 5, 3123 B.C., is by no means more certain than that the sun will rise tomorrow. We believe in both for the same reasons.   ▶

Note on Bayes's Rule. In (1.9) and (2.2) we have calculated certain conditional probabilities directly from the definition. The beginner is advised always to do so and not to memorize the formula (2.12), which we shall now derive. It traces in a general way what we did in special cases, but it is only a way of rewriting (1.3). We had a collection of events $H_1, H_2, \ldots$ which are mutually exclusive and exhaustive, that is, every sample point belonging to one, and only one, among the H_j. We were interested in

(2.11)
$$P\{H_k \mid A\} = \frac{P\{AH_k\}}{P\{A\}} .$$

If (1.5) and (1.8) are introduced into (2.11), it takes the form

(2.12)
$$P\{H_k \mid A\} = \frac{P\{A \mid H_k\}P\{H_k\}}{\sum_j P\{A \mid H_j\}P\{H_j\}} .$$

If the events H_k are called causes, then (2.12) becomes "Bayes's rule for the probability of causes." Mathematically, (2.12) is a special way of writing (1.3) and nothing more. The formula is useful in many statistical applications of the type described in examples (b) and (d), and we have used it there. Unfortunately, Bayes's rule has been somewhat discredited by metaphysical applications of the type described in example (e). In routine practice this kind of argument can be dangerous. A quality control engineer is concerned with one particular machine and not with an infinite population of machines from which one was chosen at random. He has been advised to use Bayes's rule on the grounds that it is logically acceptable and corresponds to our way of thinking. Plato used this type of argument to prove the existence of Atlantis, and philosophers used it to prove the absurdity of Newton's mechanics. But for our engineer the argument overlooks the circumstance that he desires success and that he will do better by estimating and minimizing the sources of various types of errors in prediction and guessing. The modern method of statistical tests and estimation is less intuitive but more realistic. It may be not only defended but also applied.

3. STOCHASTIC INDEPENDENCE

In the examples above the conditional probability $P\{A \mid H\}$ generally does not equal the absolute probability $P\{A\}$. Popularly speaking, the information whether H has occurred changes our way of betting on the event A. Only when $P\{A \mid H\} = P\{A\}$ this information does not permit any inference about the occurrence of A. In this case we shall say that A is stochastically independent of H. Now (1.5) shows that the condition $P\{A \mid H\} = P\{A\}$ can be written in the form

$$(3.1) \qquad P\{AH\} = P\{A\} \cdot P\{H\}.$$

This equation is symmetric in A and H and shows that whenever A is stochastically independent of H, so is H of A. It is therefore preferable to start from the following symmetric

Definition 1. *Two events A and H are said to be stochastically independent (or independent, for short) if equation* (3.1) *holds.* This definition is accepted also if $P\{H\} = 0$, in which case $P\{A \mid H\}$ is not defined. The term *statistically* independent is synonymous with stochastically independent.

In practice one usually has the correct feeling that certain events must be stochastically independent, or else the probabilistic model would be absurd. As the following examples will show, there exist nevertheless situations in which the stochastic independence can be discovered only by computation.

Examples. (*a*) A card is chosen at random from a deck of playing cards. For reasons of symmetry we expect the events "spade" and "ace" to be independent. As a matter of fact, their probabilities are $\frac{1}{4}$ and $\frac{1}{13}$, and the probability of their simultaneous realization is $\frac{1}{52}$.

(*b*) Two true dice are thrown. The events "ace with first die" and "even face with second" are independent since the probability of their simultaneous realization, $\frac{3}{36} = \frac{1}{12}$, is the product of their probabilities, namely $\frac{1}{6}$ and $\frac{1}{2}$.

(c) In a random permutation of the four letters (a, b, c, d) the events "a precedes b" and "c precedes d" are independent. This is intuitively clear and easily verified.

(d) *Sex distribution.* We return to example (1.c) but now consider families with three children. We assume that each of the eight possibilities $bbb, bbg, \ldots, ggg$ has probability $\frac{1}{8}$. Let H be the event "the family has children of both sexes," and A the event "there is at most one girl." Then $\mathbf{P}\{H\} = \frac{6}{8}$, and $\mathbf{P}\{A\} = \frac{4}{8}$. The simultaneous realization of A and H means one of the possibilities bbg, bgb, gbb, and therefore $\mathbf{P}\{AH\} = = \frac{3}{8} = \mathbf{P}\{A\} \cdot \mathbf{P}\{H\}$. Thus in families with three children the two events are independent. Note that this is not true for families with two or four children. This shows that it is not always obvious whether or not we have independence. ▶

If H occurs, the complementary event H' does not occur, and vice versa. Stochastic independence implies that no inference can be drawn from the occurrence of H to that of A; therefore stochastic independence of A and H should mean the same as independence of A and H' (and, because of symmetry, also of A' and H, and of A' and H'). This assertion is easily verified, using the relation $\mathbf{P}\{H'\} = 1 - \mathbf{P}\{H\}$. Indeed, if (3.1) holds, then (since $AH' = A - AH$)

$$(3.2) \quad \mathbf{P}\{AH'\} = \mathbf{P}\{A\} - \mathbf{P}\{AH\} = \mathbf{P}\{A\} - \mathbf{P}\{A\} \cdot \mathbf{P}\{H\} = $$
$$= \mathbf{P}\{A\} \cdot \mathbf{P}\{H'\},$$

as expected.

Suppose now that three events A, B, and C are pairwise independent so that

$$\mathbf{P}\{AB\} = \mathbf{P}\{A\} \cdot \mathbf{P}\{B\}$$
$$(3.3) \quad \mathbf{P}\{AC\} = \mathbf{P}\{A\} \cdot \mathbf{P}\{C\}$$
$$\mathbf{P}\{BC\} = \mathbf{P}\{B\} \cdot \mathbf{P}\{C\}.$$

One might think that these three relations should imply that also

$$\mathbf{P}\{ABC\} = \mathbf{P}\{A\}\mathbf{P}\{B\}\mathbf{P}\{C\},$$

in other words, that the pairwise independence of the three events should imply that the two events AB and C are independent. This is almost always true, but in principle it is possible that (3.3) holds and yet

$$\mathbf{P}\{ABC\} = 0.$$

Actually such occurrences are so rare that their possibility passed unnoticed until S. Bernstein constructed an artificial example. It still takes some search to find a plausible natural example.

Example. (*e*) Consider the six permutations of the letters a, b, c as well as the three triples (a, a, a), (b, b, b), and (c, c, c). We take these nine triples as points of a sample space and attribute probability $\frac{1}{9}$ to each. Denote by A_k the event that the kth place is occupied by the letter a. Obviously each of these three events has probability $\frac{1}{3}$ while

$$\mathbf{P}\{A_1A_2\} = \mathbf{P}\{A_1A_3\} = \mathbf{P}\{A_2A_3\} = \tfrac{1}{9}.$$

The three events are therefore *pairwise independent*, but they are *not* mutually independent because also $\mathbf{P}\{A_1A_2A_3\} = \frac{1}{9}$. (The occurrence of A_1 and A_2 implies the occurrence of A_3, and so A_3 is not independent of A_1A_2.)

We obtain further examples by considering also the events B_k and C_k consisting, respectively, in the occurrence of the letters b and c at the kth place. We have now nine events in all, each with probability $\frac{1}{3}$. Clearly $\mathbf{P}\{A_1B_2\} = \frac{1}{9}$ and generally *any two events with different subscripts are independent*. On the other hand, the letters appearing at the first two places uniquely determine the letter at the third place, and so C_3 is not independent of any among the nine events $A_1A_2, \ldots, C_1C_2$ involving the first two places.[3] We shall return to this example at the end of IX, 1. A further example is contained in problem 26.　　　　　▶

It is desirable to reserve the term stochastic independence for the case where not only (3.3) holds, but in addition

(3.4)　　　　　　　$\mathbf{P}\{ABC\} = \mathbf{P}\{A\}\mathbf{P}\{B\}\mathbf{P}\{C\}.$

This equation ensures that A and BC are independent and also that the same is true of B and AC, and C and AB. Furthermore, it can now be proved also that $A \cup B$ and C are independent. In fact, by the fundamental relation I, (7.4) we have

(3.5)　　　　　$\mathbf{P}\{A \cup B)C\} = \mathbf{P}\{AC\} + \mathbf{P}\{BC\} - \mathbf{P}\{ABC\}.$

Again applying (3.3) and (3.4) to the right side, we can factor out $\mathbf{P}\{C\}$. The other factor is $\mathbf{P}\{A\} + \mathbf{P}\{B\} - \mathbf{P}\{AB\} = \mathbf{P}\{A \cup B\}$ and so

(3.6)　　　　　　$\mathbf{P}\{A \cup B)C\} = \mathbf{P}\{(A \cup B)\}\mathbf{P}\{C\}.$

---

[3] The construction generalizes to r-tuples with $r > 3$. The sample space then contains $r! + r$ points, namely of the $r!$ permutations of the symbols $a_1, \ldots, a_r$ and of the r repetitions of the same symbol a_j. To each permutation we attribute probability $1/r^2(r-2)!$, and to each repetition probability $1/r^2$. If A_k is the event that a_1 occurs at the kth place, then the events A_k are pairwise independent, but no three among them are mutually independent.

This makes it plausible that the conditions (3.3) and (3.4) together suffice to avoid embarrassment; any event expressible in terms of A and B will be independent of C.

Definition 2. *The events* $A_1, A_2, \ldots, A_n$ *are called mutually independent if for all combinations* $1 \leq i < j < k < \cdots \leq n$ *the multiplication rules*

$$\mathbf{P}\{A_i A_j\} = \mathbf{P}\{A_i\}\,\mathbf{P}\{A_j\}$$
$$\mathbf{P}\{A_i A_j A_k\} = \mathbf{P}\{A_i\}\,\mathbf{P}\{A_j\}\,\mathbf{P}\{A_k\}$$

(3.7) $\cdots\cdots\cdots\cdots\cdots\cdots\cdots\cdots\cdots\cdots\cdots\cdots\cdots$
$\cdots\cdots\cdots\cdots\cdots\cdots\cdots\cdots\cdots\cdots\cdots\cdots\cdots$

$$\mathbf{P}\{A_1 A_2 \cdots A_n\} = \mathbf{P}\{A_1\}\,\mathbf{P}\{A_2\} \cdots \mathbf{P}\{A_n\}$$

apply

The first line stands for $\binom{n}{2}$ equations, the second for $\binom{n}{3}$, etc. We have, therefore,

$$\binom{n}{2} + \binom{n}{3} + \cdots + \binom{n}{n} = (1+1)^n - \binom{n}{1} - \binom{n}{0} = 2^n - n - 1$$

conditions which must be satisfied. On the other hand, the $\binom{n}{2}$ conditions stated in the first line suffice to insure *pairwise independence*. The whole system (3.7) looks like a complicated set of conditions, but it will soon become apparent that its validity is usually obvious and requires no checking. It is readily seen by induction [starting with $n = 2$ and (3.2)] that

In definition 2 the system (3.7) *may be replaced by the system of the* 2^n *equations obtained from the last equation in* (3.7) *on replacing an arbitrary number of events* A_j *by their complements* A_j'.

4. PRODUCT SPACES. INDEPENDENT TRIALS

We are now finally in a position to introduce the mathematical counterpart of empirical procedures which are commonly described by phrases such as continued experimentation, repeated observation, merging of two samples, combining two experiments and treating them as parts of a whole, etc. Specifically, the notion of independent trials corresponds to the intuitive concept of "experiments repeated under identical conditions." This notion is basic for probability theory and will add more realism to the examples treated so far.

We first require a notion that is by no means specific for probability theory. The *combinatorial product* of two sets A and B is the set of all ordered pairs (a, b) of their elements. We shall denote[4] it by (A, B). The definition carries over trivially to triples (A, B, C), quadruples (A, B, C, D), and even to infinite sequences.

The notion of combinatorial product is so natural that we have used it implicitly several times. For example, the conceptual experiment of tossing a coin three times is described by a sample space of eight points, namely the triples that can be formed with two letters H and T. This amounts to saying that the sample space is the combinatorial product of three spaces, each of which consists of the two points (elements) H and T. More generally, when we speak of two successive trials we refer to a sample space $\mathfrak{S}$ whose points represent the pairs of possible outcomes, and so $\mathfrak{S}$ is the combinatorial product of the two sample spaces corresponding to the individual trials. Given any two conceptual experiments with sample spaces $\mathfrak{A}$ and $\mathfrak{B}$, it is possible to consider them simultaneously or in succession. This amounts to considering pairs of possible outcomes, that is, to introduce the combinatorial product $(\mathfrak{A}, \mathfrak{B})$ as a new sample space. The question then arises as to how probabilities should be defined in this new sample space. The answer varies with circumstances, but before considering this point we turn to two examples which will clarify ideas and explain the prevalent terminology.

Examples. (*a*) *Cartesian spaces.* When the points of the plane are represented by pairs (x, y) of real numbers, the plane becomes the combinatorial product of the two axes. (The fact that geometry in the plane can be studied without use of coordinates shows that the same space can be considered from different viewpoints.) The three-dimensional space with points (x, y, z) may be viewed either as the triple product of the three axes, or else as the product of the x,y-plane and the z-axis.

In the plane, the set of points satisfying the two conditions $0 < x < 1$ and $0 < y < 1$ is the combinatorial product of two unit intervals. Note, however, that such a description is not possible for arbitrary sets such as triangles and ellipses. Finally we note that in the (x, y, z)-space the set defined by the same two inequalities is an infinite cylinder with a square cross-section. More generally, when interpreted in space, any set whose definition involves only the x- and y-coordinates may be viewed as a cylinder with generators parallel to the z-axis.

(*b*) *Alphabets and words.* Let A consist of the 26 standard letters. The triple product (A, A, A) is then the aggregate of all triples of letters or, as

---

[4] Another commonly used notation is $A \times B$. The terms combinatorial product and Cartesian product are synonymous.

we shall say, all three-letter "words." This viewpoint is used in communication and coding theory, but then it is not natural to consider words of a fixed length. Indeed, a message of arbitrary length may be considered a "word" provided a new symbol for separation (a blank) is added to the alphabet. It is then no longer necessary to introduce any assumptions concerning the length of words: Any finite message may be considered as the beginning of a potentially unending message, just as any written word is potentially the first of a series. Incidentally, communication theory uses arbitrary codes, and under its influence it has become common usage to refer to arbitrary symbols as letters of an alphabet. In this sense one describes the outcome of n repeated trials as a "message" or "word" of length n. ▶

If $\mathfrak{S}$ is an arbitrary sample space with points $E_1, E_2, \ldots$ the n-fold combinatorial product $(\mathfrak{S}, \mathfrak{S}, \ldots, \mathfrak{S})$ of $\mathfrak{S}$ with itself is referred to as sample space for a succession of n trials corresponding to $\mathfrak{S}$. It is convenient to describe its points generically by symbols such as $(x_1, \ldots, x_n)$ where each x_i stands for some point of $\mathfrak{S}$. By analogy with example (a) it is usual to refer to the x_i as *coordinates*. The terms set and event are, of course, interchangeable. What we describe as *an event that depends only on the outcome of the first two trials* is generally called a set depending only on the first two coordinates.[5]

As already mentioned, all these notions and notations carry over to infinite sequences. Conceptually these present no difficulties; after all, the decimal expansion 3.1415... represents the number π as a point in an infinite product space, except that one speaks of the nth decimal rather than of the nth coordinate. *Infinite product spaces are the natural habitat of probability theory.* It is undesirable to specify a fixed number of coin tossings or a fixed length for a random walk. The theory becomes more flexible and simpler if we conceive of potentially unending sequences of trials and then direct our attention to events depending only on the first few trials. This conceptually simpler and more satisfactory approach unfortunately requires the technical apparatus of measure theory. The plan of this volume is to present the basic ideas of probability theory unobscured by technical difficulties. For this reason we are restricted to discrete sample spaces and must be satisfied with the study of finitely many trials. This means dealing with unspecified or variable sample spaces as the price for technical simplicity. This solution is unsatisfactory theoretically, but has little practical effect.

---

[5] That is to say, if $(x_1, x_2, \ldots)$ is a point of this set so are all points $(x_1', x_2', \ldots)$ such that $x_1' = x_1$ and $x_2' = x_2$. By analogy with example (a), sets depending only on specified coordinates (in any number) are called *cylindrical*.

We turn to the assignment of probabilities in product spaces. The various urn models of section 2 can be rephrased in terms of repeated trials and we have seen that probabilities of different types can be defined by means of conditional probabilities. Intuitively speaking, various forms of dependence between successive trials can be imagined, but nothing surpasses in importance the notion of independent trials or, more generally, independent experiments.

To be specific, consider two sample spaces $\mathfrak{A}$ and $\mathfrak{B}$, with points $\alpha_1, \alpha_2, \ldots$ and $\beta_1, \beta_2, \ldots$ carrying probabilities $p_1, p_2, \ldots$ and $q_1, q_2, \ldots$, respectively. We interpret the product space $(\mathfrak{A}, \mathfrak{B})$ as the sample space describing the succession of the two experiments corresponding to $\mathfrak{A}$ and $\mathfrak{B}$. Saying that these two experiments are independent implies that the two events "first outcome is α_i" and "second outcome is β_k" are stochastically independent. But this is so only if probabilities in $(\mathfrak{A}, \mathfrak{B})$ are defined by the product rule

$$(4.1) \qquad \mathbf{P}\{(\alpha_i, \beta_k)\} = p_i q_k.$$

Such an assignment of probabilities is legitimate[6] because these probabilities add to unity. In fact, summation over all points leads to the double sum $\sum\sum p_i q_k$, which is the product of the two sums $\sum p_i$ and $\sum q_k$.

We now establish the convention that *the phrase "two independent experiments" refers to the combinatorial product of two sample spaces with probabilities defined by the product rule* (4.1). *This convention applies equally to the notion of n successive independent experiments.*

We speak of repeated independent trials if the component sample spaces (and the probabilities in them) are identical.

This convention enables us, for example, to speak of n independent coin tossings as an abbreviation of a sample space of 2^n points, each carrying probability 2^{-n}.

An intuitively obvious property of independent experiments deserves mention. Let A be an event in $\mathfrak{A}$ containing the points $\alpha_{s_1}, \alpha_{s_2}, \ldots$; let similarly B be an event in $\mathfrak{B}$ containing the points $\beta_{t_1}, \beta_{t_2}, \ldots$. Then (A, B) is the event in $(\mathfrak{A}, \mathfrak{B})$ which consists of all pairs $(\alpha_{s_i}, \beta_{t_k})$, and clearly

$$(4.2) \qquad \mathbf{P}\{(A, B)\} = \sum\sum p_{s_i} q_{t_k} = (\sum p_{s_i})(\sum q_{t_k}) = \mathbf{P}\{A\}\mathbf{P}\{B\}.$$

The multiplication rule thus extends to arbitrary events in the two component spaces. This argument applies equally to n independent experiments and shows that *if a system of n events $A_1, \ldots, A_n$ is such that*

---

[6] Measures defined similarly occur outside probability theory and are called *product measures*.

A_k *depends exclusively on the kth experiment, then the events* $A_1, \ldots, A_n$
are mutually independent.

The theory of independent experiments is the analytically simplest and most advanced part of probability theory. It is therefore desirable, when possible, to interpret complicated experiments as the result of a succession of simpler independent experiments. The following examples illustrate situations where this procedure is possible.

Examples. (c) *Permutations.* We have considered the $n!$ permutations of a_1, $a_2, \ldots, a_n$ as points of a sample space and attributed probability $1/n!$ to each. We may consider the *same sample space* as representing $n - 1$ successive independent experiments as follows. Begin by writing down a_1. The first experiment consists in putting a_2 either before or after a_1. This done, we have three places for a_3 and the second experiment consists of a choice among them, deciding on the relative order of a_1, a_2, and a_3. In general, when $a_1, \ldots, a_k$ are put into some relative order, we proceed with experiment number k, which consists in selecting one of the $k + 1$ places for a_{k+1}. In other words, we have a succession of $n - 1$ experiments of which the kth can result in k different choices (sample points), each having probability $1/k$. The experiments are independent, that is, the probabilities are multiplicative. Each permutation of the n elements has probability $\frac{1}{2} \cdot \frac{1}{3} \cdots 1/n$, in accordance with the original definition.

(d) *Sampling without replacement.* Let the population be $(a_1, \ldots, a_n)$. In sampling without replacement each choice removes an element. After k steps there remain $n - k$ elements, and the next choice can be described by specifying the number v of the place of the element chosen ($v = 1, 2, \ldots, n - k$). In this way the taking of a sample of size r without replacement becomes a succession of r experiments where the first has n possible results, the second $n - 1$, the third $n - 2$, etc. We attribute equal probabilities to all results of the individual experiments and postulate that the r experiments are independent. This amounts to attributing probability $1/(n)_r$ to each sample in accordance with our definition of random samples. Note that for $n = 100$, $r = 3$, the sample (a_{13}, a_{40}, a_{81}) means choices number 13, 39, 79, respectively: At the third experiment the seventy-ninth element of the reduced population of $n - 2$ was chosen. (With the original numbering the outcomes of the third experiment would depend on the first two choices.) We see that the notion of repeated independent experiments permits us to study sampling as a succession of independent operations. ▶

*5. APPLICATIONS TO GENETICS

The theory of heredity, originated by G. Mendel (1822–1884), provides instructive illustrations for the applicability of simple probability models. We shall restrict ourselves to indications concerning the most elementary problems. In describing the biological background, we shall necessarily oversimplify and concentrate on such facts as are pertinent to the mathematical treatment.

Heritable characters depend on special carriers, called *genes*. All cells of the body, except the reproductive cells or gametes, carry exact replicas

---

* This section treats a special subject and may be omitted.

of the same gene structure. The salient fact is that genes appear in pairs. The reader may picture them as a vast collection of beads on short pieces of string, the chromosomes. These also appear in pairs, and paired genes occupy the same position on paired chromosomes. In the simplest case each gene of a particular pair can assume two forms (alleles), A and a. Then three different pairs can be formed, and, with respect to this particular pair, the organism belongs to one of the three *genotypes* AA, Aa, aa (there is no distinction between Aa and aA). For example, peas carry a pair of genes such that A causes red blossom color and a causes white. The three genotypes are in this case distinguishable as red, pink, and white. Each pair of genes determines one heritable factor, but the majority of observable properties of organisms depend on several factors. For some characteristics (e.g., eye color and left-handedness) the influence of one particular pair of genes is predominant, and in such cases the effects of Mendelian laws are readily observable. Other characteristics, such as height, can be understood as the cumulative effect of a very large number of genes [cf. example X, (5.c)]. Here we shall study genotypes and inheritance for only one particular pair of genes with respect to which we have the three genotypes AA, Aa, aa. Frequently there are N different forms $A_1, \ldots, A_N$ for the two genes and, accordingly, $N(N+1)/2$ genotypes $A_1A_1, A_1A_2, \ldots, A_NA_N$. The theory applies to this case with obvious modifications (cf. problem 27). The following calculations apply also to the case where A is *dominant* and a *recessive*. By this is meant that Aa-individuals have the same observable properties as AA, so that only the pure aa-type shows an observable influence of the a-gene. All shades of partial dominance appear in nature. Typical partially recessive properties are blue eyes, left-handedness, etc.

The reproductive cells, or gametes, are formed by a splitting process and receive *one* gene only. Organisms of the pure AA- and aa-genotypes (or homozygotes) produce therefore gametes of only one kind, but Aa-organisms (hybrids or heterozygotes) produce A- and a-gametes in equal numbers. New organisms are derived from two parental gametes from which they receive their genes. Therefore each pair includes a paternal and a maternal gene, and any gene can be traced back to one particular ancestor in any generation, however remote.

The genotypes of offspring depend on a chance process. At every occasion, each parental gene has probability $\frac{1}{2}$ to be transmitted, and the successive trials are independent. In other words, we conceive of the genotypes of n offspring as the result of n independent trials, each of which corresponds to the tossing of two coins. For example, the genotypes of descendants of an $Aa \times Aa$ pairing are AA, Aa, aa with respective probabilities $\frac{1}{4}, \frac{1}{2}, \frac{1}{4}$. An $AA \times aa$ union can have only Aa-offspring, etc.

Looking at the population as a whole, we conceive of the pairing of parents as the result of a second chance process. We shall investigate only the so-called *random mating*, which is defined by this condition: If descendants in the first filial generation are chosen at random, then their parents form a random sample of size r, with possible repetitions, from the aggregate of all possible parental pairs. In other words, each descendant is to be regarded as the product of a random selection of parents, and all selections are mutually independent. Random mating is an idealized model of the conditions prevailing in many natural populations and in field experiments. However, if red peas are sown in one corner of the field and white peas in another, parents of like color will unite more often than under random mating. Preferential selectivity (such as blondes preferring blondes) also violates the condition of random mating. Extreme non-random mating is represented by self-fertilizing plants and artificial inbreeding. Some such assortative mating systems will be analyzed mathematically, but for the most part we shall restrict our attention to random mating.

The genotype of an offspring is the result of four independent random choices. The genotypes of the two parents can be selected in $3 \cdot 3$ ways, their genes in $2 \cdot 2$ ways. It is fortunately possible to combine two selections and describe the process as one of double selection thus: The paternal and maternal genes are each selected independently and at random from the population of all genes carried by males or females, respectively, of the parental population.

Suppose that the three genotypes AA, Aa, aa occur among males and females in the same ratios, $u:2v:w$. We shall suppose $u + 2v + w = 1$ and call u, $2v$, w, the *genotype frequencies*. Put

$$(5.1) \qquad p = u + v, \qquad q = v + w.$$

Clearly the numbers of A- and a-genes are as $p:q$, and since $p + q = 1$ we shall call p and q the *gene frequencies* of A and a. In each of the two selections an A-gene is selected with probability p, and, because of the assumed independence, the probability of an offspring being AA is p^2. The genotype Aa can occur in two ways, and its probability is therefore $2pq$. Thus, under random mating conditions *an offspring belongs to the genotypes* AA, Aa, *or* aa *with probabilities*

$$(5.2) \qquad u_1 = p^2, \qquad 2v_1 = 2pq, \qquad w_1 = q^2.$$

Examples. (*a*) All parents are Aa (heterozygotes); then $u = w = 0$, $2v = 1$, and $p = q = \frac{1}{2}$. (*b*) AA- and aa-parents are mixed in equal proportions; then $u = w = \frac{1}{2}$, $v = 0$, and again $p = q = \frac{1}{2}$. (*c*)

Finally, $u = w = \frac{1}{4}$, $2v = \frac{1}{2}$; again $p = q = \frac{1}{2}$. In all three cases we have for the filial generation $u_1 = \frac{1}{4}$, $2v_1 = \frac{1}{2}$, $w_1 = \frac{1}{4}$. ▶

For a better understanding of the implications of (5.2) let us fix the gene frequencies p and q $(p + q = 1)$ and consider all systems of genotype frequencies $u, 2v, w$ for which $u + v = p$ and $v + w = q$. They all lead to the same probabilities (5.2) for the first filial generation. Among them there is the particular distribution

$$(5.3) \qquad u = p^2, \qquad 2v = 2pq, \qquad w = q^2.$$

Consider now a population—as in example (c)—in which the frequencies u, v, w of the three genotypes are given by (5.3). In accordance with (5.2) these frequencies are then transmitted unchanged as genotype probabilities in the next generation. For this reason genotype distributions of the particular form (5.3) are called *stationary* or equilibrium distributions. To every ratio $p:q$ there corresponds such a distribution.

In a large population the actually observed frequencies of the three genotypes in the filial generation will be close to the theoretical probabilities as given by (5.2).[7] It is highly remarkable that this distribution is stationary irrespective of the distribution $u:2v:w$ in the parental generation. In other words, if the observed frequencies coincided exactly with the calculated probabilities, then the first filial generation would have a stationary genotype distribution which would perpetuate itself without change in all succeeding generations. In practice, deviations will be observed, but for large populations we can say: *Whatever the composition of the parent population may be, random mating will within one generation produce an approximately stationary genotype distribution with unchanged gene frequencies.* From the second generation on, there is no tendency toward a systematic change; a steady state is reached with the first filial generation. This was first noticed by G. H. Hardy,[8] who thus resolved assumed difficulties in Mendelian laws. It follows in particular that under conditions of random mating the frequencies of the three genotypes must stand in the ratios $p^2:2pq:q^2$. This can in turn be used to check the assumption of random mating.

---

[7] Without this our probability model would be void of operational meaning. The statement is made precise by the law of large numbers and the central limit theorem, which permit us to estimate the effect of chance fluctuations.

[8] G. H. Hardy, *Mendelian proportions in a mixed population, Letter to the Editor*, Science, N.S., vol. 28 (1908), pp. 49–50. Anticipating the language of chapters IX and XV, we can describe the situation as follows. The frequencies of the three genotypes in the nth generation are three random variables whose expected values are given by (5.2) and do not depend on n. Their actual values will vary from generation to generation and form a stochastic process of the Markov type.

Hardy also pointed out that emphasis must be put on the word "approximately." Even with a stationary distribution we must expect small changes from generation to generation, which leads us to the following picture. Starting from any parent population, random mating tends to establish the stationary distribution (5.3) within *one* generation. For a stationary distribution there is no tendency toward a systematic change of any kind, but chance fluctuations will change the gene frequencies p and q from generation to generation, and the genetic composition will slowly drift. There are no restoring forces seeking to re-establish original frequencies. On the contrary, our simplified model leads to the conclusion [cf. example XV, (2.*i*)] that, for a population bounded in size, one gene should ultimately die out, so that the population would eventually belong to one of the pure types, *AA* or *aa*. In nature this does not necessarily occur because of the creation of new genes by mutations, selections, and many other effects.

Hardy's theorem is frequently interpreted to imply a strict stability for all times. It is a common fallacy to believe that the law of large numbers acts as a force endowed with memory seeking a return to the original state, and many wrong conclusions have been drawn from this assumption. Note that Hardy's law does not apply to the distribution of two pairs of genes (e.g., eye color and left-handedness) with the nine genotypes *AABB*, *AABb*, . . . , *aabb*. There is still a tendency toward a stationary distribution, but equilibrium is not reached in the first generation (cf. problem 31).

*6. SEX-LINKED CHARACTERS

In the introduction to the preceding section it was mentioned that genes lie on chromosomes. These appear in pairs and are transmitted as units, so that all genes on a chromosome stick together.[9] Our scheme for the inheritance of genes therefore applies also to chromosomes as units. Sex is determined by two chromosomes; females are *XX*, males *XY*. The mother necessarily transmits an *X*-chromosome, and the sex of offspring depends on the chromosome transmitted by the father. Accordingly, male and female gametes are produced in equal numbers. The difference in birth rate for boys and girls is explained by variations in prenatal survival chances.

We said that both genes and chromosomes appear in pairs, but there is an exception inasmuch as the genes situated on the *X*-chromosome have

---

* This section treats a special topic and may be omitted.

[9] This picture is somewhat complicated by occasional breakings and recombinations of chromosomes (cf. problem 12 of II,10).

no corresponding gene on Y. Females have two X-chromosomes, and hence two of such X-linked genes; however, in males the X-genes appear as singles. Typical are two sex-linked genes causing colorblindness and haemophilia. With respect to each of them, females can still be classified into the three genotypes, AA, Aa, aa, but, having only *one* gene, males have only the two genotypes A and a. Note that a son always has the father's Y-chromosome so that a sex-linked character cannot be inherited from father to son. However, it can pass from father to daughter and from her to a grandson.

We now proceed to adapt the analysis of the preceding section to the present situation. Assume again random mating and let the frequencies of the genotypes AA, Aa, aa in the *female* population be u, $2v$, w, respectively. As before put $p = u + v$, $q = v + w$. The frequencies of the two *male* genotypes A and a will be denoted by p' and q' $(p' + q' = 1)$. Then p and p' are the frequencies of the A-gene in the female and male populations, respectively. The probability for a female descendant to be of genotype AA, Aa, aa will be denoted by u_1, $2v_1$, w_1; the analogous probabilities for the male types A and a are p_1', q_1'. Now a male offspring receives his X-chromosome from the female parent, and hence

$$(6.1) \qquad\qquad p_1' = p, \qquad q_1' = q.$$

For the three female genotypes we find, as in section 5,

$$(6.2) \qquad u_1 = pp', \qquad 2v_1 = pq' + qp', \qquad w_1 = qq'.$$

Hence

$$(6.3) \qquad p_1 = u_1 + v_1 = \tfrac{1}{2}(p+p'), \qquad q_1 = v_1 + w_1 = \tfrac{1}{2}(q+q').$$

This means that among the male descendants the genes A and a appear approximately with the frequencies p, q of the maternal population; the gene frequencies among female descendants are approximately p_1 and q_1, or halfway between those of the paternal and maternal populations. We discern here a tendency toward equalization of the gene frequencies. In fact, from (6.1) and (6.3) we get

$$(6.4) \qquad p_1' - p_1 = \tfrac{1}{2}(p-p'), \qquad q_1' - q_1 = \tfrac{1}{2}(q-q'),$$

and so random mating will in one generation reduce approximately by one-half the differences between gene frequencies among males and females. However, it will not eliminate the differences, and a tendency toward further reduction will subsist. In contrast to Hardy's law, no stationary situation is reached after one generation. We can pursue the systematic component of the changes from generation to generation by neglecting chance fluctuations and identifying the theoretical probabilities (6.2) and (6.3) with corresponding actual frequencies in the first filial generation.[10] For the second generation we obtain by the same process

$$(6.5) \quad p_2 = \tfrac{1}{2}(p_1 + p_1') = \tfrac{3}{4}p + \tfrac{1}{4}p', \qquad q_2 = \tfrac{1}{2}(q_1 + q_1') = \tfrac{3}{4}q + \tfrac{1}{4}q',$$

and, of course, $p_2' = p_1$, $q_2' = q_1$. A few more trials will lead to the general expression for the probabilities p_n and q_n among females of the nth descendant generation. Put

$$(6.6) \qquad \alpha = \tfrac{1}{3}(2p + p'), \qquad \beta = \tfrac{1}{3}(2q + q').$$

Then

$$(6.7) \qquad \begin{aligned} p_n &= \frac{p_{n-1} + p_{n-1}'}{2} = \alpha + (-1)^n \frac{p - p'}{3 \cdot 2^n}, \\ q_n &= \frac{q_{n-1} + q_{n-1}'}{2} = \beta + (-1)^n \frac{q - q'}{3 \cdot 2^n}, \end{aligned}$$

and $p_n' = p_{n-1}$, $q_n' = q_{n-1}$. Hence

$$(6.8) \qquad p_n \to \alpha, \qquad p_n' \to \alpha, \qquad q_n \to \beta, \qquad q_n' \to \beta.$$

The genotype frequencies in the female population, as given by (6.2), are

$$(6.9) \quad u_n = p_{n-1}p_{n-1}', \qquad 2v_n = p_{n-1}q_{n-1}' + q_{n-1}p_{n-1}', \qquad w_n = q_{n-1}q_{n-1}'.$$

Hence

$$(6.10) \qquad u_n \to \alpha^2, \qquad 2v_n \to 2\alpha\beta, \qquad w_n \to \beta^2.$$

(Note that $\alpha + \beta = 1$.)

These formulas show that there is a strong systematic tendency, from generation to generation, toward a state where the genotypes A and a appear among males with frequencies α and β, and the female genotypes AA, Aa, aa have probabilities α^2, $2\alpha\beta$, β^2, respectively. In practice, an approximate equilibrium will be reached after three or four generations. To be sure, small chance fluctuations will be superimposed on the described changes, but the latter represent the prevailing systematic tendency.

Our main conclusion is that under random mating we can expect the sex-linked genotypes A and a among males, and AA, Aa, aa among

---

[10] In the terminology introduced in footnote 8, p_n and q_n are the expected values of the gene frequencies in the nth female generation. With this interpretation the formulas for p_n and q_n are no longer approximations but exact.

females to occur approximately with the frequencies α, β, α^2, $2\alpha\beta$, β^2, respectively, where $\alpha + \beta = 1$.

Application. Many sex-linked genes, like colorblindness, are *recessive* and cause defects. Let a be such a gene. Then all a-males and all aa-females show the defect. Females of Aa-type may transmit the defect to their offspring but are not themselves affected. Hence we expect that a *recessive sex-linked defect which occurs among males with frequency* α *occurs among females with frequency* α^2. If one man in 100 is colorblind, one woman in 10,000 should be affected.

*7. SELECTION

As a typical example of the influence of selection we shall investigate the case where aa-individuals cannot multiply. This happens when the a-gene is recessive and lethal, so that aa-individuals are born but cannot survive. Another case occurs when artificial interference by breeding or by laws prohibits mating of aa-individuals.

Assume random mating among AA- and Aa-individuals but no mating of aa-types. Let the frequencies with which the genotypes AA, Aa, aa appear in the *total* population be u, $2v$, w. The corresponding frequencies for *parents* are then

$$(7.1) \qquad u^* = \frac{u}{1-w}, \qquad 2v^* = \frac{2v}{1-w}, \qquad w^* = 0.$$

We can proceed as in section 5, but we must use the quantities (7.1) instead of u, $2v$, w. Hence, (5.1) is to be replaced by

$$(7.2) \qquad p = \frac{u+v}{1-w}, \qquad q = \frac{v}{1-w}.$$

The probabilities of the three genotypes in the first filial generation are again given by (5.2); that is, $u_1 = p^2$, $2v_1 = 2pq$, and $w_1 = q^2$.

As before, in order to investigate the systematic changes from generation to generation, we have to replace u, v, w by u_1, v_1, w_1 and thus obtain probabilities u_2, v_2, w_2 for the second descendant generation, etc. In general we get from (7.2)

$$(7.3) \qquad p_n = \frac{u_n + v_n}{1 - w_n}, \qquad q_n = \frac{v_n}{1 - w_n}$$

and

$$(7.4) \qquad u_{n+1} = p_n^2, \qquad 2v_{n+1} = 2p_n q_n, \qquad w_{n+1} = q_n^2.$$

---

* This section treats a special subject and may be omitted.

A comparison of (7.3) and (7.4) shows that

$$(7.5) \qquad p_{n+1} = \frac{u_{n+1} + v_{n+1}}{1 - w_{n+1}} = \frac{p_n}{1 - q_n^2} = \frac{1}{1 + q_n}$$

and similarly

$$(7.6) \qquad q_{n+1} = \frac{v_{n+1}}{1 - w_{n+1}} = \frac{q_n}{1 + q_n}.$$

From (7.6) we can calculate q_n explicitly. In fact, taking reciprocals we get

$$(7.7) \qquad q_{n+1}^{-1} = 1 + q_n^{-1}$$

whence successively

$$(7.8) \qquad \begin{aligned} &q_1^{-1} = 1 + q^{-1}, \qquad q_2^{-1} = 2 + q^{-1}, \\ &q_3^{-1} = 3 + q^{-1}, \quad \ldots, \quad q_n^{-1} = n + q^{-1} \end{aligned}$$

or

$$(7.9) \qquad q_n = \frac{q}{1 + nq}, \qquad w_{n+1} = \left(\frac{q}{1 + qn}\right)^2.$$

We see that the unproductive (or undesirable) genotype gradually drops out, but the process is extremely slow. For $q = 0.1$ it takes ten generations to reduce the frequency of a-genes by one-half; this reduces the frequency of the aa-type approximately from 1 to $\frac{1}{4}$ per cent. (If a is sex-linked, the elimination proceeds much faster; see problem 29. For a generalized selection scheme see problem 30.)[11]

8. PROBLEMS FOR SOLUTION

1. Three dice are rolled. If no two show the same face, what is the probability that one is an ace?

2. Given that a throw with ten dice produced at least one ace, what is the probability p of two or more aces?

3. *Bridge.* In a bridge party West has no ace. What probability should he attribute to the event of his partner having (*a*) no ace, (*b*) two or more aces? Verify the result by a direct argument.

4. *Bridge.* North and South have ten trumps between them (trumps being cards of a specified suit). (*a*) Find the probability that all three remaining trumps are in the same hand (that is, either East or West has no trumps). (*b*)

---

[11] For a further analysis of various eugenic effects (which are frequently different from the ideas of enthusiastic proponents of sterilization laws) see G. Dahlberg, *Mathematical methods for population genetics*, New York and Basel, 1948.

If it is known that the king of trumps is included among the three, what is the probability that he is "unguarded" (that is, one player has the king, the other the remaining two trumps)?

5. Discuss the key problem in example II, (7.b) in terms of conditional probabilities following the pattern of example (2.a).

6. In a bolt factory machines A, B, C manufacture, respectively, 25, 35, and 40 per cent of the total. Of their output 5, 4, and 2 per cent are defective bolts. A bolt is drawn at random from the produce and is found defective. What are the probabilities that it was manufactured by machines A, B, C?

7. Suppose that 5 men out of 100 and 25 women out of 10,000 are colorblind. A colorblind person is chosen at random. What is the probability of his being male? (Assume males and females to be in equal numbers.)

8. Seven balls are distributed randomly in seven cells. Given that two cells are empty, show that the (conditional) probability of a triple occupancy of some cells equals $\frac{1}{4}$. Verify this numerically using table 1 of II, 5.

9. A die is thrown as long as necessary for an ace to turn up. Assuming that the ace does not turn up at the first throw, what is the probability that more than three throws will be necessary?

10. *Continuation.* Suppose that the number, n, of throws is even. What is the probability that $n = 2$?

11. Let[12] the probability p_n that a family has exactly n children be αp^n when $n \geq 1$, and $p_0 = 1 - \alpha p(1 + p + p^2 + \cdots)$. Suppose that all sex distributions of n children have the same probability. Show that for $k \geq 1$ the probability that a family has exactly k boys is $2\alpha p^k / (2 - p)^{k+1}$.

12. *Continuation.* Given that a family includes at least one boy, what is the probability that there are two or more?

13. Die A has four red and two white faces, whereas die B has two red and four white faces. A coin is flipped *once*. If it falls heads, the game continues by throwing die A alone; if it falls tails, die B is to be used. (a) Show that the probability of red at any throw is $\frac{1}{2}$. (b) If the first two throws resulted in red, what is the probability of red at the third throw? (c) If red turns up at the first n throws, what is the probability that die A is being used? (d) To which urn model is this game equivalent?

14. In example (2.a) let x_n be the conditional probability that the winner of the nth trial wins the entire game given that the game does not terminate at the nth trial; let y_n and z_n be the corresponding probabilities of victory for the losing and the pausing player, respectively, of the nth trial. (a) Show that

$$(*) \qquad x_n = \tfrac{1}{2} + \tfrac{1}{2}y_{n+1}, \qquad y_n = \tfrac{1}{2}z_{n+1}, \qquad z_n = \tfrac{1}{2}x_{n+1}.$$

(b) Show by a direct simple argument that in reality $x_n = x$, $y_n = y$, $z_n = z$ are independent of n. (c) Conclude that the probability that player a wins the game is $\frac{5}{14}$ (in agreement with problem 5 in I, 8). (d) Show that $x_n = \frac{4}{7}$, $y_n = \frac{1}{7}$, $z_n = \frac{2}{7}$ is the only bounded solution of $(*)$.

---

[12] According to A. J. Lotka, American family statistics satisfies our hypothesis with $p = 0.7358$. See *Théorie analytique des associations biologiques II*, Actualités scientifiques et industrielles, no. 780, Paris, 1939.

15. Let the events $A_1, A_2, \ldots, A_n$ be independent and $\mathbf{P}\{A_k\} = p_k$. Find the probability p that none of the events occurs.

16. *Continuation.* Show that always $p \leq e^{-\Sigma p_k}$.

17. *Continuation.* From Bonferroni's inequality IV, (5.7) deduce that the probability of k or more of the events $A_1, \ldots, A_n$ occurring simultaneously is less than $(p_1 + \cdots + p_n)^k / k!$.

18. *To Polya's urn scheme, example (2.c).* Given that the second ball was black, what is the probability that the first was black?

19. *To Polya's urn scheme, example (2.c).* Show by induction that the probability of a black ball at any trial is $b/(b+r)$.

20. *Continuation.* Prove by induction: for any $m < n$ the probabilities that the mth and the nth drawings produce (black, black) or (black, red) are

$$\frac{b(b+c)}{(b+r)(b+r+c)}, \qquad \frac{br}{(b+r)(b+r+c)},$$

respectively. Generalize to more than two drawings.

21. *Time symmetry of Polya's scheme.* Let A and B stand for either black or red (so that AB can be any of the four combinations). Show that the probability of A at the nth drawing, given that the mth drawing yields B, is the same as the probability of A at the mth drawing when the nth drawing yields B.

22. In Polya scheme let $p_k(n)$ be the probability of k black balls in the first n drawings. Prove the recurrence relation

$$p_k(n+1) = p_k(n) \frac{r + (n-k)c}{b + r + nc} + p_{k-1}(n) \frac{b + (k-1)c}{b - r + nc}$$

where $p_{-1}(n)$ is to be interpreted as 0. Use this relation for a new proof of (2.3).

23. *The Polya distribution.* In (2.4) set

(8.1) $$\frac{b}{b+r} = p, \qquad \frac{r}{b+r} = q, \qquad \frac{c}{b+r} = \gamma.$$

Show that

(8.2) $$p_{n_1, n} = \frac{\binom{-p/\gamma}{n_1}\binom{-q/\gamma}{n_2}}{\binom{-1/\gamma}{n}},$$

remains meaningful for arbitrary (not necessarily rational) constants $p > 0$, $q > 0$, $\gamma > 0$ such that $p + q = 1$. Verify that $p_{n_1, n} > 0$ and

$$\sum_{v=0}^{n} p_{v, n} = 1.$$

In other words, (8.2) defines a probability distribution on the integers $0, 1, \ldots,$ n. It is called the Polya distribution.

24. *Limiting form of the Polya distribution.* If $n \to \infty$, $p \to 0$, $\gamma \to 0$ so that $np \to \lambda$, $n\gamma \to \rho^{-1}$, then for fixed n_1

$$p_{n_1,n} \to \binom{\lambda\rho + n_1 - 1}{n_1} \left(\frac{\rho}{1+\rho}\right)^{\lambda\rho} \left(\frac{1}{1+\rho}\right)^{n_1}.$$

Verify this and show that for fixed λ, ρ the terms on the right add to unity. (The right side represents the so-called *negative binomial distribution;* cf. VI, 8, and problem 37 in VI, 9.)

25. Interpret II, (11.8) in terms of conditional probabilities.

26. *Pairwise but not totally independent events.* Two dice are thrown and three events are defined as follows: A means "odd face with first die"; B means "odd face with second die"; finally, C means "odd sum" (one face even, the other odd). If each of the 36 sample points has probability $\frac{1}{36}$, then any two of the events are independent. The probability of each is $\frac{1}{2}$. Nevertheless, the three events cannot occur simultaneously.

Applications in Biology

27. Generalize the results of section 5 to the case where each gene can have any of the forms $A_1, A_2, \ldots, A_k$, so that there are $k(k+1)/2$ genotypes instead of three (multiple alleles).

28. *Brother-sister mating.* Two parents are selected at random from a population in which the genotypes AA, Aa, aa occur with frequencies u, $2v$, w. This process is repeated in their progeny. Find the probabilities that both parents of the first, second, third filial generation belong to AA [cf. examples XV, (2.j) and XVI, (4.b)].

29. *Selection.* Let a be a recessive sex-linked gene, and suppose that a selection process makes mating of a-males impossible. If the genotypes AA, Aa, aa appear among females with frequencies u, $2v$, w, show that for female descendants of the first generation $u_1 = u + v$, $2v_1 = v + w$, $w_1 = 0$, and hence $p_1 = p + \frac{1}{2}q$, $q_1 = \frac{1}{2}q$. That is to say, the frequency of the a-gene among females is reduced to one-half.

30. The selection problem of section 7 can be generalized by assuming that only the fraction λ $(0 < \lambda \leq 1)$ of the aa-class is eliminated. Show that

$$p = \frac{u + v}{1 - \lambda w}, \qquad q = \frac{v + (1 - \lambda)w}{1 - \lambda w}.$$

More generally, (7.3) is to be replaced by

$$p_{n+1} = \frac{p_n}{1 - \lambda q_n^2}, \qquad q_{n+1} = \frac{1 - \lambda q_n}{1 - \lambda q_n^2}.$$

(The general solution of these equations appears to be unknown.)

31. Consider simultaneously two pairs of genes with possible forms (A, a) and (B, b), respectively. Any person transmits to each descendant one gene of each pair, and we shall suppose that each of the four possible combinations has probability $\frac{1}{4}$. (This is the case if the genes are on separate chromosomes; otherwise there is dependence.) There exist nine genotypes, and we assume that

their frequencies in the parent population are U_{AABB}, U_{aaBB}, U_{AAbb}, U_{aabb}, $2U_{AaBB}$, $2U_{Aabb}$, $2U_{AABb}$, $2U_{aaBb}$, $4U_{AaBb}$. Put

$$p_{AB} = U_{AABB} + U_{AABb} + U_{AaBB} + U_{AaBb},$$

$$p_{Ab} = U_{AAbb} + U_{Aabb} + U_{AABb} + U_{AaBb},$$

$$p_{aB} = U_{aaBB} + U_{aaBb} + U_{AaBB} + U_{AaBb},$$

$$p_{ab} = U_{aabb} + U_{Aabb} + U_{aaBb} + U_{AaBb}.$$

Compute the corresponding quantities for the first descendant generation. Show that for it

$$p_{AB}^{(1)} = p_{AB} - \delta, \qquad p_{Ab}^{(1)} = p_{Ab} + \delta,$$

$$p_{aB}^{(1)} = p_{aB} + \delta, \qquad p_{ab}^{(1)} = p_{ab} - \delta$$

with $2\delta = p_{AB}p_{ab} - p_{Ab}p_{aB}$. The stationary distribution is given by

$$p_{AB} - 2\delta = p_{Ab} + 2\delta, \text{ etc.}$$

(Notice that Hardy's law does *not* apply; the composition changes from generation to generation.)

32. Assume that the genotype frequencies in a population are $u = p^2$, $2v = 2pq$, $w = q^2$. Given that a man is of genotype Aa, the probability that his brother is of the same genotype is $(1 + pq)/2$.

Note: *The following problems are on family relations and give a meaning to the notion of degree of relationship. Each problem is a continuation of the preceding one. Random mating and the notations of section 5 are assumed. We are here concerned with a special case of Markov chains (cf. chapter XV). Matrix algebra simplifies the writing.*

33. Number the genotypes AA, Aa, aa by 1, 2, 3, respectively, and let p_{ik} $(i, k = 1, 2, 3)$ be the conditional probability that an offspring is of genotype k if it is known that the male (or female) parent is of genotype i. Compute the nine probabilities p_{ik}, assuming that the probabilities for the other parent to be of genotype 1, 2, 3 are p^2, $2pq$, q^2, respectively.

34. Show that p_{ik} is also the conditional probability that the parent is of genotype k if it is known that the first offspring is of genotype i.

35. Prove that the conditional probability of a grandson (grandfather) to be of genotype k if it is known that the grandfather (grandson) is of genotype i is given by

$$p_{ik}^{(2)} = p_{i1}p_{1k} + p_{i2}p_{2k} + p_{i3}p_{3k}.$$

[The matrix $(p_{ik}^{(2)})$ is the square of the matrix (p_{ik}).]

36.[13] Show that $p_{ik}^{(2)}$ is also the conditional probability that a man is of genotype k if it is known that a specified half-brother is of genotype i.

---

[13] The first edition contained an error since the word brother (two common parents) was used where a *half*-brother was meant. This is pointed out in C. C. Li and Louis Sacks, Biometrika, vol. 40 (1954), pp. 347–360.

37. Show that the conditional probability of a man to be of genotype k when it is known that a specified great-grandfather (or great-grandson) is of genotype i is given by

$$p_{ik}^{(3)} = p_{i1}^{(2)}p_{1k} + p_{i2}^{(2)}p_{2k} + p_{i3}^{(2)}p_{3k} = p_{i1}p_{1k}^{(2)} + p_{i2}p_{2k}^{(2)} + p_{i3}p_{3k}^{(2)}.$$

[The matrix $(p_{ik}^{(3)})$ is the third power of the matrix (p_{ik}). This procedure gives a precise meaning to the notion of the degree of family relationship.]

38. More generally, define probabilities $p_{ik}^{(n)}$ that a descendant of the nth generation is of genotype k if a specified ancestor was of genotype i. Prove by induction that the $p_{ik}^{(n)}$ are given by the elements of the following matrix:

$$\begin{pmatrix} p^2 + pq/2^{n-1} & 2pq + q(q-p)/2^{n-1} & q^2 - q^2/2^{n-1} \\ p^2 + p(q-p)/2^n & 2pq + (1-4pq)/2^n & q^2 + q(p-q)/2^n \\ p^2 - p^2/2^{n-1} & 2pq + p(p-q)/2^{n-1} & q^2 + pq/2^{n-1} \end{pmatrix}.$$

(This shows that the influence of an ancestor decreases from generation to generation by the factor $\frac{1}{2}$.)

39. Consider the problem 36 for a *full* brother instead of a half-brother. Show that the corresponding matrix is

$$\begin{pmatrix} \frac{1}{4}(1+p)^2 & \frac{1}{2}q(1+p) & \frac{1}{4}q^2 \\ \frac{1}{4}p(1+p) & \frac{1}{4}(1+pq) & \frac{1}{4}q(1+q) \\ \frac{1}{4}p^2 & \frac{1}{2}p(1+q) & \frac{1}{4}(1+q)^2 \end{pmatrix}.$$

40. Show that the degree of relationship between uncle and nephew is the same as between grandfather and grandson.

CHAPTER VI

The Binomial
and the Poisson Distributions

1. BERNOULLI TRIALS[1]

Repeated independent trials are called Bernoulli trials if there are only two possible outcomes for each trial and their probabilities remain the same throughout the trials. It is usual to denote the two probabilities by p and q, and to refer to the outcome with probability p as "*success*," S, and to the other as "*failure*," F. Clearly, p and q must be non-negative, and

$$(1.1) \qquad\qquad p + q = 1.$$

The sample space of each individual trial is formed by the two points S and F. The sample space of n Bernoulli trials contains 2^n points or successions of n symbols S and F, each point representing one possible outcome of the compound experiment. Since the trials are independent, the probabilities multiply. In other words, *the probability of any specified sequence is the product obtained on replacing the symbols S and F by p and q, respectively.* Thus $\mathbf{P}\{(SSFSF \cdots FFS)\} = ppqpq \cdots qqp$.

Examples. The most familiar example of Bernoulli trials is provided by successive tosses of a true or symmetric coin; here $p = q = \frac{1}{2}$. If the coin is unbalanced, we still assume that the successive tosses are independent so that we have a model of Bernoulli trials in which the probability p for success can have an arbitrary value. Repeated random drawings from an urn of constant composition represent Bernoulli trials. Such trials arise also from more complicated experiments if we decide not to distinguish among several outcomes and describe any result simply as A or non-A. Thus with good dice the distinction between ace (S) and non-ace (F) leads

---

[1] James Bernoulli (1654–1705). His main work, the *Ars conjectandi*, was published in 1713.

to Bernoulli trials with $p = \frac{1}{6}$, whereas distinguishing between even or odd leads to Bernoulli trials with $p = \frac{1}{2}$. If the die is unbalanced, the successive throws still form Bernoulli trials, but the corresponding probabilities p are different. Royal flush in poker or double ace in rolling dice may represent success; calling all other outcomes failure, we have Bernoulli trials with $p = \dfrac{1}{649,740}$ and $p = \frac{1}{36}$, respectively. Reductions of this type are usual in statistical applications. For example, washers produced in mass production may vary in thickness, but, on inspection, they are classified as conforming (S) or defective (F) according as their thickness is, or is not, within prescribed limits.   ▶

The Bernoulli scheme of trials is a theoretical model, and only experience can show whether it is suitable for the description of specified observations. Our knowledge that successive tossings of physical coins conform to the Bernoulli scheme is derived from experimental evidence. The man in the street, and also the philosopher K. Marbe,[2] believe that after a run of seventeen heads tail becomes more probable. This argument has nothing to do with imperfections of physical coins; it endows nature with memory, or, in our terminology, it denies the stochastic independence of successive trials. Marbe's theory cannot be refuted by logic but is rejected because of lack of empirical support.

In sampling practice, industrial quality control, etc., the scheme of Bernoulli trials provides an ideal standard even though it can never be fully attained. Thus, in the above example of the production of washers, there are many reasons why the output cannot conform to the Bernoulli scheme. The machines are subject to changes, and hence the probabilities do not remain constant; there is a persistence in the action of machines, and therefore long runs of deviations of like kind are more probable than they would be if the trials were truly independent. From the point of view of quality control, however, it is desirable that the process conform to the Bernoulli scheme, and it is an important discovery that, within certain limits, production can be made to behave in this way. The purpose of continuous control is then to discover at an early stage flagrant departures from the ideal scheme and to use them as an indication of impending trouble.

2. THE BINOMIAL DISTRIBUTION

Frequently we are interested only in the total number of successes produced in a succession of n Bernoulli trials but not in their order.

---

[2] *Die Gleichförmigkeit in der Welt*, Munich, 1916. Marbe's theory found wide acceptance; its most prominent opponent was von Mises.

The number of successes can be $0, 1, \ldots, n$, and our first problem is to determine the corresponding probabilities. Now the event "n trials result in k successes and $n - k$ failures" can happen in as many ways as k letters S can be distributed among n places. In other words, our event contains $\binom{n}{k}$ points, and, by definition, each point has the probability $p^k q^{n-k}$. This proves the

Theorem. *Let $b(k; n, p)$ be the probability that n Bernoulli trials with probabilities p for success and $q = 1 - p$ for failure result in k successes and $n - k$ failures. Then*

$$(2.1) \qquad b(k; n, p) = \binom{n}{k} p^k q^{n-k}.$$

In particular, the probability of no success is q^n, and the probability of at least one success is $1 - q^n$. ▶

We shall treat p as a constant and denote the number of successes in n trials by $\mathbf{S}_n$; then $b(k; n, p) = \mathbf{P}\{\mathbf{S}_n = k\}$. In the general terminology $\mathbf{S}_n$ is a *random variable*, and the function (2.1) is the "distribution" of this random variable; we shall refer to it as the *binomial distribution*. The attribute "binomial" refers to the fact that (2.1) represents the kth term of the binomial expansion of $(q+p)^n$. This remark shows also that

$$b(0; n, p) + b(1; n, p) + \cdots + b(n; n, p) = (q+p)^n = 1,$$

as is required by the notion of probability. The binomial distribution has been tabulated.[3]

Examples. (*a*) *Weldon's dice data.* Let an experiment consist in throwing twelve dice and let us count fives and sixes as "success." With perfect dice the probability of success is $p = \frac{1}{3}$ and the number of successes should follow the binomial distribution $b(k; 12, \frac{1}{3})$. Table 1 gives these probabilities, together with the corresponding observed average frequencies in 26,306 actual experiments. The agreement looks good, but for such extensive data it is really very bad. Statisticians usually judge closeness of fit by the chi-square criterion. According to it, deviations as large as those observed would happen with true dice only once in 10,000 times.

---

[3] For $n \leq 50$, see National Bureau of Standards, *Tables of the binomial probability distribution*, Applied Mathematics Series, vol. 6 (1950). For $50 \leq n \leq 100$, see H. C. Romig, *50–100 Binomial tables*, New York (John Wiley and Sons), 1953. For a wider range see *Tables of the cumulative binomial probability distribution*, by the Harvard Computation Laboratory, 1955, and *Tables of the cumulative binomial probabilities*, by the Ordnance Corps, ORDP 20-11 (1952).

TABLE 1
WELDON'S DICE DATA

k	$b(k; 12, \frac{1}{3})$	Observed frequency	$b(k; 12, 0.3377)$
0	0.007 707	0.007 033	0.007 123
1	0.046 244	0.043 678	0.043 584
2	0.127 171	0.124 116	0.122 225
3	0.211 952	0.208 127	0.207 736
4	0.238 446	0.232 418	0.238 324
5	0.190 757	0.197 445	0.194 429
6	0.111 275	0.116 589	0.115 660
7	0.047 689	0.050 597	0.050 549
8	0.014 903	0.015 320	0.016 109
9	0.003 312	0.003 991	0.003 650
10	0.000 497	0.000 532	0.000 558
11	0.000 045	0.000 152	0.000 052
12	0.000 002	0.000 000	0.000 002

It is, therefore, reasonable to assume that the dice were biased. A bias with probability of success $p = 0.3377$ would fit the observations.[4]

(b) In IV, 4, we have encountered the binomial distribution in connection with a card-guessing problem, and the columns b_m of table 3 exhibit the terms of the distribution for $n = 3, 4, 5, 6, 10$ and $p = n^{-1}$. In the occupancy problem II, (4.c) we found another special case of the binomial distribution with $p = n^{-1}$.

(c) How many trials with $p = 0.01$ must be performed to ensure that the probability for at least one success be $\frac{1}{2}$ or greater? Here we seek the smallest integer n for which $1 - (0.99)^n \geq \frac{1}{2}$, or $-n \log (0.99) \geq \log 2$; therefore $n \geq 70$.

(d) *A power supply problem.* Suppose that $n = 10$ workers are to use electric power intermittently, and we are interested in estimating the total load to be expected. For a crude approximation imagine that at any given time each worker has the same probability p of requiring a unit of power. If they work independently, the probability of exactly k workers requiring power at the same time should be $b(k; n, p)$. If, on the average, a worker uses power for 12 minutes per hour, we would put $p = \frac{1}{5}$. The probability of seven or more workers requiring current at the same time is then

---

[4] R. A. Fisher, *Statistical methods for research workers*, Edinburgh-London, 1932, p. 66.

$b(7; 10, 0.2) + \cdots + b(10; 10, 0.2) = 0.0008643584$. In other words, if the supply is adjusted to six power units, an overload has probability $0.00086 \ldots$ and should be expected for about one minute in 1157, that is, about one minute in twenty hours. The probability of eight or more workers requiring current at the same time is only 0.0000779264 or about eleven times less.

(*e*) *Testing sera or vaccines.*[5] Suppose that the normal rate of infection of a certain disease in cattle is 25 per cent. To test a newly discovered serum n healthy animals are injected with it. How are we to evaluate the result of the experiment? For an absolutely worthless serum the probability that exactly k of the n test animals remain free from infection may be equated to $b(k; n, 0.75)$. For $k = n = 10$ this probability is about 0.056, and for $k = n = 12$ only 0.032. Thus, if out of ten or twelve test animals none catches infection, this may be taken as an indication that the serum has had an effect, although it is not a conclusive proof. Note that, without serum, the probability that out of seventeen animals at most one catches infection is about 0.0501. It is therefore *stronger evidence* in favor of the serum if out of seventeen test animals only one gets infected than if out of ten all remain healthy. For $n = 23$ the probability of at most two animals catching infection is about 0.0492, and thus two failures out of twenty-three is again better evidence for the serum than one out of seventeen or none out of ten.

(*f*) *Another statistical test.* Suppose n people have their blood pressure measured with and without a certain drug. Let the observations be $x_1, \ldots, x_n$ and $x_1', \ldots, x_n'$. We say that the ith trial resulted in success if $x_i < x_i'$, and in failure if $x_i > x_i'$. (For simplicity we may assume that no two measurements lead to *exactly* the same result.) If the drug has no effect, then our observation should correspond to n Bernoulli trials with $p = \frac{1}{2}$, and an excessive number of successes is to be taken as evidence that the drug has an effect. ▶

3. THE CENTRAL TERM AND THE TAILS

From (2.1) we see that

$$(3.1) \qquad \frac{b(k; n, p)}{b(k-1; n, p)} = \frac{(n-k+1)p}{kq} = 1 + \frac{(n+1)p - k}{kq}.$$

Accordingly, the term $b(k; n, p)$ is greater than the preceding one for $k < (n+1)p$ and is smaller for $k > (n+1)p$. If $(n+1)p = m$ happens

[5] P. V. Sukhatme and V. G. Panse, *Size of experiments for testing sera or vaccines*, Indian Journal of Veterinary Science and Animal Husbandry, vol. 13 (1943), pp. 75–82.

to be an integer, then $b(m; n, p) = b(m - 1; n, p)$. There exists exactly one integer m such that

$$(3.2) \qquad\qquad (n+1)p - 1 < m \leq (n+1)p,$$

and we have the

Theorem. *As* k *goes from* 0 *to* n, *the terms* $b(k; n, p)$ *first increase monotonically, then decrease monotonically, reaching their greatest value when* $k = m$, *except that* $b(m-1; n, p) = b(m; n, p)$ *when* $m = (n+1)p$.

We shall call $b(m; n, p)$ the *central* term. Often m is called "the most probable number of successes," but it must be understood that for large values of n *all* terms $b(k; n, p)$ are small. In 100 tossings of a true coin the most probable number of heads is 50, but its probability is less than 0.08. In the next chapter we shall find that $b(m; n, p)$ is approximately $1/\sqrt{2\pi npq}$.

The probability of having exactly r successes is less interesting than the probability of at least r successes; that is,

$$(3.3) \qquad\qquad \mathbf{P}\{S_n \geq r\} = \sum_{\nu=0}^{\infty} b(r+\nu; n, p)$$

(The series is only formally infinite since the terms with $\nu > n-r$ vanish.) We shall now derive an upper bound for this probability which is useful even though more sophisticated estimates will be found in the next chapter. Suppose $r > np$. It is obvious from (3.1) that the terms of the series in (3.3) decrease faster than the terms of a geometric series with ratio $1 - (r-np)/rq$, and so

$$(3.4) \qquad\qquad \mathbf{P}\{S_n \geq r\} \leq b(r; n, p) \frac{rq}{r - np}.$$

On the other hand, there are more than $r - np$ integers k such that $m \leq k \leq r$. The corresponding terms of the binomial distribution add to less than unity, and none is smaller than $b(r; n, p)$. It follows that this quantity is at most $(r-np)^{-1}$, and hence

$$(3.5) \qquad\qquad \mathbf{P}\{S_n \geq r\} \leq \frac{rq}{(r-np)^2} \qquad\qquad \text{if } r > np.$$

The same argument could be applied to the left tail, but no calculations are necessary. In fact, saying that there are at most r successes amounts to saying that there are at least $n - r$ failures; applying the equivalent of (3.5) for failures we see that

$$(3.6) \qquad\qquad \mathbf{P}\{S_n \leq r\} \leq \frac{(n-r)p}{(np-r)^2} \qquad\qquad \text{if } r < np.$$

The next section will illustrate the usefulness of these inequalities for estimating the probability of large deviations from the most probable value m.

4. THE LAW OF LARGE NUMBERS

On several occasions we have mentioned that our *intuitive notion of probability* is based on the following assumption. If in n identical trials A occurs ν times, and if n is very large, then ν/n should be near the probability p of A. Clearly, a formal mathematical theory can never refer directly to real life, but it should at least provide theoretical counterparts to the phenomena which it tries to explain. Accordingly, we require that the vague introductory remark be made precise in the form of a theorem. For this purpose we translate "identical trials" as "Bernoulli trials" with probability p for success. If $\mathbf{S}_n$ is the number of successes in n trials, then $\mathbf{S}_n/n$ is the average number of successes and should be near p. It is now easy to give a precise meaning to this. Consider, for example, the probability that $\mathbf{S}_n/n$ exceeds $p + \epsilon$, where $\epsilon > 0$ is arbitrarily small but fixed. This probability is the same as $\mathbf{P}\{\mathbf{S}_n > n(p+\epsilon)\}$, and by (3.5) this is greater than $1/(n\epsilon^2)$. It follows that as n increases,

$$\mathbf{P}\{\mathbf{S}_n > n(p+\epsilon)\} \to 0.$$

We see in the same way that $\mathbf{P}\{\mathbf{S}_n < n(p-\epsilon)\} \to 0$, and thus

$$(4.1) \qquad \mathbf{P}\left\{\left|\frac{\mathbf{S}_n}{n} - p\right| < \epsilon\right\} \to 1.$$

In words: As n increases, the probability that the average number of successes deviates from p by more than any preassigned ϵ tends to zero. This is one form of the *law of large numbers* and serves as a basis for the intuitive notion of probability as a measure of relative frequencies. For practical applications it must be supplemented by a more precise estimate of the probability on the left side in (4.1); such an estimate is provided by the normal approximation to the binomial distribution [cf. the typical example VII, (4.h)]. Actually (4.1) is a simple consequence of the latter (problem 12 of VII, 7).

The assertion (4.1) is the classical law of large numbers. It is of very limited interest and should be replaced by the more precise and more useful *strong law of large numbers* (see VIII, 4).

Warning. It is usual to read into the law of large numbers things which it definitely does not imply. If Peter and Paul toss a perfect coin 10,000 times, it is customary to expect that Peter will be in the lead roughly half the time. *This is not true.* In a large number of *different* coin-tossing

games it is reasonable to expect that at any *fixed* moment heads will be in
the lead in roughly half of all cases. But it is quite likely that the player
who ends at the winning side has been in the lead for practically the whole
duration of the game. Thus, contrary to widespread belief, the time
average for any individual game has nothing to do with the ensemble
average at any given moment. For closer study of other unexpected and
paradoxical properties of chance fluctuations the reader is referred to
chapter III, in particular to the discussion of the arc sine laws.

5. THE POISSON APPROXIMATION[6]

In many applications we deal with Bernoulli trials where, comparatively
speaking, n is large and p is small, whereas the product

$$(5.1) \qquad\qquad \lambda = np$$

is of moderate magnitude. In such cases it is convenient to use an approximation to $b(k; n, p)$ which is due to Poisson and which we proceed to
derive. For $k = 0$ we have

$$(5.2) \qquad b(0; n, p) = (1-p)^n = \left(1 - \frac{\lambda}{n}\right)^n.$$

Passing to logarithms and using the Taylor expansion II, (8.10), we find

$$(5.3) \qquad \log b(0; n, p) = n \log\left(1 - \frac{\lambda}{n}\right) = -\lambda - \frac{\lambda^2}{2n} - \cdots$$

so that for large n

$$(5.4) \qquad\qquad b(0; n, p) \approx e^{-\lambda},$$

where the sign $\approx$ is used to indicate approximate equality (in the present
case up to terms of order of magnitude n^{-1}). Furthermore, from (3.1) it is
seen that for any fixed k and sufficiently large n

$$(5.5) \qquad \frac{b(k; n, p)}{b(k-1; n, p)} = \frac{\lambda - (k-1)p}{kq} \approx \frac{\lambda}{k}.$$

From this we conclude successively that

$$b(1; n, p) \approx \lambda \cdot b(0; n, p) \approx \lambda e^{-\lambda},$$

$$b(2; n, p) \approx \tfrac{1}{2}\lambda \cdot b(1; n, p) \approx \tfrac{1}{2}\lambda^2 e^{-\lambda},$$

------

[6] Siméon D. Poisson (1781–1840). His book, *Recherches sur la probabilité des juge-
ments en matière criminelle et en matière civile, précedées des règles générales du calcul
des probabilités*, appeared in 1837.

and generally by induction

$$(5.6) \qquad b(k; n, p) \approx \frac{\lambda^k}{k!} e^{-\lambda}.$$

This is the classical *Poisson approximation to the binomial distribution.*[7] In view of its great importance we introduce the notation

$$(5.7) \qquad p(k; \lambda) = e^{-\lambda} \frac{\lambda^k}{k!}.$$

With this notation $p(k; \lambda)$ should be an approximation to $b(k; n, \lambda/n)$ when n is sufficiently large.

Examples. (*a*) Table 3 of IV,4 tabulates the Poisson probabilities (5.7) with $\lambda = 1$ and, for comparison, the binomial distributions with $p = 1/n$ and $n = 3, 4, 5, 6, 10$. It will be seen that the agreement is surprisingly good despite the small values of n.

(*b*) *An empirical illustration.* The occurrence of the pair (7, 7) among 100 pairs of random digits should follow the binomial distribution with $n = 100$ and $p = 0.01$. The accompanying table 2 shows actual counts, N_k, in 100 batches of 100 pairs of random digits.[8] The ratios $N_k/100$ are

TABLE 2

AN EXAMPLE OF THE POISSON APPROXIMATION

k	$b(k; 100, 0.01)$	$p(k; 1)$	N_k
0	0.366 032	0.367 879	41
1	0.369 730	0.367 879	34
2	0.184 865	0.183 940	16
3	0.060 999	0.061 313	8
4	0.014 942	0.015 328	0
5	0.002 898	0.003 066	1
6	0.000 463	0.000 511	0
7	0.000 063	0.000 073	0
8	0.000 007	0.000 009	0
9	0.000 001	0.000 001	0

The first columns illustrate the Poisson approximation to the binomial distribution. The last column records the number of batches of 100 pairs of random digits each in which the combination (7, 7) appears exactly k times.

---

[7] For the degree of approximation see problems 33 and 34.

[8] M. G. Kendall and Babington Smith, *Tables of random sampling numbers*, Tracts for Computers No. 24, Cambridge, 1940.

compared with the theoretical binomial probabilities as well as with the corresponding Poisson approximations. The observed frequencies agree reasonably with the theoretical probabilities. (As judged by the χ^2-criterion, chance fluctuations should, in about 75 out of 100 similar cases, produce large deviations of observed frequencies from the theoretical probabilities.)

(c) *Birthdays.* What is the probability, p_k, that in a company of 500 people exactly k will have birthdays on New Year's Day? If the 500 people are chosen at random, we may apply the scheme of 500 Bernoulli trials with probability of success $p = \frac{1}{365}$. For the Poisson approximation we put $\lambda = \frac{500}{365} = 1.3699 \ldots$.

The correct probabilities and their Poisson approximations are as follows:

k	0	1	2	3	4	5	6
Binomial	0.2537	0.3484	0.2388	0.1089	0.0372	0.0101	0.0023
Poisson	0.2541	0.3481	0.2385	0.1089	0.0373	0.0102	0.0023

(d) *Defective items.* Suppose that screws are produced under statistical quality control so that it is legitimate to apply the Bernoulli scheme of trials. If the probability of a screw being defective is $p = 0.015$, then the probability that a box of 100 screws does not contain a defective one is $(0.985)^{100} = 0.22061$. The corresponding Poisson approximation is $e^{-1.5} = 0.22313 \ldots$, which should be close enough for most practical purposes. We now ask: How many screws should a box contain in order that the probability of finding at least 100 conforming screws be 0.8 or better? If $100 + x$ is the required number, then x is a small integer. To apply the Poisson approximation for $n = 100 + x$ trials we should put $\lambda = np$, but np is approximately $100p = 1.5$. We then require the smallest integer x for which

$$(5.8) \qquad e^{-1.5}\left\{ 1 + \frac{1.5}{1} + \cdots + \frac{(1.5)^x}{x!} \right\} \geq 0.8.$$

In tables[9] we find that for $x = 1$ the left side is approximately 0.56, and for $x = 2$ it is 0.809. Thus the Poisson approximation would lead to the conclusion that 102 screws are required. Actually the probability of finding at least 100 conforming screws in a box of 102 is $0.8022 \ldots$.

---

[9] E. C. Molina, *Poisson's exponential binomial limit*, New York (Van Nostrand), 1942. [These are tables giving $p(k; \lambda)$ and $p(k; \lambda) + p(k+1; \lambda) + \cdots$ for k ranging from 0 to 100.]

(e) *Centenarians.* At birth any particular person has a small chance of living 100 years, and in a large community the number of yearly births is large. Owing to wars, epidemics, etc., different lives are not stochastically independent, but as a first approximation we may compare n births to n Bernoulli trials with death after 100 years as success. In a stable community, where neither size nor mortality rate changes appreciably, it is reasonable to expect that the frequency of years in which exactly k centenarians die is approximately $p(k; \lambda)$, with λ depending on the size and health of the community. Records of Switzerland confirm this conclusion.[10]

(f) *Misprints, raisins, etc.* If in printing a book there is a constant probability of any letter being misprinted, and if the conditions of printing remain unchanged, then we have as many Bernoulli trials as there are letters. The frequency of pages containing exactly k misprints will then be approximately $p(k; \lambda)$, where λ is a characteristic of the printer. Occasional fatigue of the printer, difficult passages, etc., will increase the chances of errors and may produce clusters of misprints. Thus the Poisson formula may be used to discover radical departures from uniformity or from the state of statistical control. A similar argument applies in many cases. For example, if many raisins are distributed in the dough, we should expect that thorough mixing will result in the frequency of loaves with exactly k raisins to be approximately $p(k; \lambda)$ with λ a measure of the density of raisins in the dough.   ▶

6. THE POISSON DISTRIBUTION

In the preceding section the Poisson probabilities (5.7) appear merely as a convenient approximation to the binomial distribution in the case of large n and small p. In connection with the matching and occupancy problems of chapter IV we have studied different probability distributions, which have also led to the Poisson expressions $p(k; \lambda)$ as a limiting form. We have here a special case of the remarkable fact that there exist a few distributions of great universality which occur in a surprisingly great variety of problems. The three principal distributions, with ramifications throughout probability theory, are the binomial distribution, the normal distribution (to be introduced in the following chapter), and the *Poisson distribution*

$$(6.1) \qquad p(k; \lambda) = e^{-\lambda} \frac{\lambda^k}{k!},$$

which we shall now consider on its own merits.

---

[10] E. J. Gumbel, *Les centenaires*, Aktuárske Vedy, Prague, vol. 7 (1937), pp. 1–8.

We note first that on adding the quantities (6.1) for $k = 0, 1, 2, \ldots$ we get on the right side $e^{-\lambda}$ times the Taylor series for e^{λ}. Hence for any fixed λ the quantities $p(k; \lambda)$ add to unity, and therefore it is possible to conceive of an ideal experiment in which $p(k; \lambda)$ is the probability of exactly k successes. We shall now indicate why many physical experiments and statistical observations actually lead to such an interpretation of (6.1). The examples of the next section will illustrate the wide range and the importance of various applications of (6.1). The true nature of the Poisson distribution will become apparent only in connection with the theory of stochastic processes (cf. the new approaches in XII,2 and XVII,2).

Consider a sequence of random events occurring in time, such as radioactive disintegrations, or incoming calls at a telephone exchange. Each event is represented by a point on the time axis, and we are concerned with chance distributions of points. There exist many different types of such distributions, but their study belongs to the domain of continuous probabilities which we have postponed to the second volume. Here we shall be content to show that the simplest physical assumptions lead to $p(k; \lambda)$ as the probability of finding exactly k points (events) within a fixed interval of specified length. Our methods are necessarily crude, and we shall return to the same problem with more adequate methods in chapters XII and XVII.

The physical assumptions which we want to express mathematically are that the conditions of the experiment remain constant in time, and that non-overlapping time intervals are stochastically independent in the sense that information concerning the number of events in one interval reveals nothing about the other. The theory of probabilities in a continuum makes it possible to express these statements directly, but being restricted to discrete probabilities, we have to use an approximate finite model and pass to the limit.

Imagine a unit time interval partitioned into n subintervals of length $1/n$. A given collection of finitely many points in the interval may be regarded as the result of a chance process such that each subinterval has the same probability p_n to contain one or more points of the collection. A subinterval is then either occupied or empty, and the assumed independence of non-overlapping time intervals implies that we are dealing with Bernoulli trials: We assume that the probability for exactly k occupied subintervals is given by $b(k; n, p_n)$. We now refine this discrete model indefinitely by letting $n \to \infty$. The probability that the whole interval contains no point of the collection must tend to a finite limit. But this is the event that no cell is occupied, and its probability is $(1-p_n)^n$. Passing to logarithms it is seen that this quantity approaches a limit only if np_n

does. The contingency $np_n \to \infty$ is excluded because it would imply infinitely many points of the collection in even the smallest interval. Accordingly our model requires that there exists a number λ such that $np_n \to \lambda$. In this case the probability of exactly k occupied subintervals tends to $p(k; \lambda)$, and since we are dealing with individual points, the number of occupied cells agrees in the limit with the number of points of the collection contained in our unit time interval.[11]

In applications it is necessary to replace the unit time interval by an interval of arbitrary length t. If we divide it again into subintervals of length $1/n$ then the probabilities p_n remain unchanged, but the number of subintervals is given by the integer nearest to nt. The passage to the limit is the same except that λ is replaced by λt. This leads us to consider

$$(6.2) \qquad p(k; \lambda t) = e^{-\lambda t} \frac{(\lambda t)^k}{k!}$$

as the probability of finding exactly k *points in a fixed interval of length* t. *In particular, the probability of no point in an interval of length* t *is*

$$(6.3) \qquad p(0; \lambda t) = e^{-\lambda t},$$

and the probability of one or more points is therefore $1 - e^{-\lambda t}$.

The parameter λ is a physical constant which determines the density of points on the t-axis. The larger λ is, the smaller is the probability (6.3) of finding no point. Suppose that a physical experiment is repeated a great number N of times, and that each time we count the number of events in an interval of fixed length t. Let N_k be the number of times that exactly k events are observed. Then

$$(6.4) \qquad N_0 + N_1 + N_2 + \cdots = N.$$

The total number of points observed in the N experiments is

$$(6.5) \qquad N_1 + 2N_2 + 3N_3 + \cdots = T,$$

and T/N is the average. If N is large, we expect that

$$(6.6) \qquad N_k \approx Np(k; \lambda t)$$

---

[11] Other possibilities are conceivable. Our model may be a reasonable approximation in the study of automobile accidents, but it does not apply when one counts the number of cars smashed rather than the number of accidents as such. This is so because some accidents involve more than one car, and so it is necessary to consider single points, doublets, triplets, etc. In the limit we are lead to the compound Poisson distribution of XII,2. From the point of view of more general processes one could say that we are counting only the number of jumps, but leave their magnitude out of consideration.

(this lies at the root of all applications of probability and will be justified and made more precise by the law of large numbers in chapter X). Substituting from (6.6) into (6.5), we find

$$(6.7) \quad T \approx N\{p(1; \lambda t) + 2p(2; \lambda t) + 3p(3; \lambda t) + \cdots\} =$$
$$= Ne^{-\lambda t}\lambda t\left\{1 + \frac{\lambda t}{1} + \frac{(\lambda t)^2}{2!} + \cdots\right\} = N\lambda t$$

and hence

$$(6.8) \qquad\qquad \lambda t \approx T/N.$$

This relation gives us a means of estimating λ from observations and of comparing theory with experiments. The examples of the next section will illustrate this point.

Spatial Distributions

We have considered the distribution of random events or points along the t-axis, but the same argument applies to the distribution of points in plane or space. Instead of intervals of length t we have domains of area or volume t, and the fundamental assumption is that the probability of finding k points in any specified domain depends only on the area or volume of the domain but not on its shape. Otherwise we have the same assumptions as before: (1) if t is small, the probability of finding more than one point in a domain of volume t is small as compared to t; (2) non-overlapping domains are mutually independent. To find the probability that a domain of volume t contains exactly k random points, we subdivide it into n subdomains and approximate the required probability by the probability of k successes in n trials. This means neglecting the possibility of finding more than one point in the same subdomain, but our assumption (1) implies that the error tends to zero as $n \rightarrow \infty$. In the limit we get again the Poisson distribution (6.2). Stars in space, raisins in cake, weed seeds among grass seeds, flaws in materials, animal litters in fields are distributed in accordance with the Poisson law. See examples (7.b) and (7.e).

7. OBSERVATIONS FITTING THE POISSON DISTRIBUTION[12]

(a) *Radioactive disintegrations.* A radioactive substance emits α-particles; the number of particles reaching a given portion of space during

---

[12] The Poisson distribution has become known as the law of small numbers or of rare events. These are misnomers which proved detrimental to the realization of the fundamental role of the Poisson distribution. The following examples will show how misleading the two names are.

time t is the best-known example of random events obeying the Poisson law. Of course, the substance continues to decay, and in the long run the density of α-particles will decline. However, with radium it takes years before a decrease of matter can be detected; for relatively short periods the conditions may be considered constant, and we have an ideal realization of the hypotheses which led to the Poisson distribution.

In a famous experiment[13] a radioactive substance was observed during $N = 2608$ time intervals of 7.5 seconds each; the number of particles reaching a counter was obtained for each period. Table 3 records the

TABLE 3
EXAMPLE (a): RADIOACTIVE DISINTEGRATIONS

k	N_k	$Np(k; 3.870)$	k	N_k	$Np(k; 3.870)$
0	57	54.399	5	408	393.515
1	203	210.523	6	273	253.817
2	383	407.361	7	139	140.325
3	525	525.496	8	45	67.882
4	532	508.418	9	27	29.189
			$k \geq 10$	16	17.075
			Total	2608	2608.000

number N_k of periods with exactly k particles. The total number of particles is $T = \sum kN_k = 10{,}094$, the average $T/N = 3.870$. The theoretical values $Np(k; 3.870)$ are seen to be rather close to the observed numbers N_k. To judge the closeness of fit, an estimate of the probable magnitude of chance fluctuations is required. Statisticians judge the closeness of fit by the χ^2-criterion. Measuring by this standard, we should expect that under ideal conditions about 17 out of 100 comparable cases would show worse agreement than exhibited in table 3.

(b) *Flying-bomb hits on London.* As an example of a spatial distribution of random points consider the statistics of flying-bomb hits in the south of London during World War II. The entire area is divided into $N = 576$ small areas of $t = \frac{1}{4}$ square kilometers each, and table 4 records the number N_k of areas with exactly k hits.[14] The total number of hits is $T = \sum kN_k = 537$, the average $\lambda t = T/N = 0.9323 \ldots$. The fit of the

---

[13] Rutherford, Chadwick, and Ellis, *Radiations from radioactive substances*, Cambridge, 1920, p. 172. Table 3 and the χ^2-estimate of the text are taken from H. Cramér *Mathematical methods of statistics*, Uppsala and Princeton, 1945, p. 436.

[14] The figures are taken from R. D. Clarke, *An application of the Poisson distribution*, Journal of the Institute of Actuaries, vol. 72 (1946), p. 48.

Poisson distribution is surprisingly good; as judged by the χ^2-criterion, under ideal conditions some 88 per cent of comparable observations should show a worse agreement. It is interesting to note that most people believed in a tendency of the points of impact to cluster. If this were true, there would be a higher frequency of areas with either many hits or no hit and a deficiency in the intermediate classes. Table 4 indicates perfect randomness and homogeneity of the area; we have here an instructive illustration of the established fact that to the untrained eye randomness appears as regularity or tendency to cluster.

TABLE 4
EXAMPLE (b): FLYING-BOMB HITS ON LONDON

k	0	1	2	3	4	5 and over
N_k	229	211	93	35	7	1
$Np(k; 0.9323)$	226.74	211.39	98.54	30.62	7.14	1.57

(c) *Chromosome interchanges in cells.* Irradiation by X-rays produces certain processes in organic cells which we call chromosome interchanges. As long as radiation continues, the probability of such interchanges remains constant, and, according to theory, the numbers N_k of cells with exactly k interchanges should follow a Poisson distribution. The theory is also able to predict the dependence of the parameter λ on the intensity of radiation, the temperature, etc., but we shall not enter into these details. Table 5 records the result of eleven different series of experiments.[15] These are arranged according to goodness of fit. The last column indicates the approximate percentage of ideal cases in which chance fluctuations would produce a worse agreement (as judged by the χ^2-standard). The agreement between theory and observation is striking.

(d) *Connections to wrong number.* Table 6 shows statistics of telephone connections to a wrong number.[16] A total of $N = 267$ numbers was observed; N_k indicates how many numbers had exactly k wrong connections. The Poisson distribution $p(k; 8.74)$ shows again an excellent fit. (As judged by the χ^2-criterion the deviations are near the median value.) In Thorndike's paper the reader will find other telephone statistics

---

[15] D. G. Catcheside, D. E. Lea, and J. M. Thoday, *Types of chromosome structural change induced by the irradiation* of Tradescantia *microspores*, Journal of Genetics, vol. 47 (1945–46), pp. 113–136. Our table is table IX of this paper, except that the χ^2-levels were recomputed, using a single degree of freedom.

[16] The observations are taken from F. Thorndike, *Applications of Poisson's probability summation*, The Bell System Technical Journal, vol. 5 (1926), pp. 604–624. This paper contains a graphical analysis of 32 different statistics.

TABLE 5
EXAMPLE (c): CHROMOSOME INTERCHANGES INDUCED BY X-RAY IRRADIATION

Experiment number		Cells with k interchanges				Total N	χ^2-level in per cent
		0	1	2	≥ 3		
1	Observed N_k	753	266	49	5	1073	95
	$Np(k; 0.35508)$	752.3	267.1	47.4	6.2		
2	Observed N_k	434	195	44	9	682	85
	$Np(k; 0.45601)$	432.3	197.1	44.9	7.7		
3	Observed N_k	280	75	12	1	368	65
	$Np(k; 0.27717)$	278.9	77.3	10.7	1.1		
4	Observed N_k	2278	273	15	0	2566	65
	$Np(k; 0.11808)$	2280.2	269.2	15.9	0.7		
5	Observed N_k	593	143	20	3	759	45
	$Np(k; 0.25296)$	589.4	149.1	18.8	1.7		
6	Observed N_k	639	141	13	0	793	45
	$Np(k; 0.21059)$	642.4	135.3	14.2	1.1		
7	Observed N_k	359	109	13	1	482	40
	$Np(k; 0.28631)$	362.0	103.6	14.9	1.5		
8	Observed N_k	493	176	26	2	697	35
	$Np(k; 0.33572)$	498.2	167.3	28.1	3.4		
9	Observed N_k	793	339	62	5	1199	20
	$Np(k; 0.39867)$	804.8	320.8	64.0	9.4		
10	Observed N_k	579	254	47	3	883	20
	$Np(k; 0.40544)$	588.7	238.7	48.4	7.2		
11	Observed N_k	444	252	59	1	756	5
	$Np(k; 0.49339)$	461.6	227.7	56.2	10.5		

TABLE 6
EXAMPLE (d): CONNECTIONS TO WRONG NUMBER

k	N_k	$Np(k;\ 8.74)$	k	N_k	$Np(k;\ 8.74)$
0–2	1	2.05	11	20	24.34
3	5	4.76	12	18	17.72
4	11	10.39	13	12	11.92
5	14	18.16	14	7	7.44
6	22	26.45	15	6	4.33
7	43	33.03	≥16	2	4.65
8	31	36.09		267	267.00
9	40	35.04			
10	35	30.63			

following the Poisson law. Sometimes (as with party lines, calls from groups of coin boxes, etc.) there is an obvious interdependence among the events, and the Poisson distribution no longer fits.

(e) *Bacteria and blood counts.* Figure 1 reproduces a photograph of a Petri plate with bacterial colonies, which are visible under the microscope as dark spots. The plate is divided into small squares. Table 7 reproduces the observed numbers of squares with exactly k dark spots in eight experiments with as many different kinds of bacteria.[17] We have here a

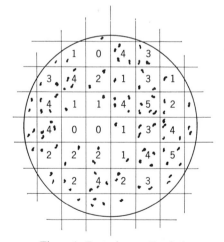

Figure 1. Bacteria on a Petri plate.

[17] The table is taken from J. Neyman, *Lectures and conferences on mathematical statistics* (mimeographed), Dept. of Agriculture, Washington, 1938.

TABLE 7
EXAMPLE (e): COUNTS OF BACTERIA

k	0	1	2	3	4	5	6	7	χ^2-Level
Observed N_k	5	19	26	26	21	13	8		97
Poisson theor.	6.1	18.0	26.7	26.4	19.6	11.7	9.5		
Observed N_k	26	40	38	17	7				66
Poisson theor.	27.5	42.2	32.5	16.7	9.1				
Observed N_k	59	86	49	30	20				26
Poisson theor.	55.6	82.2	60.8	30.0	15.4				
Observed N_k	83	134	135	101	40	16	7		63
Poisson theor.	75.0	144.5	139.4	89.7	43.3	16.7	7.4		
Observed N_k	8	16	18	15	9	7			97
Poisson theor.	6.8	16.2	19.2	15.1	9.0	6.7			
Observed N_k	7	11	11	11	7	8			53
Poisson theor.	3.9	10.4	13.7	12.0	7.9	7.1			
Observed N_k	3	7	14	21	20	19	7	9	85
Poisson theor.	2.1	8.2	15.8	20.2	19.5	15	9.6	9.6	
Observed N_k	60	80	45	16	9				78
Poisson theor.	62.6	75.8	45.8	18.5	7.3				

The last entry in each row includes the figures for higher classes and should be labeled "k" or more."

representative of an important practical application of the Poisson distribution to spatial distributions of random points.   ▶

8. WAITING TIMES. THE NEGATIVE BINOMIAL DISTRIBUTION

Consider a succession of n Bernoulli trials and let us inquire how long it will take for the rth success to turn up. Here r is a fixed positive integer. The total number of successes in n trials may, of course, fall short of r, but the probability that the rth success occurs at the trial number $v \leq n$

is clearly independent of n and depends only on v, r, and p. Since necessarily $v \geq r$, it is preferable to write $v = k + r$. *The probability that the rth success occurs at the trial number* $r + k$ (*where* $k = 0, 1, \ldots$) *will be denoted by* $f(k; r, p)$. It equals *the probability that exactly* k *failures precede the rth success.* This event occurs if, and only if, among the $r + k - 1$ trials there are exactly k failures and the following, or $(r+k)$th, trial results in success; the corresponding probabilities are $\binom{r+k-1}{k} \cdot p^{r-1}q^k$ and p, whence

$$(8.1) \qquad f(k; r, p) = \binom{r+k-1}{k} \cdot p^r q^k.$$

Rewriting the binomial coefficient in accordance with II,(12.4), we find the alternative form

$$(8.2) \qquad f(k; r, p) = \binom{-r}{k} p^r (-q)^k, \qquad k = 0, 1, 2, \ldots .$$

Suppose now that *Bernoulli trials are continued as long as necessary for r successes to turn up.* A typical sample point is represented by a sequence containing an arbitrary number, k, of letters F and exactly r letters S, the sequence terminating by an S; the probability of such a point is, by definition, $p^r q^k$. We must ask, however, whether it is possible that the trials *never* end, that is, whether an infinite sequence of trials may produce fewer than r successes. Now $\sum_{k=0}^{\infty} f(k; r, p)$ is the probability that the rth success occurs after finitely many trials; accordingly, the possibility of an infinite sequence with fewer than r successes can be discounted if, and only if,

$$(8.3) \qquad \sum_{k=0}^{\infty} f(k; r, p) = 1.$$

This is so because by the binomial theorem

$$(8.4) \qquad \sum_{k=0}^{\infty} \binom{-r}{k}(-q)^k = (1-q)^{-r} = p^{-r}.$$

Multiplying (8.4) by p^r we get (8.3).

In our waiting time problem r is necessarily a positive integer, but the quantity defined by either (8.1) or (8.2) is non-negative and (8.3) holds for any positive r. *For arbitrary fixed real* $r > 0$ *and* $0 < p < 1$ *the sequence* $\{f(k; r, p)\}$ *is called a negative binomial distribution.* It occurs in many applications (and we have encountered it in problem 24 of V, as

TABLE 8
THE PROBABILITIES (8.5) IN THE MATCH BOX PROBLEM

r	u_r	U_r	r	u_r	U_r
0	0.079 589	0.079 589	15	0.023 171	0.917 941
1	0.079 589	0.159 178	16	0.019 081	0.937 022
2	0.078 785	0.237 963	17	0.015 447	0.952 469
3	0.077 177	0.315 140	18	0.012 283	0.964 752
4	0.074 790	0.389 931	19	0.009 587	0.974 338
5	0.071 674	0.461 605	20	0.007 338	0.981 676
6	0.067 902	0.529 506	21	0.005 504	0.987 180
7	0.063 568	0.593 073	22	0.004 041	0.991 220
8	0.058 783	0.651 855	23	0.002 901	0.944 121
9	0.053 671	0.705 527	24	0.002 034	0.996 155
10	0.048 363	0.753 890	25	0.001 392	0.997 547
11	0.042 989	0.796 879	26	0.000 928	0.998 475
12	0.037 676	0.834 555	27	0.000 602	0.999 077
13	0.032 538	0.867 094	28	0.000 379	0.999 456
14	0.027 676	0.894 770	29	0.000 232	0.999 688

u_r is the probability that, at the moment for the first time a match box is found empty, the other contains exactly r matches, assuming that initially each box contained 50 matches. $U_r = u_0 + u_1 + \cdots + u_r$ is the corresponding probability of having not more than r matches.

the limiting form of the Polya distribution). When r is a positive integer, $\{f(k; r, p)\}$ may be interpreted as the *probability distribution for the waiting time to the rth success;* as such it is also called the *Pascal* distribution. For $r = 1$ it reduces to the *geometric distribution* $\{pq^k\}$.

Examples. (*a*) *The problem of Banach's match boxes.*[18] A certain mathematician always carries one match box in his right pocket and one in his left. When he wants a match, he selects a pocket at random, the successive choices thus constituting Bernoulli trials with $p = \frac{1}{2}$. Suppose that initially each box contained exactly N matches and consider the moment when, for the first time, our mathematician *discovers* that a box is empty.

[18] This example was inspired by a humorous reference to Banach's smoking habits made by H. Steinhaus in an address honoring Banach. It became unexpectedly popular in the literature and for this reason I leave the name unchanged. References to Banach's *Oeuvres complètes* are, of course, spurious.

At that moment the other box may contain $0, 1, 2, \ldots, N$ matches, and we denote the corresponding probabilities by u_r. Let us identify "success" with choice of the left pocket. The left pocket will be found empty at a moment when the right pocket contains exactly r matches if, and only if, exactly $N - r$ failures precede the $(N+1)$st success. The probability of this event is $f(N-r; N+1, \frac{1}{2})$. The same argument applies to the right pocket and therefore the required probability is

$$(8.5) \qquad u_r = 2f(N-r; N+1, \tfrac{1}{2}) = \binom{2N-r}{N} 2^{-2N+r}.$$

Numerical values for the case $N = 50$ are given in table 8. (Cf. problems 21, and 22, and problem 11 of IX,9).

(b) *Generalization: Table tennis.* The nature of the preceding problem becomes clearer when one attributes different probabilities to the two boxes. For a change we interpret this variant differently. Suppose that Peter and Paul play a game which may be treated as a sequence of Bernoulli trials in which the probabilities p and q serve as measures for the players' skill. In ordinary table tennis the player who first accumulates 21 individual victories wins the whole game. For comparison with the preceding example we consider the general situation where $2\nu + 1$ individual successes are required. The game lasts at least $2\nu + 1$ and at most $4\nu + 1$ trials. Denote by a_r the probability that Peter wins at the trial number $4\nu + 1 - r$. This event occurs if, and only if, in the first $4\nu - r$ trials Peter has scored 2ν successes and thereafter wins the $(2\nu+1)$st trial. Thus

$$(8.6) \qquad a_r = \binom{4\nu-r}{2\nu} p^{2\nu+1} q^{2\nu-r}.$$

In our game $a_0 + \cdots + a_{2N}$ is the probability that Peter wins. The probability that the game ends exactly at the trial number $4\nu + 1 - r$ is given by $a_r + b_r$, where b_r is defined by (8.6) with p and q interchanged.

If we put $2\nu = N$ and $p = q = \frac{1}{2}$, the probabilities $a_r + b_r$ reduce to the probabilities u_r of the preceding example. ▶

9. THE MULTINOMIAL DISTRIBUTION

The binomial distribution can easily be generalized to the case of n repeated independent trials where each trial can have one of several outcomes. Denote the possible outcomes of each trial by $E_1, \ldots, E_r$, and suppose that the probability of the realization of E_i in each trial is

p_i $(i = 1, \ldots, r)$. For $r = 2$ we have Bernoulli trials; in general, the numbers p_i are subject only to the condition

$$(9.1) \qquad\qquad p_1 + \cdots + p_r = 1, \qquad\qquad p_i \geq 0.$$

The result of n trials is a succession like $E_3 E_1 E_2 \ldots$. *The probability that in n trials E_1 occurs k_1 times, E_2 occurs k_2 times, etc., is*

$$(9.2) \qquad\qquad \frac{n!}{k_1! \, k_2! \cdots k_r!} \, p_1^{k_1} p_2^{k_2} p_3^{k_3} \cdots p_r^{k_r};$$

here the k_i are arbitrary non-negative integers subject to the obvious condition

$$(9.3) \qquad\qquad k_1 + k_1 + \cdots + k_r = n.$$

If $r = 2$, then (9.2) reduces to the binomial distribution with $p_1 = p$, $p_2 = q$, $k_1 = k$, $k_2 = n - k$. The proof in the general case proceeds along the same lines, starting with II, (4.7).

Formula (9.2) is called the *multinomial distribution* because the right-hand member is the general term of the *multinomial* expansion of $(p_1 + \cdots + p_r)^n$. Its main application is to *sampling with replacement* when the individuals are classified into more than two categories (e.g., according to professions).

Examples. (*a*) In rolling twelve dice, what is the probability of getting each face twice? Here $E_1, \ldots, E_6$ represent the six faces, all k_i equal 2, and all p_i equal $\frac{1}{6}$. Therefore, the answer is $12! \, 2^{-6} 6^{-12} = 0.0034 \ldots$.

(*b*) *Sampling.* Let a population of N elements be divided into subclasses $E_1, \ldots, E_r$ of sizes $Np_1, \ldots, Np_r$. The multinomial distribution gives the probabilities of the several possible compositions of a random sample with replacement of size n taken from this population.

(*c*) *Multiple Bernoulli trials.* Two sequences of Bernoulli trials with probabilities of success and failure p_1, q_1, and p_2, q_2, respectively, may be considered one compound experiment with four possible outcomes in each trial, namely, the combinations (S, S), (S, F), (F, S), (F, F). The assumption that the two original sequences are independent is translated into the statement that the probabilities of the four outcomes are $p_1 p_2$, $p_1 q_2$, $q_1 p_2$, $q_1 q_2$, respectively. If k_1, k_2, k_3, k_4 are four integers adding to n, the probability that in n trials SS will appear k_1 times, SF k_2 times, etc., is

$$(9.4) \qquad\qquad \frac{n!}{k_1! \, k_2! \, k_3! \, k_4!} \, p_1^{k_1+k_2} q_1^{k_3+k_4} p_2^{k_1+k_3} q_2^{k_2+k_4}.$$

A special case occurs in *sampling inspection*. An item is conforming or defective with probabilities p and q. It may or may not be inspected with corresponding probabilities p' and q'. The decision of whether an item is inspected is made without knowledge of its quality, so that we have independent trials. (Cf. problems 25 and 26, and problem 12 of IX, 9.)

10. PROBLEMS FOR SOLUTION

1. Assuming all sex distributions to be equally probable, what proportion of families with exactly six children should be expected to have three boys and three girls?

2. A bridge player had no ace in three consecutive hands. Did he have reason to complain of ill luck?

3. How long has a series of random digits to be in order for the probability of the digit 7 appearing to be at least $\frac{9}{10}$?

4. How many independent bridge dealings are required in order for the probability of a preassigned player having four aces at least once to be $\frac{1}{2}$ or better? Solve again for some player instead of a given one.

5. If the probability of hitting a target is $\frac{1}{5}$ and ten shots are fired independently, what is the probability of the target being hit at least twice?

6. In problem 5, find the conditional probability that the target is hit at least twice, assuming that at least one hit is scored.

7. Find the probability that a hand of thirteen bridge cards selected at random contains exactly two red cards. Compare it with the corresponding probability in Bernoulli trials with $p = \frac{1}{2}$. (For a definition of bridge see footnote 1, in I, 1.)

8. What is the probability that the birthdays of six people fall in two calendar months leaving exactly ten months free? (Assume independence and equal probabilities for all months.)

9. In rolling six true dice, find the probability of obtaining (*a*) at least one, (*b*) exactly one, (*c*) exactly two, aces. Compare with the Poisson approximations.

10. If there are on the average 1 per cent left-handers, estimate the chances of having at least four left-handers among 200 people.

11. A book of 500 pages contains 500 misprints. Estimate the chances that a given page contains at least three misprints.

12. Colorblindness appears in 1 per cent of the people in a certain population. How large must a random sample (with replacements) be if the probability of its containing a colorblind person is to be 0.95 or more?

13. In the preceding exercise, what is the probability that a sample of 100 will contain (*a*) no, (*b*) two or more, colorblind people?

14. Estimate the number of raisins which a cookie should contain on the average if it is desired that not more than one cookie out of a hundred should be without raisin.

15. The probability of a royal flush in poker is $p = \dfrac{1}{649,740}$. How large has n to be to render the probability of no royal flush in n hands smaller than $1/e \approx \frac{1}{3}$? (*Note:* No calculations are necessary for the solution.)

16. A book of n pages contains on the average λ misprints per page. Esti-mate the probability that at least one page will contain more than k misprints.

17. Suppose that there exist two kinds of stars (or raisins in a cake, or flaws in a material). The probability that a given volume contains j stars of the first kind is $p(j; a)$, and the probability that it contains k stars of the second kind is $p(k; b)$; the two events are assumed to be independent. Prove that the probability that the volume contains a total of n stars is $p(n; a+b)$. (Interpret the assertion and the assumptions abstractly.)

18. *A traffic problem.* The flow of traffic at a certain street crossing is described by saying that the probability of a car passing during any given second is a con-stant p; and that there is no interaction between the passing of cars at different seconds. Treating seconds as indivisible time units, the model of Bernoulli trials applies. Suppose that a pedestrian can cross the street only if no car is to pass during the next three seconds. Find the probability that the pedestrian has to wait for exactly $k = 0, 1, 2, 3, 4$ seconds. (The corresponding general formulas are not obvious and will be derived in connection with the theory of success runs in XIII, 7.)

19. Two people toss a true coin n times each. Find the probability that they will score the same number of heads.

20. In a sequence of Bernoulli trials with probability p for success, find the probability that a successes will occur before b failures. (*Note:* The issue is decided after at most $a + b - 1$ trials. This problem played a role in the classical theory of games in connection with the question of how to divide the pot when the game is interrupted at a moment when one player lacks a points to victory, the other b points.)

21. In *Banach's match box problem* [example (8.a)] find the probability that at the moment when the first box is emptied (not found empty) the other contains exactly r matches (where $r = 1, 2, \ldots, N$).

22. *Continuation.* Using the preceding result, find the probability x that the box first emptied is not the one first found to be empty. Show that the expression thus obtained reduces to $x = \binom{2N}{N} 2^{-2N-1}$ or $\frac{1}{2}(N\pi)^{-\frac{1}{2}}$, approxi-mately.

23. Proofs of a certain book were read independently by two proofreaders who found, respectively, k_1 and k_2 misprints; k_{12} misprints were found by both. Give a reasonable estimate of the unknown number, n, of misprints in the proofs. (Assume that proofreading corresponds to Bernoulli trials in which the two proofreaders have, respectively, probabilities p_1 and p_2 of catching a misprint. Use the law of large numbers.)

Note: The problem describes in simple terms an experimental setup used by Rutherford for the count of scintillations.

24. To estimate the size of an animal population by trapping,[19] traps are set r times in succession. Assuming that each animal has the same probability q of being trapped; that originally there were n animals in all; and that the only changes in the situation between the successive settings of traps are that

---

[19] P. A. P. Moran, *A mathematical theory of animal trapping*, Biometrika, vol. 38 (1951), pp. 307–311.

animals have been trapped (and thus removed); find the probability that the r trappings yield, respectively, $n_1, n_2, \ldots, n_r$ animals.

25. *Multiple Bernoulli trials.* In example (9.*c*) find the conditional probabilities p and q of (S, F) and (F, S), respectively, assuming that one of these combinations has occurred. Show that $p > \frac{1}{2}$ or $p < \frac{1}{2}$, according as $p_1 > p_2$ or $p_2 > p_1$.

26. *Continuation.*[20] If in n pairs of trials exactly m resulted in one of the combinations (S, F) or (F, S), show that the probability that (S, F) has occurred exactly k times is $b(k; m, p)$.

27. *Combination of the binomial and Poisson distributions.* Suppose that the probability of an insect laying r eggs is $p(r; \lambda)$ and that the probability of an egg developing is p. Assuming mutual independence of the eggs, show that the probability of a total of k survivors is given by the Poisson distribution with parameter λp.

Note: Another example for the same situation: the probability of k chromosome breakages is $p(k; \lambda)$, and the probability of a breakage healing is p. [For additional examples of a similar nature see IX, (1.*d*) and XII, 1.]

---

28. Prove the *theorem*:[21] The maximal term of the multinomial distribution (9.2) satisfies the inequalities

$$(10.1) \qquad\qquad np_i - 1 < k_i \le (n+r-1)p_i, \qquad\qquad i = 1, 2, \ldots, r.$$

Hint: Prove first that the term is maximal if, and only if, $p_i k_j \le p_j(k_i+1)$ for each pair (i, j). Add these inequalities for all j, and also for all $i \ne j$.

29. The terms $p(k; \lambda)$ of the Poisson distribution reach their maximum when k is the largest integer not exceding λ.

Note: *Problems 30–34 refer to the Poisson approximation of the binomial distribution. It is understood that* $\lambda = np$.

30. Show that as k goes from 0 to ∞ the ratios $a_k = b(k; n, p)/p(k; \lambda)$ first increase, then decrease, reaching their maximum when k is the largest integer not exceeding $\lambda + 1$.

31. As k increases, the terms $b(k; n, p)$ are first smaller, then larger, and then again smaller than $p(k; \lambda)$.

32. If $n \to \infty$ and $p \to 0$ so that $np = \lambda$ remains constant, then

$$b(k; n, p) \to p(k; \lambda)$$

uniformly for all k.

---

[20] A. Wald, *Sequential tests of statistical hypotheses*, Ann. Math. Statist., vol. 16 1945), p. 166. Wald uses the results given above to devise a practical method of comparing two empirically given sequences of trials (say, the output of two machines), with a view of selecting the one with the greater probability of success. He reduces this problem to the simpler one of finding whether in a sequence of Bernoulli trials the frequency of success differs significantly from $\frac{1}{2}$.

[21] In the first edition it was only asserted that $|k_i - np_i| \le r$. The present improvement and its elegant proof are due to P. A. P. Moran.

33. Show that

(10.2) $$\frac{\lambda^k}{k!}\left(1 - \frac{\lambda}{n}\right)^{n-k} \geq b(k; n, p) \geq \frac{\lambda^k}{k!}\left(1 - \frac{k}{n}\right)^k\left(1 - \frac{\lambda}{n}\right)^n.$$

34. Conclude from (10.2) that

(10.3) $$p(k; \lambda)e^{k\lambda/n} > b(k; n, p) > p(k; \lambda)e^{-k^2/(n-k)-\lambda^2/(n-\lambda)}.$$

Hint: Use II, (12.26).

Note: Although (10.2) is very crude, the inequalities (10.3) provide excellent error estimates. It is easy to improve on (10.3) by calculations similar to those used in II, 9. Incidentally, using the result of problem 30, it is obvious that the exponent on the left in (10.3) may be replaced by $m\lambda/n$ which is $\leq (p + n^{-1})\lambda$.

Further Limit Theorems

35. *Binomial approximation to the hypergeometric distribution.* A population of N elements is divided into red and black elements in the proportion $p:q$ (where $p + q = 1$). A sample of size n is taken without replacement. The probability that it contains exactly k red elements is given by the hypergeometric distribution of II, 6. Show that as $N \to \infty$ this probability approaches $b(k; n, p)$.

36. In the preceding problem let p be small, n large, and $\lambda = np$ of moderate magnitude. The hypergeometric distribution can then be approximated by the Poisson distribution $p(k; \lambda)$. Verify this directly without using the binomial approximation.

37. In the *negative binomial distribution* $\{f(k; r, p)\}$ of section 8 let $q \to 0$ and $r \to \infty$ in such a way that $rq = \lambda$ remains fixed. Show that

$$f(k; r, p) \to p(k; \lambda).$$

(*Note:* This provides a limit theorem for the *Polya distribution:* cf. problem 24 of V, 8.)

38. *Multiple Poisson distribution.* When n is large and $np_j = \lambda_j$ is moderate for $j = 1, \ldots, r - 1$, the multinomial distribution (9.2) can be approximated by

$$e^{-(\lambda_1 + \cdots + \lambda_{r-1})} \frac{\lambda_1^{k_1}\lambda_2^{k_2} \cdots \lambda_{r-1}^{k_{r-}}}{k_1! \, k_2! \cdots k_{r-1}!}.$$

Prove also that the terms of this distribution add to unity. (Note that problem 17 refers to a double Poisson distribution.)

---

39. (a) Derive (3.6) directly from (3.5) using the obvious relation

$$b(k; n, p) = b(n-k; n, q).$$

(b) Deduce the binomial distribution both by induction and from the general summation formula IV, (3.1).

40. Prove $\sum kb(k; n, p) = np$, and $\sum k^2 b(k; n, p) = n^2 p^2 + npq$.

41. Prove $\sum k^2 p(k; \lambda) = \lambda^2 + \lambda$.

42. Verify the identity

$$(10.4) \qquad \sum_{v=0}^{k} b(v; n_1, p) b(k-v; n_2, p) = b(k; n_1+n_2, p)$$

and interpret it probabilistically. *Hint:* Use II, (6.4).

Note: Relation (10.4) is a special case of *convolutions*, to be introduced in chapter XI; another example is (10.5).

43. Verify the identity

$$(10.5) \qquad \sum_{v=0}^{k} p(v; \lambda_1) p(k-v; \lambda_2) = p(k; \lambda_1+\lambda_2)$$

44. Let

$$(10.6) \qquad B(k; n, p) = \sum_{v=0}^{k} b(v; n, p)$$

be the probability of at most k successes in n trials. Then

$$(10.7) \qquad B(k; n+1, p) = B(k; n, p) - p b(k; n, p),$$

$$B(k+1; n+1, p) = B(k; n, p) + q b(k+1; n, p).$$

Verify this (a) from the definition, (b) analytically.

45. With the same notation[22]

$$(10.8) \qquad B(k; n, p) = (n-k)\binom{n}{k} \int_0^q t^{n-k-1}(1-t)^k \, dt$$

and

$$(10.9) \qquad 1 - B(k; n, p) = n\binom{n-1}{k} \int_0^p t^k(1-t)^{n-k-1} \, dt.$$

Hint: Integrate by parts or differentiate both sides with respect to p. Deduce one formula from the other.

46. Prove

$$(10.10) \qquad p(0; \lambda) + \cdots + p(n; \lambda) = \frac{1}{n!} \int_{\lambda}^{\infty} e^{-x} x^n \, dx.$$

---

[22] The integral in (10.9) is the *incomplete beta function*. Tables of $1 - B(k; n, p)$ to 7 decimals for k and n up to 50 and $p = 0.01, 0.02, 0.03, \ldots$ are given in K. Pearson, *Tables of the incomplete beta function*, London (Biometrika Office), 1934.

CHAPTER VII

The Normal Approximation
to the Binomial Distribution

The normal approximation to the binomial distribution is of considerable theoretical and practical value. It played an important role in the
development of probability theory because it lead to the first limit theorem.
From a modern point of view it is only a special case of *the central limit
theorem* to which we shall return in chapter X, but whose full treatment
must be postponed to volume 2.

The special case $p = \frac{1}{2}$ was used in chapter III to obtain limit theorems
for first passages, the number of changes of sign, etc. This special case is
particularly simple, and is therefore treated separately in section 2.

1. THE NORMAL DISTRIBUTION

In order to avoid later interruptions we pause here to introduce two
functions of great importance.

Definition. *The function defined by*

(1.1)
$$\mathfrak{n}(x) = \frac{1}{\sqrt{2\pi}} \, e^{-\frac{1}{2}x^2}$$

is called the normal density function; its integral

(1.2)
$$\mathfrak{N}(x) = \frac{1}{\sqrt{2\pi}} \int_{-\infty}^{x} e^{-\frac{1}{2}y^2} \, dy$$

is the normal distribution function.

The graph of $\mathfrak{n}(x)$ is the symmetric, bell-shaped curve shown in figure 1.
Note that different units are used along the two axes: The maximum of
$\mathfrak{n}(x)$ is $1/\sqrt{2\pi} = 0.399$, approximately, so that in an ordinary Cartesian

system the curve $y = \mathfrak{n}(x)$ would be much flatter. [The notations $\mathfrak{n}$ and $\mathfrak{N}$ are not standard. In the first two editions the more customary ϕ and Φ were used, but in volume 2 consistency required that we reserve these letters for other purposes.]

Lemma 1. *The domain bounded by the graph of* $\mathfrak{n}(x)$ *and the x-axis has unit area, that is,*

$$(1.3) \qquad \int_{-\infty}^{+\infty} \mathfrak{n}(x)\, dx = 1.$$

Proof. We have

$$(1.4) \qquad \left\{ \int_{-\infty}^{+\infty} \mathfrak{n}(x)\, dx \right\}^2 = \int_{-\infty}^{+\infty} \int_{-\infty}^{+\infty} \mathfrak{n}(x)\mathfrak{n}(y)\, dx\, dy =$$

$$= \frac{1}{2\pi} \int_{-\infty}^{+\infty} \int_{-\infty}^{+\infty} e^{-\frac{1}{2}(x^2+y^2)}\, dx\, dy.$$

This double integral can be expressed in polar coordinates thus:

$$(1.5) \qquad \frac{1}{2\pi} \int_0^{2\pi} d\theta \int_0^\infty e^{-\frac{1}{2}r^2} r\, dr = \int_0^\infty e^{-\frac{1}{2}r^2} r\, dr = -e^{-\frac{1}{2}r^2} \Big|_0^\infty = 1$$

which proves the assertion.   ▶

It follows from the definition and the lemma that $\mathfrak{N}(x)$ *increases steadily from* 0 *to* 1. Its graph (figure 2) is an S-shaped curve with

$$(1.6) \qquad \mathfrak{N}(-x) = 1 - \mathfrak{N}(x).$$

Table 1 gives the values[1] of $\mathfrak{N}(x)$ for positive x, and from (1.6) we get $\mathfrak{N}(-x)$.

For many purposes it is convenient to have an elementary estimate of the "tail," $1 - \mathfrak{N}(x)$, for large x. Such an estimate is given by

Lemma 2. *As* $x \to \infty$

$$(1.7) \qquad 1 - \mathfrak{N}(x) \sim x^{-1}\mathfrak{n}(x);$$

more precisely, the double inequality

$$(1.8) \qquad [x^{-1}-x^{-3}]\mathfrak{n}(x) < 1 - \mathfrak{N}(x) < x^{-1}\mathfrak{n}(x)$$

holds for every $x > 0$. (See problem 1.)

---

[1] For larger tables cf. *Tables of probability functions*, vol. 2, National Bureau of Standards, New York, 1942. There $\mathfrak{n}(x)$ and $\mathfrak{N}(x) - \mathfrak{N}(-x)$ are given to 15 decimals for x from 0 to 1 in steps of 0.0001 and for $x > 1$ in steps of 0.001.

[2] Here and in the sequel the sign $\sim$ is used to indicate that the *ratio* of the two sides tends to one.

Table 1. Normal Distribution Function $\mathfrak{N}(x)$

	0.00	0.01	0.02	0.03	0.04	0.05	0.06	0.07	0.08	0.09
0.0	0.5000	0.5040	0.5080	0.5120	0.5159	0.5199	0.5239	0.5279	0.5319	0.5359
0.1	0.5398	0.5438	0.5478	0.5517	0.5557	0.5596	0.5636	0.5675	0.5714	0.5753
0.2	0.5793	0.5832	0.5871	0.5910	0.5948	0.5987	0.6026	0.6064	0.6103	0.6141
0.3	0.6179	0.6217	0.6255	0.6293	0.6331	0.6368	0.6406	0.6443	0.6480	0.6517
0.4	0.6554	0.6591	0.6628	0.6664	0.6700	0.6736	0.6772	0.6808	0.6844	0.6879
0.5	0.6915	0.6950	0.6985	0.7019	0.7054	0.7088	0.7123	0.7157	0.7190	0.7224
0.6	0.7257	0.7291	0.7324	0.7357	0.7389	0.7422	0.7454	0.7486	0.7518	0.7549
0.7	0.7580	0.7612	0.7642	0.7673	0.7704	0.7734	0.7764	0.7794	0.7823	0.7852
0.8	0.7881	0.7910	0.7939	0.7967	0.7995	0.8023	0.8051	0.8078	0.8016	0.8133
0.9	0.8159	0.8186	0.8212	0.8238	0.8264	0.8289	0.8315	0.8340	0.8365	0.8380
1.0	0.8413	0.8438	0.8461	0.8485	0.8508	0.8531	0.8554	0.8577	0.8599	0.8621
1.1	0.8643	0.8665	0.8686	0.8718	0.8729	0.8749	0.8770	0.8790	0.8810	0.8836
1.2	0.8849	0.8869	0.8888	0.8907	9.9099	0.8944	0.8962	0.8980	0.8997	0.9015
1.3	0.9032	0.9049	0.9066	0.9083	0.9099	0.9115	0.9131	0.9147	0.9162	0.9177
1.4	0.9192	0.9207	0.9222	0.9236	0.9251	0.9265	0.9279	0.9292	0.9306	0.9319

x	.00	.01	.02	.03	.04	.05	.06	.07	.08	.09
1.5	0.9332	0.9345	0.9357	0.9370	0.9382	0.9394	0.9406	0.9418	0.9430	0.9441
1.6	0.9452	0.9463	0.9474	0.9485	0.9495	0.9505	0.9515	0.9525	0.9535	0.9545
1.7	0.9554	0.9564	0.9573	0.9582	0.9591	0.9599	0.9608	0.9616	0.9625	0.9633
1.8	0.9641	0.9649	0.9656	0.9664	0.9671	0.9678	0.9686	0.9693	0.9699	0.9706
1.9	0.9713	0.9719	0.9726	0.9732	0.9738	0.9744	0.9750	0.9758	0.9762	0.9767
2.0	0.9773	0.9778	0.9783	0.9788	0.9793	0.9798	0.9803	0.9808	0.9812	0.9817
2.1	0.9821	0.9826	0.9830	0.9834	0.9838	0.9842	0.9846	0.9850	0.9854	0.9857
2.2	0.9861	0.9865	0.9868	0.9871	0.9875	0.9878	0.9881	0.9884	0.9887	0.9890
2.3	0.9893	0.9896	0.9898	0.9901	0.9904	0.9906	0.9909	0.9911	0.9913	0.9916
2.4	0.9918	0.9920	0.9922	0.9925	0.9927	0.9929	0.9931	0.9932	0.9934	0.9936
2.5	0.9938	0.9940	0.9941	0.9943	0.9945	0.9946	0.9948	0.9949	0.9951	0.9952
2.6	0.9953	0.9955	0.9956	0.9957	0.9959	0.9960	0.9961	0.9962	0.9963	0.9964
2.7	0.9965	0.9966	0.9967	0.9968	0.9969	0.9970	0.9971	0.9972	0.9973	0.9974
2.8	0.9974	0.9975	0.9976	0.9977	0.9977	0.9978	0.9979	0.9980	0.9980	0.9981
2.9	0.9981	0.9982	0.9983	0.9984	0.9984	0.9984	0.9985	0.9985	0.9986	0.9986
3.0	0.9986	0.9987	0.9987	0.9988	0.9988	0.9989	0.9989	0.9989	0.9989	0.9990
3.1	0.9990	0.9991	0.9991	0.9991	0.9992	0.9992	0.9992	0.9992	0.9993	0.9993
3.2	0.9993	0.9993	0.9993	0.9994	0.9994	0.9994	0.9994	0.9994	0.9995	0.9995

For $x < 0$ use the relation $\mathfrak{N}(-x) = 1 - \mathfrak{N}(x)$.

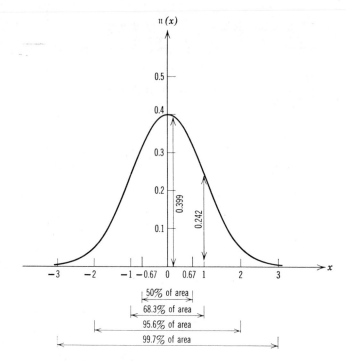

Figure 1. The normal density function $\mathfrak{n}$.

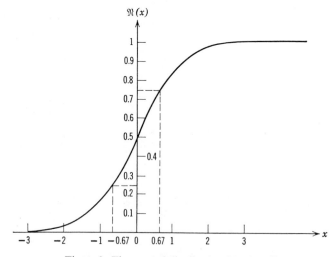

Figure 2. The normal distribution function $\mathfrak{N}$.

Proof. Obviously

(1.9) $[1-3x^{-4}]\mathfrak{n}(x) < \mathfrak{n}(x) < [1+x^{-2}]\mathfrak{n}(x).$

The members are the negatives of the derivatives of those in (1.8), and so (1.8) follows by integration between x and ∞.   ▶

Note on Terminology. The term *distribution function* is used in the mathematical literature for never-decreasing functions of x which tend to 0 as $x \to -\infty$, and to 1 as $x \to \infty$. Statisticians currently prefer the term *cumulative distribution function*, but the adjective "cumulative" is redundant. A *density function* is a non-negative function $f(x)$ whose integral, extended over the entire x-axis, is unity. The integral from $-\infty$ to x of any density function is a distribution function. The older term *frequency function* is a synonym for density function.

The normal distribution function is often called the *Gaussian distribution*, but it was used in probability theory earlier by DeMoivre and Laplace. If the origin and the unit of measurement are changed, then $\mathfrak{N}(x)$ is transformed into $\mathfrak{N}((x-a)/b)$; this function is called the normal distribution function with mean a and variance b^2 (or standard deviation $|b|$). The function $2\mathfrak{N}(x\sqrt{2}) - 1$ is often called *error function*.

2. ORIENTATION: SYMMETRIC DISTRIBUTIONS

We proceed to explain the use of the normal distribution as an approximation to the binomial with $p = \frac{1}{2}$.

There are two reasons for treating the special case $p = \frac{1}{2}$ separately. First, the calculations are much simpler and therefore convey a better idea of how the normal distribution enters the problem. Second, this special case was used in connection with random walks (see III,2), and it is therefore desirable to supply a proof which is not obscured by the technicalities required for unsymmetric distributions.

For definiteness we take $n = 2\nu$ even, and to simplify notations we put

(2.1) $a_k = b(\nu+k; \; 2\nu, \tfrac{1}{2});$

that is, the a_k are the terms of the symmetric binomial distribution renumbered so as to indicate the distance from the central term; a_0 is the central term, and k runs from $-\nu$ to ν. Since $a_{-k} = a_k$ we shall consider only $k \geq 0$.

(*In the notation of chapter* III *we have* $a_k = p_{2\nu,2k}$; the following proof does not depend on notions developed after III,2 and could be inserted there.)

To get an idea concerning the behavior of the sequence $a_0, a_1, a_2, \ldots$ we shall compare its general term with a_0 using the relation

(2.2) $a_k = a_0 \cdot \dfrac{\nu(\nu-1) \cdots (\nu-k+1)}{(\nu+1)(\nu+2) \cdots (\nu+k)}$

which follows trivially from the definition.

We are interested only in large values of ν, and it will turn out that we need consider only values k such that k/ν is small, because for other k the terms a_k will be negligible. On dividing numerator and denominator by ν^k the individual factors take on the form $1 + j/\nu$ with j running from $-(k-1)$ to k. Now

$$(2.3) \qquad 1 + \frac{j}{\nu} = e^{j/\nu + \cdots}$$

where the dots indicate terms which add to less than $(j/\nu)^2$. Within this approximation the fraction in (2.2) reduces to an exponential with exponent

$$-\frac{2}{\nu}[1 + \cdots + (k-1)] - \frac{k}{\nu} = \frac{k^2}{\nu},$$

and the error is less than k^3/ν^2. Accordingly, if $\nu \to \infty$ and k varies within a range $0 < k < K_\nu$ such that

$$(2.4) \qquad K_\nu^3/\nu^2 \to 0$$

we have the approximation

$$(2.5) \qquad a_k \sim a_0 e^{-k^2/\nu}.$$

When the binomial coefficient is expressed in terms of factorials it is seen from Stirling's formula[3] II,(9.1) that

$$(2.6) \qquad a_0 = \binom{2\nu}{\nu} 2^{-2\nu} \sim \frac{1}{\sqrt{\pi\nu}}.$$

Substituting into (2.5) we get

$$(2.7) \qquad a_k \sim h \mathfrak{n}(kh) \qquad where \quad h = \sqrt{2/\nu} = 2/\sqrt{n}.$$

---

[3] *Note on the constant in Stirling's formula.* It will be recalled from II,9 that we have not yet proved that the constant in Stirling formula coincides with $\sqrt{2\pi}$. We now fill this gap as follows. The constant π in (2.6) must be replaced by an unknown constant; this does not affect the approximation theorem except that the right side in (2.10) must be multiplied by an unknown constant c, and we have to prove that $c = 1$. We use the amended form with $z_1 = 0$. The ratio of the two sides tends to 1 as $n \to \infty$. But the tail estimate VI,(3.5) shows that the left side lies between $\frac{1}{2}$ and $\frac{1}{2} - 4z_2^{-2}$, whereas for the right side (1.8) yields the double inequality

$$c > c[\mathfrak{N}(z_2) - \tfrac{1}{2}] = \tfrac{1}{2}c - c[1 - \mathfrak{N}(z_2)] > \tfrac{1}{2}c - c\mathfrak{n}(z_2)/z_2.$$

For z_2 sufficiently large the two sides are arbitrarily close to $\frac{1}{2}$ and to $\frac{1}{2}c$, respectively, and hence $c = 1$ as asserted.

This basic relation is valid when $v \to \infty$ *and* k *is restricted to values* $k < K_v$ *satisfying* (2.4). We shall use (2.7) principally for values k of the order of magnitude of $\sqrt{v}$, and then (2.4) is trivially satisfied.

In practice we require approximations for the probabilities carried by various intervals, that is, to partial sums of the form[4]

$$(2.8) \qquad A(x_1, x_2) = \sum_{x_1 \le k \le x_2} a_k$$

the summation extending over all integers between 0 and x, inclusive. We now show how $A(x)$ can be approximated by an area under the graph of $\mathfrak{n}$ which, in turn, can be expressed in terms of the integral $\mathfrak{N}$. Because of the monotone character of $\mathfrak{n}$ it is clear that the area under the graph of $\mathfrak{n}$ between kh and $(k+1)h$ is smaller than $h\mathfrak{n}(kh)$, but larger than $h\mathfrak{n}((k+1)h)$. It follows that

$$(2.9) \qquad \int_{x_1 h}^{x_2 h + h} \mathfrak{n}(s)\, ds < \sum_{x_1 \le k \le x_2} h\mathfrak{n}(kh) < \int_{x_1 h - h}^{x_2 h} \mathfrak{n}(s)\, ds.$$

In view of (2.9) the middle term is an approximation to $A(x_1, x_2)$; it is good when v is large and k^2/v moderate, that is, when h is small and xh moderate. The two extreme members in (2.9) equal $\mathfrak{N}(x_2 h + h) - \mathfrak{N}(x_1 h)$ and $\mathfrak{N}(x_2 h) - \mathfrak{N}(x_1 h - h)$, respectively; their difference tends to 0 with h, and so we can replace them by $\mathfrak{N}(x_2 h) - \mathfrak{N}(x_1 h)$.

We express this result in the form of a limit theorem, but replace the variable x by $z = xh$.

Approximation Theorem.   *For fixed* $z_1 < z_2$

$$(2.10) \qquad \sum_{\frac{1}{2} z_1 \sqrt{n} \le k \le \frac{1}{2} z_2 \sqrt{n}} a_k \to \mathfrak{N}(z_2) - \mathfrak{N}(z_1).$$

We shall see presently that this result extends meaningfully to certain situations in which z_1 and z_2 are allowed to vary with n without remaining bounded. Note that the limit theorem of III, (2.7) is contained in (2.10), and that this is only a special case of the general theorem of the next section.

Bounds for the Error. We need not concern ourselves with the error committed in replacing the sum by an integral because (2.9) contains upper and lower bounds.

---

[4] We refrain from referring to S_n because this letter appears in different meanings in chapters III and VI. In the terminology of random walks $A(x_1, x_2)$ is the probability that at epoch $n = 2v$ the particle is between $2x_1$ and $2x_2$; in the present terminology $A(x_1, x_2)$ is the probability that $n = 2v$; trials yield a number of successes between $v + x_1$ and $v + x_2$. In the next section this number will be again denoted by S_n.

To estimate the error in the approximation (2.7) we put

$$(2.11) \qquad a_k = a_0 e^{-k^2/\nu + \epsilon_1} = \mathfrak{n}(kh)e^{\epsilon_1 - \epsilon_2}$$

so that ϵ_1 represents the error committed by dropping the higher-order terms in (2.3) while ϵ_2 derives from (2.6). From our derivation it is clear that

$$(2.12) \qquad \epsilon_1 = \sum_{j=1}^{k-1} \left(\log \frac{1 + j/\nu}{1 - j/\nu} - \frac{2j}{\nu} \right) + \left(\log \left(1 + \frac{k}{\nu} \right) - \frac{k}{\nu} \right).$$

The error estimates are most interesting for relatively small ν, and to cover such cases we shall assume only that $k < \frac{1}{3}\nu$. Comparing the expansion II, (8.11) with a geometric series with ratio $1/3$ it is seen that the general term in the series in (2.12) is positive and is less than $(j/\nu)^3$. The whole series is therefore positive and less than $k^4/(4\nu^3)$. From II,(8.9) it is similarly seen that the last term is negative and greater than $-3k^2/(4\nu^2)$. Thus

$$(2.13) \qquad -\frac{3k^2}{n^2} < \epsilon_1 < \frac{2k^4}{n^3}, \qquad\qquad provided \quad k < \tfrac{1}{6}n.$$

In most applications k and $\sqrt{n}$ are of comparable magnitude, and the condition $k < n/6$ is then trivally satisfied. Under such circumstances (2.13) is rather sharp.

As for (2.6), it follows from the improved version of Stirling's formula II,(9.15) that a better approximation for a_0 is obtained on multiplying the right side by $e^{1/(4n)}$, and that under any circumstances

$$(2.14) \qquad \frac{1}{4n} - \frac{1}{20n^3} < \epsilon_2 < \frac{1}{4n} + \frac{1}{360n^3}.$$

We have thus found *precise bounds for the error in the approximations* (2.7) *and* (2.10). These estimates are applicable even for relatively small values of n.

The main result of this investigation is that *the percentage error in* (2.7) *is of the order* k^2/n^2 *or* k^4/n^3, whichever is larger. In practice the estimate is usually applied when k^2/n is large, and in this case the relative error is of the order k^4/n^3. Our estimates also point the way how to improve the approximation by appropriate correction terms (problem 14).

3. THE DEMOIVRE-LAPLACE LIMIT THEOREM

We proceed to show how our approximations can be extended to the general binomial distribution with $p \neq \frac{1}{2}$. The procedure is the same, but the calculations are more involved. The first complication arises in connection with the central term of the distribution. As we saw in VI, (3.2), the index m of the central term is the unique integer of the form

$$(3.1) \qquad m = np + \delta \qquad\qquad with \quad -q < \delta \leq p.$$

The quantity δ will be ultimately neglected, but it occurs in the calculations. (In the case $p = \frac{1}{2}$ this was avoided by assuming $n = 2\nu$ even.)

As in the preceding section we now renumber the terms of the binomial distribution and write

$$(3.2) \qquad a_k = b(m+k; n, p) = \binom{n}{m+k} p^{m+k} q^{n-m-k}.$$

For definiteness we consider $k > 0$, but the same argument applies to $k < 0$. (Alternatively, the range $k < 0$ is covered by interchanging p and q.) In analogy with (2.2) we have now

$$(3.3) \qquad a_k = a_0 \frac{(n-m)(n-m-1)\cdots(n-m-k+1)p^k}{(m+1)(m+2)\cdots(m+k)q^k}.$$

This can be rewritten in the form

$$(3.4) \qquad a_k = a_0 \frac{(1-pt_0)(1-pt_1)\cdots(1-pt_{k-1})}{(1+qt_0)(1+qt_1)\cdots(1+qt_{k-1})}$$

where we put for abbreviation

$$(3.5) \qquad t_j = \frac{j+\delta+q}{(n+1)pq}.$$

We shall use (3.4) only for values of k for which t_k is small, say $t_k < \frac{1}{2}$. From the Taylor expansion II,(8.9) for the logarithm it is then clear that

$$(3.6) \qquad \frac{1-pt_j}{1+qt_j} = e^{-t_j+\cdots}$$

where the omitted quantity is in absolute value less than t_j^2. Thus

$$(3.7) \qquad a_k = a_0 e^{-(t_0+\cdots+t_{k-1})+\cdots}$$

where the dots indicate a quantity that is in absolute value less than[5] $kt_{k-1}^2 < k^3/(npq)^2$. Now

$$(3.8) \qquad t_0 + t_1 + \cdots + t_{k-1} = \frac{\frac{1}{2}k(k-1) + k(\delta+q)}{(n+1)pq}.$$

For simplicity we replace the right side by $k^2/(2npq)$ thereby committing an error less than $2k/(npq)$. Thus, if we write

$$(3.9) \qquad a_k = a_0 e^{-k^2/(2npq)+\rho_k},$$

---

[5] We shall be satisfied with very rough bounds for the error term.

the error term ρ_k satisfies the inequality

$$(3.10) \qquad |\rho_k| < \frac{k^3}{(npq)^2} + \frac{2k}{npq}.$$

We next show that

$$(3.11) \qquad a_0 = \frac{n!}{m!\,(n-m)!}\,p^m q^{n-m} \sim \frac{1}{\sqrt{2\pi npq}},$$

which generalizes the analogous relation (2.6) in the symmetric case. In the ideal case where $p = m/n$ the estimate (3.11) is an immediate consequence of Stirling's formula II,(9.1). A straightforward differentiation shows that the middle term in (3.11) assumes its maximum when $p = m/n$. For given m we need consider only values of p such that (3.1) holds, and the minimum of a_0 is then assumed at one of the endpoints, that is, for $p = m/(n+1)$ or $p = (m+1)/(n+1)$. With these values for p a direct application of Stirling's formula again leads to (3.11) except that n is replaced by $n + 1$. It follows that (3.11) holds for all possible values of p. If we put for abbreviation

$$(3.12) \qquad h = \frac{1}{\sqrt{2\pi npq}}$$

then (3.9) shows that

$$(3.13) \qquad a_k \sim h\mathfrak{n}(kh)$$

provided only that k varies with n in such a way that $\rho_k \to 0$. We have thus proved

Theorem 1. *If $n \to \infty$ and k is constrained to an interval $k < K_n$ such that $K_n^3/n^2 \to 0$, then (3.13) holds[6] uniformly in k; that is, for every $\epsilon > 0$ and n sufficiently large*

$$(3.14) \qquad 1 - \epsilon < \frac{a_k}{h\mathfrak{n}(kh)} < 1 + \epsilon.$$

Example. Figure 3 illustrates the case $n = 10$ and $p = \frac{1}{5}$ where $npq = 1.6$. Considering that n is extremely small the approximation seems surprisingly good. For $k = 0, \ldots, 6$ the probabilities $b(k; n, p)$ are 0.1074, 0.2684, 0.3020, 0.2013, 0.0880, 0.0264, 0.0055. The corresponding approximations (3.13) are 0.0904, 0.2307, 0.3154, 0.2307, 0.0904, 0.0189, 0.0021. ▶

---

[6] When k varies with n in such a way that $k^3/n^2 \to \infty$ the normal approximation is replaced by a limit theorem of a different type; see problems 13 and 15.

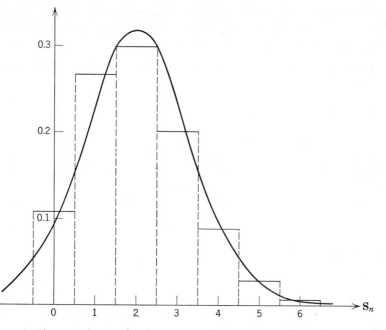

Figure 3. The normal approximation to the binomial distribution. The step function gives the probabilities $b(k; 10, \frac{1}{5})$ of k successes in ten Bernoulli trials with $p = \frac{1}{5}$. The continuous curve gives for each integer k the corresponding normal approximation.

The main application of theorem 1 is to obtain approximations to probabilities of the form

$$(3.15) \qquad \mathbf{P}\{\alpha \leq \mathbf{S}_n \leq \beta\} = \sum_{\nu=\alpha}^{\beta} b(\nu; n, p) = \sum_{k=\alpha-m}^{\beta-m} a_k.$$

Within the range of applicability of theorem 1 we obtain a good approximation when we replace a_k by $h\mathfrak{n}(kh)$. This quantity may be interpreted as the area of a rectangle with height $\mathfrak{n}(kh)$ whose basis is an interval of length h centered at kh (see figure 3). As usual we replace the area of the rectangle by the corresponding area between the x-axis and the graph of $\mathfrak{n}$; as is well known, the error thus committed is negligible in the limit when $h \to 0$. When α and β are integers we arrive thus at the approximation

$$(3.16) \qquad \mathbf{P}\{\alpha \leq \mathbf{S}_n \leq \beta\} \approx \mathfrak{N}((\alpha-m+\tfrac{1}{2})h) - \mathfrak{N}((\beta-m-\tfrac{1}{2})h).$$

It is advisable to use the normal approximation in this form when h is only moderately small and the greatest possible accuracy is desired. For the final formulation, however, it is preferable to replace the arguments on the right by the simpler expressions $z_1 = \alpha - np$ and $z_2 = \beta - np$; the error introduced by this simplification obviously tends to zero with h. We have thus proved the fundamental

Theorem 2. (*DeMoivre-Laplace limit theorem.*) *For fixed*[7] z_1 *and* z_2 *as* $n \to \infty$

$$(3.17) \qquad \mathbf{P}\{np + z_1\sqrt{npq} \leq \mathbf{S}_n \leq np + z_2\sqrt{nqp}\} \to \mathfrak{N}(z_2) - \mathfrak{N}(z_1).$$

Besides being of theoretical importance this theorem justifies the use of the right side as an approximation to the left. From (3.10) it is easy to obtain good estimates of the error, but we shall not dwell on this point. Practical examples will be found in the next section.

The limit relation (3.17) takes on a more pleasing form if $\mathbf{S}_n$ is replaced by the reduced number of successes $\mathbf{S}_n^*$ defined by

$$(3.18) \qquad \mathbf{S}_n^* = \frac{\mathbf{S}_n - np}{\sqrt{npq}}.$$

This amounts to measuring the deviations of $\mathbf{S}_n$ from np in units of $\sqrt{npq}$. In the terminology of random variables (chapter IX) np would be called *the expectation,* and npq *the variance* of $\mathbf{S}_n$. (The square root $\sqrt{npq}$ is the standard deviation.) The inequality on the left side in (3.17) is the same as $z_1 \leq \mathbf{S}_n^* \leq z_2$ and hence we can *restate* (3.17) *in the form*

$$(3.19) \qquad \mathbf{P}\{z_1 \leq \mathbf{S}_n^* \leq z_2\} \to \mathfrak{N}(z_2) - \mathfrak{N}(z_1).$$

In most cases we shall refer to the limit theorem in this form. It shows, in particular, that for large n the probability on the left is practically independent of p. This permits us to compare fluctuations in different series of Bernoulli trials simply by referring to our standard units.

Note on Optional Stopping

It is essential to note that our approximation theorems are valid only if the number n of trials is fixed in advance independently of the outcome of the trials. If a gambler has the privilege of stopping at a moment favorable to him, his ultimate gain cannot be judged from the normal approximation, for now the duration of the game depends on chance. For every fixed n it is very improbable that $\mathbf{S}_n^*$ is large, but, in the long run, even the most improbable thing is bound to happen, and we shall see that in a continued game $\mathbf{S}_n^*$ is practically certain to have a sequence of maxima of the order of magnitude $\sqrt{2 \log \log n}$ (this is the law of the iterated logarithm of VIII, 5).

---

[7] It is obvious from theorem 1 that this condition can be weakened. See also section 6 as well as problems 14 and 16.

4. EXAMPLES

(a) Let $p = \frac{1}{2}$ and $n = 200$. We consider $\mathbf{P}\{95 \leq \mathbf{S}_n \leq 105\}$, which is the probability that in 200 tosses of a coin the number of heads deviates from 100 by at most 5. Here $h = 1/\sqrt{50} = 0.141421 \cdots$ is relatively large, and it pays to be careful about the limits of the interval. The use of (3.16) leads us to the approximation

$$\mathbf{P}\{95 \leq \mathbf{S}_n \leq 105\} \approx \mathfrak{N}(5.5h) - \mathfrak{N}(-5.5h) =$$
$$= 2\mathfrak{N}(0.7778 \cdots) - 1 = 0.56331.$$

The true value is $0.56325 \ldots$. The smallness of the error is due largely to the symmetry of the distribution.

(b) Let $p = \frac{1}{10}$ and $n = 500$. Here $h = 1/\sqrt{45} = 0.14907 \ldots$. Proceeding as before we get

$$\mathbf{P}\{50 \leq \mathbf{S}_n \leq 55\} \approx \mathfrak{N}(5.5h) - \mathfrak{N}(-0.5h) =$$
$$= \mathfrak{N}(5.5h) + \mathfrak{N}(0.5h) - 1 = 0.3235 \cdots$$

against the correct value $0.3176 \ldots$. The error is about 2 per cent.

(c) The probability that $\mathbf{S}_n$ lies within the limits $np \pm 2\sqrt{npq}$ is about $\mathfrak{N}(2) - \mathfrak{N}(-2) = 0.9545$; for $np \pm 3\sqrt{npq}$ the probability is about 0.9973. It is surprising within how narrow limits the chance fluctuations are likely to lie. For example in 10^6 tosses of a coin the probability that the number of heads deviates from the mean 500000 by more than 1000 is less than 0.0455.

(d) Let $n = 100$, $p = 0.3$. Table 2 shows in a typical example (for relatively small n) how the normal approximation deteriorates as the interval (α, β) moves away from the central term.

(e) Let us find a number a such that, for large n, the inequality $|\mathbf{S}_n^*| > a$ has a probability near $\frac{1}{2}$. For this it is necessary that

$$\mathfrak{N}(a) - \mathfrak{N}(-a) = \tfrac{1}{2}$$

or $\mathfrak{N}(a) = \frac{3}{4}$. From tables of the normal distribution we find that $a = 0.6745$, and hence the two inequalities

(4.1) $|\mathbf{S}_n - np| < 0.6745\sqrt{npq}$ and $|\mathbf{S}_n - np| > 0.6745\sqrt{npq}$

are about equally probable. In particular, the probability is about $\frac{1}{2}$ that in n tossings of a coin the number of heads lies within the limits $\frac{1}{2}n \pm 0.337\sqrt{n}$, and, similarly, that in n throws of a die the number of aces lies within the interval $\frac{1}{6}n \pm 0.251\sqrt{n}$.

TABLE 2

COMPARISON OF THE BINOMIAL DISTRIBUTION FOR $n = 100$,
$p = 0.3$ AND THE NORMAL APPROXIMATION

Number of successes	Probability	Normal approximation	Percentage error
$9 \leq S_n \leq 11$	0.000 006	0.000 03	+400
$12 \leq S_n \leq 14$	0.000 15	0.000 33	+100
$15 \leq S_n \leq 17$	0.002 01	0.002 83	+40
$18 \leq S_n \leq 20$	0.014 30	0.015 99	+12
$21 \leq S_n \leq 23$	0.059 07	0.058 95	0
$24 \leq S_n \leq 26$	0.148 87	0.144 47	−3
$27 \leq S_n \leq 29$	0.237 94	0.234 05	−2
$31 \leq S_n \leq 33$	0.230 13	0.234 05	+2
$34 \leq S_n \leq 36$	0.140 86	0.144 47	+3
$37 \leq S_n \leq 39$	0.058 89	0.058 95	0
$40 \leq S_n \leq 42$	0.017 02	0.015 99	−6
$43 \leq S_n \leq 45$	0.003 43	0.002 83	−18
$46 \leq S_n \leq 48$	0.000 49	0.000 33	−33
$49 \leq S_n \leq 51$	0.000 05	0.000 03	−40

(f) *A competition problem.* This example illustrates practical applications of formula (3.17). Two competing railroads operate one train
each between Chicago and Los Angeles; the two trains leave and arrive
simultaneously and have comparable equipment. We suppose that n
passengers select trains independently and at random so that the number
of passengers in each train is the outcome of n Bernoulli trials with
$p = \frac{1}{2}$. If a train carries $s < n$ seats, then there is a positive probability
$f(s)$ that more than s passengers will turn up, in which case not all
patrons can be accommodated. Using the approximation (3.17), we find

(4.2) $$f(s) \approx 1 - \Re\left(\frac{2s - n}{\sqrt{n}}\right).$$

If s is so large that $f(s) < 0.01$, then the number of seats will be sufficient
in 99 out of 100 cases. More generally, the company may decide on an
arbitrary risk level α and determine s so that $f(s) < \alpha$. For that
purpose it suffices to put

(4.3) $$s \geq \tfrac{1}{2}(n + t_\alpha\sqrt{n}),$$

where t_α is the root of the equation $\alpha = 1 - \Re(t_\alpha)$, which can be found from tables. For example, if $n = 1000$ and $\alpha = 0.01$, then $t_\alpha \approx 2.33$ and $s = 537$ seats should suffice. If both railroads accept the risk level $\alpha = 0.01$, the two trains will carry a total of 1074 seats of which 74 will be empty. The loss from competition (or chance fluctuations) is remarkably small. In the same way, 514 seats should suffice in about 80 per cent of all cases, and 549 seats in 999 out of 1000 cases.

Similar considerations apply in other competitive supply problems. For example, if m movies compete for the same n patrons, each movie will put for its probability of success $p = 1/m$, and (4.3) is to be replaced by $s \geq m^{-1}[n + t_\alpha \sqrt{n(m-1)}]$. The total number of empty seats under this system is $ms - n \approx t_\alpha \sqrt{n(m-1)}$. For $\alpha = 0.01$, $n = 1000$, and $m = 2$, 3, 4, 5 this number is about 74, 105, 126, and 147, respectively. The loss of efficiency because of competition is again small.

(g) *Random digits.* In example II, (3.a) we considered $n = 1200$ trials with $p = 0.3024$ and an average of 0.3142 successes per trial. The discrepancy is $\epsilon = 0.0118$. Here

$$\mathbf{P}\left\{\left|\frac{\mathbf{S}_n}{n} - p\right| > \epsilon\right\} = \mathbf{P}\{|\mathbf{S}_n - np| > \epsilon n\} \approx$$

$$\approx \mathbf{P}\{|\mathbf{S}_n - np| > 0.880\sqrt{npq}\} \approx 2(1 - \Re(0.88)) \approx 0.379.$$

This means that in about 38 out of 100 similar experiments the average number of successes should deviate from p by more than it does in our material.

(h) *Sampling.* An unknown fraction p of a certain population are smokers, and random sampling with replacement is to be used to determine p. It is desired to find p with an error not exceeding 0.005. How large should the sample size n be?

Denote the fraction of smokers in the sample by p'. Clearly no sample size can give absolute guarantee that $|p' - p| < 0.005$ because it is conceivable that by chance the sample contains only smokers. The best we can do is to render an error exceeding the preassigned bound 0.005 very improbable. For this purpose we settle for an arbitrary confidence level α, say $\alpha = 0.95$, and choose n so large that the event $|p' - p| < 0.005$ will have a probability $\geq \alpha$. Since np' can be interpreted as the number of successes in n trials we have

(4.4) $\mathbf{P}\{|p' - p| < 0.005\} = \mathbf{P}\{|\mathbf{S}_n - np| < 0.005n\}$

and we wish to choose n so large that this probability is $\geq \alpha$. From the tables we first find the number z_α for which $\mathfrak{N}(z_\alpha) - \mathfrak{N}(-z_\alpha) = \alpha$. Relying on the normal approximation it is then necessary to choose n so large that $\dfrac{0.005\sqrt{n}}{\sqrt{pq}} \geq z_\alpha$, or $n \geq 40{,}000pqz_\alpha^2$. This involves the unknown probability p, but we have under any circumstances $pq \leq \frac{1}{4}$, and so a *sample size* $n \geq 10{,}000z_\alpha^2$ *should suffice.*

For the confidence level $\alpha = 0.95$ we find $z_\alpha = 1.960$ and hence a sample size of $n = 40{,}000$ would certainly suffice. A sample of this size would be costly, but the requirement that $|p' - p| < 0.005$ is exceedingly stringent. If it is only required that $|p' - p| < 0.01$, a sample size of 10,000 will suffice (on the same confidence level). The so-called accuracy to four percentage points means the event $|p' - p| < 0.045$ and requires only a sample size of 475: On the average only five out of one hundred random samples of this size will result in an estimate with a greater error. (The practical difficulty is usually to obtain a representative sample of any size.)

▶

5. RELATION TO THE POISSON APPROXIMATION

The error of the normal approximation will be small if npq is large. On the other hand, if n is large and p small, the terms $b(k; n, p)$ will be found to be near the Poisson probabilities $p(k; \lambda)$ with $\lambda = np$. For small λ only the Poisson approximation can be used, but for large λ we can use either the normal or the Poisson approximation. This implies that for large values of λ it must be possible to approximate the Poisson distribution by the normal distribution, and in example X, (1.c) we shall see that this is indeed so (cf. also problem 9). Here we shall be content to illustrate the point by a numerical and a practical example.

Examples. (a) The Poisson distribution with $\lambda = 100$ attributes to the set of integers $a, a + 1, \ldots, b$ the probability

$$P(a, b) = p(a; 100) + p(a+1; 100) + \cdots + p(b; 100).$$

This Poisson distribution may be considered as an approximation to the binomial distribution with $n = 100{,}000{,}000$ and $p = 10^{-6}$. Then $npq \approx 100$ and so it is not far-fetched to approximate this binomial distribution by the normal, at least for values close to the central term 100. But this means that $P(a, b)$ is being approximated by

$$\mathfrak{N}((b-99.5)/10) - \mathfrak{N}((a-100.5)/10).$$

The following sample gives an idea of the degree of approximation.

	Correct values	Normal approximation
$P(85, 90)$	0.113 84	0.110 49
$P(90, 95)$	0.184 85	0.179 50
$P(95, 105)$	0.417 63	0.417 68
$P(90, 110)$	0.706 52	0.706 28
$P(110, 115)$	0.107 38	0.110 49
$P(115, 120)$	0.053 23	0.053 35

(b) *A telephone trunking problem.* The following problem is, with some simplifications, taken from actual practice.[8] A telephone exchange A is to serve 2000 subscribers in a nearby exchange B. It would be too expensive and extravagant to install 2000 trunklines from A to B. It suffices to make the number N of lines so large that, under ordinary conditions, only one out of every hundred calls will fail to find an idle trunkline immediately at its disposal. Suppose that during the busy hour of the day each subscriber requires a trunkline to B for an average of 2 minutes. At a fixed moment of the busy hour we compare the situation to a set of 2000 trials with a probability $p = \frac{1}{30}$ in each that a line will be required. Under ordinary conditions these trials can be assumed to be independent (although this is not true when events like unexpected showers or earthquakes cause many people to call for taxicabs or the local newspaper; the theory no longer applies, and the trunks will be "jammed"). We have, then, 2000 Bernoulli trials with $p = \frac{1}{30}$, and the smallest number N is required such that the probability of more than N "successes" will be smaller than 0.01; in symbols $\mathbf{P}\{S_{2000} \geq N\} < 0.01$.

For the *Poisson approximation* we should take $\lambda = \frac{2000}{30} \approx 66.67$. From the tables we find that the probability of 87 or more successes is about 0.0097, whereas the probability of 86 or more successes is about 0.013. This would indicate that 87 *trunklines should suffice.* For the *normal approximation* we first find from tables the root x of $1 - \mathfrak{N}(x) = 0.01$, which is $x = 2.327$. Then it is required that

$$(N - \tfrac{1}{2} - np)/\sqrt{npq} \geq 2.327.$$

Since $n = 2000$, $p = \frac{1}{30}$, this means $N \geq 67.17 + (2.327)(8.027) \approx 85.8$. Hence the normal approximation would indicate that 86 *trunklines should suffice.*

---

[8] E. C. Molina, *Probability in engineering*, Electrical Engineering, vol. 54 (1935), pp. 423–427, or *Bell Telephone System Technical Publications Monograph* B-854. There the problem is treated by the Poisson method given in the text, which is preferable from the engineer's point of view.

For practical purposes the two solutions agree. They yield further useful information. For example, it is conceivable that the installation might be cheaper if the 2000 subscribers were divided into two groups of 1000 each, and two separate groups of trunklines from A to B were installed. Using the method above, we find that actually some ten additional trunklines would be required so that the first arrangement is preferable. ▶

*6. LARGE DEVIATIONS

The DeMoivre-Laplace theorem describes the asymptotic behavior of $\mathbf{P}\{z_1 < \mathbf{S}_n^* < z_2\}$ for fixed z_1 and z_2. From its derivation it is clear that the theorem applies also when z_1 and z_2 are permitted to vary with n in such a way that $z_1 \to \infty$, provided that the growth is sufficiently slow. In this case both sides in (3.17) tend to 0, and the theorem is meaningful only if the *ratio* of the two sides tends to unity. The next theorem shows to what extent this is true. To simplify the formulation the double inequality $z_1 < \mathbf{S}_n^* < z_2$ is replaced by $\mathbf{S}_n^* > z_1$. This is justified by the following lemma, which shows that when $z_1 \to \infty$ the upper limit z_2 plays no role.

Lemma. *If $x_n \to \infty$ then for every fixed[9] $\eta > 0$*

(6.1)
$$\frac{\mathbf{P}\{\mathbf{S}_n^* > x_n + \eta\}}{\mathbf{P}\{\mathbf{S}_n^* > x_n\}} \to 0,$$

that is,

(6.2)
$$\mathbf{P}\{x_n < \mathbf{S}_n^* \leq x_n + \eta\} \sim \mathbf{P}\{\mathbf{S}_n^* > x_n\}.$$

In other words: When $\mathbf{S}_n^*$ exceeds x_n it is likely to be very close to x_n, and larger values play no role in the limit.

Proof. With the notation (3.2) for the binomial distribution we have

(6.3) $$\mathbf{P}\{\mathbf{S}_n^* > x_n\} = \sum_{\nu=0}^{\infty} a_{r_n+\nu}, \qquad \mathbf{P}\{\mathbf{S}_n^* > x_n + \eta\} = \sum_{\nu=0}^{\infty} a_{s_n+\nu},$$

where r_n and s_n are integers that differ at most by one unit from $x_n\sqrt{npq}$ and $(x_n+\eta)\sqrt{npq}$, respectively. Now it is obvious from (3.4)

---

* The theorem of this section is in general use, but in this volume it will be applied only in VII, 4 and VIII, 5.

[9] The proof will show that it suffices that $x_n\eta \to \infty$. For a stronger and more interesting version see problem 18.

that for large n

(6.4) $$\frac{a_{k+1}}{a_k} < 1 - pt_k < 1 - \frac{k}{n} < e^{-k/n},$$

and hence

(6.5) $$\frac{a_{s_n+v}}{a_{r_n+v}} < e^{-(s_n-r_n)r_n/n} < e^{-\frac{1}{2}\eta x_n pq}.$$

By assumption $x_n \to \infty$, and so the terms of the second series in (6.3) tend to become negligible in comparison with the corresponding terms of the first series. ▶

We are now in a position to extend the limit theorem as follows.

Theorem. *If $x_n \to \infty$ in such a way that $x_n^3/\sqrt{n} \to 0$, then*

(6.6) $$\mathbf{P}\{S_n^* > x_n\} \sim 1 - \mathfrak{N}(x_n).$$

In view of (1.7) the asymptotic relation (6.6) *is fully equivalent to*

(6.7) $$\mathbf{P}\{S_n^* > x_n\} \sim \frac{1}{\sqrt{2\pi}} \cdot \frac{1}{x_n} e^{-\frac{1}{2}x_n^2}.$$

Proof. In view of the preceding lemma and theorem 3.1

(6.8) $$\mathbf{P}\{S_n^* > x_n\} \sim \sum_{k=r_n}^{\infty} h\mathfrak{n}(kh)$$

where r_n is an integer such that $|r_n h - x_n| < h$. The sum on the right therefore lies between $1 - \mathfrak{N}(x_n-2h)$ and $1 - \mathfrak{N}(x_n+2h)$. For the difference of these two quantities we get, using (1.7),

(6.9) $\mathfrak{N}(x_n+2h) - \mathfrak{N}(x_n-2h) < 4h\mathfrak{n}(x_n-2h) \to 0,$

and so the sum in (6.8) is $\sim 1 - \mathfrak{N}(x_n)$, as asserted. ▶

For generalizations see problems 14 and 16.

7. PROBLEMS FOR SOLUTION

1. Generalizing (1.7), prove that

(7.1) $$1 - \mathfrak{N}(x) \sim \frac{1}{\sqrt{2\pi}} e^{-\frac{1}{2}z^2} \left\{ \frac{1}{x} - \frac{1}{x^3} + \frac{1\cdot3}{x^5} - \frac{1\cdot3\cdot5}{x^7} + - \cdots + \right.$$
$$\left. + (-1)^k \frac{1\cdot3\cdots(2k-1)}{x^{2k+1}} \right\}$$

and that for $x > 0$ the right side *overestimates* $1 - \Re(x)$ if k is even, and *underestimates* if k is odd.

2. For every constant $a > 0$

$$(7.2) \qquad \frac{1 - \Re(x + a/x)}{1 - \Re(x)} \to e^{-a}$$

as $x \to \infty$.

3. Find the probability that among 10,000 random digits the digit 7 appears not more than 968 times.

4. Find an approximation to the probability that the number of aces obtained in 12,000 rollings of a die is between 1900 and 2150.

5. Find a number k such that the probability is about 0.5 that the number of heads obtained in 1000 tossings of a coin will be between 490 and k.

6. A sample is taken in order to find the fraction f of females in a population. Find a sample size such that the probability of a sampling error less than 0.005 will be 0.99 or greater.

7. In 10,000 tossings, a coin fell heads 5400 times. Is it reasonable to assume that the coin is skew?

------

8. Find an approximation to the maximal term of the trinomial distribution

$$\frac{n!}{k! \, r! \, (n - k - r)!} \, p_1^k p_2^r (1 - p_1 - p_2)^{n-k-r}$$

9. *Normal approximation to the Poisson distribution.* Using Stirling's formula, show that, if $\lambda \to \infty$, then for fixed $\alpha < \beta$

$$(7.3) \qquad \sum_{\lambda + \alpha \sqrt{\lambda} < k < \lambda + \beta \sqrt{\lambda}} p(k; \lambda) \to \Re(\beta) - \Re(\alpha).$$

10. *Normal approximation to the hypergeometric distribution.* Let n, m, k be positive integers and suppose that they tend to infinity in such a way that

$$(7.4) \qquad \frac{r}{n + m} \to t, \quad \frac{n}{n + m} \to p, \quad \frac{m}{n + m} \to q, \quad h\{k - rp\} \to x$$

where $h = 1/\sqrt{(n + m)pqt(1 - t)}$. Prove that

$$(7.5) \qquad \binom{n}{k}\binom{m}{r - k} \Big/ \binom{n + m}{r} \sim h\mathfrak{n}(x).$$

Hint: Use the normal approximation to the binomial distribution rather than Stirling's formula.

11. *Normal distribution and combinatorial runs.*[10] In II, (11.19) we found that in an arrangement of n alphas and m betas the probability of having exactly

------

[10] A. Wald and J. Wolfowitz, *On a test whether two samples are from the same population*, Ann. Math. Statist., vol. 11 (1940), pp. 147–162. For more general results, see A. M. Mood, *The distribution theory of runs, ibid.*, pp. 367–392.

k runs of alphas is

$$(7.6) \qquad \pi_k = \binom{n-1}{k-1}\binom{m+1}{k}\bigg/\binom{n+m}{n}.$$

Let $n \to \infty$, $m \to \infty$ so that (7.4) holds. For fixed $\alpha > \beta$ the probability that the number of alpha runs lies between $npq + \alpha\sqrt{pqn}$ and $npq + \beta\sqrt{pqn}$ tends to $\mathfrak{N}(\beta) - \mathfrak{N}(\alpha)$.

12. *A new derivation of the law of large numbers.* Derive the law of large numbers of VI, 4 from the de Moivre-Laplace limit theorem.

Limit Theorems for Large Deviations

13. Using the notations of section 3 show that if k varies with n in such a way that $k^4/n^2 \to 0$, then

$$(7.7) \qquad b(k; n, p) \sim h\mathfrak{n}(kh) \cdot e^{-(p-q)k^3h^4/6}, \qquad\qquad h = \frac{1}{\sqrt{npq}}.$$

This generalizes theorem 3.1.

14. Using the preceding problem and the lemma of section 6 prove the following

Theorem. *If* x_n *varies with* n *in such a way that* $x_n^4/n \to 0$ *but* $x_n \to \infty$, *then*

$$(7.8) \qquad P\{S_n^* > x_n\} \sim [1 - \mathfrak{N}(x_n)]e^{-(p-q)x_n^3/(\sqrt{npq})}.$$

15. *Generalization of problem* 13. Put

$$(7.9) \qquad f(x) = \sum_{\nu=3}^{\infty} \frac{p^{\nu-1} - q^{\nu-1}}{\nu(\nu-1)} h^{\nu-2}x^\nu = \frac{p-q}{6} x^3h + \frac{p^3+q^3}{12} x^4h^2 + \cdots$$

where $h = 1/\sqrt{npq}$. If k varies with n in such a way that $k/n \to 0$ then

$$(7.10) \qquad a_k \sim h\mathfrak{n}(kh) \cdot e^{-f(kh)}.$$

[When $k^3/n^2 \to 0$ this reduces to theorem 3.1; when $k^4/n^3 \to 0$ we get (7.7); when $k^5/n^4 \to 0$ we get (7.7) with a fourth-degree term added in the exponent, etc.]

16. *Generalization of problem* 14. If x_n *varies with* n *in such a way that* $x_n \to \infty$ *but* $x_n/\sqrt{n} \to 0$, *then*

$$(7.11) \qquad P\{S_n > x_n\} \sim [1 - \mathfrak{N}(x_n)]e^{-f(x_n)}.$$

When $x_n^4/n \to 0$ this reduces to (7.8). When $x_n^5/n^{\frac{3}{2}}$ one may replace $f(x_n^{\frac{3}{2}})$ by the fourth-degree polynomial appearing on the right in (7.9), etc.

17. If $p > q$ then $P\{S_n > x\} > P\{S_n < -x\}$ for all large n. *Hint:* Use problem 15.

18. If $x_n \to \infty$ and $x_n/\sqrt{n} \to 0$ show that

$$(7.12) \qquad P\{x_n < S_n < x_n + a/x_n\} \sim (1-e^{-a})P\{S_n > x_n\}.$$

In words: The conditional probability of the event $\{S_n \geq x_n + a/x_n\}$ given that $S_n > x_n$ tends to e^{-a}. (A weaker version of this theorem was proved by Khintchine.)

CHAPTER VIII *

Unlimited Sequences
of Bernoulli Trials

This chapter discusses certain properties of randomness and the important law of the iterated logarithm for Bernoulli trials. A different aspect of the fluctuation theory of Bernoulli trials (at least for $p = \frac{1}{2}$) is covered in chapter III.

1. INFINITE SEQUENCES OF TRIALS

In the preceding chapter we have dealt with probabilities connected with n Bernoulli trials and have studied their asymptotic behavior as $n \to \infty$. We turn now to a more general type of problem where the events themselves cannot be defined in a finite sample space.

Example. *A problem in runs.* Let α and β be positive integers, and consider a potentially unlimited sequence of Bernoulli trials, such as tossing a coin or throwing dice. Suppose that Paul bets Peter that a run of α consecutive successes will occur before a run of β consecutive failures. It has an intuitive meaning to speak of the event that Paul wins, but it must be remembered that in the mathematical theory the term event stands for "aggregate of sample points" and is meaningless unless an appropriate sample space has been defined. The model of a finite number of trials is insufficient for our present purpose, but the difficulty is solved by a simple passage to the limit. In n trials Peter wins or loses, or the game remains undecided. Let the corresponding probabilities be x_n, y_n, z_n ($x_n + y_n + z_n = 1$). As the number n of trials increases, the probability z_n of a tie can only decrease, and both x_n and y_n necessarily increase. Hence $x = \lim x_n$, $y = \lim y_n$, and $z = \lim z_n$ exist. Nobody would

---

* This chapter is not directly connected with the material covered in subsequent chapters and may be omitted at first reading.

hesitate to call them the probabilities of Peter's ultimate gain or loss or of a tie. However, the corresponding three events are defined only in the sample space of infinite sequences of trials, and this space is not discrete.

The example was introduced for illustration only, and the numerical values of x_n, y_n, z_n are not our immediate concern. We shall return to their calculation in example XIII, (8.b). The limits x, y, z may be obtained by a simpler method which is applicable to more general cases. We indicate it here because of its importance and intrinsic interest. ·

Let A be the event that *a run of α consecutive successes occurs before a run of β consecutive failures*. In the event A Paul wins and $x = \mathbf{P}\{A\}$. If u and v are the conditional probabilities of A under the hypotheses, respectively, that the first trial results in success or failure, then $x = pu + qv$ [see V, (1.8)]. Suppose first that the first trial results in success. In this case the event A can occur in α mutually exclusive ways: (1) The following $\alpha - 1$ trials result in successes; the probability for this is $p^{\alpha-1}$. (2) The first failure occurs at the νth trial where $2 \leq \nu \leq \alpha$. Let this event be H_ν. Then $\mathbf{P}\{H_\nu\} = p^{\nu-2}q$, and $\mathbf{P}\{A \mid H_\nu\} = v$. Hence (using once more the formula for compound probabilities)

$$(1.1) \qquad u = p^{\alpha-1} + qv(1+p+ \cdots +p^{\alpha-2}) = p^{\alpha-1} + v(1-p^{\alpha-1}).$$

If the first trial results in failure, a similar argument leads to

$$(1.2) \qquad v = pu(1+q+ \cdots +q^{\beta-2}) = u(1-q^{\beta-1}).$$

We have thus two equations for the two unknowns u and v and find for $x = pu + qv$

$$(1.3) \qquad x = p^{\alpha-1} \frac{1 - q^\beta}{p^{\alpha-1} + q^{\beta-1} - p^{\alpha-1}q^{\beta-1}} \cdot$$

To obtain y we have only to interchange p and q, and α and β. Thus

$$(1.4) \qquad y = q^{\beta-1} \frac{1 - p^\alpha}{p^{\alpha-1} + q^{\beta-1} - p^{\alpha-1}q^{\beta-1}} \cdot$$

Since $x + y = 1$, we have $z = 0$; *the probability of a tie is zero.*

For example, in tossing a coin ($p = \frac{1}{2}$) the probability that a run of two heads appears before a run of three tails is 0.7; for two consecutive heads before four consecutive tails the probability is $\frac{5}{6}$, for three consecutive heads before four consecutive tails $\frac{15}{22}$. In rolling dice there is probability 0.1753 that two consecutive aces will appear before five consecutive non-aces, etc.   ▶

In the present volume we are confined to the theory of discrete sample spaces, and this means a considerable loss of mathematical elegance. The general theory considers n Bernoulli trials only as the beginning of an infinite sequence of trials. A sample point is then represented by an infinite sequence of letters S and F, and the sample space is the aggregate of all such sequences. A finite sequence, like $SSFS$, stands for the aggregate of all points with this beginning, that is, for the compound event that in an infinite sequence of trials the first four result in S, S, F, S, respectively. In the infinite sample space the game of our example can be interpreted without a limiting process. Take any point, that is, a sequence $SSFSFF\ldots$ In it a run of α consecutive S's may or may not occur. If it does, it may or may not be preceded by a run of β consecutive F's. In this way we get a classification of all sample points into three classes, representing the events "Peter wins," "Peter loses," "no decision." Their probabilities are the numbers x, y, z, computed above. The only trouble with this sample space is that it is not discrete, and we have not yet defined probabilities in general sample spaces.

Note that we are discussing a question of terminology rather than a genuine difficulty. In our example there was no question about the proper definition or interpretation of the number x. The trouble is only that for consistency we must either decide to refer to the number x as "the limit of the probability x_n that Peter wins in n trials" or else talk of the event "that Peter wins," which means referring to a non-discrete sample space. We propose to do both. For simplicity of language we shall refer to events even when they are defined in the infinite sample space; for precision, the theorems will also be formulated in terms of finite sample spaces and passages to the limit. The events to be studied in this chapter share the following salient feature of our example. The event "Peter wins," although defined in an infinite space, is the union of the events "Peter wins at the nth trial" $(n = 1, 2, \ldots)$, each of which depends only on a finite number of trials. The required probability x is the limit of a monotonic sequence of probabilities x_n which depend only on finitely many trials. We require no theory going beyond the model of n Bernoulli trials; we merely take the liberty of simplifying clumsy expressions[1] by calling certain numbers probabilities instead of using the term "limits of probabilities."

2. SYSTEMS OF GAMBLING

The painful experience of many gamblers has taught us the lesson that no system of betting is successful in improving the gambler's chances. If the theory of probability is true to life, this experience must correspond to a provable statement.

For orientation let us consider a potentially unlimited sequence of Bernoulli trials and suppose that at each trial the bettor has the free choice

---

[1] For the reader familiar with general measure theory the situation may be described as follows. We consider only events which either depend on a finite number of trials or are limits of *monotonic* sequences of such events. We calculate the obvious limits of probabilities and clearly require no measure theory for that purpose. But only general measure theory shows that our limits are independent of the particular passage to the limit and are completely additive.

of whether or not to bet. A "system" consists in fixed rules selecting those trials on which the player is to bet. For example, the bettor may make up his mind to bet at every seventh trial or to wait as long as necessary for seven heads to occur between two bets. He may bet only following a head run of length 13, or bet for the first time after the first head, for the second time after the first run of two consecutive heads, and generally, for the kth time, just after k heads have appeared in succession. In the latter case he would bet less and less frequently. We need not consider the stakes at the individual trials; we want to show that no "system" changes the bettor's situation and that he can achieve the same result by betting every time. It goes without saying that this statement can be proved only for systems in the ordinary meaning where the bettor does not know the future (the existence or non-existence of genuine prescience is not our concern). It must also be admitted that the rule "go home after losing three times" does change the situation, but we shall rule out such uninteresting systems.

We define a system as a set of fixed rules which for every trial uniquely determine whether or not the bettor is to bet; at the kth trial the decision may depend on the outcomes of the first $k-1$ trials, but not on the outcome of trials number $k, k+1, k+2, \ldots$; finally the rules must be such as to ensure an indefinite continuation of the game. Since the set of rules is fixed, the event "in n trials the bettor bets more than r times" is well defined and its probability calculable. The last condition requires that for every r, as $n \to \infty$, this probability tends to 1.

We now formulate our fundamental theorem to the effect that *under any system the successive bets form a sequence of Bernoulli trials with unchanged probability for success.* With an appropriate change of phrasing this theorem holds for all kinds of independent trials; the successive bets form in each case an exact replica of the original trials, so that no system can affect the bettor's fortunes. The importance of this statement was first recognized by von Mises, who introduced the impossibility of a successful gambling system as a fundamental axiom. The present formulation and proof follow Doob.[2] For simplicity we assume that $p = \frac{1}{2}$.

Let A_k be the event "first bet occurs at the kth trial." Our definition of system requires that as $n \to \infty$ the probability that the first bet has occurred before the nth trial tends to 1. This means that

$$\mathbf{P}\{A_1\} + \mathbf{P}\{A_2\} + \cdots + \mathbf{P}\{A_n\} \to 1,$$

or

(2.1) $$\sum \mathbf{P}\{A_k\} = 1.$$

Next, let B_k be the event "head at kth trial" and B the event "the trial

---

[2] J. L. Doob, *Note on probability*, Annals of Mathematics, vol. 37 (1936), pp. 363–367.

of the first bet results in heads." Then the event B is the union of the events A_1B_1, A_2B_2, A_3B_3, $\ldots$ which are mutually exclusive. Now A_k depends only on the outcome of the first $k-1$ trials, and B_k only on the trial number k. Hence A_k and B_k are independent and $\mathbf{P}\{A_kB_k\} =$ $= \mathbf{P}\{A_k\}\mathbf{P}\{B_k\} = \frac{1}{2}\mathbf{P}\{A_k\}$. Thus $\mathbf{P}\{B\} = \sum \mathbf{P}\{A_kB_k\} = \frac{1}{2}\sum \mathbf{P}\{A_k\} = \frac{1}{2}$. This shows that under this system the probability of heads at the first bet is $\frac{1}{2}$, and the same statement holds for all subsequent bets.

It remains to show that the bets are stochastically independent. This means that the probability that the coin falls heads at both the first and the second bet should be $\frac{1}{4}$ (and similarly for all other combinations and for the subsequent trials). To verify this statement let A_k^* be the event that the second bet occurs at the kth trial. Let E represent the event "heads at the first two bets"; it is the union of all events $A_jB_jA_k^*B_k$ where $j < k$ (if $j \geq k$, then A_j and A_k^* are mutually exclusive and $A_jA_k^* = 0$). Therefore

$$(2.2) \qquad \mathbf{P}\{E\} = \sum_{j=1}^{\infty} \sum_{k=j+1}^{\infty} \mathbf{P}\{A_jB_jA_k^*B_k\}.$$

As before, we see that for fixed j and $k > j$, the event B_k (heads at kth trial) is independent of the event $A_jB_jA_k^*$ (which depends only on the outcomes of the first $k-1$ trials). Hence

$$(2.3) \qquad \mathbf{P}\{E\} = \frac{1}{2}\sum_{j=1}^{\infty} \sum_{k=j+1}^{\infty} \mathbf{P}\{A_jB_jA_k^*\} =$$

$$= \frac{1}{2}\sum_{j=1}^{\infty}\mathbf{P}\{A_jB_j\} \sum_{k=j+1}^{\infty} \mathbf{P}\{A_k^* \mid A_jB_j\}$$

[cf. V, (1.8)]. Now, whenever the first bet occurs and whatever its outcome, the game is sure to continue, that is, the second bet occurs sooner or later. This means that for given A_jB_j with $\mathbf{P}\{A_jB_j\} > 0$ the conditional probabilities that the second bet occurs at the kth trial must add to unity. The second series in (2.3) is therefore unity, and we have already seen that $\sum \mathbf{P}\{A_jB_j\} = \frac{1}{2}$. Hence $\mathbf{P}\{E\} = \frac{1}{4}$ as contended. A similar argument holds for any combination of trials.   ▶

Note that the situation is different when the player is permitted to vary his stakes. In this case there exist advantageous strategies, and the game depends on the strategy. We shall return to this point in XIV, 2.

3. THE BOREL-CANTELLI LEMMAS

Two simple lemmas concerning infinite sequences of trials are used so frequently that they deserve special attention. We formulate them for Bernoulli trials, but they apply to more general cases.

We refer again to an infinite sequence of Bernoulli trials. Let $A_1, A_2, \ldots$ be an infinite sequence of events each of which depends only on a finite number of trials; in other words, we suppose that there exists an integer n_k such that A_k is an event in the sample space of the first n_k Bernoulli trials. Put

$$(3.1) \qquad\qquad a_k = \mathbf{P}\{A_k\}.$$

(For example, A_k may be the event that the $2k$th trial concludes a run of at least k consecutive successes. Then $n_k = 2k$ and $a_k = p^k$.)

For every infinite sequence of letters S and F it is possible to establish whether it belongs to $0, 1, 2, \ldots$ or infinitely many among the $\{A_k\}$. This means that we can speak of the event U_r, that an unending sequence of trials produces more than r among the events $\{A_k\}$, and also of the event U_∞, that infinitely many among the $\{A_k\}$ occur. The event U_r is defined only in the infinite sample space, and its probability is the limit of $\mathbf{P}\{U_{n,r}\}$, the probability that n trials produce more than r among the events $\{A_k\}$. Finally, $\mathbf{P}\{U_\infty\} = \lim \mathbf{P}\{U_r\}$; this limit exists since $\mathbf{P}\{U_r\}$ decreases as r increases.

Lemma 1. *If $\sum a_k$ converges, then with probability one only finitely many events A_k occur.* More precisely, it is claimed that for r sufficiently large, $\mathbf{P}\{U_r\} < \epsilon$ or: *to every $\epsilon > 0$ it is possible to find an integer r such that the probability that n trials produce one or more among the events $A_{r+1}, A_{r+2}, \ldots$ is less than ϵ for all n.*

Proof. Determine r so that $a_{r+1} + a_{r+2} + \cdots < \epsilon$; this is possible since $\sum a_k$ converges. Without loss of generality we may suppose that the A_k are ordered in such a way that $n_1 \leq n_2 \leq n_3 \leq \ldots$. Let N be the last subscript for which $n_N \leq n$. Then $A_1, \ldots, A_N$ are defined in the space of n trials, and the lemma asserts that the probability that one or more among the events $A_{r+1}, A_{r+2}, \ldots, A_N$ occur is less than ϵ. This is true, since by the fundamental inequality I, (7.6) we have

$$(3.2) \quad \mathbf{P}\{A_{r+1} \cup A_{r+2} \cup \cdots \cup A_N\} \leq a_{r+1} + a_{r+2} + \cdots + a_N \leq \epsilon,$$

as contended. ▶

A satisfactory converse to the lemma is known only for the special case of mutually independent A_k. This situation occurs when the trials are divided into non-overlapping blocks and A_k depends only on the trials in the kth block (for example, A_k may be the event that the kth thousand of trials produces more than 600 successes).

Lemma 2. *If the events A_k are mutually independent, and if $\sum a_k$ diverges, then with probability one infinitely many A_k occur.* In other words, it is claimed that for every r the probability that n trials produce more than r among the events A_k tends to 1 as $n \to \infty$.

Proof. Assume the contrary. There exists then an n such that with positive probability u no event A_k with $k > n$ is realized. But

$$(3.3) \qquad u \leq (1-a_n)(1-a_{n+1}) \cdots (1-a_{n+r})$$

because the product on the right is the probability that no A_k with $n \leq k \leq n + r$ occurs. Since $1 - x \leq e^{-x}$ the product on the right is $\leq e^{-(a_n + \cdots + a_{n+r})}$, and the sum in the exponent can be made arbitrarily large by choosing r sufficiently large. Thus $u = 0$ against the hypothesis. ▶

Examples. (a) What is the probability that in a sequence of Bernoulli trials the pattern *SFS* appears infinitely often? Let A_k be the event that the trials number k, $k + 1$, and $k + 2$ produce the sequence *SFS*. The events A_k are not mutually independent, but the sequence A_1, A_4, A_7, $A_{10}, \ldots$ contains only mutually independent events (since no two depend on the outcome of the same trials). Since $a_k = p^2q$ is independent of k, the series $a_1 + a_4 + a_7 + \cdots$ diverges, and hence with probability one the pattern *SFS* occurs infinitely often. A similar argument obviously applies for arbitrary patterns of any length.

(b) *Books produced by coin tossing.* Consider a message such as PROB-ABILITY IS FUN written in the Morse code as a finite sequence of dots and dashes. When we write H for dot and T for dash this message will appear as a finite succession of heads and tails. It follows from the preceding example that a prolonged tossing of a coin is certain sooner or later to produce the given message and to repeat it infinitely often. By the same token the record of a prolonged coin-tossing game is bound to contain every conceivable book in the Morse code, from *Hamlet* to eight-place logarithmic tables. It has been suggested that an army of monkeys might be trained to pound typewriters at random in the hope that ultimately great works of literature would be produced. Using a coin for the same purpose may save feeding and training expenses and free the monkeys for other monkey business. ▶

4. THE STRONG LAW OF LARGE NUMBERS

The intuitive notion of probability is based on the expectation that the following is true: If S_n is the number of successes in the first n trials of a sequence of Bernoulli trials, then

$$(4.1) \qquad \frac{S_n}{n} \to p.$$

In the abstract theory this cannot be true for *every* sequence of trials; in fact, our sample space contains a point representing the conceptual possibility of an infinite sequence of uninterrupted successes, and for it $S_n/n = 1$. However, it is demonstrable that (4.1) holds with probability one, so that the cases where (4.1) does not hold form a negligible exception.

Note that we deal with a statement much stronger than the weak law of large numbers [VI, (4.1)]. The latter says that for every sufficiently large *fixed* n the average S_n/n is likely to be near p, but it does not say that S_n/n is bound to stay near p if the number of trials is increased. It leaves open the possibility that in n additional trials there occurs at least one among the events $k^{-1}S_k < p - \epsilon$ with $n < k \leq 2n$. The probability for this is the sum of a large number of probabilities of which we know only that they are individually small. We shall now prove that with probability one $S_n/n - p$ becomes *and remains* small.

Strong Law of Large Numbers. *For every $\epsilon > 0$ with probability one there occur only finitely many of the events*

$$(4.2) \qquad \left| \frac{S_n}{n} - p \right| > \epsilon.$$

This implies that (4.1) holds with probability one. In terms of finite sample spaces, it is asserted that to every $\epsilon > 0$, $\delta > 0$ there corresponds an r such that for all ν the probability of the simultaneous realization of the ν inequalities

$$(4.3) \qquad \left| \frac{S_{r+k}}{r + k} - p \right| < \epsilon, \qquad\qquad k = 1, 2, \ldots, \nu,$$

is greater than $1 - \delta$.

Proof. We shall prove a much stronger statement. Let A_k be the event

$$(4.4) \qquad \left| S_k^* \right| = \left| \frac{S_k - kp}{\sqrt{kpq}} \right| \geq \sqrt{2a \log k},$$

where $a > 1$. It is then obvious from VII, (6.7) that, at least for all k sufficiently large,

$$(4.5) \qquad P\{A_k\} < e^{-a \log k} = \frac{1}{k^a}.$$

Hence $\sum P\{A_k\}$ converges, and lemma 1 of the preceding section ensures that *with probability one only finitely many inequalities* (4.4) *hold.* On the other hand, if (4.2) holds, then

(4.6)
$$\left| \frac{\mathbf{S}_n - np}{\sqrt{npq}} \right| > \frac{\epsilon}{\sqrt{pq}} \cdot \sqrt{n}$$

and for large n the right side is larger than $\sqrt{2a \log n}$. Hence, the realization of infinitely many inequalities (4.2) implies the realization of infinitely many A_k and has therefore probability zero.   ▶

The strong law of large numbers was first formulated by Cantelli (1917), after Borel and Hausdorff had discussed certain special cases. Like the weak law, it is only a very special case of a general theorem on random variables. Taken in conjunction with our theorem on the impossibility of gambling systems, the law of large numbers implies the existence of the limit (4.1) not only for the original sequence of trials but also for all subsequences obtained in accordance with the rules of section 2. *Thus the two theorems together describe the fundamental properties of randomness which are inherent in the intuitive notion of probability* and whose importance was stressed with special emphasis by von Mises.

5. THE LAW OF THE ITERATED LOGARITHM

As in chapter VII let us again introduce the reduced number of successes in n trials

(5.1)
$$\mathbf{S}_n^* = \frac{\mathbf{S}_n - np}{\sqrt{npq}}.$$

The Laplace limit theorem asserts that $\mathbf{P}\{\mathbf{S}_n^* > x\} \sim 1 - \mathfrak{N}(x)$. Thus, for every particular value of n it is improbable to have a large $\mathbf{S}_n^*$, but it is intuitively clear that in a prolonged sequence of trials $\mathbf{S}_n^*$ will sooner or later take on arbitrarily large values. Moderate values of $\mathbf{S}_n^*$ are most probable, but the maxima will slowly increase. How fast? In the course of the proof of the strong law of large numbers we have concluded from (4.5) that with probability one the inequality $\mathbf{S}_n^* < \sqrt{2a \log n}$ holds for each $a > 1$ and all sufficiently large n. This provides us with an upper bound for the fluctuations of $\mathbf{S}_n^*$, but this bound is bad. To see this, let us apply the same argument to the subsequence $\mathbf{S}_2^*, \mathbf{S}_4^*, \mathbf{S}_8^*, \mathbf{S}_{16}^*, \ldots$; that is, let us define the event A_k by $\mathbf{S}_{2^k}^* \geq \sqrt{2a \log k}$. The inequality (4.5) implies that $\mathbf{S}_{2^k}^* < \sqrt{2a \log k}$ holds for $a > 1$ and all sufficiently large k. But for $n = 2^k$ we have $\log k \sim \log \log n$, and we conclude that for each $a > 1$ and all n of the form $n = 2^k$ the inequality

(5.2)
$$\mathbf{S}_n^* < \sqrt{2a \log \log n}$$

will hold from some k onward. It is now a fair guess that in reality (5.2) holds for *all* n sufficiently large and, in fact, this is one part of the law of the iterated logarithm. This remarkable theorem[3] asserts that $\sqrt{2 \log \log n}$ is the *precise* upper bound in the sense that for each $a < 1$ the reverse of the inequality (5.2) will hold for infinitely many n.

Theorem. *With probability one we have*

$$(5.3) \qquad \limsup_{n \to \infty} \frac{S_n^*}{\sqrt{2 \log \log n}} = 1.$$

This means: For $\lambda > 1$ with probability one only finitely many of the events

$$(5.4) \qquad S_n > np + \lambda \sqrt{2npq \log \log n}$$

occur; for $\lambda < 1$ with probability one (5.4) holds for infinitely many n.
For reasons of symmetry (5.3) implies that

$$(5.3a) \qquad \liminf_{n \to \infty} \frac{S_n^*}{\sqrt{2 \log \log n}} = -1.$$

Proof. We start with two preliminary remarks.

(1) There exists a constant $c > 0$ which depends on p, but not on n, such that

$$(5.5) \qquad P\{S_n > np\} > c$$

for all n. In fact, an inspection of the binomial distribution shows that the left side in (5.5) is never zero, and the Laplace limit theorem shows that it tends to $\frac{1}{2}$ as $n \to \infty$. Accordingly, the left side is bounded away from zero, as asserted.

(2) We require the following *lemma*: Let x be fixed, and let A be the event that for at least one k with $k \leq n$

$$(5.6) \qquad S_k - kp > x.$$

Then

$$(5.7) \qquad P\{A\} \leq c^{-1} P\{S_n - np > x\}.$$

---

[3] A. Khintchine, *Über einen Satz der Wahrscheinlichkeitsrechnung*, Fundamenta Mathematicae, vol. 6 (1924), pp. 9–20. The discovery was preceded by partial results due to other authors. The present proof is arranged so as to permit straightforward generalization to more general random variables.

For a proof of the lemma let A_ν be the event that (5.6) holds for $k = \nu$ but not for $k = 1, 2, \ldots, \nu - 1$ (here $1 \leq \nu \leq n$). The events $A_1, A_2, \ldots, A_n$ are mutually exclusive, and A is their union. Hence

$$\text{(5.8)} \qquad\qquad \mathbf{P}\{A\} = \mathbf{P}\{A_1\} + \cdots + \mathbf{P}\{A_n\}.$$

Next, for $\nu < n$ let U_ν be the event that the total number of successes in the trials number $\nu + 1, \nu + 2, \ldots, n$ exceeds $(n-\nu)p$. If both A_ν and U_ν occur, then $\mathbf{S}_n > \mathbf{S}_\nu + (n-\nu)p > np + x$, and since the $A_\nu U_\nu$ are mutually exclusive, this implies

$$\text{(5.9)} \qquad \mathbf{P}\{\mathbf{S}_n - np > x\} \geq \mathbf{P}\{A_1 U_1\} + \mathbf{P}\{A_{n-1}U_{n-1}\} + \mathbf{P}\{A_n\}.$$

Now A_ν depends only on the first ν trials and U_ν only on the following $n - \nu$ trials. Hence A_ν and U_ν are independent, and $\mathbf{P}\{A_\nu U_\nu\} = \mathbf{P}\{A_\nu\}\mathbf{P}\{U_\nu\}$. From the preliminary remark (5.5) we know that $\mathbf{P}\{U_\nu\} > c$, and since $c < 1$, we get from (5.9) and (5.8)

$$\text{(5.10)} \qquad\qquad \mathbf{P}\{\mathbf{S}_n - np > x\} \geq c \sum \mathbf{P}\{A_\nu\} = c\mathbf{P}\{A\}.$$

This proves (5.7).

(3) We now prove the part of the theorem relating to (5.4) with $\lambda > 1$. Let γ be a number such that

$$\text{(5.11)} \qquad\qquad 1 < \gamma < \lambda$$

and let n_r be the integer nearest to γ^r. Let B_r be the event that the inequality

$$\text{(5.12)} \qquad\qquad \mathbf{S}_n - np > \lambda\sqrt{2n_r pq \log \log n_r}$$

holds for at least one n with $n_r \leq n < n_{r+1}$. Obviously (5.4) can hold for infinitely many n only if infinitely many B_r occur. Using the first Borel-Cantelli lemma, we see therefore that it suffices to prove that

$$\text{(5.13)} \qquad\qquad \sum \mathbf{P}\{B_r\} \quad \text{converges.}$$

By the inequality (5.7)

$$\mathbf{P}\{B_r\} \leq c^{-1}\mathbf{P}\{\mathbf{S}_{n_{r+1}} - n_{r+1}p > \lambda\sqrt{2n_r pq \log \log n_r}\} =$$

$$\text{(5.14)} \qquad\qquad = c^{-1}\mathbf{P}\left\{\mathbf{S}^*_{n_{r+1}} > \lambda\sqrt{2\frac{n_r}{n_{r+1}}\log\log n_r}\right\}.$$

Now $n_{r+1}/n_r \sim \gamma < \lambda$, and hence for sufficiently large r

$$\text{(5.15)} \qquad\qquad \mathbf{P}\{B_r\} \leq c^{-1}\mathbf{P}\{\mathbf{S}^*_{n_{r+1}} > \sqrt{2\lambda \log \log n_r}\}.$$

From VII, (5.2) we get, therefore, for large r,

$$(5.16) \qquad \mathbf{P}\{B_r\} \leq c^{-1}e^{-\lambda \log \log n_r} = \frac{1}{c(\log n_r)^{\lambda}} \sim \frac{1}{c(r \log \gamma)^{\lambda}}.$$

Since $\lambda > 1$, the assertion (5.13) is proved.

(4) Finally, we prove the assertion concerning (5.4) with $\lambda < 1$. This time we choose for γ an integer so large that

$$(5.17) \qquad \frac{\gamma - 1}{\gamma} > \eta > \lambda$$

where η is a constant to be determined later, and put $n_r = \gamma^r$. The second Borel-Cantelli lemma applies only to independent events, and for this reason we introduce

$$(5.18) \qquad \mathbf{D}_r = \mathbf{S}_{n_r} - \mathbf{S}_{n_{r-1}};$$

$\mathbf{D}_r$ is the total number of successes following trial number n_{r-1} and up to and including trial n_r; for it we have the binomial distribution $b(k; n, p)$ with $n = n_r - n_{r-1}$. Let A_r be the event

$$(5.19) \qquad \mathbf{D}_r - (n_r - n_{r-1})p > \eta\sqrt{2pqn_r \log \log n_r}.$$

We claim that *with probability one infinitely many A_r occur*. Since the various A_r depend on non-overlapping blocks of trials (namely, $n_{r-1} < n \leq n_r$), they are mutually independent, and, according to the second Borel-Cantelli lemma, it suffices to prove that $\sum \mathbf{P}\{A_r\}$ diverges. Now

$$(5.20) \quad \mathbf{P}\{A_r\} = \mathbf{P}\left\{\frac{\mathbf{D}_r - (n_r - n_{r-1})p}{\sqrt{(n_r - n_{r-1})pq}} > \eta\sqrt{2\frac{n_r}{n_r - n_{r-1}} \log \log n_r}\right\}.$$

Here $n_r/(n_r - n_{r-1}) = \gamma/(\gamma - 1) < \eta^{-1}$, by (5.17). Hence

$$(5.21) \qquad \mathbf{P}\{A_r\} \geq \mathbf{P}\left\{\frac{\mathbf{D}_r - (n_r - n_{r-1})p}{\sqrt{(n_r - n_{r-1})pq}} > \sqrt{2\eta \log \log n_r}\right\}.$$

Using again the estimate VII, (6.7) we find for large r

$$(5.22) \qquad \mathbf{P}\{A_r\} > \frac{1}{\log \log n_r} e^{-\eta \log \log n_r} = \frac{1}{(\log \log n_r)(\log n_r)^{\eta}}.$$

Since $n_r = \gamma^r$ and $\eta < 1$, we find that for large r we have $\mathbf{P}\{A_r\} > 1/r$, which proves the divergence of $\sum \mathbf{P}\{A_r\}$.

The last step of the proof consists in showing that $\mathbf{S}_{n_{r-1}}$ in (5.18) can be neglected. From the first part of the theorem, which has already been proved, we know that to every $\epsilon > 0$ we can find an N so that, with probability $1 - \epsilon$ or better, for all $r > N$,

$$(5.23) \qquad |\mathbf{S}_{n_{r-1}} - n_{r-1}p| < 2\sqrt{2pqn_{r-1} \log \log n_{r-1}} \,.$$

Now suppose that η is chosen so close to 1 that

$$(5.24) \qquad 1 - \eta < \left(\frac{\eta - \lambda}{2}\right)^2.$$

Then from (5.17)

$$(5.25) \qquad 4n_{r-1} = 4^r\gamma^{-1} < n_r(\eta-\lambda)^2$$

and hence (5.23) implies

$$(5.26) \qquad \mathbf{S}_{n_{r-1}} - n_{r-1}p > -(\eta-\lambda)\sqrt{2pqn_r \log \log n_r} \,.$$

Adding (5.26) to (5.19), we obtain (5.4) with $n = n_r$. It follows that, with probability $1 - \epsilon$ or better, this inequality holds for infinitely many r, and this accomplishes the proof.   ▶

The law of the iterated logarithm for Bernoulli trials is a special case of a more general theorem first formulated by Kolmogorov.[4] At present it is possible to formulate stronger theorems (cf. problems 7 and 8).

6. INTERPRETATION IN NUMBER THEORY LANGUAGE

Let x be a real number in the interval $0 \leq x < 1$, and let

$$(6.1) \qquad x = .a_1a_2a_3 \cdots$$

be its decimal expansion (so that each a_j stands for one of the digits $0, 1, \ldots, 9$). This expansion is unique except for numbers of the form $a/10^n$ (where a is an integer), which can be written either by means of an expansion containing infinitely many zeros or by means of an expansion containing infinitely many nines. To avoid ambiguities we now agree not to use the latter form.

The decimal expansions are connected with Bernoulli trials with $p = \frac{1}{10}$, the digit 0 representing success and all other digits failure. If we replace in

---

[4] A. Kolmogoroff, *Das Gesetz des iterierten Logarithmus*, Mathematische Annalen, vol. 101 (1929), pp. 126–135.

(6.1) all zeros by the letter S and all other digits by F, then (6.1) represents a possible outcome of an infinite sequence of Bernoulli trials with $p = \frac{1}{10}$. Conversely, an arbitrary sequence of letters S and F can be obtained in the described manner from the expansion of certain numbers x. In this way every event in the sample space of Bernoulli trials is represented by a certain aggregate of numbers x. For example, the event "success at the nth trial" is represented by all those x whose nth decimal is zero. This is an aggregate of 10^{n-1} intervals each of length 10^{-n}, and the total length of these intervals equals $\frac{1}{10}$, which is the probability of our event. Every particular finite sample sequence of length n corresponds to an aggregate of certain intervals; for example, the sequence SFS is represented by the nine intervals $0.01 \leq x < 0.011, 0.02 \leq x < 0.021, \ldots,$ $0.09 \leq x < 0.091$. The probability of each such sample sequence equals the total length of the corresponding intervals on the x-axis. Probabilities of more complicated events are always expressed in terms of probabilities of finite sample sequences, and the calculation proceeds according to the same addition rule that is valid for the familiar Lebesgue measure on the x-axis. Accordingly, our probabilities will always coincide with the measure of the corresponding aggregate of points on the x-axis. We have thus a means of translating all limit theorems for Bernoulli trials with $p = \frac{1}{10}$ into theorems concerning decimal expansions. The phrase "with probability one" is equivalent to "for almost all x" or "almost everywhere."

We have considered the random variable $\mathbf{S}_n$ which gives the number of successes in n trials. Here it is more convenient to emphasize the fact that $\mathbf{S}_n$ is a function of the sample point, and we write $\mathbf{S}_n(x)$ *for the number of zeros among the first n decimals of x.* Obviously the graph of $\mathbf{S}_n(x)$ is a step polygon whose discontinuities are necessarily points of the form $a/10^n$, where a is an integer. The ratio $\mathbf{S}_n(x)/n$ is called the *frequency of zeros* among the first n decimals of x.

In the language of ordinary measure theory the weak law of large numbers asserts that $\mathbf{S}_n(x)/n \to \frac{1}{10}$ in measure, whereas the strong law states that $\mathbf{S}_n(x)/n \to \frac{1}{10}$ almost everywhere. Khintchine's law of the iterated logarithm shows that

$$(6.2) \qquad \limsup \frac{\mathbf{S}_n(x) - n/10}{\sqrt{n \log \log n}} = 0.3\sqrt{2}$$

for almost all x. It gives an answer to a problem treated in a series of papers initiated by Hausdorff[5] (1913) and Hardy and Littlewood[6] (1914). For a further improvement of this result see problems 7 and 8.

[5] F. Hausdorff, *Grundzüge der Mengenlehre*, Leipzig, 1913.

[6] Hardy and Littlewood, *Some problems of Diophantine approximation*, Acta Mathematica. vol. 37 (1914), pp. 155–239.

Instead of the digit zero we may consider any other digit and can formulate the strong law of large numbers to the effect that the frequency of each of the ten digits tends to $\frac{1}{10}$ for almost all x. A similar theorem holds if the base 10 of the decimal system is replaced by any other base. This fact was discovered by Borel (1909) and is usually expressed by saying that almost all numbers are "normal."

7. PROBLEMS FOR SOLUTION

1. Find an integer β such that in rolling dice there are about even chances that a run of three consecutive aces appears before a non-ace run of length β.

2. Consider repeated independent trials with three possible outcomes A, B, C and corresponding probabilities p, q, r $(p + q + r = 1)$. Find the probability that a run of α consecutive A's will occur before a B-run of length β.

3. *Continuation.* Find the probability that an A-run of length α will occur before either a B-run of length β or a C-run of length γ.

4. In a sequence of Bernoulli trials let A_n be the event that a run of n consecutive successes occurs between the 2^nth and the 2^{n+1}st trial. If $p \geq \frac{1}{2}$, there is probability one that infinitely many A_n occur; if $p < \frac{1}{2}$, then with probability one only finitely many A_n occur.

5.[7] Denote by $\mathbf{N}_n$ the length of the success run beginning at the nth trial (i.e., $\mathbf{N}_n = 0$ if the nth trial results in F, etc.). Prove that with probability one

$$(7.1) \qquad\qquad \limsup \frac{\mathbf{N}_n}{\mathrm{Log}\, n} = 1.$$

where Log denotes the logarithm to the basis $1/p$.

Hint: Consider the event A_n that the nth trial is followed by a run of more than $a\,\mathrm{Log}\,n$ successes. For $a > 1$ the calculation is straightforward. For $a < 1$ consider the subsequence of trials number $a_1, a_2, \ldots$ where a_n is an integer very close to $n\,\mathrm{Log}\,n$.

6. From the law of the iterated logarithm conclude: With probability one it will happen for infinitely many n that all $\mathbf{S}_k$ with $n < k < 17n$ are positive. (*Note:* Considerably stronger statements can be proved using the results of chapter III.)

7. Let $\phi(t)$ be a positive monotonically increasing function, and let n_r be the nearest integer to $e^{r/\log r}$. If

$$(7.2) \qquad\qquad \sum \frac{1}{\phi(n_r)} e^{-\frac{1}{2}\phi^2(n_r)}$$

converges, then with probability one, the inequality

$$(7.3) \qquad\qquad \mathbf{S}_n > np + \sqrt{npq}\; \phi(n)$$

---

[7] Suggested by a communication from D. J. Newman.

takes place only for infinitely many n. Note that without loss of generality we may suppose that $\phi(n) < 10\sqrt{\log\log n}$;   the law of the iterated logarithm takes care of the larger $\phi(n)$.

8. Prove[8] that the series (7.2) converges if, and only if,

(7.4)
$$\sum \frac{\phi(n)}{n} e^{-\frac{1}{2}\phi^2(n)}$$

converges. *Hint:* Collect the terms for which $n_{r-1} < n < n_r$ and note that $n_r - n_{r-1} \sim n_r(1 - 1/\log r)$;   furthermore, (7.4) can converge only if $\phi^2(n) > 2\log\log n$.

9. From the preceding problem conclude that with probability one

(7.5)
$$\lim\sup [S_n^* - \sqrt{2\log\log n}\,]\frac{\sqrt{2\log\log n}}{\log\log\log n} = \frac{3}{2}.$$

---

[8] Problems 7 and 8 together show that in case of convergence of (7.4) the inequality (7.3) holds with probability one only for finitely many n. Conversely, if (7.4) diverges, the inequality (7,3) holds with probability one for infinitely many n. This converse is much more difficult to prove; cf. W. Feller, *The general form of the so-called law of the iterated logarithm*, Trans. Amer. Math. Soc., vol. 54 (1943), pp. 373–402, where more general theorems are proved for arbitrary random variables. For the special case of Bernoulli trials with $p = \frac{1}{2}$ cf. P. Erdös, *On the law of the iterated logarithm,* Ann. of Math. (2), vol. 43 (1942), pp. 419–436. The law of the iterated logarithm follows from the particular case $\phi(t) = \lambda\sqrt{2\log\log t}$.

CHAPTER IX

Random Variables; Expectation

1. RANDOM VARIABLES

According to the definition given in calculus textbooks, the quantity y is called a *function* of the real number x if to every x there corresponds a value y. This definition can be extended to cases where the independent variable is not a real number. Thus the distance is a function of a pair of points; the perimeter of a triangle is a function defined on the set of triangles; a sequence $\{a_n\}$ is a function defined for all positive integers; the binomial coefficient $\binom{x}{k}$ is a function defined for pairs of numbers (x, k) of which the second is a non-negative integer. In the same sense we can say that the number S_n of successes in n Bernoulli trials is a function defined on the sample space; to each of the 2^n points in this space there corresponds a number S_n.

A function defined on a sample space is called a random variable. Throughout the preceding chapters we have been concerned with random variables without using this term. Typical random variables are the number of aces in a hand at bridge, of multiple birthdays in a company of n people, of success runs in n Bernoulli trials. In each case there is a unique rule which associates a number X with any sample point. The classical theory of probability was devoted mainly to a study of the gambler's gain, which is again a random variable; in fact, every random variable can be interpreted as the gain of a real or imaginary gambler in a suitable game. The position of a particle under diffusion, the energy, temperature, etc., of physical systems are random variables; but they are defined in non-discrete sample spaces, and their study is therefore deferred. In the case of a discrete sample space we can theoretically tabulate any random variable X by enumerating in some order all points of the space and associating with each the corresponding value of X.

The term random variable is somewhat confusing; random function would be more appropriate (the independent variable being a point in sample space, that is, the outcome of an experiment).

Let **X** be a random variable and let $x_1, x_2, \ldots$ be the values which it assumes;[1] in most of what follows the x_j will be integers. The aggregate of all sample points on which **X** assumes the fixed value x_j forms the event that $\mathbf{X} = x_j$; its probability is denoted by $\mathbf{P}\{\mathbf{X} = x_j\}$. *The function*

$$(1.1) \qquad\qquad \mathbf{P}\{\mathbf{X} = x_j\} = f(x_j) \qquad\qquad (j = 1, 2, \ldots)$$

is called the (probability) distribution[2] of the random variable **X**. Clearly

$$(1.2) \qquad\qquad f(x_j) \geq 0, \qquad \sum f(x_j) = 1.$$

With this terminology we can say that in Bernoulli trials the number of successes $\mathbf{S}_n$ is a random variable with probability distribution $\{b(k; n, p)\}$, whereas the number of trials up to and including the first success is a random variable with the distribution $\{q^{k-1}p\}$.

Consider now two random variables **X** and **Y** defined on the same sample space, and denote the values which they assume, respectively, by $x_1, x_2, \ldots$, and $y_1, y_2, \ldots$; let the corresponding probability distributions be $\{f(x_j)\}$ and $\{g(y_k)\}$. The aggregate of points in which the two conditions $\mathbf{X} = x_j$ and $\mathbf{Y} = y_k$ are satisfied forms an event whose probability will be denoted by $\mathbf{P}\{\mathbf{X} = x_j, \mathbf{Y} = y_k\}$. *The function*

$$(1.3) \qquad \mathbf{P}\{\mathbf{X} = x_j, \mathbf{Y} = y_k\} = p(x_j, y_k) \qquad (j, k = 1, 2, \ldots)$$

is called the joint probability distribution of **X** *and* **Y**. It is best exhibited in the form of a double-entry table as exemplified in tables 1 and 2. Clearly

$$(1.4) \qquad\qquad p(x_j, y_k) \geq 0, \qquad \sum_{j,k} p(x_j, y_k) = 1.$$

---

[1] In the standard mathematical terminology the set of values $x_1, x_2, \ldots$ should be called *the range of* **X**. Unfortunately the statistical literature uses the term range for the difference between the maximum and the minimum of **X**.

[2] For a discrete variable **X** the probability distribution is the function $f(x_j)$ defined on the aggregate of values x_j assumed by **X**. This term must be distinguished from the term "distribution function," which applies to non-decreasing functions which tend to 0 as $x \to -\infty$ and to 1 as $x \to \infty$. The distribution function $F(x)$ of **X** is defined by

$$F(x) = \mathbf{P}\{\mathbf{X} \leq x\} = \sum_{x_j \leq x} f(x_j),$$

the last sum extending over all those x_j which do not exceed x. Thus the distribution function of a variable can be calculated from its probability distribution and vice versa. In this volume we shall not be concerned with distribution functions in general.

TABLE 1
JOINT DISTRIBUTION OF (N, X_1) IN EXAMPLE (a)

N \ X_1	0	1	2	3	Distribution of N
1	2/27	0	0	1/27	1/9
2	6/27	6/27	6/27	0	2/3
3	0	6/27	0	0	2/9
Distribution of X_1	8/27	12/27	6/27	1/27	

$$E(N) = 19/9, \quad E(N^2) = 129/27, \quad \text{Var}(N) = 26/81$$
$$E(X_1) = 1, \quad E(X_1^2) = 45/27, \quad \text{Var}(X_1) = 2/3$$
$$E(NX_1) = 19/9, \quad \text{Cov}(N, X_1) = 0.$$

N is the number of occupied cells, X_1 the number of balls in the first cell when 3 balls are distributed randomly in 3 cells.

TABLE 2
JOINT DISTRIBUTION OF (X_1, X_2) IN EXAMPLE (a)

X_2 \ X_1	0	1	2	3	Distribution of X_2
0	1/27	3/27	3/27	1/27	8/27
1	3/27	6/27	3/27	0	12/27
2	3/27	3/27	0	0	6/27
3	1/27	0	0	0	1/27
Distribution of X_1	8/27	12/27	6/27	1/27	

$$E(X_i) = 1, \quad E(X_i^2) = 45/27, \quad \text{Var}(X_i) = 2/3$$
$$E(X_1X_2) = 2/3, \quad \text{Cov}(X_1, X_2) = -1/3.$$

X_i is the number of balls in the ith cell when 3 balls are distributed randomly in 3 cells.

Moreover, for every fixed j

(1.5) $p(x_j, y_1) + p(x_j, y_2) + p(x_j, y_3) + \cdots = \mathbf{P}\{\mathbf{X} = x_j\} = f(x_j)$

and for every fixed k

(1.6) $p(x_1, y_k) + p(x_2, y_k) + p(x_3, y_k) + \cdots = \mathbf{P}\{\mathbf{Y} = y_k\} = g(y_k)$.

In other words, by adding the probabilities in individual rows and columns, we obtain the probability distributions of $\mathbf{X}$ and $\mathbf{Y}$. They may be exhibited as shown in tables 1 and 2 and are then called *marginal distributions*. The adjective "marginal" refers to the outer appearance in the double-entry table and is also used for stylistic clarity when the joint distribution of two variables as well as their individual (marginal) distributions appear in the same context. Strictly speaking, the adjective "marginal" is redundant.

The notion of joint distribution carries over to *systems of more than two random variables.*

Examples. (*a*) *Random placements of* 3 *balls into* 3 *cells.* We refer to the sample space of 27 points defined formally in table 1 accompanying example I, (2.*a*); to each point we attach probability $\frac{1}{27}$. Let $\mathbf{N}$ denote the number of occupied cells, and for $i = 1, 2, 3$ let $\mathbf{X}_i$ denote the number of balls in the cell number i. These are picturesque descriptions. Formally $\mathbf{N}$ is the function assuming the value 1 on the sample points number 1–3; the value 2 on the points number 4–21; and the value 3 on the points number 22–27. Accordingly, the probability distribution of $\mathbf{N}$ is defined by $\mathbf{P}\{\mathbf{N}=1\} = \frac{1}{9}$, $\mathbf{P}\{\mathbf{N}=2\} = \frac{2}{3}$, $\mathbf{P}\{\mathbf{N}=3\} = \frac{2}{9}$. The joint distributions of $(\mathbf{N}, \mathbf{X}_1)$ and of $(\mathbf{X}_1, \mathbf{X}_2)$ are given in tables 1 and 2.

(*b*) *Multinomial distribution.* There are many situations in which the joint distribution of three random variables is given by the multinomial distribution (see VI, 9), that is,

(1.7)

$$\mathbf{P}\{\mathbf{X}_1 = k_1, \mathbf{X}_2 = k_2, \mathbf{X}_3 = k_3\} = \frac{n!\; p_1^{k_1} p_2^{k_2} p_3^{k_3}(1-p_1-p_2-p_3)^{n-k_1-k_2-k_3}}{k_1!\, k_2!\, k_3!\, (n-k_1-k_2-k_3)!};$$

here k_1, k_2, and k_3 are non-negative integers such that $k_1 + k_2 + k_3 \leq n$. For example if $\mathbf{X}_1$, $\mathbf{X}_2$, and $\mathbf{X}_3$ represent the numbers of ones, twos, and threes scored in n throws of an ideal die, then their joint distribution is given by (1.7) with $p_1 = p_2 = p_3 = \frac{1}{6}$. Again, suppose a sample with replacement is taken from a population consisting of several subpopulations or strata. If $\mathbf{X}_j$ stands for the number of elements in the sample that belong to the jth subpopulation, then the joint distribution of $(\mathbf{X}_1, \mathbf{X}_2, \mathbf{X}_3)$ is of the form (1.7).

To obtain the (marginal) distribution of (X_1, X_2) we have to keep k_1 and k_2 fixed and sum (1.7) over all possible values of k_3, that is, $k_3 = 0, \ldots, n - k_1 - k_2$. Using the binomial theorem we get the trinomial distribution

$$(1.8) \qquad P\{X_1 = k_1, X_2 = k_2\} = \frac{n!\, p_1^{k_1} p_2^{k_2} (1 - p_1 - p_2)^{n-k_1-k_2}}{k_1!\, k_2!\, (n-k_1-k_2)!}.$$

Summing over $k_2 = 0, \ldots, n - k$, we get the distribution of X_1 alone: It reduces to the binomial distribution with $p = p_1$.

(c) *Geometric distributions.* Consider a sequence of Bernoulli trials continued at least as long as necessary to obtain two successes. Let X_1 be the number of failures preceding the first success, and X_2 the number of failures between the first two successes. The joint distribution of (X_1, X_2) is given by

$$(1.9) \qquad P\{X_1 = j, X_2 = k\} = q^{j+k} p^2$$

(see VI, 8). Summing over k we get the obvious geometric distribution for X_1. (This example shows incidentally how the use of random variable avoids difficulties connected with non-denumerable sample spaces.)

(d) *Randomized sampling.* A somewhat surprising result is obtained from a variant of example (b). Suppose that the number of trials is not fixed in advance but depends on the outcome of a chance experiment in such a way that the probability of having exactly n trials equals $e^{-\lambda}\lambda^n/n!$. In other words, the number of trials itself is now a random variable with the Poisson distribution $\{e^{-\lambda}\lambda^n/n!\}$. Given the number n of trials, the event $\{X_1 = k_1, X_2 = k_2, X_3 = k_3\}$ has the (conditional) probability given by the right side in (1.7). To obtain the absolute probability of this event we must multiply the right side in (1.7) by $e^{-\lambda}\lambda^n/n!$ and sum over all possible n. For given k_j it is, of course, necessary that

$$n \geq k_1 + k_2 + k_3.$$

Introducing the difference r as a new summation index we get

$$(1.10) \quad P\{X_1 = k_1, X_2 = k_2, X_3 = k_3\} =$$

$$= e^{-\lambda} \frac{(\lambda p_1)^{k_1} (\lambda p_2)^{k_2} (\lambda p_3)^{k_3}}{k_1!\, k_2!\, k_3!} \sum_{r=0}^{\infty} \frac{\lambda^r (1 - p_1 - p_2 - p_3)^r}{r!}.$$

On the right we recognize the exponential series and we can write the final result in the form

$$(1.11) \quad P\{X_1 = k_1, X_2 = k_2, X_3 = k_3\} =$$

$$= e^{-\lambda p_1} \frac{(\lambda p_1)^{k_1}}{k_1!} \cdot e^{-\lambda p_2} \frac{(\lambda p_2)^{k_2}}{k_2!} \cdot e^{-\lambda p_3} \frac{(\lambda p_3)^{k_3}}{k_3!}.$$

Summation over k_2 and k_3 eliminates the second and third factors, and we see that X_1 itself has a Poisson distribution. The curious fact is that the joint distribution assumes the form of a multiplication table; this will be described by saying that *the three variables* X_j *are mutually independent.* (This example is essentially a reformulation of problem 27 in VI, 10.) ▶

With the notation (1.3) the conditional probability of the event $Y = y_k$, given that $X = x_j$ [with $f(x_j) > 0$], becomes

$$(1.12) \qquad P\{Y = y_k \mid X = x_j\} = \frac{p(x_j, y_k)}{f(x_j)}.$$

In this way a number is associated with every value of X, and so (1.12) defines a function of X. It is called the *conditional distribution of* Y *for given* X, and is denoted by $P\{Y = y_k \mid X\}$. A glance at tables 1 and 2 shows that the conditional probability (1.12) is in general different from $g(y_k)$. This indicates that inference can be drawn from the values of X to those of Y and vice versa; the two variables are (stochastically) *dependent.* The strongest degree of dependence exists when Y is a function of X, that is, when the value of X uniquely determines Y. For example, if a coin is tossed n times and X and Y are the numbers of heads and tails, then $Y = n - X$. Similarly, when $Y = X^2$, we can compute Y from X. In the joint distribution this means that in each row all entries but one are zero. If, on the other hand, $p(x_j, y_k) = f(x_j)g(y_k)$ for all combinations of x_j, y_k, then the events $X = x_j$ and $Y = y_k$ are independent; the joint distribution assumes the form of a multiplication table. In this case we speak of *independent* random variables. They occur in particular in connection with independent trials; for example, the numbers scored in two throws of a die are independent. An example of a different nature is found in example (*d*).

Note that the joint distribution of X and Y determines the distributions of X and Y, but that we cannot calculate the joint distribution of X and Y from their marginal distributions. If two variables X and Y have the same distribution, they may or may not be independent. For example, the two variables X_1 and X_2 in table 2 have the same distribution and are dependent.

All our notions apply also to the case of more than two variables. We recapitulate in the formal

Definition. *A random variable* X *is a function defined on a given sample space, that is, an assignment of a real number to each sample point. The probability distribution of* X *is the function defined in* (1.1). *If two random variables* X *and* Y *are defined on the same sample space, their joint distribution is given by* (1.3) *and assigns probabilities to all combinations*

(x_j, y_k) of values assumed by **X** and **Y**. This notion carries over, in an obvious manner, to any finite set of variables **X, Y, ... , W** defined on the same sample space. These variables are called mutually independent if, for any combination of values $(x, y, \ldots , w)$ assumed by them,

(1.13) $\mathbf{P}\{\mathbf{X} = x, \mathbf{Y} = y, \ldots , \mathbf{W} = w\} =$

$$= \mathbf{P}\{\mathbf{X} = x\}\, \mathbf{P}\{\mathbf{Y} = y\} \cdots \mathbf{P}\{\mathbf{W} = w\}.$$

In V, 4 we have defined the sample space corresponding to n mutually independent trials. Comparing this definition to (1.13), we see that if $\mathbf{X}_k$ depends only on the outcome of the kth trial, then the variables $\mathbf{X}_1, \ldots , \mathbf{X}_n$ are mutually independent. More generally, if a random variable **U** depends only on the outcomes of the first k trials, and another variable **V** depends only on the outcomes of the last $n-k$ trials, then **U** and **V** are independent (cf. problem 39).

We may conceive of a random variable as a labeling of the points of the sample space. This procedure is familiar from dice, where the faces are numbered, and we speak of numbers as the possible outcomes of individual trials. In conventional mathematical terminology we could say that a random variable **X** is a mapping of the original sample space onto a new space whose points are $x_1, x_2, \ldots$. Therefore:

Whenever $\{f(x_j)\}$ satisfies the obvious conditions (1.2) it is legitimate to talk of a random variable **X**, assuming the values $x_1, x_2, \ldots$ with probabilities $f(x_1), f(x_2), \ldots$ without further reference to the old sample space; a new one is formed by the sample points $x_1, x_2, \ldots$ Specifying a probability distribution is equivalent to specifying a sample space whose points are real numbers. Speaking of two independent random variables **X** and **Y** with distributions $\{f(x_j)\}$ and $\{g(y_k)\}$ is equivalent to referring to a sample space whose points are pairs of numbers (x_j, y_k) to which probabilities are assigned by the rule $\mathbf{P}\{(x_j, y_k)\} = f(x_j)g(y_k)$. Similarly, for the sample space corresponding to a set of n random variables $(\mathbf{X}, \mathbf{Y}, \ldots , \mathbf{W})$ we can take an aggregate of points $(x, y, \ldots , w)$ in the n-dimensional space to which probabilities are assigned by the joint distribution. The variables are mutually independent if their joint distribution is given by (1.13).

Example.   (e) Bernoulli trials with variable probabilities. Consider n independent trials, each of which has only two possible outcomes, S and F. The probability of S at the kth trial is p_k, that of F is $q_k = 1 - p_k$. If $p_k = p$, this scheme reduces to Bernoulli trials. The simplest way of describing it is to attribute the values 1 and 0 to S and F. The model is then completely described by saying that we have n mutually independent random variables $\mathbf{X}_k$ with distributions $\mathbf{P}\{\mathbf{X}_k = 1\} = p_k$, $\mathbf{P}\{\mathbf{X}_k = 0\} = q_k$. This scheme is known under the confusing name of "*Poisson trials.*" [See examples (5.b) and XI, (6.b).]   ▶

It is clear that the same distribution can occur in conjunction with different sample spaces. If we say that the random variable **X** assumes the values 0 and 1 with probabilities $\frac{1}{2}$, then we refer tacitly to a sample space consisting of the two points 0 and 1. But the variable **X** might have been defined by stipulating that it equals 0 or 1 according as the tenth tossing of a coin produces heads or tails; in this case **X** is defined in a sample space of sequences $(HHT\ldots)$, and this sample space has 2^{10} points.

In principle, it is possible to restrict the theory of probability to sample spaces defined in terms of probability distributions of random variables. This procedure avoids references to abstract sample spaces and also to terms like "trials" and "outcomes of experiments." The reduction of probability theory to random variables is a short-cut to the use of analysis and simplifies the theory in many ways. However, it also has the drawback of obscuring the probability background. The notion of random variable easily remains vague as "something that takes on different values with different probabilities." But random variables are ordinary functions, and this notion is by no means peculiar to probability theory.

Example. (f) Let **X** be a random variable with possible values $x_1, x_2, \ldots$ and corresponding probabilities $f(x_1), f(x_2), \ldots$ If it helps the reader's imagination, he may always construct a conceptual experiment leading to **X**. For example, subdivide a roulette wheel into arcs $l_1, l_2, \ldots$ whose lengths are as $f(x_1){:}f(x_2){:}\ldots$ Imagine a gambler receiving the (positive or negative) amount x_j if the roulette comes to rest at a point of l_j. Then **X** is the gambler's gain. In n trials, the gains are assumed to be n independent variables with the common distribution $\{f(x_j)\}$. To obtain two variables with a given joint distribution $\{p(x_j, y_k)\}$ let an arc correspond to each combination (x_j, y_k) and think of two gamblers receiving the amounts x_j and y_k, respectively. ▶

If **X, Y, Z,** $\ldots$ are random variables defined on the same sample space, then any function $F(\mathbf{X}, \mathbf{Y}, \mathbf{Z}, \ldots)$ is again a random variable. Its distribution can be obtained from the joint distribution of **X, Y, Z,** $\ldots$ simply by collecting the terms which correspond to combinations of $(\mathbf{X}, \mathbf{Y}, \mathbf{Z}, \ldots)$ giving the same value of $F(\mathbf{X}, \mathbf{Y}, \mathbf{Z}, \ldots)$.

Example. (g) In the example illustrated by table 2 the sum $\mathbf{X}_1 + \mathbf{X}_2$ is a random variable assuming the values 0, 1, 2, 3 with probabilities $\frac{1}{27}, \frac{6}{27}, \frac{12}{27}$, and $\frac{8}{27}$. The product $\mathbf{X}_1\mathbf{X}_2$ assumes the values 0, 1, and 2 with probabilities $\frac{15}{27}, \frac{6}{27}$, and $\frac{6}{27}$.

(h) We return to example (c) and consider various functions of $\mathbf{X}_1$ and $\mathbf{X}_2$. Most interesting is the sum $\mathbf{S} = \mathbf{X}_1 + \mathbf{X}_2$. To obtain $\mathbf{P}\{\mathbf{S} = \nu\}$ we have to sum (1.9) over all values j, k such that $j + k = \nu$. There are

$\nu + 1$ such pairs, and in this special case they all have the same probability $p^\nu q^2$. Thus $P\{X = \nu\} = (\nu+1)q^k p^2$, which is a special case of VI, (8.1).

Next let U be defined as the smaller of the two variables X_1, X_2; in other words, $U = X_1$ if $X_2 \geq X_1$ and $U = X_2$ if $X_2 \leq X_1$. To obtain $P\{U = \nu\}$ we have to sum (1.9) over all pairs (j, k) such that $j = \nu$ and $k \geq \nu$, or else $j > \nu$ and $k = \nu$. This leads to two geometric series and

$$(1.14) \qquad P\{U = \nu\} = \frac{q^{2\nu}p^2}{1 - q} + \frac{q^{2\nu+1}p^2}{1 - q} = q^{2\nu}(1+q)p.$$

Here $\nu = 0, 1, \ldots$.

A similar calculation shows that

$$(1.15) \qquad P\{X_1 - X_2 = \nu\} = \frac{q^{|\nu|}p}{1 + q}, \qquad \nu = 0, \pm 1, \pm 2, \ldots.$$

▶

Note on pairwise independence. As a matter of curiosity we have shown in example V,(3.e) that three events can be pairwise independent without being mutually independent. To formulate an analogous result for random variables we consider the simplest case, namely a sample space consisting of nine points, each carrying probability $\frac{1}{9}$. Six of these points we identify with the various permutations of the numbers 1, 2, 3 while the remaining three points stand for the triples $(1, 1, 1)$, $(2, 2, 2)$, and $(3, 3, 3)$. We now introduce three random variables X_1, X_2, X_3 such that X_k equals the number appearing at the kth place. The possible values of these variables are 1, 2, 3 and it is easily verified that their distributions and joint distributions are given by

$$(1.16) \qquad P\{X_j = r\} = \tfrac{1}{3}, \qquad P\{X_j = r, X_k = s\} = \tfrac{1}{9}.$$

[This differs only notationally from the conclusions in example V, (3.e).] It follows that our three random variables are pairwise independent. On the other hand, the knowledge of X_1 and X_2 uniquely determines X_3, and so the variables are not mutually independent.

To go a step further, define a triple (X_4, X_5, X_6) exactly as the triple (X_1, X_2, X_3) but independent of it. In this way we obtain six pairwise independent variables satisfying (1.16). Continuing in like manner we obtain *a sequence of variables* $X_1, X_2, \ldots, X_n, \ldots$ *satisfying* (1.16) *and such that the* X_k *are pairwise independent without being mutually independent.*[3] We shall return to this example in XV, (13.f).

2. EXPECTATIONS

To achieve reasonable simplicity it is often necessary to describe probability distributions rather summarily by a few "typical values." An example is provided by the median used in the waiting-time problems of

---

[3] The construction can be modified to achieve that no three consecutive variables are independent. Further modifications lead to various counterexamples in the theory of stochastic processes. See W. Feller, *Non-Markovian processes with the semi-group property*, Ann. Math. Statist., vol. 30 (1959), pp. 1252–1253.

II, 7, and the central term of the binomial distribution. Among the typical values the expectation, or mean, is by far the most important. It lends itself best to analytical manipulations, and it is preferred by statisticians because of a property known as sampling stability. Its definition follows the customary notion of an average. If in a certain population n_k families have exactly k children, the total number of families is $n = = n_0 + n_1 + n_2 + \cdots$ and the total number of children

$$m = n_1 + 2n_2 + 3n_3 + \cdots.$$

The average number of children per family is m/n. The analogy between probabilities and frequencies suggests the following

Definition. *Let* X *be a random variable assuming the values* $x_1, x_2, \ldots$ *with corresponding probabilities* $f(x_1), f(x_2), \ldots$ *. The mean or expected value of* X *is defined by*

(2.1) $$E(X) = \sum x_k f(x_k)$$

provided that the series converges absolutely. In this case we say that X *has a finite expectation. If* $\sum |x_k| f(x_k)$ *diverges, then we say that* X *has no finite expectation.*

It is sometimes convenient to think of probabilities intuitively as limits of observable frequencies in repeated experiments. This would lead to the following intuitive interpretation of the expectation. Let an experiment be repeated n times "under identical conditions," and denote by $X_1, \ldots, X_n$ the values of X that were actually observed. For large n the average $(X_1 + \cdots + X_n)/n$ should be close to $E(X)$. The laws of large numbers give substance and precision to this vague intuitive description.

It goes without saying that the most common random variables have finite expectations; otherwise the concept would be impractical. However, variables without finite expectations occur in connection with important recurrence problems in physics. The terms *mean, average,* and *mathematical expectation* are synonymous. We also speak of the *mean of a distribution* instead of referring to a corresponding random variable. The notation $E(X)$ is generally accepted in mathematics and statistics. In physics $\bar{X}$, $\langle X \rangle$, and $\langle X \rangle_{\mathrm{Av}}$ are common substitutes for $E(X)$.

We wish to calculate expectations of functions such as X^2. This function is a new random variable assuming the values x_k^2; in general, the probability of $X^2 = x_k^2$ is not $f(x_k)$ but $f(x_k) + f(-x_k)$ and $E(X^2)$ is defined as the sum of $x_k^2\{f(x_k) + f(-x_k)\}$. Obviously under all circumstances

(2.2) $$E(X^2) = \sum x_k^2 f(x_k)$$

provided the series converges. The same procedure leads to the general

Theorem 1. *Any function $\phi(x)$ defines a new random variable $\phi(\mathbf{X})$. If $\phi(\mathbf{X})$ has finite expectation, then*

$$(2.3) \qquad \mathbf{E}(\phi(\mathbf{X})) = \sum \phi(x_k) f(x_k);$$

the series converges absolutely if, and only if, $\mathbf{E}(\phi(\mathbf{X}))$ exists. For any constant a we have $\mathbf{E}(a\mathbf{X}) = a\mathbf{E}(\mathbf{X})$.

If several random variables $\mathbf{X}_1, \ldots, \mathbf{X}_n$ are defined on the same sample space, then their sum $\mathbf{X}_1 + \cdots + \mathbf{X}_n$ is a new random variable. Its possible values and the corresponding probabilities can be readily found from the joint distribution of the $\mathbf{X}_\nu$ and thus $\mathbf{E}(\mathbf{X}_1 + \cdots + \mathbf{X}_n)$ can be calculated. A simpler procedure is furnished by the following important

Theorem 2. *If $\mathbf{X}_1, \mathbf{X}_2, \ldots, \mathbf{X}_n$ are random variables with expectations, then the expectation of their sum exists and is the sum of their expectations:*

$$(2.4) \qquad \mathbf{E}(\mathbf{X}_1 + \cdots + \mathbf{X}_n) = \mathbf{E}(\mathbf{X}_1) + \cdots + \mathbf{E}(\mathbf{X}_n).$$

Proof. It suffices to prove (2.4) for two variables $\mathbf{X}$ and $\mathbf{Y}$. Using the notation (1.3), we can write

$$(2.5) \qquad \mathbf{E}(\mathbf{X}) + \mathbf{E}(\mathbf{Y}) = \sum_{j,k} x_j p(x_j, y_k) + \sum_{j,k} y_k p(x_j, y_k),$$

the summation extending over all possible values x_j, y_k (which need not be all different). The two series converge absolutely; their sum can therefore be rearranged to give $\sum_{j,k} (x_j + y_k) p(x_j, y_k)$, which is by definition the expectation of $\mathbf{X} + \mathbf{Y}$. This accomplishes the proof. ▶

Clearly, no corresponding general theorem holds for products; for example, $\mathbf{E}(\mathbf{X}^2)$ is generally different from $(\mathbf{E}(\mathbf{X}))^2$. Thus, if $\mathbf{X}$ is the number scored with a balanced die,

$$\mathbf{E}(\mathbf{X}) = \tfrac{7}{2}, \quad \text{but} \quad \mathbf{E}(\mathbf{X}^2) = (1+4+9+16+25+36)/6 = 91/6.$$

However, the simple multiplication rule holds for mutually independent variables.

Theorem 3. *If $\mathbf{X}$ and $\mathbf{Y}$ are mutually independent random variables with finite expectations, then their product is a random variable with finite expectation and*

$$(2.6) \qquad \mathbf{E}(\mathbf{XY}) = \mathbf{E}(\mathbf{X})\mathbf{E}(\mathbf{Y}).$$

Proof. To calculate $E(XY)$ we must multiply each possible value $x_j y_k$ with the corresponding probability. Hence

$$(2.7) \qquad E(XY) = \sum_{j,k} x_j y_k f(x_j) g(y_k) = \left\{ \sum_j x_j f(x_j) \right\} \left\{ \sum_k y_k g(y_k) \right\},$$

the rearrangement being justified since the series converge absolutely. ▶

By induction the same multiplication rule holds for any number of mutually independent random variables.

It is convenient to have a notation also for the expectation of a conditional probability distribution. If X and Y are two random variables with the joint distribution (1.3), the *conditional expectation* $E(Y \mid X)$ *of* Y *for given* X *is the function which at the place* x_j *assumes the value*

$$(2.8) \qquad \sum_k y_k P\{Y = y_k \mid X = x_j\} = \frac{\sum_k y_k p(x_j, y_k)}{f(x_j)} ;$$

this definition is meaningful only if the series converges absolutely and $f(x_j) > 0$ for all j.

The conditional expectation $E(Y \mid X)$ is a new random variable. To calculate its expectation we have to multiply (2.8) by $f(x_j)$ and sum over x_j. The result is

$$(2.9) \qquad E(E(Y \mid X)) = E(Y).$$

3. EXAMPLES AND APPLICATIONS

(*a*) *Binomial distribution.* Let S_n be the number of successes in n Bernoulli trials with probability p for success. We know that S_n has the binomial distribution $\{b(k; n, p)\}$, whence $E(S_n) = \sum k b(k; n, p) = np \sum b(k-1; n-1, p)$. The last sum includes all terms of the binomial distribution for $n - 1$ and hence equals 1. Therefore *the mean of the binomial distribution* is

$$(3.1) \qquad E(S_n) = np.$$

The same result could have been obtained without calculation by a method which is often expedient. Let X_k be the number of successes scored at the kth trial. This random variable assumes only the values 0 and 1 with corresponding probabilities q and p. Hence

$$E(X_k) = 0 \cdot q + 1 \cdot p = p,$$

and since

(3.2) $$\mathbf{S}_n = \mathbf{X}_1 + \mathbf{X}_2 + \cdots + \mathbf{X}_n,$$

we get (3.1) directly from (2.4).

(b) *Poisson distribution.* If $\mathbf{X}$ has the Poisson distribution $p(k; \lambda) = e^{-\lambda}\lambda^k/k!$ (where $k = 0, 1, \ldots$) then

$$\mathbf{E}(\mathbf{X}) = \sum kp(k; \lambda) = \lambda \sum p(k-1; \lambda).$$

The last series contains all terms of the distribution and therefore adds to unity. Accordingly, *the Poisson distribution* $\{e^{-\lambda}\lambda^k/k!\}$ *has the mean* λ.

(c) *Negative binomial distribution.* Let $\mathbf{X}$ be a variable with the *geometric distribution* $\mathbf{P}\{\mathbf{X} = k\} = q^k p$ where $k = 0, 1, 2, \ldots$. Then $\mathbf{E}(\mathbf{X}) = qp(1+2q+3q^2+\cdots)$. On the right we have the derivative of a geometric series so that $\mathbf{E}(\mathbf{X}) = qp(1-q)^{-2} = q/p$. We have seen in VI, 8, that $\mathbf{X}$ may be interpreted as the number of failures preceding the first success in a sequence of Bernoulli trials. More generally, we have studied the sample space corresponding to Bernoulli trials which are continued until the nth success. For $r < n$, let $\mathbf{X}_1 = \mathbf{X}$, and let $\mathbf{X}_r$ be the number of failures between the $(r-1)$st and the rth success. Then each $\mathbf{X}_\nu$ has the geometric distribution $\{q^k p\}$, and $\mathbf{E}(\mathbf{X}_\nu) = q/p$. The sum

$$\mathbf{Y}_r = \mathbf{X}_1 + \cdots + \mathbf{X}_r$$

is the number of failures preceding the rth success. In other words, $\mathbf{Y}_r$ is a random variable whose distribution is the negative binomial defined by either of the two equivalent formulas VI, (8.1) or VI, (8.2). It follows that *the mean of this negative binomial is* rq/p. This can be verified by direct computation. From VI, (8.2) it is clear that

$$kf(k; r, p) = rp^{-1}qf(k-1; r+1, p),$$

and the terms of the distribution $\{f(k-1; r+1, p)\}$ add to unity. This direct calculation has the advantage that it applies also to *non-integral* r. On the other hand, the first argument leads to the result without requiring knowledge of the explicit form of the distribution of $\mathbf{X}_1 + \cdots + \mathbf{X}_r$.

(d) *Waiting times in sampling.* A population of N distinct elements is sampled with replacement. Because of repetitions a random sample of size r will in general contain fewer than r distinct elements. As the sample size increases, new elements will enter the sample more and more rarely. We are interested in the sample size $\mathbf{S}_r$ necessary for the acquisition of r distinct elements. (As a special case, consider the population of $N = 365$ possible birthdays; here $\mathbf{S}_r$ represents the number of people

sampled up to the moment where the sample contains r different birthdays. A similar interpretation is possible with random placements of balls
into cells. Our problem is of particular interest to collectors of coupons
and other items where the acquisition can be compared to random
sampling.[4])

To simplify language let us call a drawing successful if it results in
adding a new element to the sample. Then $\mathbf{S}_r$ is the number of drawings
up to and including the rth success. Put $\mathbf{X}_k = \mathbf{S}_{k+1} - \mathbf{S}_k$. Then $\mathbf{X}_k - 1$
is the number of unsuccessful drawings between the kth and $(k+1)$st
success. During these drawings the population contains $N - k$ elements
that have not yet entered the sample, and so $\mathbf{X}_k - 1$ is the number of
failures preceding the first success in Bernoulli trials with $p = (N-k)/N$.
In accordance with example (c) therefore $\mathbf{E}(\mathbf{X}_k) = 1 + q/p = N/(N-k)$.
Since $\mathbf{S}_r = 1 + \mathbf{X}_1 + \cdots + \mathbf{X}_r$ we get finally

$$(3.3) \qquad \mathbf{E}(\mathbf{S}_r) = N\left\{\frac{1}{N} + \frac{1}{N-1} + \cdots + \frac{1}{N-r+1}\right\}.$$

In particular, $\mathbf{E}(\mathbf{S}_N)$ is the expected number of drawings necessary to
exhaust the entire population. For $N = 10$ we have $\mathbf{E}(\mathbf{S}_5) \approx 6.5$ and
$\mathbf{E}(\mathbf{S}_{10}) \approx 29.3$. This means that, on the average, seven drawings suffice
to cover the first half of a population of 10, but the second half will require
an average of some 23 drawings.

To obtain an approximation to (3.3) we interpret $(N-k)^{-1}$ as area of
a rectangle whose basis is a unit interval centered at $N - k$, and whose
height is the ordinate of x^{-1} at that point. Replacing the area of this
rectangle by the area under the graph of x^{-1} we get the approximation

$$(3.4) \qquad \mathbf{E}(\mathbf{S}_r) \approx N \int_{N-r+\frac{1}{2}}^{N+\frac{1}{2}} x^{-1}\,dx = N \log \frac{N + \frac{1}{2}}{N - r + \frac{1}{2}}.$$

As an application choose $\alpha < 1$ arbitrary and consider the *expected
number of drawings to obtain a sample containing the fraction* α *of the
entire population.* This equals $\mathbf{E}(\mathbf{S}_r)$ when r is the smallest integer
$\geq \alpha N$. When $N \to \infty$ the error committed in (3.4) tends to 0, and we find
for the desired expectation in the limit $N \log (1-\alpha)^{-1}$. Note that all
these results are obtained without use of the probability distribution itself.
[The latter can be derived easily from the occupancy probabilities found
in IV, (2.3).]

---

[4] G. Polya, *Eine Wahrscheinlichkeitsaufgabe zur Kundenwerbung*, Zeitschrift für Angewandte Mathematik und Mechanik, vol. 10 (1930), pp. 96–97. Polya treats a slightly
more general problem with different methods. There exists a huge literature treating
variants of the coupon collector's problem. (Cf. problems 24, 25; problems 12–14 in
XI,7; and 12 in II,11.)

(e) *An estimation problem.* An urn contains balls numbered 1 to N. Let $\mathbf{X}$ *be the largest number drawn in* n drawings when random sampling with replacement is used. The event $\mathbf{X} \leq k$ means that each of n numbers drawn is less than or equal to k and therefore $\mathbf{P}\{\mathbf{X} \leq k\} = (k/N)^n$. Hence the probability distribution of $\mathbf{X}$ is given by

$$(3.5) \qquad p_k = \mathbf{P}\{\mathbf{X} = k\} = \mathbf{P}\{\mathbf{X} \leq k\} - \mathbf{P}\{\mathbf{X} \leq k - 1\} =$$
$$= \{k^n - (k-1)^n\}N^{-n}.$$

It follows that

$$(3.6) \qquad \mathbf{E}(\mathbf{X}) = \sum_{k=1}^{N} k p_k = N^{-n} \sum_{k=1}^{N} \{k^{n+1} - (k-1)^{n+1} - (k-1)^n\} =$$
$$= N^{-n}\left\{N^{n+1} - \sum_{k=1}^{N}(k-1)^n\right\}.$$

For large N the last sum is approximately the area under the curve $y = x^n$ from $x = 0$ to $x = N$, that is, $N^{n+1}/(n+1)$. It follows that for large N

$$(3.7) \qquad\qquad\qquad \mathbf{E}(\mathbf{X}) \approx \frac{n}{n+1}\, N.$$

If a town has $N = 1000$ cars and a sample of $n = 10$ is observed, the expected number of the highest observed license plate (assuming randomness) is about 910. The practical statistician uses the observed maximum in a sample to estimate the unknown true number N. This method was used during the last war to estimate enemy production (cf. problems 8–9.)

(f) *Application to a statistical test.* This example[5] illustrates the practical use of expectations to avoid cumbersome calculations of probability distributions.

Spores of the fungus Sordaria are produced in chains of eight. The chain may break into several parts, and ultimately the spores escape in projectiles containing from 1 to 8 spores. There are reasons to suppose that the breakages at the seven links are stochastically independent and that the links have the same probability p to break. Under this hypothesis it is theoretically possible to calculate the joint distribution of singlets, doublets, etc., but this would involve tedious calculations. On the other hand, for an empirical test of the hypothesis it suffices to know the expected numbers of singlets, doublets, etc., and these are easily found.

---

[5] Taken from the Inaugural Address of D. R. Cox at Birbeck College (London) 1961. Cox refers to C. T. Ingold and S. A. Hadland, New Phytologist, vol. 58 (1959), pp. 46–57.

For example, the spores located at the ends of the chain have probability p to become singlets whereas for all other spores this probability equals p^2. By the addition rule therefore the expected number of singlets arising from one chain is given by $\epsilon_1 = 2p + 6p^2$. A similar argument shows that the expected number of doublets is $\epsilon_2 = 2qp + 5qp^2$ where $q = 1 - p$. In like manner $\epsilon_3 = 2q^2p + 4q^2p^2, \ldots, \epsilon_8 = q^7$. The expected number of projectiles is $\epsilon_1 + \cdots + \epsilon_8 = 1 + 7p$. (This is obvious without calculations because the expected number of breaks equals $7p$, and each break increases the number of projectiles by 1.)

TABLE 3

OBSERVED NUMBERS f_k AND EXPECTED NUMBERS $N\epsilon_k$
OF PROJECTILES OF SIZE k IN EXAMPLE (f)

k	f_k	$N\epsilon_k$	k	f_k	$N\epsilon_k$
1	490	458.3	5	200	170.6
2	343	360.8	6	134	131.7
3	265	281.8	7	72	101.1
4	199	219.7	8	272	250.3

In an actual field observation a total of 7251 spores were counted, apparently coming from a total of $N = 907$ chains (with 5 spores undetected). If our probabilistic model is applicable we should have approximately $(1+7p)N = 7251$, or $p = 0.168$. (This argument depends on the intuitive meaning of expectation, to be justified by the weak law of large numbers.) The observed number f_k of projectiles should be close to the expected number $N\epsilon_k$. As table 3 shows, the discrepancies were not startling and there is no reason to reject the model.   ▶

4. THE VARIANCE

Let $\mathbf{X}$ be a random variable with distribution $\{f(x_j)\}$, and let $r \geq 0$ be an integer. *If the expectation of the random variable* $\mathbf{X}^r$, *that is,*

$$(4.1) \qquad E(\mathbf{X}^r) = \sum x_j^r f(x_j),$$

exists, then it is called the rth moment of $\mathbf{X}$ *about the origin.* If the series does not converge absolutely, we say that the rth moment does not exist. Since $|\mathbf{X}|^{r-1} \leq |\mathbf{X}|^r + 1$, it follows that *whenever the rth moment exists so does the* $(r-1)$st, *and hence all preceding moments.*

Moments play an important role in the general theory, but in the present volume we shall use only the second moment. If it exists, so does the mean

$$(4.2) \qquad \mu = E(\mathbf{X}).$$

It is then natural to replace the random variable $\mathbf{X}$ by its *deviation from the mean*, $\mathbf{X} - \mu$. Since $(x-\mu)^2 \leq 2(x^2+\mu^2)$ the second moment of $\mathbf{X} - \mu$ exists whenever $\mathbf{E}(\mathbf{X}^2)$ exists. It is given by

$$(4.3) \qquad \mathbf{E}((\mathbf{X}-\mu)^2) = \sum_j (x_j^2 - 2\mu x_j + \mu^2) f(x_j).$$

Splitting the right side into three individual sums, we find it equal to $\mathbf{E}(\mathbf{X}^2) - 2\mu\mathbf{E}(\mathbf{X}) + \mu^2 = \mathbf{E}(\mathbf{X}^2) - \mu^2$.

Definition. *Let $\mathbf{X}$ be a random variable with second moment $\mathbf{E}(\mathbf{X}^2)$ and let $\mu = \mathbf{E}(\mathbf{X})$ be its mean. We define a number called the variance of $\mathbf{X}$ by*

$$(4.4) \qquad \mathrm{Var}\,(\mathbf{X}) = \mathbf{E}((\mathbf{X}-\mu)^2) = \mathbf{E}(\mathbf{X}^2) - \mu^2.$$

Its positive square root (or zero) is called the standard deviation of $\mathbf{X}$.

For simplicity we often speak of the variance of a distribution without mentioning the random variable. "Dispersion" is a synonym for the now generally accepted term "variance."

Examples. (*a*) If $\mathbf{X}$ assumes the values $\pm c$, each with probability $\frac{1}{2}$, then $\mathrm{Var}\,(\mathbf{X}) = c^2$.

(*b*) If $\mathbf{X}$ is the number of points scored with a symmetric die, then $\mathrm{Var}\,(\mathbf{X}) = \frac{1}{6}(1^2+2^2+ \cdots +6^2) - (\frac{7}{2})^2 = \frac{35}{12}$.

(*c*) For the *Poisson distribution* $p(k;\lambda)$ the mean is λ [cf. example (3.*b*)] and hence the variance $\sum k^2 p(k;\lambda) - \lambda^2 = \lambda \sum kp(k-1;\lambda) - \lambda^2 = \lambda \sum (k-1)p(k-1;\lambda) + \lambda \sum p(k-1;\lambda) - \lambda^2 = \lambda^2 + \lambda - \lambda^2 = \lambda$. In this case mean and variance are equal.

(*d*) For the *binomial distribution* [cf. example (3.*a*)] a similar computation shows that the variance is

$$\sum k^2 b(k;n,p) - (np)^2 = np \sum kb(k-1;n-1,p) - (np)^2 =$$
$$= np\{(n-1)p + 1\} - (np)^2 = npq. \quad \blacktriangleright$$

The usefulness of the notion of variance will appear only gradually, in particular, in connection with limit theorems of chapter X. Here we observe that the variance is a rough *measure of spread*. In fact, if $\mathrm{Var}\,(\mathbf{X}) = \sum (x_j-\mu)^2 f(x_j)$ is small, then each term in the sum is small. A value x_j for which $|x_j - \mu|$ is large must therefore have a small probability $f(x_j)$. In other words, in case of small variance large deviations of $\mathbf{X}$ from the mean μ are improbable. Conversely, a large variance indicates that not all values assumed by $\mathbf{X}$ lie near the mean.

Some readers may be helped by the following interpretation in mechanics. Suppose that a unit mass is distributed on the x-axis so that the mass $f(x_j)$ is concentrated at the point x_j. Then the mean μ is the abscissa of the *center of gravity*, and the variance is the *moment of inertia*. Clearly different mass distributions may have the same center of gravity and the same moment of inertia, but it is well known that some important mechanical properties can be described in terms of these two quantities.

If **X** represents a measurable quantity like length or temperature, then its numerical values depend on the origin and the unit of measurement. A change of the latter means passing from **X** to a new variable $a\mathbf{X} + b$, where a and b are constants. Clearly Var $(\mathbf{X}+b) =$ Var $(\mathbf{X})$, and hence

$$(4.5) \qquad \text{Var } (a\mathbf{X}+b) = a^2 \text{ Var } (\mathbf{X}).$$

The choice of the origin and unit of measurement is to a large degree arbitrary, and often it is most convenient to take the mean as origin and the standard deviation as unit. We have done so in VII, 3 when we introduced the normalized number of successes $\mathbf{S}_n^* = (\mathbf{S}_n - np)/\sqrt{npq}$. In general, if **X** has mean μ and variance σ^2, then $\mathbf{X} - \mu$ has mean zero and variance σ^2, and hence *the variable*

$$(4.6) \qquad \mathbf{X}^* = (\mathbf{X}-\mu)/\sigma \qquad\qquad (\sigma > 0)$$

has mean 0 and variance 1. It is called the normalized variable corresponding to **X**. In the physicist's language, the passage from **X** to **X*** would be interpreted as the introduction of dimensionless quantities.

5. COVARIANCE; VARIANCE OF A SUM

Let **X** and **Y** be two random variables on the same sample space. Then $\mathbf{X} + \mathbf{Y}$ and **XY** are again random variables, and their distributions can be obtained by a simple rearrangement of the joint distribution of **X** and **Y**. Our aim now is to calculate Var $(\mathbf{X}+\mathbf{Y})$. For that purpose we introduce the notion of covariance, which will be analyzed in greater detail in section 8. If the joint distribution of **X** and **Y** is $\{p(x_j, y_k)\}$, then the expectation of **XY** is given by

$$(5.1) \qquad \mathbf{E}(\mathbf{XY}) = \sum x_j y_k p(x_j, y_k),$$

provided, of course, that the series converges absolutely. Now $|x_j y_k| \leq \leq (x_j^2 + y_k^2)/2$ and therefore $\mathbf{E}(\mathbf{XY})$ certainly exists if $\mathbf{E}(\mathbf{X}^2)$ and $\mathbf{E}(\mathbf{Y}^2)$ exist. In this case there exist also the expectations

$$(5.2) \qquad \mu_x = \mathbf{E}(\mathbf{X}), \qquad \mu_y = \mathbf{E}(\mathbf{Y}),$$

and the variables $\mathbf{X} - \mu_x$ and $\mathbf{Y} - \mu_y$ have means zero. For their product we have from the addition rule of section 2

$$(5.3) \quad \mathbf{E}((\mathbf{X}-\mu_x)(\mathbf{Y}-\mu_y)) = \mathbf{E}(\mathbf{XY}) - \mu_x\mathbf{E}(\mathbf{Y}) - \mu_y\mathbf{E}(\mathbf{X}) + \mu_x\mu_y =$$
$$= \mathbf{E}(\mathbf{XY}) - \mu_x\mu_y.$$

Definition. *The covariance of* **X** *and* **Y** *is defined by*

$$(5.4) \qquad \text{Cov}(\mathbf{X}, \mathbf{Y}) = \mathbf{E}((\mathbf{X}-\mu_x)(\mathbf{Y}-\mu_y)) = \mathbf{E}(\mathbf{XY}) - \mu_x\mu_y.$$

This definition is meaningful whenever **X** *and* **Y** *have finite variances.*

We know from section 2 that for independent variables $\mathbf{E}(\mathbf{XY}) = \mathbf{E}(\mathbf{X})\mathbf{E}(\mathbf{Y})$. Hence from (5.4) we have

Theorem 1. *If* **X** *and* **Y** *are independent, then* $\text{Cov}(\mathbf{X}, \mathbf{Y}) = 0$.

Note that *the converse is not true*. For example, a glance at table 1 shows that the two variables are dependent, but their covariance vanishes nevertheless. We shall return to this point in section 8. The next theorem is important, and the addition rule (5.6) for independent variables is constantly applied.

Theorem 2. *If* $\mathbf{X}_1, \ldots, \mathbf{X}_n$ *are random variables with finite variances* $\sigma_1^2, \ldots, \sigma_n^2$, *and* $\mathbf{S}_n = \mathbf{X}_1 + \cdots + \mathbf{X}_n$, *then*

$$(5.5) \qquad \text{Var}(\mathbf{S}_n) = \sum_{k=1}^{n} \sigma_k^2 + 2 \sum_{j,k} \text{Cov}(\mathbf{X}_j, \mathbf{X}_k)$$

the last sum extending over each of the $\binom{n}{2}$ *pairs* $(\mathbf{X}_j, \mathbf{X}_k)$ *with* $j < k$.

In particular, if the $\mathbf{X}_j$ *are mutually independent,*

$$(5.6) \qquad \text{Var}(\mathbf{S}_n) = \sigma_1^2 + \sigma_2^2 + \cdots + \sigma_n^2.$$

Proof. Put $\mu_k = \mathbf{E}(\mathbf{X}_k)$ and $m_n = \mu_1 + \cdots + \mu_n = \mathbf{E}(\mathbf{S}_n)$. Then $\mathbf{S}_n - m_n = \sum(\mathbf{X}_k-\mu_k)$ and

$$(5.7) \qquad (\mathbf{S}_n-m_n)^2 = \sum(\mathbf{X}_k-\mu_k)^2 + 2\sum(\mathbf{X}_j-\mu_j)(\mathbf{X}_k-\mu_k).$$

Taking expectations, we get (5.5). ▶

Examples. *(a) Binomial distribution* $\{b(k; n, p)\}$. In example (3.a), the variables $\mathbf{X}_k$ are mutually independent. We have

$$\mathbf{E}(\mathbf{X}_k^2) = 0^2 \cdot q + 1^2 \cdot p = p,$$

and $\mathbf{E}(\mathbf{X}_k) = p$. Hence $\sigma_k^2 = p - p^2 = pq$, and from (5.6) we see that *the variance of the binomial distribution* is npq. The same result was derived by direct computation in example (4.d).

(b) Bernoulli trials with variable probabilities. Let $\mathbf{X}_1, \ldots, \mathbf{X}_n$ be mutually independent random variables such that $\mathbf{X}_k$ assumes the values 1 and 0 with probabilities p_k and $q_k = 1 - p_k$ respectively. Then

$E(X_k) = p_k$ and $\text{Var}(X_k) = p_k - p_k^2 = p_k q_k$. Putting again

$$S_n = X_1 + \cdots + X_n$$

we have from (5.6)

(5.8) $$\text{Var}(S_n) = \sum_{k=1}^{n} p_k q_k.$$

As in example (1.e) the variable S_n may be interpreted as the total number of successes in n independent trials, each of which results in success or failure. Then $p = (p_1 + \cdots + p_n)/n$ is the average probability of success, and it seems natural to compare the present situation to Bernoulli trials with the constant probability of success p. Such a comparison leads us to a striking result. We may rewrite (5.8) in the form

$$\text{Var}(S_n) = np - \sum p_k^2.$$

Next, it is easily seen (by elementary calculus or induction) that among all combinations $\{p_k\}$ such that $\sum p_k = np$ the sum $\sum p_k^2$ assumes its minimum value when all p_k are equal. It follows that, if the average probability of success p is kept constant, $\text{Var}(S_n)$ *assumes its maximum value when* $p_1 = \cdots = p_n = p$. We have thus the surprising result that the *variability of* p_k, *or lack of uniformity, decreases the magnitude of chance fluctuations* as measured by the variance.[6] For example, the number of annual fires in a community may be treated as a random variable; for a given average number, the variability is *maximal* if all households have the *same* probability of fire. Given a certain average quality p of n machines, the *output will be least uniform if all machines are equal*. (An application to modern education is obvious but hopeless.)

(c) *Card matching.* A deck of n numbered cards is put into random order so that all $n!$ arrangements have equal probabilities. The number of matches (cards in their natural place) is a random variable S_n which assumes the values $0, 1, \ldots, n$. Its probability distribution was derived in IV, 4. From it the mean and variance could be obtained, but the following way is simpler and more instructive.

Define a random variable X_k which is either 1 or 0, according as card number k is or is not at the kth place. Then $S_n = X_1 + \cdots + X_n$. Now each card has probability $1/n$ to appear at the kth place. Hence $P\{X_k = 1\} = 1/n$ and $P\{X_k = 0\} = (n-1)/n$. Therefore $E(X_k) = 1/n$, and it follows that $E(S_n) = 1$: the average is one match per deck. To

---

[6] For stronger results in the same direction see W. Hoeffding, *On the distribution of the number of successes in independent trials*, Ann. Math. Statist., vol. 27 (1956), pp. 713–721. For an approximation by Poisson distributions see example XI, (6.b).

find $\text{Var}(S_n)$ we first calculate the variance σ_k^2 of X_k:

(5.9) $$\sigma_k^2 = \frac{1}{n} - \left(\frac{1}{n}\right)^2 = \frac{n-1}{n^2}.$$

Next we calculate $E(X_j X_k)$. The product $X_j X_k$ is 0 or 1; the latter is true if both card number j and card number k are at their proper places, and the probability for that is $1/n(n-1)$. Hence

(5.10) $$E(X_j X_k) = \frac{1}{n(n-1)},$$

$$\text{Cov}(X_j, X_k) = \frac{1}{n(n-1)} - \frac{1}{n^2} = \frac{1}{n^2(n-1)}.$$

Thus finally

(5.11) $$\text{Var}(S_n) = n\frac{n-1}{n^2} + 2\binom{n}{2}\frac{1}{n^2(n-1)} = 1.$$

We see that both mean and variance of the number of matches are equal to one. This result may be applied to the problem of *card guessing* discussed in IV, 4. There we considered three methods of guessing, one of which corresponds to card matching. The second can be described as a sequence of n Bernoulli trials with probability $p = 1/n$, in which case the expected number of correct guesses is $np = 1$ and the variance $npq = (n-1)/n$. The expected numbers are the same in both cases, but the larger variance with the first method indicates greater chance fluctuations about the mean and thus promises a slightly more exciting game. (With more complicated decks of cards the difference between the two variances is somewhat larger but never really big.) With the last mode of guessing the subject keeps calling the same card; the number of correct guesses is necessarily one, and chance fluctuations are completely eliminated (variance 0). We see that the strategy of calling cannot influence the expected number of correct guesses but has some influence on the magnitude of chance fluctuations.

(d) *Sampling without replacement.* Suppose that a population consists of b black and g green elements, and that a random sample of size r is taken (without repetitions). The number S_k of black elements in the sample is a random variable with the *hypergeometric distribution* (see II, 6) from which the mean and the variance can be obtained by direct computation. However, the following method is preferable. Define the random variable X_k to assume the values 1 or 0 according as the kth element in the sample is or is not black $(k \leq r)$. For reasons of symmetry the probability that $X_k = 1$ is $b/(b+g)$, and hence

$$(5.12) \qquad E(X_k) = \frac{b}{b+g}, \qquad \text{Var}(X_k) = \frac{bg}{(b+g)^2}.$$

Next, if $j \neq k$, then $X_j X_k = 1$ if the jth and kth elements of the sample are black, and otherwise $X_j X_k = 0$. The probability of $X_j X_k = 1$ is $b(b-1)/(b+g)(b+g-1)$, and therefore

$$(5.13) \qquad E(X_j X_k) = \frac{b(b-1)}{(b+g)(b+g-1)},$$

$$\text{Cov}(X_j X_k) = \frac{-bg}{(b+g)^2(b+g-1)}.$$

Thus

$$(5.14) \qquad E(S_r) = \frac{rb}{b+g}, \qquad \text{Var}(S_r) = \frac{rbg}{(b+g)^2}\left\{1 - \frac{r-1}{b+g-1}\right\}.$$

In sampling with replacement we would have the same mean, but the variance would be slightly larger, namely, $rbg/(b+g)^2$. ▶

6. CHEBYSHEV'S INEQUALITY[7]

We saw that a small variance indicates that large deviations from the mean are improbable. This statement is made more precisely by Chebyshev's inequality, which is an exceedingly useful tool. It presupposes the existence of a second moment.

Theorem. *For any* $t > 0$

$$(6.1) \qquad P\{|X| \geq t\} \leq t^{-2} E(X^2).$$

In particular, if $E(X) = \mu$ *then*

$$(6.2) \qquad P\{X - \mu| \geq t\} < t^{-2} \text{Var}(X).$$

Proof. The second inequality is obtained by applying the first to the variable $X - \mu$. Using the notations of section 4 we have

$$(6.3) \qquad P\{|X| > t\} = \sum_{|x_j| \geq t} f(x_j) \leq t^{-2} \sum_{|x_j| \geq t} x_j^2 f(x_j)$$

the sums extending over those x_j that exceed t in absolute value. The last sum is $\leq E(X^2)$, and so (6.1) is true. ▶

---

[7] P. L. Chebyshev (1821–1894).

Chebyshev's inequality must be regarded as a theoretical tool rather than a practical method of estimation. Its importance is due to its universality, but no statement of great generality can be expected to yield sharp results in individual cases.

Examples. (a) If $\mathbf{X}$ is the number scored in a throw of a true die, then [cf. example (4.b)], $\mu = \frac{7}{2}$, $\sigma^2 = \frac{35}{12}$. The maximum deviation of $\mathbf{X}$ from μ is $2.5 \approx 3\sigma/2$. The probability of greater deviations is zero, whereas Chebyshev's inequality only asserts that this probability is smaller than 0.47.

(b) For the binomial distribution $\{b(k; n, p)\}$ we have [cf. example (5.a)] $\mu = np$, $\sigma^2 = npq$. For large n we know that

(6.4) $$\mathbf{P}\{|\mathbf{S}_n - np| > x\sqrt{npq}\} \approx 1 - \mathfrak{N}(x) + \mathfrak{N}(-x).$$

Chebyshev's inequality states only that the left side is less than x^{-2}; this is obviously a much poorer estimate than (6.4).

*7. KOLMOGOROV'S INEQUALITY

As an example of more refined methods we prove:

Let $\mathbf{X}_1, \ldots, \mathbf{X}_n$ *be mutually independent variables with expectations* $\mu_k = \mathbf{E}(\mathbf{X}_k)$ *and variances* σ_k^2. *Put*

(7.1) $$\mathbf{S}_k = \mathbf{X}_1 + \cdots + \mathbf{X}_k$$

(7.2) $$m_k = \mathbf{E}(\mathbf{S}_k) = \mu_1 + \cdots + \mu_k,$$

$$s_k^2 = \mathrm{Var}\,(\mathbf{S}_k) = \sigma_1^2 + \cdots + \sigma_k^2.$$

For every $t > 0$ *the probability of the simultaneous realization of the* n *inequalities*

(7.3) $$|\mathbf{S}_k - m_k| < t s_n, \qquad k = 1, 2, \ldots, n,$$

is at least $1 - t^{-2}$.

For $n = 1$ this theorem reduces to Chebyshev's inequality. For $n > 1$ Chebyshev's inequality gives the same bound for the probability of the single relation $|\mathbf{S}_n - m_n| < t s_n$, so that Kolmogorov's inequality is considerably stronger.

Proof. We want to estimate the probability x that at least one of the inequalities (7.3) does not hold. The theorem asserts that $x \leq t^{-2}$.

---

* This section treats a special topic and should be omitted at first reading.

Define n random variables $\mathbf{Y}_v$ as follows: $\mathbf{Y}_v = 1$ if

(7.4)
$$|\mathbf{S}_v - m_v| \geq t s_n$$

but

(7.5)
$$|\mathbf{S}_k - m_k| < t s_n \qquad \text{for} \quad k = 1, 2, \ldots, v-1;$$

$\mathbf{Y}_v = 0$ for all other sample points. In words, $\mathbf{Y}_v$ equals 1 at those points in which the vth of the inequalities (7.3) is the *first* to be violated. Then at any particular sample point at most one among the $\mathbf{Y}_k$ is 1, and the sum $\mathbf{Y}_1 + \mathbf{Y}_2 + \cdots + \mathbf{Y}_n$ can assume only the values 0 or 1; it is 1 if, and only if, at least one of the inequalities (7.3) is violated, and therefore

(7.6)
$$x = P\{\mathbf{Y}_1 + \cdots + \mathbf{Y}_n = 1\}.$$

Since $\mathbf{Y}_1 + \cdots + \mathbf{Y}_n$ is 0 or 1, we have $\sum \mathbf{Y}_k \leq 1$. Multiplying by $(\mathbf{S}_n - m_n)^2$ and taking expectations, we get

(7.7)
$$\sum_{k=1}^{n} \mathbf{E}(\mathbf{Y}_k(\mathbf{S}_n - m_n)^2) \leq s_n^2.$$

For an evaluation of the terms on the left we put

(7.8)
$$\mathbf{U}_k = (\mathbf{S}_n - m_n) - (\mathbf{S}_k - m_k) = \sum_{v=k+1}^{n} (\mathbf{X}_v - \mu_v).$$

Then

(7.9) $$\mathbf{E}(\mathbf{Y}_k(\mathbf{S}_n - m_n)^2) = \mathbf{E}(\mathbf{Y}_k(\mathbf{S}_k - m_k)^2) + 2\mathbf{E}(\mathbf{Y}_k \mathbf{U}_k(\mathbf{S}_k - m_k)) + \mathbf{E}(\mathbf{Y}_k \mathbf{U}_k^2).$$

Now, $\mathbf{U}_k$ depends only on $\mathbf{X}_{k+1}, \ldots, \mathbf{X}_n$ while $\mathbf{Y}_k$ and $\mathbf{S}_k$ depend only on $\mathbf{X}_1, \ldots, \mathbf{X}_k$. Hence $\mathbf{U}_k$ is independent of $\mathbf{Y}_k(\mathbf{S}_k - m_k)$ and therefore $\mathbf{E}(\mathbf{Y}_k \mathbf{U}_k(\mathbf{S}_k - m_k)) = \mathbf{E}(\mathbf{Y}_k(\mathbf{S}_k - m_k))\mathbf{E}(\mathbf{U}_k) = 0$, since $\mathbf{E}(\mathbf{U}_k) = 0$. Thus from (7.9)

(7.10)
$$\mathbf{E}(\mathbf{Y}_k(\mathbf{S}_n - m_n)^2) \geq \mathbf{E}(\mathbf{Y}_k(\mathbf{S}_k - m_k)^2).$$

But $\mathbf{Y}_k \neq 0$ only if $|\mathbf{S}_k - m_k| \geq t s_n$, so that $\mathbf{Y}_k(\mathbf{S}_k - m_k)^2 \geq t^2 s_n^2 \mathbf{Y}_k$. Combining (7.7) and (7.10), we get therefore

(7.11)
$$s_n^2 \geq t^2 s_n^2 \mathbf{E}(\mathbf{Y}_1 + \cdots + \mathbf{Y}_n).$$

Since $\mathbf{Y}_1 + \cdots + \mathbf{Y}_n$ equals either 0 or 1, the expectation to the right equals the probability x defined in (7.6). Thus $xt^2 \leq 1$ as asserted.   ▶

*8. THE CORRELATION COEFFICIENT

Let X and Y be any two random variables with means μ_x and μ_y and positive variances σ_x^2 and σ_y^2. We introduce the corresponding normalized variables X^* and Y^* defined by (4.6). Their covariance is called *the correlation coefficient of* X, Y *and is denoted by* $\rho(X, Y)$. Thus, using (5.4),

$$(8.1) \qquad \rho(X, Y) = \text{Cov}(X^*, Y^*) = \frac{\text{Cov}(X, Y)}{\sigma_x \sigma_y}.$$

Clearly this correlation coefficient is independent of the origins and units of measurements, that is, for any constants a_1, a_2, b_1, b_2, with $a_1 > 0$, $a_2 > 0$, we have $\rho(a_1X+b_1, a_2Y+b_2) = \rho(X, Y)$.

The use of the correlation coefficient amounts to a fancy way of writing the covariance.[8] Unfortunately, the term correlation is suggestive of implications which are not inherent in it. We know from section 5 that $\rho(X, Y) = 0$ whenever X and Y are independent. It is important to realize that the converse is not true. In fact, *the correlation coefficient* $\rho(X, Y)$ *can vanish even if* Y *is a function of* X.

Examples. (*a*) Let X assume the values ±1, ±2 each with probability $\frac{1}{4}$. Let $Y = X^2$. The joint distribution is given by $p(-1, 1) = p(1, 1) = p(2, 4) = p(-2, 4) = \frac{1}{4}$. For reasons of symmetry $\rho(X, Y) = 0$ even though we have a direct functional dependence of Y on X.

(*b*) Let U and V have the same distribution, and let $X = U + V$, $Y = U - V$. Then $E(XY) = E(U^2) - E(V^2) = 0$ and $E(Y) = 0$. Hence $\text{Cov}(X, Y) = 0$ and therefore also $\rho(X, Y) = 0$. For example, X and Y may be the sum and difference of points on two dice. Then X and Y are either both odd or both even and therefore dependent. ▶

It follows that the correlation coefficient is by no means a general measure of dependence between X and Y. However, $\rho(X, Y)$ is connected with the *linear* dependence of X and Y.

Theorem. *We have always* $|\rho(X, Y)| \leq 1$; *furthermore,* $\rho(X, Y) = \pm1$ *only if there exist constants* a *and* b *such that* $Y = aX + b$, *except, perhaps, for values of* X *with zero probability.*

Proof. Let X^* and Y^* be the normalized variables. Then

$$(8.2) \quad \text{Var}(X^*\pm Y^*) = \text{Var}(X^*) \pm 2\,\text{Cov}(X^*, Y^*) + \text{Var}(Y^*) =$$
$$= 2(1\pm\rho(X, Y)).$$

---

* This section treats a special topic and may be omitted at first reading.
[8] The physicist would define the correlation coefficient as "dimensionless covariance."

The left side cannot be negative; hence $|\rho(X, Y)| \leq 1$. For $\rho(X, Y) = 1$ it is necessary that $\text{Var}(X^* - Y^*) = 0$ which means that with unit probability the variable $X^* - Y^*$ assumes only one value. In this case $X^* - Y^* = \text{const.}$, and hence $Y = aX + \text{const.}$ with $a = \sigma_y/\sigma_x$. A similar argument applies to the case $\rho(X, Y) = -1$.   ▶

9. PROBLEMS FOR SOLUTION

1. Seven balls are distributed randomly in seven cells. Let X_i be the number of cells containing exactly i balls. Using the probabilities tabulated in II, 5, write down the joint distribution of (X_2, X_3).

2. Two ideal dice are thrown. Let X be the score on the first die and Y be the larger of two scores. (a) Write down the joint distribution of X and Y. (b) Find the means, the variances, and the covariance.

3. In five tosses of a coin let X, Y, Z be, respectively, the number of heads, the number of head runs, the length of the largest head run. Tabulate the 32 sample points together with the corresponding values of $X, Y,$ and Z. By simple counting derive the joint distributions of the pairs (X, Y), (X, Z), (Y, Z) and the distributions of $X + Y$ and XY. Find the means, variances, covariances of the variables.

4. Let $X, Y,$ and Z be independent random variables with the same geometric distribution $\{q^k p\}$. Find (a) $P\{X = Y\}$; (b) $P\{X \geq 2Y\}$; and (c) $P\{X + Y \leq Z\}$.

5. *Continuation.* Let U be the larger of X and Y, and put $V = X - Y$. Show that U and V are independent.[9]

6. Let X_1 and X_2 be independent random variables with Poisson distributions $\{p(k; \lambda_1)\}$ and $\{p(k; \lambda_2)\}$.
(a) Prove that $X_1 + X_2$ has the Poisson distribution $\{p(k; \lambda_1 + \lambda_2)\}$.
(b) Show that the *conditional distribution of* X_1 *given* $X_1 + X_2$ *is binomial,* namely

$$(9.1) \qquad P\{X_1 = k \mid X_1 + X_2 = n\} = b\left(k; n, \frac{\lambda_1}{\lambda_1 + \lambda_2}\right).$$

7. Let X_1 and X_2 be independent and have the common geometric distribution $\{q^k p\}$ (as in problem 4). Show without calculations that the *conditional distribution of* X_1 *given* $X_1 + X_2$ *is uniform,* that is,

$$(9.2) \qquad P\{X_1 = k \mid X_1 + X_2 = n\} = \frac{1}{n + 1}, \qquad k = 0, \ldots, n.$$

8. Let $X_1, \ldots, X_r$ be mutually independent random variables, each having the *uniform distribution* $P\{X_i = k\} = 1/N$ for $k = 1, 2, \ldots, N$. Let U_n be the smallest among the $X_1, \ldots, X_n$ and V_n the largest. Find the distributions of U_n and V_n. What is the connection with the *estimation problem* (3.e)?

---

[9] The geometric distribution is the only probability distribution on the integers for which this is true. See T. S. Ferguson, *A characterization of the geometric distribution,* Amer. Math. Monthly, vol. 72 (1965), pp. 256–260.

9. *Continuation to the estimation problem in example* (3.e). (a) Find the joint distribution of the largest and the smallest observation. Specialize to $n = 2$. (*Hint:* Calculate first $P\{X \leq r, Y \geq s\}$.)

(b) Find the conditional probability that the first two observations are j and k, given that $X = r$.

(c) Find $E(X^2)$ and hence an asymptotic expression for Var (X) as $N \to \infty$ (with n fixed).

10. *Simulating a perfect coin.* Given a biased coin such that the probability of heads is α, we simulate a perfect coin as follows. Throw the biased coin twice. Interpret *HT* as success and *TH* as failure; if neither event occurs repeat the throws until a decision is reached. (a) Show that this model leads to Bernoulli trials with $p = \frac{1}{2}$. (b) Find the distribution and the expectation of the number of throws required to reach a decision.

11. *The problem of Banach's match boxes, example* VI,(8.a). Show that the expectation of the distribution $\{u_r\}$ is given by $\mu = (2N+1)u_0 - 1$. Using Stirling's formula show that this is approximately $2\sqrt{N/\pi} - 1$. (For $N = 50$ the mean is about 7.04.)

Hint: Start from the relation

$$(N-r)u_r = \tfrac{1}{2}(2N+1)u_{r+1} - \tfrac{1}{2}(r+1)u_{r+1}.$$

Use the fact[10] that $\sum u_r = 1$.

12. *Sampling inspection.* Suppose that items with a probability p of being acceptable are subjected to inspection in such a way that the probability of an item being inspected is p'. We have four classes, namely, "acceptable and inspected," "acceptable but not inspected," etc. with corresponding probabilities pp', pq', $p'q$, qq' where $q = 1 - p$, $q' = 1 - p'$. We are concerned with double Bernoulli trials [see example VI,(9.c)]. Let N be the number of items passing the inspection desk (both inspected and uninspected) before the first defective is found, and let K be the (undiscovered) number of defectives among them. Find the joint distributions of N and K and the marginal distributions.

13. *Continuation.* Find $E\left(\dfrac{K}{N+1}\right)$ and Cov (K, N). [In industrial practice the discovered defective item is replaced by an acceptable one so that $K/(N+1)$ is the fraction of defectives and measures the quality of the lot. Note that $E\left(\dfrac{K}{N+1}\right)$ is not $E(K)/E(N+1)$.]

14. In a sequence of Bernoulli trials let X be the length of the run (of either successes or failures) started by the first trial. (a) Find the distribution of X, $E(X)$, Var (X). (b) Let Y be the length of the *second* run. Find the distribution of Y, $E(Y)$, Var (Y), and the joint distribution of X, Y.

15. Let X and Y have a common negative binomial distribution. Find the conditional probability $P\{X = j \mid X + Y = k\}$ and show that the identity II, (12.16) now becomes obvious without any calculations.[11]

---

[10] This fact is not obvious analytically; it may be verified by induction on N.

[11] This derivation permits generalizations to more than two factors. It is due to T. K. M. Wisniewski, Amer. Statistician, vol. 20 (1966), p. 25.

16. If two random variables **X** and **Y** assume only two values each, and if Cov $(\mathbf{X}, \mathbf{Y}) = 0$, then **X** and **Y** are independent.

17. *Birthdays.* For a group of n people find the expected number of days of the year which are birthdays of exactly k people. (Assume 365 days and that all arrangements are equally probable.)

18. *Continuation.* Find the expected number of multiple birthdays. How large should n be to make this expectation exceed 1?

19. A man with n keys wants to open his door and tries the keys independently and at random. Find the mean and variance of the number of trials (a) if unsuccessful keys are not eliminated from further selections; (b) if they are. (Assume that only one key fits the door. The exact distributions are given in II, 7, but are not required for the present problem.)

20. Let $(\mathbf{X}, \mathbf{Y})$ be random variables whose joint distribution is the trinomial defined by (1.8). Find $E(\mathbf{X})$, Var $(\mathbf{X})$, and Cov $(\mathbf{X}, \mathbf{Y})$ (a) by direct computation, (b) by representing **X** and **Y** as sums of n variables each and using the methods of section 5.

21. Find the covariance of the number of ones and sixes in n throws of a die.

22. In the animal trapping problem 24 of VI, 10, prove that the expected number of animals trapped at the vth trapping is nqp^{v-1}.

23. If **X** has the *geometric* distribution $P\{\mathbf{X} = k\} = q^k p$ (where $k = 0, 1, \ldots$), show that Var $(\mathbf{X}) = qp^{-2}$. Conclude that the *negative* binomial distribution $\{f(k; r, p)\}$ has variance rqp^{-2} provided r is a positive integer. Prove by direct calculation that the statement remains true for all $r > 0$.

24. In the *waiting time problem* (3.d) prove that

$$\text{Var} \, (\mathbf{S}_r) = N\left\{\frac{1}{(N-1)^2} + \frac{2}{(N-2)^2} + \cdots + \frac{r-1}{(N-r+1)^2}\right\}.$$

Conclude that $N^{-2}E(\mathbf{S}_N) \sim \sum k^{-2}$. (Incidentally, the value of this series is $\pi^2/6$.) *Hint:* Use the variance of the geometric distribution found in the preceding problem.

25. *Continuation.* Let $\mathbf{Y}_r$ be the number of drawings required to include r preassigned elements (instead of any r different elements as in the text). Find $E(\mathbf{Y}_r)$ and Var $(\mathbf{Y}_r)$. (*Note:* The exact distribution of $\mathbf{Y}_r$ was found in problem 12 of II, 11 but is not required for the present purpose.)

26. *The blood-testing problem.*[12] A large number, N, of people are subject to a blood test. This can be administered in two ways. (i) Each person can be

---

[12] This problem is based on a technique developed during World War II by R. Dorfman. In army practice Dorfman achieved savings up to 80 per cent. When the problem appeared in the first edition it caught widespread attention and led to various generalizations as well as to new industrial and biological applications. The main improvement consists in introducing more than two stages. See, for example, M. Sobel and P. A. Groll, *Group testing to eliminate efficiently all defectives in a binomial sample*, The Bell System Journal, vol. 38 (1959), pp. 1179–1252; G. S. Watson, *A study of the group screening method*, Technometrics, vol. 3 (1961), pp. 371–388; H. M. Finucan, *The blood-testing problem*, Applied Statistics, vol. 13 (1964), pp. 43–50.

tested separately. In this case N tests are required. (ii) The blood samples of k people can be pooled and analyzed together. If the test is *negative*, this *one* test suffices for the k people. If the test is *positive*, each of the k persons must be tested separately, and in all $k + 1$ tests are required for the k people.

Assume the probability p that the test is positive is the same for all people and that people are stochastically independent.

(*a*) What is the probability that the test for a pooled sample of k people will be positive?

(*b*) What is the expected value of the number, $\mathbf{X}$, of tests necessary under plan (ii)?

(*c*) Find an equation for the value of k which will minimize the expected number of tests under the second plan.

(*d*) Show that this k is close to $1/\sqrt{p}$, and hence that the minimum expected number of tests is about $2N\sqrt{p}$. (This remark is due to M. S. Raff.)

27. *Sample structure.* A population consists of r classes whose sizes are in the proportion $p_1:p_2:\,\cdots\,:p_r$. A random sample of size n is taken with replacement. Find the expected number of classes *not* represented in the sample.

28. Let $\mathbf{X}$ be the number of α runs in a random arrangement of r_1 alphas and r_2 betas. The distribution of $\mathbf{X}$ is given in problem 23 of II, 11. Find $E(\mathbf{X})$ and $\mathrm{Var}\,(\mathbf{X})$.

29. In *Polya's urn scheme* [V,(2.c)] let $\mathbf{X}_n$ be one or zero according as the nth trial results in black or red. Prove $\rho(\mathbf{X}_n, \mathbf{X}_m) = c/(b+r+c)$ for $n \neq m$.

30. *Continuation.* Let $\mathbf{S}_n$ be the total number of black balls extracted in the first n drawings (that is, $\mathbf{S}_n = \mathbf{X}_1 + \cdots + \mathbf{X}_n$). Find $E(\mathbf{S}_n)$ and $\mathrm{Var}\,(\mathbf{S}_n)$. Verify the result by means of the recursion formula in problem 22 of V, 8. *Hint:* Use problems 19, 20 of V, 8.

31. *Stratified sampling.* A city has n blocks of which n_j have x_j inhabitants each $(n_1 + n_2 + \cdots = n)$. Let $m = \Sigma n_j x_j/n$ be the mean number of inhabitants per block and put $a^2 = n^{-1}\Sigma n_j x_j^2 - m^2$. In sampling without replacement r blocks are selected at random, and in each the inhabitants are counted. Let $\mathbf{X}_1, \ldots, \mathbf{X}_r$ be the respective number of inhabitants. Show that

$$E(\mathbf{X}_1 + \cdots + \mathbf{X}_r) = mr \qquad \mathrm{Var}\,(\mathbf{X}_1 + \cdots + \mathbf{X}_r) = \frac{a^2 r(n-r)}{n-1}\,.$$

(In sampling with replacement the variance would be larger, namely, $a^2 r$.)

32. *Length of random chains.*[13] A chain in the x,y-plane consists of n links, each of unit length. The angle between two consecutive links is $\pm\alpha$ where α is a positive constant; each possibility has probability $\tfrac{1}{2}$, and the successive angles are mutually independent. The distance $\mathbf{L}_n$ from the beginning to the end of the chain is a random variable, and we wish to prove that

$$(9.3) \qquad E(\mathbf{L}_n^2) = n\frac{1 + \cos\alpha}{1 - \cos\alpha} - 2\cos\alpha\,\frac{1 - \cos^n\alpha}{(1 - \cos\alpha)^2}\,.$$

Without loss of generality the first link may be assumed to lie in the direction of the positive x-axis. The angle between the kth link and the positive x-axis

---

[13] This is the two-dimensional analogue to the problem of length of *long polymer molecules* in chemistry. The problem illustrates applications to random variables which are not expressible as sums of simple variables.

is a random variable S_{k-1} where $S_0 = 0$, $S_k = S_{k-1} + X_k\alpha$ and the X_k are mutually independent variables, assuming the values ± 1 with probability $\frac{1}{2}$. The projections on the two axes of the kth link are $\cos S_{k-1}$ and $\sin S_{k-1}$. Hence for $n \geq 1$

$$(9.4) \qquad L_n^2 = \left(\sum_{k=0}^{n-1} \cos S_k\right)^2 + \left(\sum_{k=0}^{n-1} \sin S_k\right)^2.$$

Prove by induction successively for $m < n$

$$(9.5) \qquad E(\cos S_n) = \cos^n \alpha, \qquad E(\sin S_n) = 0;$$

$$(9.6) \qquad E((\cos S_m) \cdot (\cos S_n)) = \cos^{n-m}\alpha \cdot E(\cos^2 S_m)$$

$$(9.7) \qquad E((\sin S_m) \cdot (\sin S_n)) = \cos^{n-m} \alpha \cdot E(\sin^2 S_m)$$

$$(9.8) \qquad E(L_n^2) - E(L_{n-1}^2) = 1 + 2 \cos \alpha \cdot \frac{1 - \cos^{n-1} \alpha}{1 - \cos \alpha}$$

(with $L_0 = 0$) and hence finally (9.3).

---

33. A sequence of Bernoulli trials is continued as long as necessary to obtain r successes, where r is a fixed integer. Let X be the number of trials required. Find[14] $E(r/X)$. (The definition leads to infinite series for which a finite expression can be obtained.)

34. In a random placement of r balls into n cells the probability of finding exactly m cells empty satisfies the recursion formula II,(11.8). Let m_r be the expected number of empty cells. *From the recursion formula* prove that

$$m_{r+1} = (1 - n^{-1})m_r, \qquad \text{and conclude} \qquad m_r = n\left(1 - \frac{1}{n}\right)^r.$$

35. Let S_n be the number of successes in n Bernoulli trials. Prove

$$E(|S_n - np|) = 2\nu q b(\nu; n, p)$$

where ν is the integer such that $np < \nu \leq np + 1$.

36. Let $\{X_k\}$ be a sequence of mutually independent random variables with a common distribution. Suppose that the X_k assume only positive values and that $E(X_k) = a$ and $E(X_k^{-1}) = b$ exist. Let $S_n = X_1 + \cdots + X_n$. Prove that $E(S_n^{-1})$ is finite and that $E(X_k S_n^{-1}) = n^{-1}$ for $k = 1, 2, \ldots, n$.

---

[14] This example illustrates the effect of *optional stopping*. When the number n of trials is fixed, the ratio of the number N of successes to the number n of trials is a random variable whose expectation is p. It is often erroneously assumed that the same is true in our example where the number r of successes is fixed and the number of trials depends on chance. If $p = \frac{1}{2}$ and $r = 2$, then $E(2/X) = 0.614$ instead of 0.5; for $r = 3$ we find $E(3/X) = 0.579$.

37. *Continuation.*[15] Prove that

$$\mathbf{E}\left(\frac{\mathbf{S}_m}{\mathbf{S}_n}\right) = \frac{m}{n}, \qquad\qquad \text{if } m \le n$$

$$\mathbf{E}\left(\frac{\mathbf{S}_m}{\mathbf{S}_n}\right) = 1 + (m-n)a\mathbf{E}(\mathbf{S}_n^{-1}), \qquad\qquad \text{if } m \ge n.$$

38. Let $\mathbf{X}_1, \ldots, \mathbf{X}_n$ be mutually independent random variables with a common distribution; let its mean be m, its variance σ^2. Let $\overline{\mathbf{X}} = (\mathbf{X}_1 + \cdots + \mathbf{X}_n)/n$. Prove that[16]

$$\frac{1}{n-1}\, \mathbf{E}\left(\sum_{k=1}^{n}(\mathbf{X}_k - \overline{\mathbf{X}})^2\right) = \sigma^2.$$

39. Let $\mathbf{X}_1, \ldots, \mathbf{X}_n$ be mutually independent random variables. Let $\mathbf{U}$ be a function of $\mathbf{X}_1, \ldots, \mathbf{X}_k$ and $\mathbf{V}$ a function of $\mathbf{X}_{k+1}, \ldots, \mathbf{X}_n$. Prove that $\mathbf{U}$ and $\mathbf{V}$ are mutually independent random variables.

---

40. *Generalized Chebyshev inequality.* Let $\phi(x) > 0$ for $x > 0$ be monotonically increasing and suppose that $\mathbf{E}(\phi(|\mathbf{X}|)) = M$ exists. Prove that

$$\mathbf{P}\{|\mathbf{X}| \ge t\} \le \frac{M}{\phi(t)}.$$

41. *Schwarz inequality.* For any two random variables with finite variances one has $\mathbf{E}^2(\mathbf{XY}) \le \mathbf{E}(\mathbf{X}^2)\mathbf{E}(\mathbf{Y}^2)$. Prove this from the fact that the quadratic polynomial $\mathbf{E}((t\mathbf{X}+\mathbf{Y})^2)$ is non-negative.

---

[15] The observation that problem 37 can be derived from 36 is due to K. L. Chung.

[16] This can be expressed by saying that $\sum(\mathbf{X}_k - \overline{\mathbf{X}})^2/(n-1)$ is an *unbiased estimator* of σ^2.

CHAPTER X

Law of Large Numbers

1. IDENTICALLY DISTRIBUTED VARIABLES

The limit theorems for Bernoulli trials derived in chapters VII and VIII are special cases of general limit theorems which cannot be treated in this volume. However, we shall here discuss at least some cases of the law of large numbers in order to reveal a new aspect of the expectation of a random variable.

The connection between Bernoulli trials and the theory of random variables becomes clearer when we consider the dependence of the number S_n of successes on the number n of trials. With each trial S_n increases by 1 or 0, and we can write

$$(1.1) \qquad S_n = X_1 + \cdots + X_n,$$

where the random variable X_k equals 1 if the kth trial results in success and zero otherwise. Thus S_n is a sum of n mutually independent random variables, each of which assumes the values 1 and 0 with probabilities p and q. From this it is only one step to consider sums of the form (1.1) where the X_k are mutually independent variables with an arbitrary distribution. The (weak) law of large numbers of VI,4, states that for large n the average proportion of successes S_n/n is likely to lie near p. This is a special case of the following

Law of Large Numbers. *Let $\{X_k\}$ be a sequence of mutually independent random variables with a common distribution. If the expectation $\mu = E(X_k)$ exists, then for every $\epsilon > 0$ as $n \to \infty$*

$$(1.2) \qquad P\left\{ \left| \frac{X_1 + \cdots + X_n}{n} - \mu \right| > \epsilon \right\} \to 0;$$

in words, the probability that the average S_n/n will differ from the expectation by less than an arbitrarily prescribed ϵ tends to one.

In this generality the theorem was first proved by Khintchine.[1] Older proofs had to introduce the unnecessary restriction that the variance Var (X_k) should also be finite.[2] For this case, however, there exists a much more precise result which generalizes the DeMoivre-Laplace limit theorem for Bernoulli trials, namely the

Central Limit Theorem. *Let* $\{X_k\}$ *be a sequence of mutually independent random variables with a common distribution. Suppose that* $\mu = E(X_k)$ *and* $\sigma^2 = \mathrm{Var}\,(X_k)$ *exist and let* $S_n = X_1 + \cdots + X_n$. *Then for every fixed* β

(1.3)
$$P\left\{ \frac{S_n - n\mu}{\sigma\sqrt{n}} < \beta \right\} \to \mathfrak{N}(\beta)$$

where $\mathfrak{N}(x)$ is the normal distribution introduced in VII,1. This theorem is due to Lindeberg[3]; Ljapunov and other authors had previously proved it under more restrictive conditions. It must be understood that this theorem is only a special case of a much more general theorem whose formulation and proof are deferred to the second volume. Here we note that (1.3) is stronger than (1.2), since it gives an estimate for the probability that the discrepancy $|n^{-1}S_n - \mu|$ is larger than $\sigma/\sqrt{n}$. On the other hand, the law of large numbers (1.2) holds even when the random variables X_k have no finite variance so that it is more general than the central limit theorem. For this reason we shall give an independent proof of the law of large numbers, but first we illustrate the two limit theorems.

Examples. (*a*) In a sequence of independent throws of a symmetric die let X_k be the number scored at the kth throw. Then

$$E(X_k) = (1+2+3+4+5+6)/6 = 3.5,$$

and $\mathrm{Var}\,(X_k) = (1^2+2^2+3^2+4^2+5^2+6^2)/6 - (3.5)^2 = \frac{35}{12}$. The law of large numbers states that for large n the average score S_n/n is likely to be near 3.5. The central limit theorem states that

(1.4)
$$P\{|S_n - 3.5n| < \alpha\sqrt{35n/12}\} \approx \mathfrak{N}(\alpha) - \mathfrak{N}(-\alpha).$$

For $n = 1000$ and $\alpha = 1$ this reduces to $P\{3450 < S_n < 3550\} \approx 0.68$. For $\alpha = 0.6744 \cdots$ the right side in (1.4) equals $\frac{1}{2}$, and so there are

---

[1] A. Khintchine, Comptes rendus de l'Académie des Sciences, Paris, vol. 189 (1929), pp. 477–479. Incidentally, the reader should observe the warning given in connection with the law of large numbers for Bernoulli trials at the end of VI,4.

[2] A. Markov showed that the existence of $E(|X_k|^{1+a})$ for some $a > 0$ suffices.

[3] J. W. Lindeberg, *Eine neue Herleitung des Exponentialgesetzes in der Wahrscheinlichkeitsrechnung*, Mathematische Zeitschrift, vol. 15 (1922), pp. 211–225.

roughly equal chances that $\mathbf{S}_n$ lies within or without the interval 3500 ± 36.

(b) *Sampling.* Suppose that in a population of N families there are N_k families with exactly k children $(k = 0, 1, \ldots ; \sum N_k = N)$. For a family chosen at random, the number of children is a random variable which assumes the value ν with probability $p_\nu = N_\nu/N$. A sample of size n with replacement represents n independent random variables or "observations" $\mathbf{X}_1, \ldots, \mathbf{X}_n$, each with the same distribution; $\mathbf{S}_n/n$ is the *sample average.* The law of large numbers tells us that for sufficiently large random samples the sample average is likely to be near $\mu = \sum \nu p_\nu = \sum \nu N_\nu/N$, namely the population average. The central limit theorem permits us to estimate the probable magnitude of the discrepancy and to determine the sample size necessary for reliable estimates. In practice both μ and σ^2 are unknown, but it is usually easy to obtain a preliminary estimate of σ^2, and it is always possible to keep to the safe side. If it is desired that there be probability 0.99 or better that the sample average $\mathbf{S}_n/n$ differ from the unknown population mean μ by less than $\frac{1}{10}$, then the sample size should be such that

$$(1.5) \qquad \mathbf{P}\left\{ \left| \frac{\mathbf{S}_n - n\mu}{n} \right| < \frac{1}{10} \right\} \geq 0.99.$$

The root of $\mathfrak{N}(x) - \mathfrak{N}(-x) = 0.99$ is $x = 2.57 \ldots$, and hence n should satisfy $\sqrt{n}/10\sigma \geq 2.57$ or $n \geq 660\sigma^2$. A cautious preliminary estimate of σ^2 gives us an idea of the required sample size. Similar situations occur frequently. Thus when the experimenter takes the mean of n measurements he, too, relies on the law of large numbers and uses a sample mean as an estimate for an unknown theoretical expectation. The reliability of this estimate can be judged only in terms of σ^2, and usually one is compelled to use rather crude estimates for σ^2.

(c) *The Poisson distribution.* In VII,5, we found that for large λ the Poisson distribution $\{p(k; \lambda)\}$ can be approximated by the normal distribution. This is really a direct consequence of the central limit theorem. Suppose that the variables $\mathbf{X}_k$ have a Poisson distribution $\{p(k; \gamma)\}$. Then $\mathbf{S}_n$ has a Poisson distribution $\{p(k; n\gamma)\}$ with mean and variance equal to $n\gamma$. Writing λ for $n\gamma$, we conclude that as $n \to \infty$

$$(1.6) \qquad \sum_{k < \lambda + \beta\sqrt{\lambda}} e^{-\lambda}\lambda^k/k! \to \mathfrak{N}(\beta)$$

the summation extending over all k up to $\lambda + \beta\sqrt{\lambda}$. It is now obvious that (1.6) holds also when λ approaches ∞ in an arbitrary manner. This theorem is used in the theory of summability of divergent series and is of general interest; estimates of the difference of the two sides in (1.6) are available from the general theory.   ▶

Note on Variables without Expectation

Both the law of large numbers and the central limit theorem become meaningless if the expectation μ does not exist, but they can be replaced by more general theorems supplying the same sort of information. In the modern theory variables without expectation play an important role and many waiting and recurrence times in physics turn out to be of this type. This is true even of the simple coin-tossing game.

Suppose that n coins are tossed one by one. For the kth coin let $\mathbf{X}_k$ be the waiting time up to the first equalization of the accumulated numbers of heads and tails. The $\mathbf{X}_k$ are mutually independent random variables with a common distribution: each $\mathbf{X}_k$ assumes only even positive values and $\mathbf{P}\{\mathbf{X}_k = 2r\} = f_{2r}$ with the probability distribution $\{f_{2r}\}$ defined in III,(3.7). The sum $\mathbf{S}_n = \mathbf{X}_1 + \cdots + \mathbf{X}_n$ has the same distribution as the waiting time to the nth equalization of the accumulated numbers of heads and tails or, what amounts to the same, the epoch of the nth return to the origin in a symmetric random walk. The distribution of $\mathbf{S}_n$ was found in theorem 4 of III,7, and it was shown that

$$(1.7) \qquad\qquad \mathbf{P}\{\mathbf{S}_n < n^2 x\} \rightarrow 2[1 - \mathfrak{N}(1/\sqrt{x}\,)].$$

We have here a limit theorem of the same character as the central limit theorem with the remarkable difference that this time *the variable* $\mathbf{S}_n/n^2$ *rather than* $\mathbf{S}_n/n$ *possesses a limit distribution.* In the physicist's language the $\mathbf{X}_k$ stand for independent measurements of the same physical quantity, and the theorem asserts that, in probability, *the average*

$$(\mathbf{X}_1 + \cdots + \mathbf{X}_n)/n$$

increases linearly with n. This paradoxical result cannot be shrugged off as representing a pathological case because it turns out that our $\mathbf{X}_k$ are typical of the waiting times occurring in many physical and economical processes. The limit theorem (1.7) is also typical of many modern limit theorems for variables without expectation.[4]

*2. PROOF OF THE LAW OF LARGE NUMBERS

There is no loss of generality in assuming that $\mu = \mathbf{E}(\mathbf{X}_k) = 0$, for otherwise we would replace $\mathbf{X}_k$ by $\mathbf{X}_k - \mu$, and this involves merely a

---

[4] For an analogue to the law of large numbers for variables without expectation see section 4 and problem 13. The surprising consequences of (1.7) were discussed at length in chapter III.

* This section should be omitted at first reading.

change of notation. In the special case where $\sigma^2 = \text{Var}(X_k)$ exists the law of large numbers is a trivial consequence of Chebyshev's inequality IX,(6.2) according to which

$$(2.1) \qquad P\{|S_n| > t\} \leq \frac{n\sigma^2}{t^2}.$$

For $t = \epsilon n$ the right side tends to 0, and so (1.2) is true.

The case where the second moment does not exist is more difficult. The proof depends on the versatile *method of truncation* which is a standard tool in deriving various limit theorems. Let δ be a positive constant to be determined later. For each n we define n pairs of random variables as follows.

$$(2.2) \qquad \begin{array}{llll} U_k = X_k, & V_k = 0 & \textit{if} & |X_k| \leq \delta n, \\ U_k = 0, & V_k = X_k & \textit{if} & |X_k| > \delta n. \end{array}$$

Here $k = 1, \ldots, n$ and the dependence of the U_k and V_k on n must be borne in mind. By this definition

$$(2.3) \qquad X_k = U_k + V_k$$

and to prove the law of large numbers it suffices to show that for given $\epsilon > 0$ the constant δ can be chosen so that as $n \to \infty$

$$(2.4) \qquad P\{|U_1 + \cdots + U_n| > \tfrac{1}{2}\epsilon n\} \to 0$$

and

$$(2.5) \qquad P\{|V_1 + \cdots + V_n| > \tfrac{1}{2}\epsilon n\} \to 0.$$

For the proof denote the possible values of the X_j by $x_1, x_2, \ldots$ and their probabilities by $f(x_j)$. Put $a = E(|X_j|)$, that is,

$$(2.6) \qquad a = \sum_j |x_j| \, f(x_j).$$

The variable U_1 is bounded by δn and hence clearly

$$(2.7) \qquad E(U_1^2) < a \, \delta n.$$

The variables $U_1, \ldots, U_n$ have the same distribution and are mutually independent. Therefore

$$(2.8) \qquad \text{Var}(U_1 + \cdots + U_n) = n \, \text{Var}(U_1) \leq n E(U_1^2) \leq a \, \delta n^2.$$

On the other hand, by the very definition of the U_k as $n \to \infty$

$$(2.9) \qquad E(U_1) \to E(X_1) = 0.$$

It follows that for n sufficiently large

(2.10) $E((U_1 + \cdots + U_n)^2) \leq 2a \, \delta n^2.$

The relation (2.4) is now an immediate consequence of Chebyshev's inequality IX,(6.1) according to which

(2.11) $P\{|U_1 + \cdots + U_n| > \tfrac{1}{2}\epsilon n\} \geq \dfrac{8a \, \delta}{\epsilon^2}.$

By choosing $\cdot \delta$ small enough we can make the right side as small as we please, and so (2.4) is true.

As for (2.5), note that

(2.12) $P\{V_1 + \cdots + V_n \neq 0\} \leq nP\{V_1 \neq 0\}$

by the basic inequality I,(7.6). For arbitrary $\delta > 0$ we have

$$P\{V_1 \neq 0\} = P\{|X_1| > \delta n\} = \sum_{|x_j| > \delta n} f(x_j)$$

(2.13)

$$\leq \frac{1}{\delta n} \sum_{|x_j| > \delta n} |x_j| \, f(x_j).$$

The last sum tends to 0 as $n \to \infty$. Therefore also the left side in (2.12) tends to 0. This statement is stronger than (2.5) and completes the proof.   ▶

3. THE THEORY OF "FAIR" GAMES

For a further analysis of the implications of the law of large numbers we shall use the time-honored terminology of gamblers, but our discussion bears equally on less frivolous applications, and our two basic assumptions are more realistic in statistics and physics than in gambling halls. First, we shall assume that our gambler possesses an *unlimited capital* so that no loss can force a termination of the game. (Dropping this assumption leads to the problem of the gambler's *ruin*, which from the very beginning has intrigued students of probability. It is of importance in Wald's sequential analysis and in the theory of stochastic processes, and will be taken up in chapter XIV.) Second, we shall assume that the gambler *does not have the privilege of optional stopping; the number n of trials must be fixed in advance* independently of the development of the game. (In reality a player blessed with an unlimited capital can wait for a run of good luck and quit at an opportune moment. He is not interested in the probable state at a prescribed moment, but only in the maximal fluctuations likely to occur in the long run. Light is shed on this problem by the law of the iterated logarithm rather than by the law of large numbers (see VIII,5).)

The random variable X_k will be interpreted as the (positive or negative) gain at the kth trial of a player who keeps playing the same type of game of chance. The sum $S_n = X_1 + \cdots + X_n$ is the accumulated gain in n independent trials. If the player pays for each trial an entrance fee μ' (not necessarily positive), then $n\mu'$ represents the accumulated entrance fees, and $S_n - n\mu'$ the *accumulated net gain*. The law of large numbers applies when $\mu = E(X_k)$ exists. It says roughly that for sufficiently large n the difference $S_n - n\mu$ is likely to be small in comparison to n. Therefore, if the entrance fee μ' is smaller than μ, then, for large n, the player is likely to have a positive gain of the order of magnitude $n(\mu - \mu')$. For the same reason an entrance fee $\mu' > \mu$ is practically sure to lead to a loss. In short, the case $\mu' < \mu$ is *favorable* to the player, while $\mu' > \mu$ is *unfavorable*.

Note that nothing is said about the case $\mu' = \mu$. The *only* possible conclusion in this case is that, for n sufficiently large, the accumulated gain or loss $S_n - n\mu$ will with overwhelming probability be small in comparison with n. It is not stated whether $S_n - n\mu$ is likely to be positive or negative, that is, whether the game is favorable or unfavorable. This was overlooked in the classical theory which called $\mu' = \mu$ a "fair" price and a game with $\mu' = \mu$ "*fair*." Much harm was done by the misleading suggestive power of this name. It must be understood that *a "fair" game may be distinctly unfavorable to the player.*   ▶

In applications to gambling and in other simple situations where the variables X_k have a finite second moment the notion of "fairness" can be justified, but when the variance is infinite, the term "fair game" becomes an absolute misnomer. There is no reason to believe that the accumulated net gain $S_n - n\mu'$ fluctuates around zero. In fact, *there exist examples of "fair" games*[5] *where the probability tends to one that the player will have sustained a net loss.* The law of large numbers asserts that this net loss is likely to be of smaller order of magnitude than n. However, nothing more can be asserted. If a_n is an arbitrary sequence such that $a_n/n \to 0$, it is possible to construct a "fair" game where the probability tends to one that at the nth trial the accumulated net loss exceeds a_n. Problem 15 contains an example where the player has a practical assurance that his loss will exceed $n/\log n$. This game is "fair," and the entrance fee is unity. It is difficult to imagine that a player will find it "fair" if he is practically sure to sustain a steadily increasing loss.

---

[5] W. Feller, *Note on the law of large numbers and "fair" games*, Ann. Math. Statist., vol. 16 (1945), pp. 301–304.

It would be a mistake to dismiss such phenomena as pathological or as being without practical importance. The neglect of random variables without expectations has done much harm in applications because such variables play an essential role even in the simplest stochastic processes. For example, the simple random walk (or coin-tossing game) discussed in chapter III serves as prototype for many stochastic processes in physics and economics. As was shown in chapter III, the waiting and first-passage times in this random walk do not have expectations, and they are therefore subject to chance fluctuations that appear paradoxical and do not accord with our intuition. This faulty intuition as well as many modern applications of probability theory are under the strong influence of traditional misconceptions concerning the meaning of the law of large numbers and of a popular mystique concerning a so-called law of averages. These are inherited from the classical theory in which mathematical analysis was inevitably interwoven with empirical and metaphysical considerations, and in which something mystical adhered to the various limit theorems.[6]

Let us return to the "normal" situations where not only $E(X_k)$ but also $Var(X_k)$ exists. In this case the law of large numbers is supplemented by the central limit theorem, and the latter tells us that, with a "fair" game, the long-run net gain $S_n - n\mu$ is likely to be of the order of magnitude $\sqrt{n}$ and that for large n there are about equal odds for this net gain to be positive or negative. Thus, when the central limit theorem applies, the term "fair" appears justified, but even in this case we deal with a limit theorem with emphasis on the words "long run."

For illustration, consider a slot machine where the player has a probability of 10^{-6} to win $10^6 - 1$ dollars, and the alternative of losing the entrance fee $\mu' = 1$. Here we have Bernoulli trials, and the game is "fair." In a million trials the player pays as many dollars in entrance fees. He may hit the jackpot $0, 1, 2, \ldots$ times. We know from the Poisson approximation to the binomial distribution that, with an accuracy to several decimal places, the probability of hitting the jackpot exactly k times is $e^{-1}/k!$. Thus the player has probability $0.368\ldots$ to lose a million, and the same probability of barely recovering his expenses; he has probability $0.184\ldots$ to gain exactly one million, etc. Here 10^6 trials are equivalent to one single trial in a game with the gain distributed according to a Poisson distribution. Such a game can be realized, for example, by matching two large decks of cards as described in IV,4. Nobody would expect the law of large numbers to become operative in practice after three

---

[6] The student of modern probability theory may be astonished to hear that as late as 1934 leading experts could question the possibility of formulating the basic limit theorems of probability in purely analytic terms.

or four matchings. By the same token, when applied to our slot machine the law of large numbers is operationally meaningless unless many millions of trials are involved. Now all fire, automobile, and similar insurance is of the described type; the risk involves a huge sum, but the corresponding probability is very small. Moreover, the insured plays ordinarily only one trial per year, so that the number n of trials never grows large. For him the game is necessarily "unfair," and yet it is usually economically advantageous; the law of large numbers is of no relevance to him. As for the company, it plays a large number of games, but because of the large variance the chance fluctuations are pronounced. The premiums must be fixed so as to preclude a huge loss in any specific year, and hence the company is concerned with the ruin problem rather than the law of large numbers.

*4. THE PETERSBURG GAME

In the classical theory the notion of expectation was not clearly disassociated from the definition of probability, and no mathematical formalism existed to handle it. Random variables with infinite expectations therefore produced insurmountable difficulties, and even quite recent discussions appear strange to the student of modern probability. The importance of variables without expectation has been stressed in the preceding sections, and it seems appropriate here to give an example for the analogue of the law of large numbers in the case of such variables. For that purpose we use the time-honored so-called Petersburg paradox.[7]

A single trial in the Petersburg game consists in tossing a true coin until it falls heads; if this occurs at the rth throw the player receives 2^r dollars. In other words, we are dealing with independent random variables assuming the values 2^1, 2^2, 2^3, ... with corresponding probabilities 2^{-1}, 2^{-2}, 2^{-3}, ... Their expectation is formally defined by $\sum x_r f(x_r)$ with $x_r = 2^r$ and $f(x_r) = 2^{-r}$, so that each term of the series equals 1. Thus the gain has no finite expectation, and the law of large numbers is inapplicable. Now the game becomes less favorable to the player when amended by the rule that he receives nothing if no decision is reached in N tosses (that is, if the coin falls tails N times in succession). The gain in this less favorable game has the finite expectation N, and the law of large numbers applies. It follows that the original game will be "favorable" to the player even if he pays the entrance fee N for each trial. This is true for every N, but the larger N the longer will it take to render a positive gain probable, and so it is

---

* This section should be omitted at first reading.

[7] This paradox was discussed by Daniel Bernoulli (1700–1782). Note that Bernoulli trials are named after James Bernoulli.

meaningless to speak of a "favorable" game. The classical theory concluded that $\mu' = \infty$ is a "fair" entrance fee, but the modern student will hardly understand the mysterious discussions of this "paradox."

It is perfectly possible to determine entrance fees with which the Petersburg game will have all properties of a "fair" game in the classical sense, except that these entrance fees will depend on the number of trials instead of remaining constant. Variable entrance fees are undesirable in gambling halls, but there the Petersburg game is impossible anyway because of limited resources. In the case of a finite expectation $\mu = E(X_k) > 0$, a game is called "fair" if for large n the ratio of the accumulated gain S_n to the accumulated entrance fees e_n is likely to be near 1 (that is, if the difference $S_n - e_n$ is likely to be of smaller order of magnitude than e_n). If $E(X_k)$ does not exist, we cannot keep the entrance fees constant, but must determine e_n in another way. We shall say that a *game with accumulated entrance fees* e_n *is fair in the classical sense if for every* $\epsilon > 0$

$$(4.1) \qquad\qquad P\left\{ \left| \frac{S_n}{e_n} - 1 \right| > \epsilon \right\} \to 0.$$

This is the complete analogue of the law of large numbers where $e_n = n\mu'$. The latter is interpreted by the physicist to the effect that the average of n independent measurements is bound to be near μ. In the present instance the average of n measurements is bound to be near e_n/n. Our limit theorem (4.1), when it applies, has a mathematical and operational meaning which does not differ from the law of large numbers.

We shall now show[8] that the *Petersburg game becomes "fair" in the classical sense if we put* $e_n = n \, \mathrm{Log} \, n$, where $\mathrm{Log} \, n$ is the logarithm to the base 2, that is, $2^{\mathrm{Log} \, n} = n$.

Proof. We use the method of truncation of section 2, this time defining the variables U_k and V_k $(k = 1, 2, \ldots, n)$ by

$$(4.2) \qquad
\begin{aligned}
U_k &= X_k, & V_k &= 0 & &\text{if } X_k \leq n \, \mathrm{Log} \, n; \\
U_k &= 0, & V_k &= X_k & &\text{if } X_k > n \, \mathrm{Log} \, n.
\end{aligned}$$

Then

$$(4.3) \quad P\{|e_n^{-1} S_n - 1| > \epsilon\} \leq P\{|U_1 + \cdots + U_n - e_n| > \epsilon e_n\}$$
$$+ P\{V_1 + \cdots + V_n \neq 0\}$$

because the event on the left cannot occur unless at least one of the events

---

[8] This is a special case of a generalized law of large numbers from which necessary and sufficient conditions for (4.1) can easily be derived; cf. W. Feller, Acta Scientiarum Litterarum Univ. Szeged, vol. 8 (1937), pp. 191–201.

on the right is realized. Now

$$(4.4) \quad \mathbf{P}\{\mathbf{V}_1 + \cdots + \mathbf{V}_n \neq 0\} \leq n\mathbf{P}\{\mathbf{X}_1 > n \text{ Log } n\} \leq \frac{2}{\text{Log } n} \to 0.$$

To verify (4.3) it suffices therefore to prove that

$$(4.5) \qquad \mathbf{P}\{\,|\mathbf{U}_1 + \cdots + \mathbf{U}_n - n \text{ Log } n| > \epsilon n \text{ Log } n\} \to 0.$$

Put $\mu_n = \mathbf{E}(\mathbf{U}_k)$ and $\sigma_n^2 = \text{Var}(\mathbf{U}_k)$; these quantities depend on n, but are common to $\mathbf{U}_1, \mathbf{U}_2, \ldots, \mathbf{U}_n$. If r is the largest integer such that $2^r \leq n \text{ Log } n$, then $\mu_n = r$ and hence for sufficiently large n

$$(4.6) \qquad\qquad \text{Log } n < \mu_n \leq \text{Log } n + \text{Log Log } n.$$

Similarly

$$(4.7) \quad \sigma_n^2 < \mathbf{E}(\mathbf{U}_k^2) = 2 + 2^2 + \cdots + 2^r < 2^{r+1} \leq 2n \text{ Log } n.$$

Since the sum $\mathbf{U}_1 + \cdots + \mathbf{U}_n$ has mean $n\mu_n$ and variance $n\sigma_n^2$, we have by Chebyshev's inequality

$$(4.8) \quad \mathbf{P}\{|\mathbf{U}_1 + \cdots + \mathbf{U}_n - n\mu_n| > \epsilon n\mu_n\} \leq \frac{n\sigma_n^2}{\epsilon^2 n^2 \mu_n^2} < \frac{2}{\epsilon^2 \text{ Log } n} \to 0.$$

Now by (4.6) $\mu_n \sim \text{Log } n$, and hence (4.8) is equivalent to (4.5). ▶

5. VARIABLE DISTRIBUTIONS

Up to now we have considered only variables $\mathbf{X}_k$ having the same distribution. This situation corresponds to a repetition of the same game of chance, but it is more interesting to see what happens if the type of game changes at each step. It is not necessary to think of gambling places; the statistician who applies statistical tests is engaged in a dignified sort of gambling, and in his case the distribution of the random variables changes from occasion to occasion.

To fix ideas we shall imagine that an infinite sequence of probability distributions is given so that for each n we have n mutually independent variables $\mathbf{X}_1, \ldots, \mathbf{X}_n$ with the prescribed distributions. We assume that the means and variances exist and put

$$(5.1) \qquad\qquad \mu_k = \mathbf{E}(\mathbf{X}_k), \qquad \sigma_k^2 = \text{Var}(\mathbf{X}_k).$$

The sum $\mathbf{S}_n = \mathbf{X}_1 + \cdots + \mathbf{X}_n$ has mean m_n and variance s_n^2 given by

$$(5.2) \qquad m_n = \mu_1 + \cdots + \mu_n, \qquad s_n^2 = \sigma_1^2 + \cdots + \sigma_n^2$$

[cf. IX,(2.4) and IX,(5.6)]. In the special case of identical distributions we had $m_n = n\mu$, $s_n^2 = n\sigma^2$.

The (weak) law of large numbers is said to hold for the sequence $\{X_k\}$ if for every $\epsilon > 0$

$$(5.3) \qquad \mathbf{P}\left\{\frac{|S_n - m_n|}{n} > \epsilon\right\} \to 0.$$

The sequence $\{X_k\}$ is said to obey the central limit theorem if for every fixed $\alpha < \beta$

$$(5.4) \qquad \mathbf{P}\left\{\alpha < \frac{S_n - m_n}{s_n} < \beta\right\} \to \mathfrak{N}(\beta) - \mathfrak{N}(\alpha).$$

It is one of the salient features of probability theory that both the law of large numbers and the central limit theorem hold for a surprisingly large class of sequences $\{X_k\}$. In particular, the law of large numbers holds whenever the X_k are uniformly bounded, that is, whenever there exists a constant A such that $|X_k| < A$ for all k. More generally, a sufficient condition for the law of large numbers to hold is that

$$(5.5) \qquad \frac{s_n}{n} \to 0.$$

This is a direct consequence of the Chebyshev inequality, and the proof given in the opening passage of section 2 applies. Note, however, that the condition (5.5) is not necessary (cf. problem 14).

Various sufficient conditions for the central limit theorem have been discovered, but all were superseded by the Lindeberg[9] theorem according to which the central limit theorem holds whenever for every $\epsilon > 0$ the truncated variables U_k defined by

$$(5.6) \qquad \begin{aligned} \mathbf{U}_k &= \mathbf{X}_k - \mu_k & &\text{if} \quad |X_k - \mu_k| \leq \epsilon s_n, \\ \mathbf{U}_k &= 0 & &\text{if} \quad |X_k - \mu_k| > \epsilon s_n, \end{aligned}$$

satisfy the conditions $s_n \to \infty$ and

$$(5.7) \qquad \frac{1}{s_n^2}\sum_{k=1}^{n}\mathbf{E}(\mathbf{U}_k^2) \to 1.$$

If the X_k are uniformly bounded, that is, if $|X_k| < A$, then $U_k = = X_k - \mu_k$ for all n which are so large that $s_n > 2A\epsilon^{-1}$. The left side in (5.7) then equals 1. Therefore the Lindeberg theorem implies that every uniformly bounded sequence $\{X_k\}$ of mutually independent random variables

---

[9] J. W. Lindeberg, loc. cit. (footnote 3).

obeys the central limit theorem, provided, of course, that $s_n \to \infty$. It was found that the Lindeberg conditions are also necessary for (5.4) to hold.[10] The proof is deferred to the second volume, where we shall also give estimates for the difference between the two sides in (5.4).

When variables X_k have a common distribution we found the central limit theorem to be stronger than the law of large numbers. This is not so in general, and we shall see that the central limit theorem may apply to sequences which do not obey the law of large numbers.

Examples. (*a*) Let $\lambda > 0$ be fixed, and let $X_k = \pm k^\lambda$, each with probability $\frac{1}{2}$ (e.g., a coin is tossed, and at the kth throw the stakes are $\pm k^\lambda$). Here $\mu_k = 0$, $\sigma_k^2 = k^{2\lambda}$, and

$$(5.8) \qquad s_n^2 = 1^{2\lambda} + 2^{2\lambda} + 3^{2\lambda} + \cdots + n^{2\lambda} \sim \frac{n^{2\lambda+1}}{2\lambda + 1}.$$

The condition (5.5) is satisfied if $\lambda < \frac{1}{2}$. Therefore the law of large numbers holds if $\lambda < \frac{1}{2}$; we proceed to show that it does not hold if $\lambda \geq \frac{1}{2}$.

For $k = 1, 2, \ldots, n$ we have $|X_k| = k^\lambda \leq n^\lambda$, so that for $n > (2\lambda+1)\epsilon^{-2}$ the truncated variables U_k are identical with the X_k. Hence the Lindeberg condition holds, and so

$$(5.9) \qquad P\left\{ \alpha < \sqrt{\frac{2\lambda + 1}{n^{2\lambda+1}}} \, S_n < \beta \right\} \to \mathfrak{N}(\beta) - \mathfrak{N}(\alpha).$$

It follows that S_n is likely to be of the order of magnitude $n^{\lambda+\frac{1}{2}}$, so that the law of large numbers cannot apply for $\lambda \geq \frac{1}{2}$. We see that in this example *the central limit theorem applies for all $\lambda > 0$, but the law of large numbers only if $\lambda < \frac{1}{2}$.*

(*b*) Consider two independent sequences of 1000 tossings of a coin (or emptying two bags of 1000 coins each), and let us examine the *difference* **D** of the number of heads. Let the tossings of the two sequences be numbered from 1 to 1000 and from 1001 to 2000, respectively and define 2000 random variables X_k as follows: If the kth coin falls tails, then $X_k = 0$. If it falls heads, we put $X_k = 1$ for $k \leq 1000$ and $X_k = -1$, for $k > 1000$. Then $D = X_1 + \cdots + X_{2000}$. The variables X_k have mean $\mu_k = \pm\frac{1}{2}$ and variance $\sigma_k^2 = \frac{1}{4}$, and hence $E(D) = 0$ and $Var(D) = 500$. Thus the probability that the difference **D** will lie within

---

[10] W. Feller, *Über den zentralen Grenzwertsatz der Wahrscheinlichkeitsrechnung* Mathematische Zeitschrift, vol. 40 (1935), pp. 521–559. There also a generalized central limit theorem is derived which may apply to variables without expectations. Note that we are here considering only independent variables; for dependent variables the Lindeberg condition is neither necessary nor sufficient.

the limits $\pm\sqrt{500}\alpha$ is $\mathfrak{N}(\alpha) - \mathfrak{N}(-\alpha)$, approximately, and **D** is comparable to the deviation $\mathbf{S}_{2000} - 1000$ of the number of heads in 2000 tossings from its expected number 1000.

(c) An application to the *theory of inheritance* will illustrate the great variety of conclusions based on the central limit theorem. In V,5, we studied traits which depend essentially only on one pair of genes (alleles). We conceive of other characters (like height) as the cumulative effect of many pairs of genes. For simplicity, suppose that for each particular pair of genes there exist three genotypes *AA*, *Aa*, or *aa*. Let x_1, x_2, and x_3 be the corresponding contributions. The genotype of an individual is a random event, and the contribution of a particular pair of genes to the height is a random variable **X**, assuming the three values x_1, x_2, x_3 with certain probabilities. The height is the cumulative effect of many such random variables $\mathbf{X}_1, \mathbf{X}_2, \ldots, \mathbf{X}_n$, and since the contribution of each is small, we may in first approximation assume that the height is the *sum* $\mathbf{X}_1 + \cdots + \mathbf{X}_n$. It is true that not *all* the $\mathbf{X}_k$ are mutually independent. But the central limit theorem holds also for large classes of dependent variables, and, besides, it is plausible that the great majority of the $\mathbf{X}_k$ can be treated as independent. These considerations can be rendered more precise; here they serve only as indication of how the central limit theorem explains why many biometric characters, like height, exhibit an empirical distribution close to the normal distribution. This theory permits also the prediction of properties of inheritance, e.g., the dependence of the mean height of children on the height of their parents. Such biometric investigations were initiated by F. Galton and Karl Pearson.[11]   ▶

*6. APPLICATIONS TO COMBINATORIAL ANALYSIS

We shall give two examples of applications of the central limit theorem to problems not directly connected with probability theory. Both relate to the $n!$ permutations of the n elements $a_1, a_2, \ldots, a_n$, to each of which we attribute probability $1/n!$.

(a) Inversions. In a given permutation the element a_k is said to induce r inversions if it precedes exactly r elements with smaller index (i.e., elements which precede a_k in the natural order). For example, in $(a_3a_6a_1a_5a_2a_4)$ the elements a_1 and a_2 induce no inversion, a_3 induces two, a_4 none, a_5 two, and a_6 four. In $(a_6a_5a_4a_3a_2a_1)$ the element a_k induces $k - 1$ inversions and there are fifteen inversions in all. The

---

[11] Sir Francis Galton (1822–1911); Karl Pearson (1857–1936).

* This section treats a special topic and may be omitted.

number X_k of inversions induced by a_k is a random variable, and $S_n = X_1 + \cdots + X_n$ is the total number of inversions. Here X_k assumes the values $0, 1, \ldots, k-1$, each with probability $1/k$, and therefore

$$\mu_k = \frac{k-1}{2},$$

(6.1)

$$\sigma_k^2 = \frac{1 + 2^2 + \cdots + (k-1)^2}{k} - \left(\frac{k-1}{2}\right)^2 = \frac{k^2-1}{12}.$$

The number of inversions produced by a_k does not depend on the relative order of $a_1, a_2, \ldots, a_{k-1}$, and the X_k are therefore mutually independent. From (6.1) we get

(6.2)
$$m_n = \frac{1 + 2 + \cdots + (n-1)}{2} = \frac{n(n-1)}{4} \sim \frac{n^2}{4}$$

and

(6.3)
$$s_n^2 = \frac{1}{12} \sum_{k=1}^{n} (k^2-1) = \frac{2n^3 + 3n^2 - 5n}{72} \sim \frac{n^3}{36}.$$

For large n we have $\epsilon s_n > n \geq U_k$, and hence the variables U_k of the Lindeberg condition are identical with X_k. Therefore the central limit theorem applies, and we conclude that the *number* N_n *of permutations for which the number of inversions lies between the limits* $\dfrac{n^2}{4} \pm \dfrac{\alpha}{6} \sqrt{n^3}$ *is, asymptotically, given by* $n!\{\Re(\alpha) - \Re(-\alpha)\}$. In particular, for about one-half of all permutations the number of inversions lies between the limits $\frac{1}{4}n^2 \pm 0.11\sqrt{n^3}$.

(b) Cycles. Every permutation can be broken down into cycles, that is, groups of elements permuted among themselves. Thus in $(a_3 a_6 a_1 a_5 a_2 a_4)$ we find that a_1 and a_3 are interchanged, and that the remaining four elements are permuted among themselves; this permutation contains two cycles. If an element is in its natural place, it forms a cycle so that the identity permutation $(a_1, a_2, \ldots, a_n)$ contains as many cycles as elements. On the other hand, the cyclical permutations $(a_2, a_3, \ldots, a_n, a_1)$, $(a_3, a_4, \ldots, a_n, a_1, a_2)$, etc., contain a single cycle each. For the study of cycles it is convenient to describe the permutation by means of arrows indicating the places occupied by the several elements. For example, $1 \to 3 \to 4 \to 1$ indicates that a_1 is at the third place, a_3 at the fourth, and a_4 at the first, the third step thus completing the cycle. This description continues with a_2, which is the next element in the natural order. In this notation the permutation $(a_4, a_8, a_1, a_3, a_2, a_5, a_7, a_6)$ is described by: $1 \to 3 \to 4 \to 1$; $2 \to 5 \to 6 \to 8 \to 2$; $7 \to 7$. In other words, we construct a permutation $(a_1, \ldots, a_n)$ by a succession of n decisions. First we choose the place i to be occupied by a_1, next the place to be occupied by a_i, and so forth. At the 1st, 2nd, $\ldots$, nth step we have $n, n-1, \ldots, 1$ choices and exactly one among them completes a cycle.

Let X_k equal 1 if a cycle is completed at the kth step in this build-up; otherwise let $X_k = 0$. (In the last example $X_3 = X_7 = X_8 = 1$ and $X_1 = X_2 = X_4 = X_5 = X_6 = 0$.) Clearly $X_1 = 1$ if, and only if, a_1 is at the first place. From our construction it follows that $P\{X_k = 1\} = \dfrac{1}{n-k+1}$ and $P\{X_k = 0\} = \dfrac{n-k}{n-k+1}$, and that the variables X_k are mutually independent.[12] Their means and variances are

$$(6.4) \qquad \mu_k = \frac{1}{n-k+1}, \qquad \sigma_k^2 = \frac{n-k}{(n-k+1)^2}$$

whence

$$(6.5) \qquad m_n = 1 + \frac{1}{2} + \frac{1}{3} + \cdots + \frac{1}{n} \sim \log n$$

and

$$(6.6) \qquad s_n^2 = \sum_{k=1}^{n} \frac{n-k}{(n-k+1)^2} \sim \log n.$$

$S_n = X_1 + \cdots + X_n$ is the total number of cycles. *Its average is* m_n; *and the number of permutations with cycles between* $\log n + \alpha\sqrt{\log n}$ *and* $\log n + \beta\sqrt{\log n}$ *is given by* $n!\{\mathfrak{N}(\beta) - \mathfrak{N}(\alpha)\}$, *approximately*. The refined forms of the central limit theorem give more precise estimates.[13]

*7. THE STRONG LAW OF LARGE NUMBERS

The (weak) law of large numbers (5.3) asserts that for every particular sufficiently large n the deviation $|S_n - m_n|$ is likely to be small in comparison to n. It has been pointed out in connection with Bernoulli trials

---

[12] Formally, the distribution of X_k depends not only on k but also on n. It suffices to reorder the X_k, starting from $k = n$ down to $k = 1$, to have the distribution depend only on the subscript. [See also example XI, $(2.e)$.]

[13] A great variety of asymptotic estimates in combinatorial analysis were derived by other methods by V. Gončarov, *Du domaine d'analyse combinatoire*, Bulletin de l'Académie Sciences URSS, Sér. Math. (in Russian, French summary), vol. 8 (1944), pp. 3–48. The present method is simpler but more restricted in scope; cf. W. Feller, *The fundamental limit theorems in probability*, Bull. Amer. Math. Soc., vol. 51 (1945), pp. 800–832.

* This section treats a special topic and may be omitted.

(chapter VIII) that this does not imply that $|\mathbf{S}_n - m_n|/n$ remains small for all large n; it can happen that the law of large numbers applies but that $|\mathbf{S}_n - m_n|/n$ continues to fluctuate between finite or infinite limits. The law of large numbers permits only the conclusion that large values of $|\mathbf{S}_n - m_n|/n$ occur at infrequent moments.

We say that the sequence $\mathbf{X}_k$ *obeys the strong law of large numbers if to every pair* $\epsilon > 0$, $\delta > 0$, *there corresponds an* N *such that there is probability* $1 - \delta$ *or better that for every* $r > 0$ *all* $r + 1$ *inequalities*

$$(7.1) \qquad \frac{|\mathbf{S}_n - m_n|}{n} < \epsilon, \qquad n = N, N + 1, \ldots, N + r$$

will be satisfied.

We can interpret (7.1) roughly by saying that with an overwhelming probability $|\mathbf{S}_n - m_n|/n$ *remains* small[14] for all $n > N$.

The Kolmogorov Criterion. *The convergence of the series*

$$(7.2) \qquad \sum \sigma_k^2/k^2$$

is a sufficient condition for the strong law of large numbers to apply to the sequence of mutually independent random variables $\mathbf{X}_k$ *with variances* σ_k^2.

Proof. Let A_ν be the event that for at least one n with $2^{\nu-1} < n \leq 2^\nu$ the inequality (7.1) does *not* hold. Obviously it suffices to prove that for all ν sufficiently large and all r

$$\mathbf{P}\{A_\nu\} + \mathbf{P}\{A_{\nu+1}\} + \cdots + \mathbf{P}\{A_{\nu+r}\} < \delta,$$

that is, that the series $\sum \mathbf{P}\{A_\nu\}$ converges. Now the event A_ν implies that for some n with $2^{\nu-1} < n \leq 2^\nu$

$$(7.3) \qquad |\mathbf{S}_n - m_n| \geq \epsilon \cdot 2^{\nu-1}$$

and by Kolmogorov's inequality of IV,7

$$(7.4) \qquad \mathbf{P}\{A_\nu\} \leq 4\epsilon^{-2} \cdot s_{2^\nu}^2 \cdot 2^{-2\nu}.$$

Hence

$$(7.5) \quad \sum_{\nu=1}^\infty \mathbf{P}\{A_\nu\} \leq 4\epsilon^{-2} \sum_{\nu=1}^\infty 2^{-2\nu} \sum_{k=1}^{2^\nu} \sigma_k^2 = 4\epsilon^{-2} \sum_{k=1}^\infty \sigma_k^2 \sum_{2^\nu \geq k} 2^{-2\nu} \leq 8\epsilon^{-2} \sum_{k=1}^\infty \frac{\sigma^2}{k^2}$$

which accomplishes the proof. ▶

---

[14] The general theory introduces a sample space corresponding to the infinite sequence $\{\mathbf{X}_k\}$. The strong law then states that with probability one $|\mathbf{S}_n - m_n|/n$ tends to zero. In real variable terminology the strong law asserts convergence almost everywhere, and the weak law is equivalent to convergence in measure.

As a typical application we prove the

Theorem. *If the mutually independent random variables* $\mathbf{X}_k$ *have a common distribution* $\{f(x_j)\}$ *and if* $\mu = \mathbf{E}(\mathbf{X}_k)$ *exists, then the strong law of large numbers applies to the sequence* $\{\mathbf{X}_k\}$.

This theorem is, of course, stronger than the weak law of section 1. The two theorems are treated independently because of the methodological interest of the proofs. For a converse cf. problems 17 and 18.

Proof. We again use the method of truncation. Two new sequences of random variables are introduced by

(7.6)
$$\mathbf{U}_k = \mathbf{X}_k, \qquad \mathbf{V}_k = 0 \qquad \qquad if \ \ |\mathbf{X}_k| < k,$$
$$\mathbf{U}_k = 0, \qquad \mathbf{V}_k = \mathbf{X}_k \qquad \qquad if \ \ |\mathbf{X}_k| \geq k.$$

The $\mathbf{U}_k$ are mutually independent, and we proceed to show that they satisfy Kolmogorov's criterion. For $\sigma_k^2 = \mathrm{Var}(\mathbf{U}_k)$ we get

(7.7)
$$\sigma_k^2 \leq \mathbf{E}(\mathbf{U}_k^2) = \sum_{|x_j| < k} x_j^2 f(x_j).$$

Put for abbreviation

(7.8)
$$a_v = \sum_{v-1 \leq |x_j| < v} |x_j| \, f(x_j).$$

Then the series $\sum a_v$ converges since $\mathbf{E}(\mathbf{X}_k)$ exists. Moreover, from (7.7),

(7.9)
$$\sigma_k^2 \leq a_1 + 2a_2 + 3a_3 + \cdots + ka_k$$
and

(7.10)
$$\sum_{k=1}^{\infty} \frac{\sigma_k^2}{k^2} \leq \sum_{k=1}^{\infty} \frac{1}{k^2} \sum_{v=1}^{k} v a_v = \sum_{v=1}^{\infty} v a_v \sum_{k=v}^{\infty} \frac{1}{k^2} < 2 \sum_{v=1}^{\infty} a_v < \infty.$$

Thus the criterion (7.2) holds for $\{\mathbf{U}_k\}$. Now

(7.11)
$$\mathbf{E}(\mathbf{U}_k) = \mu_k = \sum_{|x_j| < k} x_j f(x_j)$$

so that $\mu_k \to \mu$ and hence $(\mu_1 + \mu_2 + \cdots + \mu_n)/n \to \mu$. From the strong law of large numbers for $\{\mathbf{U}_k\}$ we conclude therefore that with probability $1 - \delta$ or better

(7.12)
$$\left| n^{-1} \sum_{k=1}^{n} \mathbf{U}_k - \mu \right| < \epsilon$$

for *all* $n > N$ provided N is chosen sufficiently large. It remains to prove that the same assertion holds true when the $\mathbf{U}_k$ are replaced by

X_k. It suffices obviously to show that N can be chosen so large that with a probability arbitrarily close to unity the event $U_k = X_k$ occurs for all $k > N$. This amounts to saying that with probability one only finitely many among the variables V_k are different from zero. By the first Borel-Cantelli lemma of VIII,3 this is the case whenever the series $\sum P\{V_k \neq 0\}$ converges, and we now complete the proof by establishing the convergence of this series. Obviously

$$(7.13)\quad P\{V_n \neq 0\} = \sum_{|x_j| \geq n} f(x_j) \leq \frac{a_{n+1}}{n} + \frac{a_{n+2}}{n+1} + \frac{a_{n+3}}{n+2} + \cdots$$

and hence

$$(7.14)\quad \sum P\{V_n \neq 0\} \leq \sum_{n=1}^{\infty} \sum_{v=n}^{\infty} \frac{a_{v+1}}{v} = \sum_{v=1}^{\infty} \frac{a_{v+1}}{v} \sum_{n=1}^{v} 1 = \sum_v a_{v+1} < \infty,$$

as asserted.

8. PROBLEMS FOR SOLUTION

1. Prove that the law of large numbers applies in example (5.a) also when $\lambda \leq 0$. The central limit theorem holds if $\lambda \geq -\frac{1}{2}$.

2. Decide whether the law of large numbers and the central limit theorem hold for the sequences of mutually independent variables X_k with distributions defined as follows $(k \geq 1)$:

(a) $P\{X_k = \pm 2^k\} = \frac{1}{2}$;

(b) $P\{X_k = \pm 2^k\} = 2^{-(2k+1)}$, $P\{X_k = 0\} = 1 - 2^{-2k}$;

(c) $P\{X_k = \pm k\} = 1/(2\sqrt{k})$, $P\{X_k = 0\} = 1 - 1/\sqrt{k}$.

3. *Ljapunov's condition* (1901). Show that Lindeberg's condition is satisfied if for some $\delta > 0$

$$\frac{1}{s_m^{2+\delta}} \sum_{k=1}^{n} E|(X_k|^{2+\delta}) \to 0.$$

4. Let the X_k be mutually independent random variables such that X_k assumes the $2k + 1$ values $0, \pm L_k, \pm 2L_k, \ldots, \pm k L_k$, each with probability $1/(2k+1)$. Find conditions on the constants L_k which will ensure that the law of large numbers and/or the central limit theorem holds for $\{X_k\}$.

5. Do the same problem if X_k assumes the values $a_k, -a_k,$ and 0 with probabilities p_k, p_k and $1 - 2p_k$.

Note: *The following seven problems treat the weak law of large numbers for dependent variables.*

6. In problem 13 of V, 8 let $X_k = 1$ if the kth throw results in red, and $X_k = 0$ otherwise. Show that the law of large numbers does not apply.

7. Let the $\{X_k\}$ be mutually independent and have a common distribution with mean μ and finite variance. If $S_n = X_1 + \cdots + X_n$, prove that the law

of large numbers does not hold for the sequence $\{S_n\}$ but holds for $a_n S_n$ if $n a_n \to 0$.

8. Let $\{X_k\}$ be a sequence of random variables such that X_k may depend on X_{k-1} and X_{k+1} but is independent of all other X_j. Show that the law of large numbers holds, provided the X_k have bounded variances.

9. If the joint distribution of $(X_1, \ldots, X_n)$ is defined for every n so that the variances are bounded and all covariances are negative, the law of large numbers applies.

10. *Continuation.* Replace the condition $\mathrm{Cov}\,(X_j, X_k) \leq 0$ by the assumption that $\mathrm{Cov}\,(X_j, X_k) \to 0$ uniformly as $|j - k| \to \infty$. Prove that the law of large numbers holds.

11. If $|S_n| < cn$ and $\mathrm{Var}\,(S_n) > \alpha n^2$, then the law of large numbers does not apply to $\{X_k\}$.

12. In the Polya urn scheme [example V, $(2.c)$] let X_k equal 1 or 0 according to whether the kth ball drawn is black or red. Then S_n is the number of black balls in n drawings. Prove that the law of large numbers does not apply to $\{X_k\}$. *Hint:* Use the preceding problem and problem 30 of IX, 9.

---

13. The mutually independent random variables X_k assume the values $r = 2, 3, 4, \ldots$ with probability $p_r = c/(r^2 \log r)$ where c is a constant such that $\sum p_r = 1$. Show that the generalized law of large numbers (4.1) holds if we put $e_n = c \cdot n \, \log \log n$.

14. Let $\{X_n\}$ be a sequence of mutually independent random variables such that $X_n = \pm 1$ with probability $(1 - 2^{-n})/2$ and $X_n = \pm 2^n$ with probability 2^{-n-1}. Prove that both the weak and the strong law of large numbers apply to $\{X_k\}$. [*Note:* This shows that the condition (5.5) is not necessary.]

15. *Example of an unfavorable "fair" game.* Let the possible values of the gain at each trial be $0, 2, 2^2, 2^3, \ldots$; the probability of the gain being 2^k is

$$(8.1) \qquad p_k = \frac{1}{2^k k(k+1)},$$

and the probability of 0 is $p_0 = 1 - (p_1 + p_2 + \cdots)$. The expected gain is

$$(8.2) \qquad \mu = \sum 2^k p_k = (1 - \tfrac{1}{2}) + (\tfrac{1}{2} - \tfrac{1}{3}) + (\tfrac{1}{3} - \tfrac{1}{4}) + \cdots = 1.$$

Assume that at each trial the player pays a unit amount as entrance fee, so that after n trials his net gain (or loss) is $S_n - n$. Show that for every $\epsilon > 0$ *the probability approaches unity that in n trials the player will have sustained a loss greater than* $(1 - \epsilon)n/\mathrm{Log}_2\, n$, where $\mathrm{Log}_2\, n$ denotes the logarithm to the base 2. In symbols, prove that

$$(8.3) \qquad \mathbf{P}\left\{ S_n - n < - \frac{(1 - \epsilon)n}{\mathrm{Log}_2\, n} \right\} \to 1,$$

Hint: Use the truncation method of section 4, but replace the bound $n \, \mathrm{Log}\, n$ of (4.2) by $n/\mathrm{Log}_2\, n$. Show that the probability that $U_k = X_k$ for all $k \leq n$

tends to 1 and prove that

$$(8.4) \qquad \mathbf{P}\left\{|\mathbf{U}_1 + \cdots + \mathbf{U}_n - n\mathbf{E}(\mathbf{U}_1)| < \frac{\epsilon n}{\mathrm{Log}_2\, n}\right\} \to 1.$$

$$(8.5) \qquad 1 - \frac{1}{\mathrm{Log}_2\, n} \geq \mathbf{E}(\mathbf{U}_1) \geq 1 - \frac{1 + \epsilon}{\mathrm{Log}_2\, n}.$$

For details see the paper cited in footnote 5.

16. Let $\{\mathbf{X}_n\}$ be a sequence of mutually independent random variables with a common distribution. Suppose that the $\mathbf{X}_n$ do not have a finite expectation and let A be a positive constant. The probability is one that infinitely many among the events $|\mathbf{X}_n| > An$ occur.

17. *Converse to the strong law of large numbers.* Under the assumption of problem 16 there is probability one that $|\mathbf{S}_n| > An$ for infinitely many n.

18. *A converse to Kolmogorov's criterion.* If $\sum \sigma_k^2/k^2$ diverges, then there exists a sequence $\{\mathbf{X}_k\}$ of mutually independent random variables with Var $\{\mathbf{X}_k\} = \sigma_k^2$ for which the strong law of large numbers does not apply. *Hint:* Prove first that the convergence of $\sum \mathbf{P}\{|\mathbf{X}_n| > \epsilon n\}$ is a necessary condition for the strong law to apply.

CHAPTER XI

Integral-Valued Variables.
Generating Functions

1. GENERALITIES

Among discrete random variables those assuming only the integral values $k = 0, 1, 2, \ldots$ are of special importance. Their study is facilitated by the powerful method of generating functions which will later be recognized as a special case of the method of characteristic functions on which the theory of probability depends to a large extent. More generally, the subject of generating functions belongs to the domain of operational methods which are widely used in the theory of differential and integral equations. In the theory of probability generating functions have been used since DeMoivre and Laplace, but the power and the possibilities of the method are rarely fully utilized.

Definition. *Let* $a_0, a_1, a_2, \ldots$ *be a sequence of real numbers. If*

$$(1.1) \qquad A(s) = a_0 + a_1 s + a_2 s^2 + \cdots$$

converges in some interval $-s_0 < s < s_0$, *then* $A(s)$ *is called the generating function of the sequence* $\{a_j\}$.

The variable s itself has no significance. If the sequence $\{a_j\}$ is bounded, then a comparison with the geometric series shows that (1.1) converges at least for $|s| < 1$.

Examples. If $a_j = 1$ for all j, then $A(s) = 1/(1-s)$. The generating function of the sequence $(0, 0, 1, 1, 1, \ldots)$ is $s^2/(1-s)$. The sequence $a_j = 1/j!$ has the generating function e^s. For fixed n the sequence $a_j = \binom{n}{j}$ has the generating function $(1+s)^n$. If $\mathbf{X}$ is the number scored in a throw of a perfect die, the probability distribution of $\mathbf{X}$ has the generating function $(s+s^2+s^3+s^4+s^5+s^6)/6$. ▶

Let X be a random variable assuming the values $0, 1, 2, \ldots$. It will be convenient to have a notation both for the distribution of X and for its tails, and we shall write

$$(1.2) \qquad \mathbf{P}\{X = j\} = p_j, \qquad \mathbf{P}\{X > j\} = q_j.$$

Then

$$(1.3) \qquad q_k = p_{k+1} + p_{k+2} + \cdots \qquad\qquad k \geq 0.$$

The generating functions of the sequences $\{p_j\}$ and $\{q_k\}$ are

$$(1.4) \qquad P(s) = p_0 + p_1 s + p_2 s^2 + p_3 s^3 + \cdots$$

$$(1.5) \qquad Q(s) = q_0 + q_1 s + q_2 s^2 + q_3 s^3 + \cdots.$$

As $P(1) = 1$, *the series for $P(s)$ converges absolutely at least for* $-1 \leq s \leq 1$. The coefficients of $Q(s)$ are less than unity, and so *the series for $Q(s)$ converges at least in the open interval* $-1 < s < 1$.

Theorem 1. *For* $-1 < s < 1$

$$(1.6) \qquad Q(s) = \frac{1 - P(s)}{1 - s}.$$

Proof. The coefficient of s^n in $(1-s) \cdot Q(s)$ equals $q_n - q_{n-1} = -p_n$ when $n \geq 1$, and equals $q_0 = p_1 + p_2 + \cdots = 1 - p_0$ when $n = 0$. Therefore $(1-s) \cdot Q(s) = 1 - P(s)$ as asserted. ▶

Next we examine the derivative

$$(1.7) \qquad P'(s) = \sum_{k=1}^{\infty} k p_k s^{k-1}.$$

The series converges at least for $-1 < s < 1$. For $s = 1$ the right side reduces formally to $\sum k p_k = \mathbf{E}(X)$. Whenever this expectation exists, the derivative $P'(s)$ will be continuous in the closed interval $-1 \leq s \leq 1$. If $\sum k p_k$ diverges, then $P'(s) \to \infty$ as $s \to 1$. In this case we say that X *has an infinite expectation* and write $P'(1) = \mathbf{E}(X) = \infty$. (All quantities being positive, there is no danger in the use of the symbol ∞.) Applying the mean value theorem to the numerator in (1.6), we see that $Q(s) = P'(\sigma)$ where σ is a point lying between s and 1. Since both functions are monotone this implies that $P(s)$ and $Q(s)$ have the same finite or infinite limit which we denote by $P(1)$ or $Q(1)$. This proves

Theorem 2. *The expectation $\mathbf{E}(X)$ satisfies the relations*

$$(1.8) \qquad \mathbf{E}(X) = \sum_{j=1}^{\infty} j p_j = \sum_{k=0}^{\infty} q_k,$$

or in terms of the generating functions,

(1.9) $$E(X) = P'(1) = Q(1).$$

By differentiation of (1.7) and of the relation $P'(s) = Q(s) - (1-s)Q'(s)$ we find in the same way

(1.10) $$E(X(X-1)) = \sum k(k-1)p_k = P''(1) = 2Q'(1).$$

To obtain the variance of X we have to add $E(X) - E^2(X)$ which leads us to

Theorem 3. *We have*

(1.11) $$\text{Var}(X) = P''(1) + P'(1) - P'^2(1) =$$
$$= 2Q'(1) + Q(1) - Q^2(1).$$

In the case of an infinite variance $P''(s) \to \infty$ as $s \to 1$.

The realtions (1.9) and (1.11) frequently provide the simplest means to calculate $E(X)$ and $Var(X)$.

2. CONVOLUTIONS

If a random variable X assumes only non-negative integral values, then s^X is a well-defined new random variable, and the generating function of the distribution of X can be written in the compact form $E(s^X)$. If X and Y are independent, so are s^X and s^Y, and hence

$$E(s^{X+Y}) = E(s^X)E(s^Y).$$

We proceed to give a different proof for this important result because it will lead us to a useful generalization.

Let X and Y be non-negative independent integral-valued random variables with probability distributions $P\{X = j\} = a_j$ and $P\{Y = j\} = b_j$. The event $(X = j, Y = k)$ has probability $a_j b_k$. The sum $S = X + Y$ is a new random variable, and the event $S = r$ is the union of the mutually exclusive events

$$(X = 0, Y = r), \quad (X = 1, Y = r - 1), \ldots, (X = r, Y = 0).$$

Therefore the distribution $c_r = P\{S = r\}$ is given by

(2.1) $$c_r = a_0 b_r + a_1 b_{r-1} + a_2 b_{r-2} + \cdots + a_{r-1} b_1 + a_r b_0.$$

The operation (2.1), leading from the two sequences $\{a_k\}$ and $\{b_k\}$ to a new sequence $\{c_k\}$, occurs so frequently that it is convenient to introduce a special name and notation for it.

Definition. *Let* $\{a_k\}$ *and* $\{b_k\}$ *be any two numerical sequences (not necessarily probability distributions). The new sequence* $\{c_r\}$ *defined by* (2.1) *is called the convolution[1] of* $\{a_k\}$ *and* $\{b_k\}$ *and will be denoted by*

$$(2.2) \qquad \{c_k\} = \{a_k\} * \{b_k\}.$$

Examples. (*a*) If $a_k = b_k = 1$ for all $k \geq 0$, then $c_k = k + 1$. If $a_k = k$, $b_k = 1$, then $c_k = 1 + 2 + \cdots + k = k(k+1)/2$. Finally, if $a_0 = a_1 = \frac{1}{2}$, $a_k = 0$ for $k \geq 2$, then $c_k = (b_k + b_{k-1})/2$, etc. ▶

The sequences $\{a_k\}$ and $\{b_k\}$ have generating functions $A(s) = \sum a_k s^k$ and $B(s) = \sum b_k s^k$. The product $A(s)B(s)$ can be obtained by termwise multiplication of the power series for $A(s)$ and $B(s)$. Collecting terms with equal powers of s, we find that the coefficient c_r of s^r in the expansion of $A(s)B(s)$ is given by (2.1). We have thus the

Theorem. *If* $\{a_k\}$ *and* $\{b_k\}$ *are sequences with generating functions* $A(s)$ *and* $B(s)$, *and* $\{c_k\}$ *is their convolution, then the generating function* $C(s) = \sum c_k s^k$ *is the product*

$$(2.3) \qquad C(s) = A(s)B(s).$$

If **X** *and* **Y** *are non-negative integral-valued mutually independent random variables with generating functions* $A(s)$ *and* $B(s)$, *then their sum* **X** + **Y** *has the generating function* $A(s)B(s)$.

Let now $\{a_k\}, \{b_k\}, \{c_k\}, \{d_k\}, \ldots$ be any sequences. We can form the convolution $\{a_k\} * \{b_k\}$, and then the convolution of this new sequence with $\{c_k\}$, etc. The generating function of $\{a_k\} * \{b_k\} * \{c_k\} * \{d_k\}$ is $A(s)B(s)C(s)D(s)$, and this fact shows that the order in which the convolutions are performed is immaterial. For example, $\{a_k\} * \{b_k\} * \{c_k\} = \{c_k\} * \{b_k\} * \{a_k\}$, etc. *Thus the convolution is an associative and commutative operation* (exactly as the summation of random variables).

In the study of sums of independent random variables $\mathbf{X}_n$ the special case where the $\mathbf{X}_n$ have a common distribution is of particular interest. If $\{a_j\}$ is the common probability distribution of the $\mathbf{X}_n$, then the distribution of $\mathbf{S}_n = \mathbf{X}_1 + \cdots + \mathbf{X}_n$ will be denoted by $\{a_j\}^{n*}$. Thus

$$(2.4) \qquad \{a_j\}^{2*} = \{a_j\} * \{a_j\}, \qquad \{a_j\}^{3*} = \{a_j\}^{2*} * \{a_j\}, \ldots$$

and generally

$$(2.5) \qquad \{a_j\}^{n*} = \{a_j\}^{(n-1)*} * \{a_j\}.$$

---

[1] Some writers prefer the German word *faltung*. The French equivalent is *composition*.

In words, $\{a_j\}^{n*}$ *is the sequence of numbers whose generating function is* $A^n(s)$. In particular, $\{a_j\}^{1*}$ is the same as $\{a_j\}$, and $\{a_j\}^{0*}$ *is defined as the sequence whose generating function is* $A^0(s) = 1$, *that is, the sequence* $(1, 0, 0, 0, \ldots)$.

Examples. (b) *Binomial distribution.* The generating function of the binomial distribution with terms $b(k; n, p) = \binom{n}{k} p^k q^{n-k}$ is

$$(2.6) \qquad \sum_{k=0}^{n} \binom{n}{k} (ps)^k q^{n-k} = (q+ps)^n.$$

The fact that this generating function is the nth power of $q + ps$ shows that $\{b(k; n, p)\}$ is the distribution of a sum $\mathbf{S}_n = \mathbf{X}_1 + \cdots + \mathbf{X}_n$ of n independent random variables with the common generating function $q + ps$; each variable $\mathbf{X}_j$ assumes the value 0 with probability q and the value 1 with probability p. Thus

$$(2.7) \qquad \{b(k; n, p)\} = \{b(k; 1, p)\}^{n*}.$$

The representation $\mathbf{S}_n = \mathbf{X}_1 + \cdots + \mathbf{X}_n$ has already been used [e.g., in examples IX,(3.a) and IX, (5.a)]. The preceding argument may be reversed to obtain a new derivation of the binomial distribution. The mutliplicative property $(q+ps)^m(q+ps)^n = (q+ps)^{m+n}$ shows also that

$$(2.8) \qquad \{b(k; m, p)\} * \{b(k; n, p)\} = \{b(k; m+n, p)\}$$

which is the same as VI,(10.4). Differentiation of $(q+ps)^n$ leads also to a simple proof that $\mathbf{E}(\mathbf{S}_n) = np$ and $\text{Var}(\mathbf{S}_n) = npq$.

(c) *Poisson distribution.* The generating function of the distribution $p(k; \lambda) = e^{-\lambda} \lambda^k / k!$ is

$$(2.9) \qquad \sum_{k=0}^{\infty} e^{-\lambda} \frac{(\lambda s)^k}{k!} = e^{-\lambda + \lambda s}.$$

It follows that

$$(2.10) \qquad \{p(k; \lambda)\} * \{p(k; \mu)\} = \{p(k; \lambda+\mu)\},$$

which is the same as VI,(10.5). By differentiation we find again that both mean and variance of the Poisson distribution equal λ [cf. example IX,(4.c)].

(d) *Geometric and negative binomial distributions.* Let $\mathbf{X}$ be a random variable with the geometric distribution

$$(2.11) \qquad \mathbf{P}\{\mathbf{X} = k\} = q^k p, \qquad\qquad k = 0, 1, 2, \ldots$$

where p *and* q *are positive constants with* $p + q = 1$. *The corresponding generating function is*

$$(2.12) \qquad p \sum_{k=0}^{\infty} (qs)^k = \frac{p}{1 - qs}.$$

Using the results of section 1 we find easily $E(X) = q/p$ and $Var(X) = q/p^2$, in agreement with the findings in example IX,(3.c).

In a sequence of Bernoulli trials the probability that the *first success* occurs after exactly k failures [i.e., at the $(k+1)$st trial] is $q^k p$, and so X may be interpreted as the *waiting time for the first success*. Strictly speaking, such an interpretation refers to an infinite sample space, and the advantage of the formal definition (2.11) and the terminology of random variables is that we need not worry about the structure of the original sample space. The same is true of *the waiting time for the rth success*. If X_k denotes the number of failures following the $(k-1)$st and preceding the kth success, then $S_r = X_1 + X_2, + \cdots + X_r$ is the total number of failures preceding the rth success (and $S_r + r$ is the number of trials up to and including the rth success). The notion of Bernoulli trials requires that the X_k should be mutually independent with the same distribution (2.11), and we can *define* the X_k by this property. Then S_r has the generating function

$$(2.13) \qquad \left(\frac{p}{1 - qs}\right)^r.$$

and the binomial expansion II,(8.7) shows at once that the coefficient of s^k equals

$$(2.14) \qquad f(k; r, p) = \binom{-r}{k} p^r (-q)^k, \qquad k = 0, 1, 2, \ldots.$$

It follows that $P\{S_r = k\} = f(k; r, p)$, in agreement with the distribution for the number of failures preceding the rth success derived in VI,8. We can restate this result by saying that *the distribution* $\{f(k; r, p)\}$ *is the r-fold convolution of the geometric distribution with itself*, in symbols

$$(2.15) \qquad \{f(k; r, p)\} = \{q^k p\}^{r*}.$$

So far we have considered r as an integer, but it will be recalled from VI,8, that $\{f(k; r, p)\}$ defines the *negative binomial distribution* also when $r > 0$ is not an integer. The generating function is still defined by (2.13) and we see that for arbitrary $r > 0$ the *mean and variance of the negative binomial distribution are rq/p and rq/p^2 and that*

$$(2.16) \qquad \{f(k; r_1, p)\} * \{f(k; r_2, p)\} = \{f(k; r_1 + r_2, p)\}.$$

(e) *Cycles.* In X,(6.b) we studied the number S_n of cycles in a random permutation of n elements. It was shown that it is possible to represent this random variable as the sum $S_n = X_1 + \cdots + X_n$ of n independent variables such that X_k assumes the two values 1 and 0 with probabilities $(n-k+1)^{-1}$ and $(n-k)(n-k+1)^{-1}$, respectively. It follows immediately that the generating function of S_n is given by the product

$$(2.17) \qquad \frac{n-1+s}{n} \cdot \frac{n-2+s}{n-1} \cdots \frac{1+s}{2} \cdot \frac{s}{1} = (-1)^n \binom{-s}{n}.$$

The coefficients of this polynomial determine the probability distribution of S_n, but an explicit representation requires knowledge of the Stirling numbers. We have here an example of a very usual situation, namely that the generating function is simpler than the probability distribution itself. It is therefore fortunate that much information can be extracted from the generating function. ▶

3. EQUALIZATIONS AND WAITING TIMES IN BERNOULLI TRIALS

We pause here to illustrate the power and the flexibility of the method of generating functions by a discussion of a few important problems of methodological interest. The results play a prominent role in the theory of random walks and may be considered the prototypes of related results in diffusion theory. They will be derived by different methods in chapter XIV (see, in particular, sections 4 and 9). In the special case $p = \frac{1}{2}$ the results were derived in a different form by combinatorial methods in chapter III. A comparison of the methods should prove illuminating.[2]

In the following we consider Bernoulli trials with probability p for success. We put $X_k = +1$ if the kth trial results in success, and $X_k = -1$ otherwise. In other words, the object of our investigation is a sequence of mutually independent random variables assuming the values $+1$ and -1, with probabilities p and q, respectively. This description is simplest and most natural, but since it refers to an unending sequence of trials it leads formally to nondenumerable sample spaces. Actually we shall only calculate certain probabilities involving a specified finite number of trials, and so there arise no problems of principle. We could speak of a fixed number N of trials and let $N \to \infty$, but this would be unnecessary pedantry and harmful to probabilistic intuition.

As usual we put

$$(3.1) \qquad S_n = X_1 + \cdots + X_n, \qquad S_0 = 0.$$

---

[2] It should be clear from this account that the present section is inserted for purposes of illustration as well as for its intrinsic interest, but that it is not a prerequisite for the remainder of this book.

In the time-honored gambling terminology Peter and Paul are playing for unit stakes and S_n represents Peter's accumulated gain at the conclusion of the nth trial. In random walk terminology S_n is the position of a "particle" which at regular time intervals takes a unit step to the right or to the left. The random walk is unsymmetric if $p \neq \frac{1}{2}$.

(a) Waiting Time for a Gain. The event

$$(3.2) \qquad S_1 \leq 0, \ldots, S_{n-1} \leq 0, \qquad S_n = 1$$

signifies in gambling terminology that the nth trial is the first to render Peter's accumulated gain positive. In random walk terminology *the first visit to* $+1$ takes place at the nth step; a more usual description employs the language of physical diffusion theory and refers to a *first passage* through 1. We seek the probability ϕ_n of the event (3.2). More precisely, we seek their generating function

$$(3.3) \qquad \Phi(s) = \sum_{n=0}^{\infty} \phi_n s^n$$

where we put $\phi_0 = 0$ for convenience.[3] By definition $\phi_1 = p$. If (3.2) holds for some $n > 1$ then $S_1 = -1$ and there exists a *smallest* subscript $\nu < n$ such that $S_\nu = 0$. The outcome of the first n trials may now be described in gambling terminology as follows. (1) At the first trial Peter loses a unit amount. (2) It takes exactly $\nu - 1$ further trials for Peter to reestablish the initial situation. (3) It takes exactly $n - \nu$ further trials for Peter to attain a positive net gain. These three events depend on non-overlapping blocks of trials and are therefore mutually independent. From the definition it is clear that the events (2) and (3) have probabilities $\phi_{\nu-1}$ and $\phi_{n-\nu}$, respectively, and so the probability of the simultaneous realization of all three events is given by the product $q\phi_{\nu-1}\phi_{n-\nu}$. Now the event (3.2) occurs if, and only if, the events (1)–(3) occur for some $\nu < n$. Summing over all possible ν we get

$$(3.4) \qquad \phi_n = q(\phi_1\phi_{n-2} + \phi_2\phi_{n-3} + \cdots + \phi_{n-2}\phi_1).$$

It must be remembered that this relation is valid only for $n > 1$ and that $\phi_1 = p$ and $\phi_0 = 0$. Multiplying (3.4) by s^n and summing over $n = 2, 3, \ldots$ we get therefore on the left $\Phi(s) - ps$. The quantity within the parenthesis is the $(n-1)$st term of the convolution $\{\phi_n\} * \{\phi_n\}$, and

---

[3] As will be seen later on, the generating function Φ can be obtained directly by a simple probabilistic argument. The following less elegant derivation is given because it provides a good exercise in handling convolution equations, which also appear in various contexts outside probability theory. (See, for example, problem 6.)

so the right side leads to $qs \cdot \Phi^2(s)$ by the theorem of section 2. We see thus that *the generating function* Φ *satisfies the quadratic equation*

$$(3.5) \qquad \Phi(s) - ps = qs\Phi^2(s).$$

Of the two roots one is unbounded near $s = 0$, and the unique bounded solution is given by

$$(3.6) \qquad \Phi(s) = \frac{1 - \sqrt{1 - 4pqs^2}}{2qs},$$

where $\sqrt{}$ denotes the positive root. The binomial expansion II,(8.7) enables us to write down the coefficients in the form

$$(3.7) \qquad \phi_{2k-1} = \frac{(-1)^{k-1}}{2q}\binom{\frac{1}{2}}{k}(4pq)^k, \qquad \phi_{2k} = 0.$$

We are thus in the possession of explicit expressions for the required probabilities ϕ_k, but they are of secondary interest; it is more instructive to extract the relevant information directly from the generating function.

First we note that the sum $\sum\phi_n$ is given by

$$(3.8) \qquad \Phi(1) = \frac{1 - |p - q|}{2q},$$

and so

$$(3.9) \qquad \sum \phi_n = \begin{array}{ll} p/q & \text{if } \ p < q \\ 1 & \text{if } \ p \geq q. \end{array}$$

In other words: *If* $p < q$ *the probability that the sums* $\mathbf{S}_n$ *remain negative forever equals* $(q-p)/q$. If $p \geq q$ this probability is zero so that with probability one $\mathbf{S}_n$ will sooner or later become positive. How long will it take? An easy calculation shows that $\Phi'(1) = (p-q)^{-1}$ if $p > q$ and $\Phi'(1) = \infty$ if $p = q = \frac{1}{2}$. We conclude that *when* $p = \frac{1}{2}$ *the number of trials preceding the first positive sum* $\mathbf{S}_n$ *has infinite expectation.*

It is worthwhile to restate this noteworthy result in gambling terminology. It implies that in an ideal coin-tossing game Peter is theoretically sure sooner or later to attain a positive net gain, but the expected number of trials required to achieve this goal is infinite. A player with finite capital is therefore by no means certain of ever reaching a positive net gain. We shall return to this question in connection with the ruin problem in chapter XIV.

The derivation of the quadratic equation (3.5) for Φ may be described more concisely in probabilistic terms as follows. Denote by $\mathbf{N}$ the first subscript for which $\mathbf{S_N} > 0$. Then $\mathbf{N}$ is a random variable in the slightly generalized sense that it is not defined in the event that $\mathbf{S}_n \leq 0$ for *all* n. (In the terminology of chapter XIII we should call $\mathbf{N}$ a *defective variable*.) The generating function Φ can now be written in the form $\Phi(s) = E(s^{\mathbf{N}})$. If $\mathbf{X}_1 = -1$ we have $\mathbf{N} = 1 + \mathbf{N}_1 + \mathbf{N}_2$, where $\mathbf{N}_1$ is the number of trials required to increase the partial sums $\mathbf{S}_k$ from -1 to 0, and $\mathbf{N}_2$ is the number of subsequent trials required for the increase from 0 to 1. These variables are independent and have the same distribution as $\mathbf{N}$. For the conditional expectation of $s^{\mathbf{N}}$ we get therefore

$$E(s^{\mathbf{N}} \mid \mathbf{X}_1 = -1) = E(s^{1+\mathbf{N}_1+\mathbf{N}_2} \mid \mathbf{X}_1 = -1) = s\Phi^2(s),$$

$$E(s^{\mathbf{N}} \mid \mathbf{X}_1 = 1) = s.$$

But

(3.10) $$E(s^{\mathbf{N}}) = pE(s^{\mathbf{N}} \mid \mathbf{X}_1 = 1) + qE(s^{\mathbf{N}} \mid \mathbf{X}_1 = -1),$$

which reduces to the quadratic equation (3.5) for $\Phi(s) = E(s^{\mathbf{N}})$.

(b) Returns to Equilibrium. An equalization of the accumulated numbers of successes and failures occurs at the kth trial if $\mathbf{S}_k = 0$. Borrowing a term from diffusion theory, we describe this event as a return to equilibrium. The number of trials is necessarily even, and the probability of a return at the $2n$th trial is given by

(3.11) $$u_{2n} = \binom{2n}{n} p^n q^n = (-1)^n \binom{-\frac{1}{2}}{n} (4pq)^n.$$

From the binomial expansion II,(8.7) we get for the generating function

(3.12) $$U(s) = \sum_{n=0}^{\infty} u_{2n} s^{2n} = \frac{1}{\sqrt{1 - 4pqs^2}} .$$

Note that $\{u_n\}$ is *not* a probability distribution because returns to equilibrium can occur repeatedly.

(c) The First Return to Equilibrium occurs at the $2n$th trial if $\mathbf{S}_{2n} = 0$ but $\mathbf{S}_k \neq 0$ for $k = 1, \ldots, 2n - 1$. Denote the probability of this event by f_{2n}. (Of course, $f_{2n-1} = 0$.) We consider separately the two subevents with $\mathbf{X}_1 = 1$ and $\mathbf{X}_1 = -1$ and denote their probabilities by f_{2n}^+ and f_{2n}^-. From what was said under (a) it is clear that $f_{2n}^- = q\phi_{2n-1}$ because the first $2n - 2$ partial sums $\mathbf{X}_2 + \mathbf{X}_3 + \cdots + \mathbf{X}_k$ are ≤ 0, but the next is positive. Using (3.6) we get therefore

(3.13) $$F^-(s) = \sum_{n=1}^{\infty} f_{2n}^- s^{2n} = qs\Phi(s) = \frac{1 - \sqrt{1-4pqs^2}}{2} .$$

For reasons of symmetry the generating function of $\{f_n^+\}$ is obtained by interchanging p and q. It follows that $F^+ = F^-$ and so finally[4]

(3.14) $$F(s) = \sum_{n=1}^{\infty} f_n s^n = 1 - \sqrt{1 - 4pqs^2}.$$

---

[4] An alternative derivation will be found in example XIII,(4.b).

Interesting conclusions can be drawn from this without using an explicit form for the coefficients f_n. Clearly $F(1)$ equals the probability that a return to equilibrium occurs sooner or later. Now $F(1) = 1 - |p - q|$ and so $|p - q|$ *is the probability that no return to equilibrium ever occurs.* that is, $\mathbf{S}_k \neq 0$ for all $k > 0$. Only in the symmetric case $p = \frac{1}{2}$ is a return to equilibrium certain. In this case $\{f_n\}$ represents the probability distribution for the waiting time for the first return. This waiting time has *infinite expectation.*

In the symmetric case $p = \frac{1}{2}$ we have

(3.15)
$$U(s) = \frac{1 - F(s)}{1 - s^2}.$$

Since both U and F are power series in s^2 this relation differs only notationally from (1.6), and by theorem 1.1

(3.16)
$$u_{2n} = f_{2n} + f_{2n+2} + \cdots.$$

In words, *when $p = \frac{1}{2}$ the probability that $\mathbf{S}_{2n} = 0$ equals the probability that the $2n$ sums $\mathbf{S}_1, \ldots, \mathbf{S}_{2n}$ are different from zero.* This result was derived by different methods in III,3 and played a basic role in the analysis of the paradoxical nature of the fluctuations in coin-tossing games.

(d) First Passages and Later Returns. We say that a *first passage through $r > 0$ occurs at the nth trial if $\mathbf{S}_n = r$ but $\mathbf{S}_k < r$ for all $k < n$.* The probability for this will be denoted by $\phi_n^{(r)}$. The trials following the first passage through $\nu > 0$ form a probabilistic replica of the whole sequence and hence the number of trials following the first passage through ν up to and including the first passage through $\nu + 1$ has the same distribution $\{\phi_n\}$ as the number of trials up to the first passage through 1. When $p < q$ the ϕ_n do not add to unity, but it still makes sense to say that the waiting time for the first passage is a random variable with the (possibly defective) distribution $\{\phi_n\}$. The waiting times between the successive first passages are mutually independent, and so the total waiting time for the first passage through r is the sum of r independent variables with the common distribution $\{\phi_n\}$. *The generating function of the first-passage probabilities $\phi_n^{(r)}$ is therefore given by the rth power of Φ.* [Beginners should verify this statement directly by deriving for $\phi_n^{(2)}$ a convolution equation similar to (2.4) and proceeding by induction.]

A similar argument holds for the probability $f_n^{(r)}$ that *the rth return to equilibrium occurs at the nth trial. The generating function of $\{f_n^{(r)}\}$ is given by the rth power F^r.* Comparing (3.6) and (3.14) one sees immediately that

(3.17) $$f_n^{(r)} = (2q)^r \phi_{n+r}^{(r)}.$$

In the special case $p = q = \frac{1}{2}$ this result is contained in theorem 4 of III,7.

From the generating functions it is easy to derive approximations and limit theorems, but this depends on the use of Laplace transforms which will be treated only in chapter XIII of volume 2. There is no systematic way to derive an explicit expression for $f_n^{(r)}$ from the generating function F^r, but a good guess is easily verified from the form of the generating function. From theorem 4 of III, 7 one can guess that

(3.18) $$f_{2n}^{(r)} = \frac{r}{2n-r}\binom{2n-r}{n} 2^r (pq)^n .$$

To verify this conjecture it suffices to note that the identity

$$F^r(s) = 2F^{r-1}(s) - 4pqs^2 F^{r-2}(s)$$

implies the recursion relation

(3.19) $$f_{2n}^{(r)} = 2f_{2n}^{(r-1)} - 4pq f_{2n-2}^{(r-2)},$$

which is also satisfied by the right side in (3.18). The truth of (3.18) therefore follows by induction. For an equivalent expression of a different outer appearance see problem 13 of XIV, 9.

4. PARTIAL FRACTION EXPANSIONS

Given a generating function $P(s) = \sum p_k s^k$ the coefficients p_k can be found by differentiations from the obvious formula $p_k = P^{(k)}(0)/k!$. In practice it may be impossible to obtain explicit expressions and, anyhow, such expressions are frequently so complicated that reasonable approximations are preferable. The most common method for obtaining such approximations is based on partial fraction expansions. It is known from the theory of complex variables that a large class of functions admits of such expansions, but we shall limit our exposition to the simple case of *rational functions*.

Suppose then that the generating function is of the form

(4.1) $$P(s) = \frac{U(s)}{V(s)}$$

where U and V are polynomials without common roots. For simplicity let us first assume that the degree of U is lower than the degree of V, say m. Moreover, suppose that the equation $V(s) = 0$ has m distinct (real or imaginary) roots $s_1, s_2, \ldots, s_m$. Then

(4.2) $$V(s) = (s-s_1)(s-s_2) \cdots (s-s_m),$$

and it is known from algebra that $P(s)$ can be decomposed into *partial fractions*

(4.3)
$$P(s) = \frac{\rho_1}{s_1 - s} + \frac{\rho_2}{s_2 - s} + \cdots + \frac{\rho_m}{s_m - s}$$

where $\rho_1, \rho_2, \ldots, \rho_m$ are constants. To find ρ_1 multiply (4.3) by $s_1 - s$; as $s \to s_1$ the product $(s_1-s)P(s)$ tends to ρ_1. On the other hand, from (4.1) and (4.2) we get

(4.4)
$$(s_1-s)P(s) = \frac{-U(s)}{(s-s_2)(s-s_3)\cdots(s-s_m)}.$$

As $s \to s_1$ the numerator tends to $-U(s_1)$ and the denominator to $(s_1-s_2)(s_1-s_3)\cdots(s_1-s_m)$, which is the same as $V'(s_1)$. Thus $\rho_1 = = -U(s_1)/V'(s_1)$. The same argument applies to all roots, so that for $k \leq m$

(4.5)
$$\rho_k = \frac{-U(s_k)}{V'(s_k)}.$$

Given the ρ_k, we can easily derive an exact expression for the coefficient of s^n in $P(s)$. Write

(4.6)
$$\frac{1}{s_k - s} = \frac{1}{s_k} \cdot \frac{1}{1 - s/s_k}.$$

For $|s| < |s_k|$ we expand the last fraction into a geometric series

(4.7)
$$\frac{1}{1 - s/s_k} = 1 + \frac{s}{s_k} + \left(\frac{s}{s_k}\right)^2 + \left(\frac{s}{s_k}\right)^3 + \cdots.$$

Introducing these expressions into (4.3), we find for the *coefficient p_n of s^n*

(4.8)
$$p_n = \frac{\rho_1}{s_1^{n+1}} + \frac{\rho_2}{s_2^{n+1}} + \cdots + \frac{\rho_m}{s_m^{n+1}}.$$

Thus, to get p_n we have first to find the roots $s_1, \ldots, s_m$ of the denominator and then to determine the coefficients $\rho_1, \ldots, \rho_m$ from (4.5).

In (4.8) we have an *exact* expression for the probability p_n. The labor involved in calculating all m roots is usually prohibitive, and therefore formula (4.8) is primarily of theoretical interest. Fortunately a single term in (4.8) almost always provides a satisfactory approximation. In fact, suppose that s_1 is a root which is *smaller* in absolute value than all other roots. Then the first denominator in (4.8) is smallest. Clearly, as n increases, the proportionate contributions of the other terms decrease and the first term preponderates. In other words, *if s_1 is a root of $V(s) = 0$ which is smaller in absolute value than all other roots, then, as $n \to \infty$,*

$$(4.9) \qquad\qquad p_n \sim \frac{\rho_1}{s_1^{n+1}}$$

(the sign $\sim$ indicating that the ratio of the two sides tends to 1). Usually this formula provides surprisingly good approximations even for relatively small values of n. The main advantage of (4.9) lies in the fact that it requires the computation of only one root of an algebraic equation.

It is easy to remove the restrictions under which we have derived the asymptotic formula (4.9). To begin with, the degree of the numerator in (4.1) may exceed the degree m of the denominator. Let $U(s)$ be of degree $m + r$ ($r \geq 0$); a division reduces $P(s)$ to a polynomial of degree r plus a fraction $U_1(s)/V(s)$ in which $U_1(s)$ is a polynomial of a degree lower than m. The polynomial affects only the first $r + 1$ terms of the distribution $\{p_n\}$, and $U_1(s)/V(s)$ can be expanded into partial fractions as explained above. Thus (4.9) remains true. Secondly, the restriction that $V(s)$ should have only simple roots is unnecessary. It is known from algebra that every rational function admits of an expansion into partial fractions. If s_k is a double root of $V(s)$, then the partial fraction expansion (4.3) will contain an additional term of the form $a/(s-s_k)^2$, and this will contribute a term of the form $a(n+1)s_k^{-(n+2)}$ to the exact expression (4.8) for p_n. However, this does not affect the asymptotic expansion (4.9), provided only that s_1 is a simple root. We note this result for future reference as a

Theorem. *If $P(s)$ is a rational function with a simple root s_1 of the denominator which is smaller in absolute value than all other roots, then the coefficient p_n of s^n is given asymptotically by $p_n \sim \rho_1 s_1^{-(n+1)}$, where ρ_1 is defined in (4.5).*

A similar asymptotic expansion exists also in the case where s_1 is a multiple root. (See problem 25.)

Examples.[5] (a) Let a_n be the probability that n Bernoulli trials result in an *even number of successes*. This event occurs if an initial failure at the first trial is followed by an even number of successes or if an initial success is followed by an odd number. Therefore for $n \geq 1$

$$(4.10) \qquad\qquad a_n = qa_{n-1} + p(1-a_{n-1}), \qquad\qquad a_0 = 1.$$

---

[5] A good illustration for the use of partial fractions for numerical approximations is provided by the theory of success runs in XIII, 7. The explicit expressions for the ruin probabilities in XIV, 5 and for the transition probabilities in XVI, 1 also depend on the method of partial fractions.

Multiplying by s^n and adding over $n = 1, 2, \ldots$ we get for the generating function the relation

$$A(s) - 1 = qsA(s) + ps(1-s)^{-1} - psA(s)$$

or

$$2A(s) = [1-s]^{-1} + [1-(q-p)s]^{-1}.$$

Expanding into geometric series we get finally a_n explicitly in the form

(4.11) $$2a_n = 1 + (q-p)^n,$$

which is in every way preferable to the obvious answer

$$a_n = b(0; n, p) + b(2; n, p) + \cdots.$$

(b) Let q_n be the probability that in n tosses of an ideal coin no run of three consecutive heads appears. (Note that $\{q_n\}$ is not a probability distribution; if p_n is the probability that the first run of three consecutive heads ends at the nth trial, then $\{p_n\}$ is a probability distribution, and q_n represents its "tails," $q_n = p_{n+1} + p_{n+2} + \cdots.$)

We can easily show that q_n satisfies the recurrence formula

(4.12) $$q_n = \tfrac{1}{2}q_{n-1} + \tfrac{1}{4}q_{n-2} + \tfrac{1}{8}q_{n-3},\qquad\qquad n \geq 3.$$

In fact, the event that n trials produce no sequence HHH can occur only when the trials begin with T, HT, or HHT. The probabilities that the following trials lead to no run HHH are q_{n-1}, q_{n-2}, and q_{n-3}, respectively, and the right side of (4.12) therefore contains the probabilities of the three mutually exclusive ways in which the event "no run HHH" can occur.

Evidently $q_0 = q_1 = q_2 = 1$, and hence the q_n can be calculated recursively from (4.12). To obtain the generating function $Q(s) = \sum q_n s^n$ we multiply both sides by s^n and add over $n \geq 3$. The result is

$$Q(s) - 1 - s - s^2 = \tfrac{1}{2}s\{Q(s)-1-s\} + \tfrac{1}{4}s^2\{Q(s)-1\} + \tfrac{1}{8}s^3 Q(s)$$

or

(4.13) $$Q(s) = \frac{2s^2 + 4s + 8}{8 - 4s - 2s^2 - s^3}.$$

The denominator has the root $s_1 = 1.0873778 \ldots$ and two complex roots. For $|s| < s_1$ we have $|4s + 2s^2 + s^3| < 4s_1 + 2s_1^2 + s_1^3 = 8$, and the same inequality holds also when $|s| = s_1$ unless $s = s_1$. Hence the other two roots exceed s_1 in absolute value. Thus, from (4.9)

(4.14) $$q_n \sim \frac{1.236840}{(1.0873778)^{n+1}},$$

where the numerator equals $(2s_1^2+4s_1+8)/(4+4s_1+3s_1^2)$. This is a remarkably good approximation even for small values of n. It approximates $q_3 = 0.875$ by 0.8847 and $q_4 = 0.8125$ by 0.81360. The percentage error decreases steadily, and $q_{12} = 0.41626\ldots$ is given correct to five decimal places.   ▶

5. BIVARIATE GENERATING FUNCTIONS

For a pair of integral-valued random variables $\mathbf{X}, \mathbf{Y}$ with a joint distribution of the form

$$(5.1) \qquad\qquad \mathbf{P}\{\mathbf{X} = j, \mathbf{Y} = k\} = p_{jk} \qquad\qquad j, k = 0, 1, \ldots$$

we define a generating function depending on two variables

$$(5.2) \qquad\qquad P(s_1, s_2) = \sum_{j,k} p_{jk} s_1^j s_2^k.$$

Such generating functions will be called bivariate for short.

The considerations of the first two sections apply without essential modifications, and it will suffice to point out three properties evident from (5.2):

(a) *The generating function of the marginal distributions* $\mathbf{P}\{\mathbf{X} = j\}$ *and* $\mathbf{P}\{\mathbf{Y} = k\}$ *are* $A(s) = P(s, 1)$ *and* $B(s) = P(1, s)$.

(b) *The generating function of* $\mathbf{X} + \mathbf{Y}$ *is* $P(s, s)$.

(c) *The variables* $\mathbf{X}$ *and* $\mathbf{Y}$ *are independent if, and only if,* $P(s_1, s_2) = A(s_1)B(s_2)$ *for all* s_1, s_2.

Examples. (a) *Bivariate Poisson distribution.* It is obvious that

$$(5.3) \qquad P(s_1, s_2) = e^{-a_1-a_2-b+a_1 s_1+a_2 s_2+b s_1 s_2}, \qquad a_i > 0, b > 0$$

has a power-series expansion with positive coefficients adding up to unity. Accordingly $P(s_1, s_2)$ represents the generating function of a bivariate probability distribution. The marginal distributions are Poisson distributions with mean $a_1 + b$ and $a_2 + b$, respectively, but the sum $\mathbf{X} + \mathbf{Y}$ has the generating function $e^{-a_1-a_2-b+(a_1+a_2)s+b s^2}$ and is *not* a Poisson variable. (It is a compound Poisson distribution; see XII, 2.)

(b) *Multinomial distributions.* Consider a sequence of n independent trials, each of which results in E_0, E_1, or E_2 with respective probabilities p_0, p_1, p_2. If $\mathbf{X}_i$ is the number of occurrences of E_i, then $(\mathbf{X}_1, \mathbf{X}_2)$ has a trinomial distribution with generating function $(p_0+p_1 s_1+p_2 s_2)^n$.   ▶

*6. THE CONTINUITY THEOREM

We know from chapter VI that the Poisson distribution $\{e^{-\lambda}\lambda^k/k!\}$ is the limiting form of the binomial distribution with the probability p depending on n in such a way that $np \to \lambda$ as $n \to \infty$. Then

$$b(k; n, p) \to e^{-\lambda}\lambda^k/k!.$$

The generating function of $\{b(k; n, p)\}$ is $(q+ps)^n = \{1 - \lambda(1-s)/n\}^n$. Taking logarithms, we see directly that this generating function tends to $e^{-\lambda(1-s)}$, which is the generating function of the Poisson distribution. We shall show that this situation prevails in general; a sequence of probability distributions converges to a limiting distribution if and only if the corresponding generating functions converge. Unfortunately, this theorem is of limited applicability, since the most interesting limiting forms of discrete distributions are continuous distributions (for example, the normal distribution appears as a limiting form of the binomial distribution).

Continuity Theorem. *Suppose that for every fixed* n *the sequence* $a_{0,n}, a_{1,n}, a_{2,n}, \ldots$ *is a probability distribution, that is,*

(6.1) $$a_{k,n} \geq 0, \qquad \sum_{k=0}^{\infty} a_{k,n} = 1.$$

In order that a limit

(6.2) $$a_k = \lim_{n\to\infty} a_{k,n}$$

exists for every $k \geq 0$ *it is necessary and sufficient that the limit*

(6.3) $$A(s) = \lim_{n\to\infty} \sum_{k=0}^{\infty} a_{k,n}s^k$$

exists for each s *in the open interval* $0 < s < 1$. *In this case automatically*

(6.4) $$A(s) = \sum_{k=0}^{\infty} a_k s^k.$$

It is obvious that $a_k \geq 0$ and that $\sum a_k \leq 1$. Note, however, that the sum may be strictly less than 1. For example, if $a_{k,n} = f_{k+n}$ then $a_k = 0$ for all k.

---

* The continuity theorem will be used only in the derivation of the general form for infinitely divisible distributions in XII, 2 and for the total progeny in branching processes in XII, 5.

Proof.[6] Let $A_n(s)$ stand for the series on the right side in (6.3).

(i) Assume (6.2) and define $A(s)$ by (6.4). Since $|a_{k,n} - a_k| \leq 1$ we have for $0 < s < 1$

$$(6.5) \qquad |A_n(s) - A(s)| \leq \sum_{k=0}^{r} |a_{k,n} - a_k| + \frac{s^r}{1-s}.$$

If we choose r so large that $s^r < \epsilon(1-s)$, the right side will be less than 2ϵ for all n sufficiently large. Thus the left side can be made as small as we please, and so (6.3) is true.

(ii) Assume (6.3). Clearly $A(s)$ depends monotonically on s, and so $A(0)$ exists as the limit of $A(s)$ as $s \to 0$. Now

$$(6.6) \qquad a_{0,n} \leq A_n(s) \leq a_{0,n} + s/(1-s).$$

It follows that as $n \to \infty$ all limit values of $a_{0,n}$ lie between $A(0)$ and $A(s) - s/(1-s)$. Letting $s \to 0$ we see that $a_{0,n} \to A(0)$, and so (6.2) holds when $k = 0$.

This argument extends successively to all k. Indeed, for $0 < s < 1$

$$(6.7) \qquad \frac{A_n(s) - a_{0,n}}{s} \to \frac{A(s) - A(0)}{s}.$$

On the left we have a power series with nonnegative coefficients, and (6.7) is in every way analogous to (6.3). Arguing as before we find first that the derivative $A'(0)$ exists, and then that $a_{1,n} \to A'(0)$. By induction we get (6.2) for all k.   ▶

Examples. (a) *The negative binomial distribution.* We saw in example (2.d) that the generating function of the distribution $\{f(k; r, p)\}$ is $p^r(1-qs)^{-r}$. Now let λ be fixed, and let $p \to 1$, $q \to 0$, and $r \to \infty$ so that $q \sim \lambda/r$. Then

$$(6.8) \qquad \left(\frac{p}{1-qs} \right)^r = \left(\frac{1-\lambda/r}{1-\lambda s/r} \right)^r.$$

Passing to logarithms, we see that the right side tends to $e^{-\lambda + \lambda s}$, which is the generating function of the Poisson distribution $\{e^{-\lambda}\lambda^k/k!\}$. Hence *if $r \to \infty$ and $rq \to \lambda$, then*

$$(6.9) \qquad f(k; r, p) \to e^{-\lambda} \frac{\lambda^k}{k!}.$$

---

[6] The theorem is a special case of the continuity theorem for Laplace-Stieltjes transforms, and the proof follows the general pattern. In the literature the continuity theorem for generating functions is usually stated and proved under unnecessary restrictions.

(b) *Bernoulli trials with variable probabilities.*[7] Consider n independent trials such that the kth trial results in success with probability p_k and in failure with probability $q_k = 1 - p_k$. The number $\mathbf{S}_n$ of successes can be written as the sum $\mathbf{S}_n = \mathbf{X}_1 + \cdots + \mathbf{X}_n$ of n mutually independent random variables $\mathbf{X}_k$ with the distributions $\mathbf{P}\{\mathbf{X}_k = 0\} = q_k$,

$$\mathbf{P}\{\mathbf{X}_k = 1\} = p_k.$$

The generating function of $\mathbf{X}_k$ is $q_k + p_k s$, and hence the generating function of $\mathbf{S}_n$

(6.10) $$P(s) = (q_1 + p_1 s)(q_2 + p_2 s) \cdots (q_n + p_n s).$$

As an application of this scheme let us assume that each house in a city has a small probability p_k of burning on a given day.   The sum $p_1 + \cdots + p_n$ is the expected number of fires in the city, n being the number of houses. We have seen in chapter VI that if all p_k are equal and if the houses are stochastically independent, then the number of fires is a random variable whose distribution is near the Poisson distribution. We show now that this conclusion remains valid also under the more realistic assumption that the probabilities p_k are not equal. This result should increase our confidence in the Poisson distribution as an adequate description of phenomena which are the cumulative effect of many improbable events ("successes"). Accidents and telephone calls are typical examples.

We use the now familiar model of an increasing number n of variables where the probabilities p_k depend on n in such a way that the largest p_k tends to zero, but the sum $p_1 + p_2 + \cdots + p_n = \lambda$ remains constant. Then from (6.10)

(6.11) $$\log P(s) = \sum_{k=1}^{n} \log \{1 - p_k(1 - s)\}.$$

Since $p_k \to 0$, we can use the fact that $\log(1 - x) = -x - \theta x$, where $\theta \to 0$ as $x \to 0$. It follows that

(6.12) $$\log P(s) = -(1 - s)\left\{ \sum_{k=1}^{n} (p_k + \theta_k p_k) \right\} \to -\lambda(1 - s),$$

so that $P(s)$ tends to the generating function of the Poisson distribution. Hence, $\mathbf{S}_n$ *has in the limit a Poisson distribution.* We conclude that for large n and moderate values of $\lambda = p_1 + p_2 + \cdots + p_n$ the distribution of $\mathbf{S}_n$ can be approximated by a Poisson distribution.   ▶

---

[7] See also examples IX, (1.*e*) and IX, (5.*b*).

7. PROBLEMS FOR SOLUTION

1. Let X be a random variable with generating function $P(s)$. Find the generating functions of $X + 1$ and $2X$.

2. Find the generating functions of (a) $P\{X \leq n\}$, (b) $P\{X < n\}$, (c) $P\{X \geq n\}$, (d) $P\{X > n + 1\}$, (e) $P\{X = 2n\}$.

3. In a sequence of Bernoulli trials let u_n be the probability that the combination SF occurs for the first time at trials number $n - 1$ and n. Find the generating function, mean, and variance.

4. Discuss which of the formulas of II, 12, represent convolutions and where generating functions have been used.

5. Let a_n be the number of ways in which the score n can be obtained by throwing a die any number of times. Show that the generating function of $\{a_n\}$ is $\{1 - s - s^2 - s^3 - s^4 - s^5 - s^6\}^{-1} - 1$.

6. Let a_n be the number of ways in which a convex polygon $P_0 P_1 \cdots P_n$ with $n + 1$ sides can be partitioned into triangles by drawing $n - 2$ (nonintersecting) diagonals.[8] Put $a_1 = 1$. Show that for $n \geq 2$

$$a_n = a_1 a_{n-1} + a_2 a_{n-2} + \cdots + a_{n-1} a_1.$$

Find the generating function and an explicit expression for a_n.

Hint: Assume that one of the diagonals passes through P_0 and let k be the smallest subscript such that $P_0 P_k$ appears among the diagonals.

Note: *Problems 7–11 refer to section 3. The generating functions* Φ, U, *and F refer respectively to first passages through 1, returns to equilibrium, and first returns; see (3.6), (3.12), and (3.14). No calculations are necessary.*

7. (a) The probability that a return to equilibrium occurs at or before the nth trial is given by $(1 - s)^{-1} F(s)$.

(b) Conclude: The generating function for the probability that $S_j \neq 0$ for $j = 1, \ldots, n$ is given by $\sqrt{\dfrac{1 + s}{1 - s}} = (1 + s) U(s)$.

(c) Show that this is equivalent to the proposition following (3.16).

8. The generating function for the probabilities that no return to equilibrium occurs after the nth trial (exclusive) is given by $(1 - s)^{-1} U(s) |p - q|$.

9. (a) The generating function for $P\{S_n = r\}$ (with $r > 0$ fixed) is given by $\Phi^r(s) U(s)$.

(b) When $p = \frac{1}{2}$ this is also the generating function for the probability that $S_k = r$ for exactly one subscript $k \leq n$.

10. (a) Find the generating function for the probabilities that the event $S_n = r$ will occur exactly k times ($r > 0$ and $k > 0$ fixed).

(b) Do the same problem with "exactly" replaced by "at most."

11. (a) Find the generating function for the probability that the first return to equilibrium following a first passage through $r > 0$ occurs at trial number r.

(b) Do the same problem with the words "the first" omitted.

---

[8] The problem appears in G. Polya, *Mathematics of plausible reasoning*, Princeton (Princeton University Press), 1954, p. 102.

12. In the *waiting time example* IX, (3.d) find the generating function of S_r (for r fixed). Verify formula IX, (3.3) for the mean and calculate the variance.

13. *Continuation.* The following is an alternative method for deriving the same result. Let $p_n(r) = \mathbf{P}\{S_r = n\}$. Prove the recursion formula

(7.1) $$p_{n+1}(r) = \frac{r-1}{N} p_n(r) + \frac{N-r+1}{N} p_n(r-1).$$

Derive the generating function directly from (7.1).

14. Solve the two preceding problems for r preassigned elements (instead of r arbitrary ones).

15.[9] Let the sequence of Bernoulli trials up to the first failure be called a *turn*. Find the generating function and the probabiity distribution of the accumulated numbers S_r of successes in r turns.

16. *Continuation.* (a) Let $\mathbf{R}$ be the number of successive turns up to the νth success (that is, the νth success occurs during the $\mathbf{R}$th turn). Find $\mathbf{E(R)}$ and Var $(\mathbf{R})$. Prove that

$$\mathbf{P}\{\mathbf{R} = r\} = p^\nu q^{r-1} \binom{r+\nu-2}{\nu-1}.$$

(b) Consider *two* sequences of Bernoulli trials with probabilities p_1, q_1, and p_2, q_2, respectively. Find the probability that the same number of turns will lead to the Nth success.

---

17. Let X assume the values $0, 1, \ldots, r-1$ each with the same probability $1/r$. When r is a composite number, say $r = ab$, it is possible to represent X as the sum of two independent integral-valued random variables.

18. Let $S_n = X_1 + \cdots + X_n$ be the sum of mutually independent variables each assuming the values $1, 2, \ldots, a$ with probability $1/a$. Show that the generating function is given by

$$P(s) = \left\{ \frac{s(1-s^a)}{a(1-s)} \right\}^n$$

whence for $j \geq n$

$$\mathbf{P}\{S_n = j\} = a^{-n} \sum_{\nu=0}^{\infty} (-1)^{\nu+j-n-a\nu} \binom{n}{\nu} \binom{-n}{j-n-a\nu}$$

$$= a^{-n} \sum_{\nu=0}^{\infty} (-1)^\nu \binom{n}{\nu} \binom{j-a\nu-1}{n-1}.$$

(Only finitely many terms in the sum are different from zero.)

---

[9] Problems 15–16 have a direct bearing on the *game of billiards*. The probability p of success is a measure of the player's skill. The player continues to play until he fails. Hence the number of successes he accumulates is the length of his "turn." The game continues until one player has scored N successes. Problem 15 therefore gives the probability distribution of the number of turns one player needs to score k successes, problem 16 the average duration and the probability of a tie between two players. For further details cf. O. Bottema and S. C. Van Veen, *Kansberekningen bij het biljartspel*, Nieuw Archief voor Wiskunde (in Dutch), vol. 22 (1943), pp. 16–33 and 123–158.

Note: For $a = 6$ we get the probability of scoring the sum $j + n$ in a throw with n dice. The solution goes back to De Moivre.

19. *Continuation.* The probability $P\{S_n \leq j\}$ has the generating function $P(s)/(1-s)$ and hence

$$P\{S_n \leq j\} = \frac{1}{a^n} \sum_{\nu} (-1)^{\nu} \binom{n}{\nu} \binom{j-a\nu}{-n}.$$

20. *Continuation: the limiting form.* If $a \to \infty$ and $j \to \infty$, so that $j/a \to x$, then

$$P\{S_n \leq j\} \to \frac{1}{n!} \sum_{\nu} (-1)^{\nu} \binom{n}{\nu} (x-\nu)^n,$$

the summation extending over all ν with $0 \leq \nu < x$.

Note: This result is due to Lagrange. In the theory of geometric probabilities the right-hand side represents the distribution function of the sum of n independent random variables with "uniform" distribution in the interval $(0, 1)$.

21. Let u_n be the probability that the number of successes in n Bernoulli trials is divisible by 3. Find a recursive relation for u_n and hence the generating function.

22. *Continuation: alternative method.* Let v_n and w_n be the probabilities that S_n is of the form $3v + 1$ and $3v + 2$, respectively (so that $u_n + v_n + w_n = 1$). Find three simultaneous recursive relations and hence three equations for the generating functions.

23. Let **X** and **Y** be independent variables with generating functions $U(s)$ and $V(s)$. Show that $P\{X - Y = j\}$ is the coefficient of s^j in $U(s) V(1/s)$, where $j = 0, \pm1, \pm2, \ldots$.

24. *Moment generating functions.* Let **X** be a random variable with generating function $P(s)$, and suppose that $\sum p_n s^n$ converges for some $s_0 > 1$. Then all moments $m_r = P(X^r)$ exist, and the generating function $F(s)$ of the sequence $m_r/r!$ converges at least for $|s| < \log s_0$. Moreover

$$F(s) = \sum_{r=0}^{\infty} \frac{m_r}{r!} s^r = P(e^s).$$

Note: $F(s)$ is usually called the *moment generating function*, although in reality it generates $m_r/r!$.

25. Suppose that $A(s) = \sum a_n s^n$ is a rational function $U(s)/V(s)$ and that s_1 is a root of $V(s)$, which is smaller in absolute value than all other roots. If s_1 is of multiplicity r, show that

$$a_n \sim \frac{\rho_1}{s_1^{n+r}} \binom{n+r-1}{r-1}$$

where $\rho_1 = (-1)^r r! \, U(s_1)/V^{(r)}(s_1)$.

26. *Bivariate negative binomial distributions.* Show that for positive values of the parameters $p_0^a\{1 - p_1 s_1 - p_2 s_2\}^{-a}$ is the generating function of the distribution, of a pair (X, Y) such that the marginal distributions of **X**, **Y**, and $X + Y$ are negative binomial distributions.[10]

---

[10] Distributions of this type were used by G. E. Bates and J. Neyman in investigations of accident proneness. See University of California Publications in Statistics, vol. 1, 1952.

CHAPTER XII*

Compound Distributions.
Branching Processes

A substantial part of probability theory is connected with sums of independent random variables, and in many situations the number of terms in
such sums is itself a random variable. We consider here this situation for
the special case of integral-valued random variables, partly to illustrate
the use of generating functions, partly as a preparation for the study of
infinitely divisible distributions and of processes with independent increments in volume 2.

As a particularly enticing application we describe the elements of the
beautiful theory of branching processes.

1. SUMS OF A RANDOM NUMBER OF VARIABLES

Let $\{X_k\}$ be a sequence of mutually independent random variables with
the common distribution $P\{X_k = j\} = f_j$ and generating function
$f(s) = \Sigma f_i s^i$. We are often interested in sums

$$S_N = X_1 + X_2 + \cdots + X_N,$$

where the number N of terms is a random variable independent of the
X_j. Let $P\{N = n\} = g_n$ be the distribution of N and $g(s) = \Sigma g_n s^n$
its generating function. For the distribution $\{h_j\}$ of S_N we get from the
fundamental formula for conditional probabilities

(1.1) $h_j = P\{S_N = j\} = \sum_{n=0}^{\infty} P\{N = n\}P\{X_1 + \cdots + X_n = j\}.$

If N assumes only finitely many values, the random variable S_N is
defined on the sample space of finitely many X_k. Otherwise the probabilistic definition of S_N as a sum involves the sample space of an infinite

---

* The contents of this chapter will not be used in the sequel.

sequence $\{X_k\}$, but we shall be dealing only with the distribution function of S_N: for our purposes we take the distribution (1.1) as definition of the variable S_N on the sample space with points $0, 1, 2, \ldots$.

For a fixed n the distribution of $X_1 + X_2 + \cdots + X_n$ is given by the n-fold convolution of $\{f_j\}$ with itself, and therefore (1.1) can be written in the compact form

$$(1.2) \qquad \{h_j\} = \sum_{n=0}^{\infty} g_n \{f_j\}^{n*}.$$

This formula can be simplified by the use of generating functions. The generating function of $\{f_j\}^{n*}$ is $f^n(s)$ and it is obvious from (1.2) that the generating function of the sum S_N is given by

$$(1.3) \qquad h(s) = \sum_{j=0}^{\infty} h_j s^j = \sum_{n=0}^{\infty} g_n f^n(s).$$

The right side is the Taylor expansion of $g(s)$ with s replaced by $f(s)$; hence it equals $g(f(s))$. This proves the

Theorem. *The generating function of the sum* $S_N = X_1 + \cdots + X_N$ *is the compound function* $g(f(s))$.

The proof can be reformulated in terms of conditional expectations. By definition

$$(1.4) \qquad E(s^{S_N} \mid N = n) = f^n(s),$$

and to obtain $h(s) = E(s^{S_N})$ we have to multiply this quantity by $P\{N = n\}$ and sum over n [see IX,(2.9)].

Two special cases are of interest.

(*a*) If the X_i are Bernoulli variables with $P\{X_i = 1\} = p$ and $P\{X_i = 0\} = q$, then $f(s) = q + ps$ and therefore $h(s) = g(q+ps)$.

(*b*) If N has a Poisson distribution with mean t then $h(s) = e^{-t+tf(s)}$. The distribution with this generating function will be called the *compound Poisson distribution*. In particular, if the X_i are Bernoulli variables *and* N has a Poisson distribution, then $h(s) = e^{-tp+tps}$; the sum S_N has a Poisson distribution with mean tp.

Examples. (*a*) We saw in example VI, (7.*c*) that X-rays produce chromosome breakages in cells; for a given dosage and time of exposure the number N of breakages in individual cells has a Poisson distribution. Each breakage has a fixed probability q of healing whereas with probability $p = 1 - q$ the cell dies. Here S_N is the number of *observable* breakages[1] and has a Poisson distribution with mean tp.

---

[1] See D. G. Catcheside, Genetic effects of radiations, *Advances in Genetics*, edited by M. Demerec, vol. 2, Academic Press, New York, 1948, pp. 271–358, in particular p. 339.

(b) In animal-trapping experiments[2] g_n represents the probability that a species is of size n. If all animals have the same probability p of being trapped, then (assuming stochastic independence) the number of trapped representatives of one species in the sample is a varible S_N with generating function $g(q+ps)$. This description can be varied in many ways. For example, let g_n be the probability of an insect laying n eggs, and p the probability of survival of an egg. Then S_N is the number of surviving eggs. Again, let g_n be the probability of a family having n children and let the sex ratio of boys to girls be $p:q$. Then S_N represents the number of boys in a family.

(c) Each plant has a large number of seeds, but each seed has only a small probability of survival, and it is therefore reasonable to assume that the number of survivors of an individual plant has a Poisson distribution. If $\{g_n\}$ represents the distribution of the number of parent plants, $g(e^{-\lambda+\lambda s})$ is the generating function of the number of surviving seeds.

(d) *Required service time.* Consider a telephone trunkline, a counter, or any other server with the property that the service times required by the successive customers may be regarded as independent random variables $X_1, X_2, \ldots$ with a common distribution. The number of customers (or calls) arriving during a day is itself a random variable N, and the total service time required by them is therefore a random sum $X_1 + \cdots + X_N$.

2. THE COMPOUND POISSON DISTRIBUTION

Among the random sums $S_N = X_1 + \cdots + X_N$ by far the most important are those for which N has a Poisson distribution. For reasons that will presently become apparent we denote the expectation of N by λt. If the X_j have the common distribution $\{f_i\}$ then S_N has *the compound Poisson distribution*

$$(2.1) \qquad \{h_i\}_t = e^{-\lambda t} \sum_{n=0}^{\infty} \frac{(\lambda t)^n}{n!} \{f_i\}^{n*}$$

with the generating function

$$(2.2) \qquad h_t(s) = e^{-\lambda t + \lambda t f(s)}.$$

Examples. (a) *Accumulated damage.* Suppose that the number of hits by lightning during any time interval of duration t is a Poisson variable with expectation λt. If $\{f_n\}$ is the probability distribution of the damage

caused by an individual hit by lightning, then (assuming stochastic independence) the total damage during time t has the compound Poisson
distribution (2.1).

(b) *Cosmic ray showers.* It is generally supposed that the number $\mathbf{N}$
of cosmic ray showers during a time interval of length t has a Poisson
distribution with expectation λt. For any given counter, the number of
registrations caused by a shower is a random variable with a distribution
$\{f_i\}$. The total number of registrations during a time t is again a random
sum $\mathbf{S_N}$ with the compound Poisson distribution (2.1).

(c) *In ecology* it is assumed that the number of animal litters in a plot
has a Poisson distribution with expectation proportional to the area t
of the plot. Let $\{f_k\}$ be the distribution of the number of animals in a
litter and assume that the litters are independent. Under these conditions
the number of animals in the plot is subject to the compound Poisson distribution (2.1). This model is widely used in practice.   ▶

It will be noticed that all three examples are closely related to the phenomena discussed in VI,6 in connection with the Poisson distribution. In
the first two examples a variable $\mathbf{S_N}$ is associated with every time interval.
[The same is true of example (c) if we agree to treat the area as operational
time.] It is implicit in the model that when an interval is partitioned into
two non-overlapping intervals their contributions are stochastically independent and add to $\mathbf{S_N}$. In terms of the generating function (2.2) this
means that

$$(2.3) \qquad h_{t+\tau}(s) = h_t(s)h_\tau(s).$$

Every compound Poisson generating function (2.2) satisfies (2.3). We
shall now show that also the converse is true: A family of probability
generating functions h_t satisfying (2.3) is necessarily of the form (2.2).
[It must be understood that this statement is true only for integral-valued
random variables. The notion of a compound Poisson distribution remains
meaningful even when the $\mathbf{X}_j$ have an arbitrary distribution while an
analogue to (2.3) plays an important role in the general theory of stochastic
processes with independent increments. Such processes, however, are not
necessarily subject to compound Poisson distributions.]

The following definition and theorem really refer to probability distributions on the integers $0, 1, \ldots,$ but for simplicity they are formulated in
terms of the corresponding generating functions.

Definition. *A probability generating function h is called infinitely
divisible if for each positive integer n the nth root $\sqrt[n]{h}$ is again a probability
generating function.*

It follows from the next theorem that the statement remains true even if $n > 0$ is not an integer. If a family of probability generating functions satisfy (2.3) then $\sqrt[n]{h_t} = h_{t/n}$, and so h_t is infinitely divisible. The converse to this statement is contained in

Theorem.[3] *The only infinitely divisible probability generating functions are those of the form (2.2) with $\{f_i\}$ a probability distribution on* $0, 1, \ldots$.

Proof. Put $h(s) = \sum h_k s^k$ and suppose that $\sqrt[n]{h}$ is a probability generating function for each $n \geq 1$. Then $h_0 > 0$, for otherwise the absolute term in the power series for $\sqrt[n]{h}$ would vanish, and this in turn would imply that $h_0 = h_1 = \cdots = h_{n-1} = 0$. It follows that $\sqrt[n]{h\,(s)} \to 1$ for every $0 \leq s \leq 1$ and so

$$(2.4) \qquad \log \sqrt[n]{h(s)/h_0} = \log \left[1 + (\sqrt[n]{h(s)/h_0} - 1)\right] \sim \sqrt[n]{h(s)/h_0} - 1,$$

where the sign $\sim$ indicates that the ratio of the two sides tends to unity. Combining this relation with its special case for $s = 1$ we get [since $h(1) = 1$]

$$(2.5) \qquad \frac{\log h(s) - \log h_0}{-\log h_0} = \frac{\log \sqrt[n]{h(s)/h_0}}{\log \sqrt[n]{1/h_0}} \sim \frac{\sqrt[n]{h(s)} - \sqrt[n]{h_0}}{1 - \sqrt[n]{h_0}}.$$

The right side is a power series with positive coefficients and for $s = 1$ it is seen that these coefficients add to unity. Thus for each n the right side represents a probability generating function and so the left side is the limit of a sequence of probability generating functions. By the continuity theorem of XI,6 this implies that the left side itself is the generating function. of a non-negative sequence $\{f_j\}$. Letting $s = 1$ we see that $\sum f_j = 1$. This means that h is of the form (2.2) with $\lambda t = -\log h_0$.   ▶

The theorem may be restated in the form of the

Criterion. *A function h is an infinitely divisible probability generating function if, and only if, $h(1) = 1$ and*

$$(2.6) \qquad \log \frac{h(s)}{h(0)} = \sum_{k=1}^{\infty} a_k s^k \qquad \text{where} \quad a_k \geq 0, \quad \sum a_k = \lambda < \infty.$$

Indeed, if (2.6) it suffices to put $f_k = a_k/\lambda$ to reduce h to the canonical form (2.2) (with $t = 1$), and this in turn is the generating function of the compound Poisson distribution defined in (2.1).

---

[3] This is a simple special case of an important theorem of P. Lévy.

Examples. (*d*) Comparing (2.2) with the theorem of the preceding section we see that if the distribution of **N** is infinitely divisible, the same is true of the distribution of the random sum S_N.

(*e*) *The negative binomial* distribution with generating function

$$(2.7) \qquad\qquad h_t(s) = \left(\frac{p}{1 - qs}\right)^t, \qquad\qquad p + q = 1,$$

has the property (2.3) and is therefore infinitely divisible. Passing to logarithms one sees immediately that it is indeed of the form (2.2) with

$$(2.8) \qquad\qquad f_n = q^n/\lambda n, \qquad \lambda = \log p^{-1}.$$

$\{f_n\}$ is known as the *logarithmic distribution* and is used by statisticians in various contexts.

(*f*) From the expansions II,(8.9) and (8.10) it is obvious that when $q = 1 - p > p$ the functions

$$(2.9) \qquad f(s) = \sqrt{q - p} \ \frac{q + ps}{q - ps}, \qquad g(s) = \frac{\sqrt{q - p}}{\sqrt{q^2 - p^2 s^2}}$$

satisfy the condition (2.6), and so both f *and* g *are infinitely divisible probability generating functions.* It is interesting to note that

$$(2.10) \qquad\qquad f(s) = g(s)(q + ps).$$

We have here *a factorization of the infinitely divisible f into two generating functions, of which only one is infinitely divisible.* The possibility of such factorizations came originally as a great surprise and for a while the topic attracted much attention.

A remarkable property of the compound Poisson distribution has been the object of some curious speculations. If we put for abbreviation $\lambda_i = \lambda f_i$ the generating function h_t of (2.2) can be factored in the form

$$(2.11) \qquad\qquad h_t(s) = e^{\lambda_1 t(s-1)} \cdot e^{\lambda_2 t(s^2-1)} \cdot e^{\lambda_3 t(s^3-1)} \cdots.$$

The product can be infinite, but this has no bearing on our discussion and we may suppose that only finitely many λ_i are positive. The first factor is the generating function of an ordinary Poisson distribution with expectation $\lambda_1 t$. The second factor is the generating function for two times a Poisson variable, that is, the familiar probability $e^{-\lambda_2 t}(\lambda_2 t)^n/n!$ is carried by the point $2n$ rather than n. In like manner the kth factor corresponds to a Poisson distribution attributing probabilities to the multiples of k. Thus (2.11) gives a new representation of S_N as the sum of independent variables $Y_1, Y_2, \ldots$ such that Y_k takes on only the values $0, k, 2k, \ldots$ but has otherwise a Poisson distribution. The content of (2.11) may be described as follows. Let N_j stand for the number of those variables among $X_1, \ldots, X_N$ that are equal to j. Then $N = N_1 + N_2 + \cdots$ and (2.11) states that the variables N_k *are mutually independent and subject to Poisson distributions.*

Example. (g) *Automobile accidents.* Interpret X_n as the number of automobiles involved in the nth accident. Under the standard assumption that the X_n are independent and that the number N of accidents has a Poisson distribution, the total number of cars involved in the accidents is given by $X_1 + \cdots + X_N$ and has the compound Poisson distribution (2.1). We may now consider separately the number N_k of accidents involving exactly k cars. According to (2.11) the variables N_k are mutually independent and have Poisson distributions. The practical implications of this result require no comment.   ▶

[For a generalization of the compound Poisson distribution see example XVII,(9.a).]

2a. Processes with independent increments

The preceding results gain in interest through their intimate connections with an important class of stochastic processes. These will now be indicated informally even though the theory lies beyond the scope of the present book.

To begin with the simplest example consider the number of incoming calls at a telephone exchange as a function of time. The development at an individual exchange is described by recording for each t the number $Z(t)$ of calls that arrived between 0 and t. If the successive calls arrived at $t_1, t_2, \ldots$, then $Z(t) = 0$ for $0 < t < t_1$, and generally $Z(t) = k$ for $t_k < t < t_{k+1}$. Conversely, every non-decreasing function assuming only the values $0, 1, 2, \ldots$ represents a possible development at a telephone exchange. A probabilistic model must therefore be based on a sample space whose individual points represent functions $Z(t)$ (rather than sequences as in the case of discrete trials). Probabilities must be assigned in a manner enabling us to deal with intricate events such as the event that $Z(t+1) - Z(t)$ will ever exceed 17 or that $Z(t)$ will at some time exceed $at + b$ (the latter event is the main object of the ruin problem in the collective theory of risk). In the following we shall take it for granted that such an assignment is indeed possible; our aim is to show that simple and natural assumptions concerning the nature of the process imply that for every fixed t the random variable $Z(t)$ must have a compound Poisson distribution.

Similar considerations apply to a great variety of empirical phenomena. Instead of the number of telephone calls the variable $Z(t)$ may represent the accumulated length (or cost) of the ensuing conversations, or the number of cars involved in accidents, the accumulated damage due to lightning, the total consumption of electricity, the accumulated rainfall, etc. Within the framework of the present chapter we must assume that the variables $Z(t)$ assume only non-negative integral values, but the theory can be generalized to arbitrary random variables. We focus our attention on processes satisfying the following two basic assumptions, which seem natural in many applications.

(a) The process is *time-homogeneous*, that is, the distributions of increments $\mathbf{Z}(t+h) - \mathbf{Z}(t)$ depend only on the length of the time interval, but not on its position.[4]

(b) The increments $\mathbf{Z}(t_2) - \mathbf{Z}(t_1)$ and $\mathbf{Z}(t_1) - \mathbf{Z}(t_0)$ over contiguous time intervals are mutually independent. The results of the preceding section may now be restated as follows: *If* there exists a process satisfying the postulates (a) and (b), then its increments $\mathbf{Z}(t+h) - \mathbf{Z}(t)$ have compound Poisson distributions. In particular, when $\mathbf{Z}(t)$ changes only by unit amounts the variables have simple Poisson distributions. [Cf. (2.11).]

We have thus found a characterization of the simple and compound Poisson distributions by intrinsic properties; by contrast to the derivation in chapter VI the Poisson distribution no longer appears as an approximation, but stands on its own rights (one might say: as an expression of a natural law). Of course, we are now faced with the converse problem to see whether any family of compound Poisson distributions really corresponds to a stochastic process. The answer is affirmative, but it turns out (somewhat surprisingly) that our two postulates do not suffice to describe a *unique* process. For a unique description of an interesting class of processes it is necessary to strengthen the postulate (b) by requiring that for any n the n increments corresponding to a finite partition $t_0 < t_1 < \cdots < t_n$ be mutually independent. This is the defining property of *processes with independent increments*. Any family of compound Poisson distributions determines uniquely a process with independent increments, and so no theoretical difficulties arise. But we have assumed the independence property only for two intervals. This restricted postulate suffices to determine the form of the distributions of the increments, but it is possible to construct rather pathological processes with this property.[5] This example illustrates the difficulties inherent in the construction of a complete model of a stochastic process.

3. EXAMPLES FOR BRANCHING PROCESSES

We shall describe a chance process which serves as a simplified model of many empirical processes and also illustrates the usefulness of generating functions. In words the process may be described as follows.

We consider particles which are able to produce new particles of like kind. A single particle forms the original, or zero, generation. Every particle has probability p_k $(k = 0, 1, 2, \ldots)$ of creating exactly k new particles; the direct descendants of the nth generation form the $(n+1)$st generation. The particles of each generation act independently of each other. We are interested in the size of the successive generations.

---

[4] This condition is less restrictive than might appear at first sight. For example, in a telephone exchange incoming calls are more frequent during the busiest hour of the day than, say, between midnight and 1 A.M.; the process is therefore not homogeneous in time. However, for obvious reasons telephone engineers are concerned mainly with the "busy hour" of the day, and for that period the process can be considered homogeneous. Experience shows also that during the busy hour the incoming traffic follows the Poisson distribution with surprising accuracy.

[5] In such a process the increment $\mathbf{Z}(t_3) - \mathbf{Z}(t_2)$ is independent of $\mathbf{Z}(t_2) - \mathbf{Z}(t_1)$ as well as of $\mathbf{Z}(t_1) - \mathbf{Z}(t_0)$, and yet may be completely determined by the latter pair. See W. Feller, *Non-Markovian processes with the semi-group property*, Ann. Math. Statist., vol. 30 (1959), pp. 1252–1253.

A few illustrations may precede a rigorous formulation in terms of random variables.

(a) *Nuclear chain reactions.* This application became familiar in connection with the atomic bomb.[6] The particles are neutrons, which are subject to chance hits by other particles. Let p be the probability that the particle sooner or later scores a hit, thus creating m particles; then $q = 1 - p$ is the probability that the particle has no descendants; that is, it remains inactive (is removed or absorbed in a different way). In this scheme the only possible numbers of descendants are 0 and m, and the corresponding probabilities are q and p (i.e., $p_0 = q$, $p_m = p$, $p_j = 0$ for all other j). At worst, the first particle remains inactive and the process never starts. At best, there will be m particles of the first generation, m^2 of the second, and so on. If p is near one, the number of particles is likely to increase very rapidly. Mathematically, this number may increase indefinitely. Physically speaking, for very large numbers of particles the probabilities of fission cannot remain constant, and also stochastic independence is impossible. However, for ordinary chain reactions, the mathematical description "indefinitely increasing number of particles" may be translated by "explosion."

(b) *Survival of family names.* Here (as often in life), only male descendants count; they play the role of particles, and p_k is the probability for a newborn boy to become the progenitor of exactly k boys. Our scheme introduces two artificial simplifications. Fertility is subject to secular trends, and therefore the distribution $\{p_k\}$ in reality changes from generation to generation. Moreover, common inheritance and common environment are bound to produce similarities among brothers which is contrary to our assumption of stochastic independence. Our model can be refined to take care of these objections, but the essential features remain unaffected. We shall derive the probability of finding k carriers of the family name in the nth generation and, in particular, the probability of an extinction of the line. Survival of family names appears to have been the first chain reaction studied by probability methods. The problem was first treated by F. Galton (1889); for a detailed account the reader is referred to A. Lotka's book.[7] Lotka shows that American experience is reasonably well described by the distribution $p_0 = 0.4825, p_k = (0.2126)(0.5893)^{k-1}$ ($k \geq 1$), which, except for the first term, is a geometric distribution.

---

[6] The following description follows E. Schroedinger, *Probability problems in nuclear chemistry*, Proceedings of the Royal Irish Academy, vol. 51, sect. A, No. 1 (December 1945). There the assumption of spatial homogeneity is removed.

[7] *Théorie analytique des associations biologiques*, vol. 2, *Actualités scientifiques et industrielles*, No. 780 (1939), pp. 123–136, Hermann et Cie, Paris.

(c) *Genes and mutations.* Every gene of a given organism (V,5) has a chance to reappear in 1, 2, 3, ... direct descendants, and our scheme describes the process, neglecting, of course, variations within the population and with time. This scheme is of particular use in the study of mutations, or changes of form in a gene. A spontaneous mutation produces a single gene of the new kind, which plays the role of a zero-generation particle. The theory leads to estimates of the chances of survival and of the spread of the mutant gene. To fix ideas, consider (following R. A. Fisher) a corn plant which is father to some 100 seeds and mother to an equal number. If the population size remains constant, an average of two among these 200 seeds will develop to a plant. Each seed has probability $\frac{1}{2}$ to receive a particular gene. The probability of a mutant gene being represented in exactly k new plants is therefore comparable to the probability of exactly k successes in 200 Bernoulli trials with probability $p = \frac{1}{200}$, and it appears reasonable to assume that $\{p_k\}$ is, approximately, a Poisson distribution with mean 1. If the gene carries a biological advantage, we get a Poisson distribution with mean $\lambda > 1$.

(d) *Waiting lines.*[8] Interesting applications of branching processes occur in queuing theory. Roughly speaking, a customer arriving at an empty server and receiving immediate service is termed ancestor; his direct descendants are the customers arriving during his service time and forming a waiting line. This process continues as long as the queue lasts. We shall return to it in greater detail in example (5.b), and to an even more interesting variant in example (5.c). ▶

4. EXTINCTION PROBABILITIES IN BRANCHING PROCESSES

Denote by $\mathbf{Z}_n$ the size of the nth generation, and by P_n the generating function of its probability distribution. By assumption $\mathbf{Z}_0 = 1$ and

$$(4.1) \qquad\qquad P_1(s) = P(s) = \sum_{k=0}^{\infty} p_k s^k.$$

The nth generation can be divided into $\mathbf{Z}_1$ clans according to the ancestor in the first generation. This means that $\mathbf{Z}_n$ is the sum of $\mathbf{Z}_1$ random variables $\mathbf{Z}_n^{(k)}$, each representing the size of the offspring of one member of the first generation. By assumption each $\mathbf{Z}_n^{(k)}$ has the same probability distribution as $\mathbf{Z}_{n-1}$ and (for fixed n) the variables $\mathbf{Z}_n^{(k)}$ are mutually

---

[8] D. G. Kendal, *Some problems in the theory of queues*, J. Roy. Statist. Soc. (Series B), vol. 13 (1951), pp. 151–173, and discussion 173–185.

independent. The generating function P_n is therefore given by the compound function

$$(4.2) \qquad\qquad P_n(s) = P(P_{n-1}(s)).$$

This result enables us to calculate recursively all the generating functions. In view of (4.2) we have $P_2(s) = P(P(s))$, then $P_3(s) = P(P_2(s))$, etc. The calculations are straightforward, though explicit expressions for P_n are usually hard to come by. We shall see presently that it is nevertheless possible to draw important conclusions from (4.2).

Example.   Suppose that the number of direct descendants is subject to the geometric distribution $\{qp^k\}$ where $p \neq q$. Then $P(s) = q/(1-ps)$ and an explicit calculation of P_2, P_3, etc., leads us (with some patience) to the general formula

$$(4.3) \qquad\qquad P_n(s) = q \cdot \frac{p^n - q^n - (p^{n-1}-q^{n-1})ps}{p^{n+1} - q^{n+1} - (p^n-q^n)ps}.$$

It is easy to verify that (4.3) indeed satisfies (4.2).

If $p = q$, we get, letting $p \to \frac{1}{2}$,

$$(4.4) \qquad\qquad P_n(s) = \frac{n - (n-1)s}{n + 1 - ns}.$$

Note that $P_n(0) \to q/p$ if $p > q$, but $P_n(0) \to 1$ if $p \leq q$. We shall now interpret this result and find its analogue for arbitrary distributions $\{p_k\}$.   ▶

The first question concerning our branching process is whether it will continue forever or whether the progeny will die out after finitely many generations. Put

$$(4.5) \qquad\qquad x_n = \mathbf{P}\{\mathbf{Z}_n = 0\} = P_n(0).$$

This is the probability that the process terminates at or before the nth generation. By definition $x_1 = p_0$ and from (4.2) it is clear that

$$(4.6) \qquad\qquad x_n = P(x_{n-1}).$$

The extreme cases $p_0 = 0$ and $p_0 = 1$ being trivial, we now suppose that $0 < p_0 < 1$. From the monotone character of P we conclude then that $x_2 = P(p_0) > P(0) = x_1$, and hence by induction that $x_1 < x_2 < x_3 < \cdots$. It follows that there exists a limit $x \leq 1$, and from (4.6) it is clear that

$$(4.7) \qquad\qquad x = P(x).$$

For $0 \leq s \leq 1$ the graph of $P(s)$ is a *convex* curve starting at the point $(0, p_0)$ above the bisector and ending at the point $(1, 1)$ on the bisector. Accordingly only two situations are possible:

Case (i).   The graph is entirely above the bisector. In this case $x = 1$ is the unique root of the equation (4.7), and so $x_n \to 1$. Furthermore, in this case $1 - P(s) \leq 1 - s$ for all s, and letting $s \to 1$ we see that the derivative $P'(1)$ satisfies the inequality $P'(1) \leq 1$.

Case (ii).   The graph of P intersects the bisector at some point $\sigma < 1$. Since a convex curve intersects a straight line in at most two points, in this case $P(s) > s$ for $s < \sigma$ but $P(s) < s$ for $\sigma < s < 1$. Then $x_1 = P(0) < P(\sigma) = \sigma$, and by induction $x_n = P(x_{n-1}) < P(\sigma) = \sigma$. It follows that $x_n \to \sigma$ and so $x = \sigma$. On the other hand, by the mean value theorem there exists a point between σ and 1 at which the derivative P' equals one. This derivative being monotone, it follows that $P'(1) > 1$.

We see thus that the two cases are characterized by $P'(1) \leq 1$ and $P'(1) > 1$, respectively. But

$$(4.8) \qquad\qquad \mu = P'(1) = \sum_{k=0}^{\infty} k p_k \leq \infty$$

is *the expected number of direct descendants*, and we have proved the interesting

Theorem. *If* $\mu \leq 1$ *the process dies out with probability one. If, however,* $\mu > 1$ *the probability* x_n *that the process terminates at or before the nth generation tends to the unique root* $x < 1$ *of the equation* (4.7).

In practice the convergence $x_n \to x$ is usually rapid and so with a great probability the process either stops rather soon, or else it continues forever. The expected size of the nth generation is given by $\mathbf{E}(Z_n) = P_n'(1)$. From (4.2) we get by the chain rule $P_n'(1) = P'(1)P_{n-1}'(1) = \mu \mathbf{E}(X_{n-1})$, and hence[9]

$$(4.9) \qquad\qquad\qquad \mathbf{E}(X_n) = \mu^n.$$

It is not surprising that the process is bound for extinction when $\mu < 1$, but it was not clear a priori that a stable situation is impossible even when $\mu = 1$. When $\mu > 1$ one should expect a geometric growth in accordance with (4.9). This is true in some average sense, but no matter how large μ there is a finite probability of extinction. It is easily seen that $P_n(s) \to x$ for all $s < 1$ and this means that the coefficients of s, s^2, s^3, etc., all tend to 0. After *a sufficient number of generations it is therefore likely that there*

---

[9] For further details see the comprehensive treatise by T. E. Harris, *The theory of branching processes*, Berlin (Springer), 1963.

are either no descendants or else a great many descendants (the corresponding probabilities being x and $1 - x$).

5. THE TOTAL PROGENY IN BRANCHING PROCESSES

We now turn our attention to the random variable[10]

$$(5.1) \qquad \mathbf{Y}_n = 1 + \mathbf{Z}_1 + \cdots + \mathbf{Z}_n$$

which equals the total number of descendants up to and including the nth generation and also including the ancestor (zero generation). Letting $n \to \infty$ we get the size of the total progeny which may be finite or infinite. Clearly, for each n the random variable $\mathbf{Y}_n$ is well defined and we denote by R_n the generating function of its probability distribution. Since $\mathbf{Y}_1 = 1 + \mathbf{Z}_1$ we have $R_1(s) = sP(s)$. A recursion formula for R_n can be derived by the argument of the preceding section, the only difference being that to obtain $\mathbf{Y}_n$ we must add the progenitor to the sum of the progenies of the $\mathbf{Z}_1$ members of the first generation. Accordingly

$$(5.2) \qquad R_n(s) = sP(R_{n-1}(s)).$$

From this recursion formula it is theoretically possible to calculate successively $R_1, R_2, \ldots$, but the labor is prohibitive. Fortunately it is possible to discuss the asymptotic behavior of R_n by the geometric argument used in the preceding section to derive the extinction probability x.

First we note that for each $s < 1$

$$(5.3) \qquad R_2(s) = sP(R_1(s)) < sP(s) = R_1(s)$$

and by induction it follows that $R_n(s) < R_{n-1}(s)$. Accordingly $R_n(s)$ decreases monotonically to a limit $\rho(s)$, and the latter satisfies

$$(5.4) \qquad \rho(s) = sP(\rho(s)) \qquad\qquad 0 < s < 1.$$

From the continuity theorem of XI,6 we know that as limit of probability generating functions ρ is the generating function of a sequence of non-negative numbers ρ_k such that $\sum \rho_k \leq 1$.

It follows from (5.4) that for fixed $s < 1$ the value $\rho(s)$ is a root of the equation

$$(5.5) \qquad t = sP(t).$$

---

[10] This section was inspired by I. J. Good, *The number of individuals in a cascade process*, Proc. Cambridge Philos. Soc., vol. 45 (1949), pp. 360–363.

We show that this root is unique. For that purpose we denote again by x the smallest positive root of $x = P(x)$ (so that $x \leq 1$). We observe that $y = sP(t)$ (with s fixed) is a convex function of t and so its graph intersects the line $y = t$ in at most two points. But for $t = 0$ the right side in (5.5) is greater than the left, whereas the inequality is reversed when $t = x$, and also when $t = 1$; thus (5.5) has exactly one root between 0 and x, and no root between x and 1. Accordingly, $\rho(s)$ is uniquely characterized as this root, and we see furthermore that $\rho(s) < x$. But $\rho(1)$ is obviously a root of $t = P(t)$, and since x is the smallest root of this equation it is clear that $\rho(1) = x$. In other words, ρ is an honest probability generating function if, and only if, $x = 1$. We can summarize these findings as follows.

Let p_k be the probability that the total progeny consists of k elements.
(a) $\sum p_k$ equals the extinction probability x (and $1 - x$ equals the probability of an infinite progeny).
(b) The generating function $\rho(s) = \sum p_k s^k$ is given by the unique positive root of (5.5), and $\rho(s) \leq x$.
We know already that with probability one the total progeny is finite whenever $\mu \leq 1$. By differentiation of (5.4) it is now seen that its expectation equals $1/(1 - \mu)$ when $\mu < 1$ and is infinite when $\mu = 1$.

Examples. (a) In example (4.a) we had $P(s) = q/(1-ps)$, and (5.5) reduces to the quadratic equation $pt^2 - t + q = 0$ from which we conclude that

(5.6)
$$\rho(s) = \frac{1 - \sqrt{1 - 4pqs}}{2p}.$$

(This generating function occurred also in connection with the first-passage times in XI,3.)

(b) *Busy periods.* We turn to a more detailed analysis of the queuing problem mentioned in example (3.d). Suppose for simplicity that customers can arrive only one at a time and only at integral-valued epochs.[11] We assume that the arrivals are regulated by Bernoulli trials in such a way that at epoch n a customer arrives with probability p, while with probability $q = 1 - p$ no arrival takes place. A customer arriving when the server is free is served immediately, and otherwise he joins the queue (waiting line). The server continues service without interruption as long as there are customers in the queue requiring service. We suppose finally that the

---

[11] Following a practice introduced by J. Riordan we use the term epoch for points on the time axis because the alternative terms such as time, moment, etc., are overburdened with other meanings.

successive service times are independent (integral-valued) random variables with a common distribution $\{\beta_k\}$ and generating function $\beta(s) = \sum \beta_k s^k$.

Suppose then that a customer arrives at epoch 0 and finds the server free. His service time starts immediately. If it has duration n, the counter becomes free at epoch n provided that no new customer arrives at epochs $1, 2, \ldots, n$. Otherwise the service continues without interruption. By *busy period* is meant the duration of uninterrupted service commencing at epoch 0. We show how the theory of branching process may be used to analyze the duration of the busy period.

The customer arriving at epoch 0 initiates the busy period and will be called ancestor. The first generation consists of the customers arriving prior to or at the epoch of the termination of the ancestor's service time. If there are no such direct descendants the process stops. Otherwise the direct descendants are served successively, and during their service times their direct descendants join the queue. We have here a branching process such that *the probability x of extinction equals the probability of a termination of the busy period, and the total progeny consists of all customers (including the ancestor) arriving during the busy period.* Needless to say, only queues with $x = 1$ are feasible in practice.

To apply our results we require the generating function $P(s)$ for the number of direct descendants. By definition this number is determined by the random sum $\mathbf{X}_1 + \cdots + \mathbf{X}_N$ where the $\mathbf{X}_j$ are mutually independent and assume the values 1 and 0 with probabilities p and q, while $\mathbf{N}$ is the length of the ancestor's service time. Thus in the present situation $P(s) = \beta(ps+q)$, and hence $\mu = p\sigma$ where $\sigma = \beta'(1)$ is the expected duration of the service time. It follows that *the busy period is certain to terminate only if $p\sigma \leq 1$. The expected number of customers during a busy period is finite only if $p\sigma < 1$.* In other words, congestion is guaranteed when $p\sigma = 1$, and long queues must be the order of the day unless $p\sigma$ is substantially less than 1.

(c) *Duration of the busy period.* The preceding example treats the number of customers during a busy period, but the actual duration of the busy period is of greater practical interest. It can be obtained by the elegant device[12] of considering time units as elements of a branching process. We say that the epoch n has no descendants if no customer arrives at epoch n. If such a customer arrives and his service time lasts r time units, then the epochs $n + 1, \ldots, n + r$ are counted as direct descendants of the epoch. Suppose that at epoch 0 the server is free. A little reflection now shows that

---

[12] It is due to I. J. Good. See the discussion following Kendall's paper quoted in example (3.d).

the branching process originated by the epoch 0 either does not come off at all or else lasts exactly for the duration of the uninterrupted service time initiated by a new customer. The generating function for the number of direct descendants is given by

$$(5.7) \qquad\qquad P(s) = q + p\beta(s).$$

The root x gives the probability of a termination of the busy period. The total progeny equals 1 with probability q while with probability p it equals the duration of the busy period commencing at epoch 0. The duration of the busy period itself has obviously the generating function given by $\beta(\rho(s))$.   ▶

6. PROBLEMS FOR SOLUTION

1. The distribution (1.1) of the random sum S_N has mean $E(N)E(X)$ and variance $E(N)$ Var $(X) +$ Var $(N)E^2(X)$. Verify this (a) using the generating function, (b) directly from the definition and the notion of conditional expectations.

2. *Animal trapping* [example (1.b)]. If $\{g_n\}$ is a geometric distribution, so is the resulting distribution. If $\{g_n\}$ is a logarithmic distribution [cf. (2.8)], there results a logarithmic distribution with an added term.

3. In N Bernoulli trials, where N is a random variable with a Poisson distribution, the numbers of successes and failures are stochastically independent variables. Generalize this to the multinomial distribution (a) directly, (b) using multivariate generating functions. [Cf. example IX,(1.d).]

4. *Randomization.* Let N have a Poisson distribution with mean λ, and let N balls be placed randomly into n cells. Show without calculation that the probability of finding exactly m cells empty is $\binom{n}{m}e^{-\lambda m/n}[(1-e)^{-\lambda/n}]^{n-m}$.

5. *Continuation.*[13] Show that when a fixed number r of balls is placed randomly into n cells the probability of finding exactly m cells empty equals the coefficient of $e^{-\lambda}\lambda^r/r!$ in the expression above. (a) Discuss the connection with moment generating functions (problem 24 of XI, 7). (b) Use the result for an effortless derivation of II,(11.7).

6. *Mixtures of probability distributions.* Let $\{f_i\}$ and $\{g_i\}$ be two probability distributions, $\alpha > 0$, $\beta > 0$, $\alpha + \beta = 1$. Then $\{\alpha f_i + \beta g_i\}$ is again a probability distribution. Discuss its meaning and the connection with the urn models of V,2. Generalize to more than two distributions. Show that such a mixture can be a compound Poisson distribution.

7. Using generating functions show that in the branching process Var $(X_{n+1}) = \mu$ Var $(X_n) + \mu^{2n}\sigma^2$. Using conditional expectations prove the equivalent

---

[13] This elegant derivation of various combinatorial formulas by randomizing a parameter is due to C. Domb, *On the use of a random parameter in combinatorial problems*, Proceedings Physical Society, Sec. A., vol. 65 (1952), pp. 305–309.

relation $\text{Var}\,(X_{n+1}) = \mu^2\,\text{Var}\,(X_n) + \mu^n\sigma^2$.   Conclude from either form that $\text{Var}\,(X_n) = \sigma^2(\mu^{2n-2} + \mu^{2n-3} + \cdots + \mu^{n-1})$.

8. *Continuation.* If $n > m$ show that $E(X_n X_m) = \mu^{n-m} E(X_m^2)$.

9. *Continuation.* Show that the bivariate generating function of (X_m, X_n) is $P_m(s_1 P_{n-m}(s_2))$. Use this to verify the assertion in problem 8.

10. Consider the changes introduced in the branching process when each individual has a fixed probability p to die before producing descendants.

11. *Branching processes with two types of individuals.* Assume that each individual can have descendants of either kind; the numbers of descendants of the two types are regulated by two bivariate generating functions $P_1(s_1, s_2)$ and $P_2(s_1, s_2)$. We have now two extinction probabilities x, y depending on the type of the ancestor. Show that the pair (x, y) satisfies the equations

(6.1) $$x = P_1(x, y), \qquad y = P_2(x, y).$$

Prove that these equations have at most one solution $0 \le x \le 1$, $0 \le y \le 1$ different from $(1, 1)$. The solution $(1, 1)$ is unique if, and only if, $\mu_{11} \le 1$, $\mu_{22} \le 1$ and $(1 - \mu_{11})(1 - \mu_{22}) \ge \mu_{12}\mu_{21}$ where $\mu_{ij} = \dfrac{\partial P_i(1, 1)}{\partial s_j}$.

CHAPTER XIII

Recurrent Events.
Renewal Theory

1. INFORMAL PREPARATIONS AND EXAMPLES

We shall be concerned with certain repetitive, or recurrent, patterns connected with repeated trials. Roughly speaking, a pattern $\mathcal{E}$ qualifies for the following theory if after each occurrence of $\mathcal{E}$ the trials start from scratch in the sense that the trials following an occurrence of $\mathcal{E}$ form a replica of the whole experiment. The waiting times between successive occurrences of $\mathcal{E}$ are mutually independent random variables having the same distribution.

The simplest special case arises when $\mathcal{E}$ stands as abbreviation for "a success occurs" in a sequence of Bernoulli trials. The waiting time up to the first success has a geometric distribution; when the first success occurs, the trials start anew, and the number of trials between the rth and the $(r+1)$st success has the same geometric distribution. The waiting time up to the rth success is the sum of r independent variables [example IX,(3.c)]. This situation prevails also when $\mathcal{E}$ stands for "a success followed by failure": The occurrence of the pattern SF reestablishes the initial situation, and the waiting time for the next occurrence of SF is independent of the preceding trials. By contrast, suppose that people are sampled one by one and let $\mathcal{E}$ stand for "two people in the sample have the same birthday." This $\mathcal{E}$ is not repetitive because after its first realization $\mathcal{E}$ persists forever. If we change the definition to "$\mathcal{E}$ occurs whenever the birthday of the newly added person is already present in the sample," then $\mathcal{E}$ can occur any number of times, but after an occurrence of $\mathcal{E}$ the process does *not* start from scratch. This is so because the increasing sample size makes duplications of birthdays more likely; a long waiting time for the first double birthday promises therefore a shorter waiting time for the second duplication, and so the consecutive waiting times are neither independent nor subject to a common distribution.

The importance of the theory of recurrent patterns is due to the fact that such patterns occur frequently in connection with various sequences of variables (stochastic processes). The laws governing a sequence of random variables may be so intricate as to preclude a complete analysis but the existence of a repetitive pattern makes it always possible to discuss essential features of the sequence, to prove the existence of certain limits, etc. This approach contributes greatly to the simplification and unification of many theories.

We proceed to review a few typical examples, some of which are of intrinsic interest. The first examples refer to the familiar Bernoulli trials, but the last three involve more complicated schemes. In their description we use terms such as "server" and "customer," but in each case we give a mathematical definition of a sequence of random variables which is complete in the sense that it uniquely determines the probabilities of all possible events. In practice, not even the basic probabilities can be calculated explicitly, but it will turn out that the theory of repetitive patterns nevertheless leads to significant results.

Examples. (*a*) *Return to equilibrium.* In a sequence of Bernoulli trials let $\mathcal{E}$ stand as abbreviation for "the accumulated numbers of successes and failures are equal." As we have done before, we describe the trials in terms of mutually independent random variables $\mathbf{X}_1, \mathbf{X}_2, \ldots$ assuming the values 1 and -1 with probabilities p and q, respectively. As usual, we put

$$(1.1) \qquad \mathbf{S}_0 = 0, \qquad \mathbf{S}_n = \mathbf{X}_1 + \cdots + \mathbf{X}_n.$$

Then $\mathbf{S}_n$ is the accumulated excess of heads over tails, and $\mathcal{E}$ *occurs if, and only if,* $\mathbf{S}_n = 0$. It goes without saying that the occurrence of this event reestablishes the initial situation in the sense that the subsequent partial sums $\mathbf{S}_{n+1}, \mathbf{S}_{n+2}, \ldots$ form a probabilistic replica of the whole sequence $\mathbf{S}_1, \mathbf{S}_2, \ldots$. [Continued in example (4.*b*).]

(*b*) *Return to equilibrium through negative values.* We modify the last example by stipulating that $\mathcal{E}$ occurs at the nth trial if

$$(1.2) \qquad \mathbf{S}_n = 0, \quad but \quad \mathbf{S}_1 < 0, \ldots, \mathbf{S}_{n-1} < 0.$$

Again, it is clear that the occurrence of $\mathcal{E}$ implies that we start from scratch. [Continued in example (4.*c*).]

(*c*) Another variant of example (*a*) is the event $\mathcal{E}$ that the accumulated number of successes equals λ times the accumulated number of failures (where $\lambda > 0$ is an arbitrary, but fixed, number). If $\mathcal{E}$ occurs at the nth trial, it occurs again at the $(n+m)$th trial only if among the trials number $n + 1, \ldots, n + m$ there occur exactly λ times as many successes as failures. The waiting times between successive occurrences of $\mathcal{E}$ are therefore independent and identically distributed. As a special case consider the event that $6n$ throws of a perfect die yield exactly n aces. (Continued in problems 4–5.)

(*d*) *Ladder variables.* Adhering to the notations of example (*a*) we define a new repetitive pattern $\mathcal{E}$ by stipulating that $\mathcal{E}$ *occurs at the nth trial if* S_n *exceeds all preceding sums*, that is, if

(1.3) $$S_n > 0, \qquad S_n > S_1, \ldots, S_n > S_{n-1}.$$

If $\mathcal{E}$ occurs at the nth trial the process starts from scratch in the following sense. Assuming (1.3) to hold, $\mathcal{E}$ occurs at the $(n+m)$th trial if, and only if,

(1.4) $$S_{n+m} > S_n, \ldots, S_{n+m} > S_{n+m-1}.$$

But the differences $S_{n+k} - S_n$ are simply the partial sums of the residual sequence $X_{n+1}, X_{n+2}, \ldots$ and so the reoccurrence of $\mathcal{E}$ is defined in terms of this residual sequence exactly as $\mathcal{E}$ is defined for the whole sequence. In other words, for the study of $\mathcal{E}$ the whole past becomes irrelevant every time $\mathcal{E}$ occurs. [Continued in example (4.*d*).]

(*e*) *Success runs in Bernoulli trials.* In the preceding examples the definition of $\mathcal{E}$ was straightforward, but we turn now to a situation in which a judicious definition is necessary to make the theory of recurrent patterns applicable. In the classical literature a "success run of length r" meant an uninterrupted sequence of either exactly r, or of at least r, successes. Neither convention leads to a recurrent pattern. Indeed, if exactly r successes are required, then a success at the $(n+1)$st trial may undo the run completed at the nth trial. On the other hand, if at least r successes are required, then every run may be prolonged indefinitely and it is clear that the occurrence of a run does not reestablish the initial situation. The classical theory of runs was rather messy, and a more systematic approach is possible by defining a run of length r in such a way that it becomes a recurrent pattern. A *first* run of length r is uniquely defined, and we now agree to start counting from scratch every time a run occurs. With this convention the sequence $SSS \mid SFSSS \mid SSS \mid F$ contains three success runs of length three (occurring at trials number 3, 8, and 11). It contains five runs of length two (trials number 2, 4, 7, 9, 11). The formal definition is as follows: *A sequence of n letters S and F contains as many S-runs of length r as there are non-overlapping uninterrupted blocks containing exactly r letters S each.* With this convention we say that $\mathcal{E}$ occurs at the nth trial if a new run of length r is added to the sequence. This defines a recurrent pattern and greatly simplifies the theory without affecting its basic features. (Continued in section 7.)

(*f*) *Continuation: Related patterns.* It is obvious that the considerations of the preceding example apply to more general patterns, such as the occurrence of the succession *SFSF.* More interesting is that no limitation to a fixed pattern is necessary. Thus the occurrence of "*two successes and three failures*" defines a repetitive pattern, and the same is true of "either a success run of length *r* or a failure run of length ρ." (Continued in section 8.)

(*g*) *Geiger counters.* Counters of the type used for cosmic rays and α-particles may be described by the following simplified model.[1] Bernoulli trials are performed at a uniform rate. A counter is meant to register successes, but the mechanism is locked for exactly *r*−1 trials following each registration. In other words, a success at the *n*th trial is registered if, and only if, no registration has occurred in the preceding *r*−1 trials. The counter is then locked at the conclusion of trials number $n, . . , n + r - 1$, and is freed at the conclusion of the (*n*+*r*)th trial provided this trial results in failure. The output of the counter represents dependent trials. Each registration has an aftereffect, but, whenever the counter is free (not locked) the situation is exactly the same, and the trials start from scratch. Letting ℰ stand for "at the conclusion of the trial the counter is free," we have a typical recurrent pattern. [Continued in example (4.*e*).]

(*h*) *The simplest queuing process* is defined in terms of a sequence of Bernoulli trials and a sequence of random variables $X_1, X_2, . . .$ assuming only positive integral values. The X_k have a common distribution $\{\beta_k\}$ and are independent of each other and of the Bernoulli trials. We interpret success at the *n*th trial as the arrival at epoch[2] *n* of a customer at a server (or a call at a telephone trunk line). The variable X_n represents the service time of the *n*th customer arriving at the server. At any epoch the server is either "free" or "busy" and the process proceeds according to the following rules. Initially (at epoch 0) the server is free. A customer arriving when the counter is free is served immediately, but following his arrival the server is busy for the duration of the service time. Customers arriving when the server is busy form a waiting line (queue). The server serves customers without interruption as long as there is a demand.

These rules determine the process uniquely, for given a sample sequence $(S, F, S, S, S, F, F, . . .)$ for the arrival process and a sample sequence $(3, 1, 17, 2, . . .)$ for the successive service times, it is not difficult to find

---

[1] This is the discrete analogue of the so-called counters of type I. Type II is described in problem 8.

[2] We use the term *epoch* to denote points on the time axis. Terms such as waiting time will refer to durations. This practice was introduced by J. Riordan because in queuing theory the several meanings of words like time, moment, etc., are apt to cause confusion.

the size of the queue at any epoch, and the waiting time of the nth customer. In principle, therefore, we should be able to calculate all pertinent probabilities, but it is not easy to find practicable methods. Now it is clear that every time the server is free the situation is exactly the same as it is at epoch 0. In our terminology therefore the contingency "the server is free" constitutes a recurrent pattern. We shall see that the very existence of such a recurrent pattern has important consequences; for example, it implies that the probability distributions for the size of the queue at epoch n, for the waiting time of the nth customer, and for similar random variables tend to definite limits when $n \to \infty$ (theorem 5.2). In other words, the existence of a recurrent pattern enables us to prove the existence of a steady state and to analyze its dominant features.

(i) *Servicing of machines.* The scope of the method of recurrent patterns may be illustrated by a variant of the preceding example in which the arrivals are no longer regulated by Bernoulli trials. To fix ideas, let us interpret the "customers" as identical machines subject to occasional breakdowns, and the "server" as a repairman. We adhere to the same conventions concerning servicing and the formation of queues, but introduce a new chance mechanism for the "arrivals," that is, for the breakdowns. Suppose there are N machines in all, and consider two extreme cases.

(a) Suppose first that as long as a machine is in working condition it has a fixed probability p to break down at the next epoch; when it breaks down it is replaced by an identical new machine, and the serving time is interpreted as the time required for the installation of a new machine. We treat the machines as independent, and the breakdowns are regulated by N independent sequences of Bernoulli trials. Note that the more machines are in the queue, the fewer machines are in working condition, and hence the length of the queue at any epoch influences the probability of new arrivals (or service calls). This is in marked contrast to the preceding example, but the contingency "server is idle" constitutes nevertheless a recurrent pattern because we are confronted with precisely the same situation whenever it occurs.

(b) Suppose now that every repair has an aftereffect in that it increases the probabilities of further breakdowns. This implies that the machines deteriorate steadily and so once a machine breaks down it is impossible that the favorable initial situation should be repeated. In this case there is no recurrent pattern to help the analysis.   ▶

2. DEFINITIONS

We consider a sequence of repeated trials with possible outcomes E_j ($j = 1, 2, \ldots$). They need not be independent (applications to Markov chains being of special interest). As usual, we suppose that it is in principle possible to continue the trials indefinitely, the probabilities $\mathbf{P}\{E_{j_1}, E_{j_2}, \ldots, E_{j_n}\}$ being defined consistently for all finite sequences. Let $\mathcal{E}$ be an attribute of finite sequences; that is, we suppose that it is uniquely determined whether a sequence $(E_{j_1}, \ldots, E_{j_n})$ has, or has not, the characteristic $\mathcal{E}$. We agree that the expression "$\mathcal{E}$ occurs at the nth place in the (finite or infinite) sequence $E_{j_1}, E_{j_2}, \ldots$" is an abbreviation for "The subsequence $E_{j_1}, E_{j_2}, \ldots, E_{j_n}$ has the attribute $\mathcal{E}$." This convention implies that the occurrence of $\mathcal{E}$ at the nth trial depends soley on the outcome of the first n trials. It is also understood that *when speaking of a "recurrent event $\mathcal{E}$," we are really referring to a class of events* defined by the property that $\mathcal{E}$ occurs. Clearly $\mathcal{E}$ itself is a label rather than an event. We are here abusing the language in the same way as is generally accepted in terms such as "a two-dimensional problem"; the problem itself is dimensionless.

Definition 1. *The attribute $\mathcal{E}$ defines a recurrent event if:*

(a) In order that $\mathcal{E}$ occurs at the nth and the $(n+m)$th place of the sequence $(E_{j_1}, E_{j_2}, \ldots, E_{j_{n+m}})$ it is necessary and sufficient that $\mathcal{E}$ occurs at the last place in each of the two subsequences $(E_{j_1}, E_{j_2}, \ldots, E_{j_n})$ and $(E_{j_{n+1}}, E_{j_{n+2}}, \ldots, E_{j_{n+m}})$.

(b) If $\mathcal{E}$ occurs at the nth place then identically

$$\mathbf{P}\{E_{j_1}, \ldots, E_{j_{n+m}}\} = \mathbf{P}\{E_{j_1}, \ldots, E_{j_n}\} \, \mathbf{P}\{E_{j_{n+1}}, \ldots, E_{j_{n+m}}\}.$$

It has now an obvious meaning to say that $\mathcal{E}$ occurs in the sequence $(E_{j_1}, E_{j_2}, \ldots)$ *for the first time* at the nth place, etc. It is also clear that with each recurrent event $\mathcal{E}$ there are associated the two sequences of numbers defined for $n = 1, 2, \ldots$ as follows

(2.1)
$$u_n = \mathbf{P}\{\mathcal{E} \text{ occurs at the } n\text{th trial}\},$$

$$f_n = \mathbf{P}\{\mathcal{E} \text{ occurs for the first time at the } n\text{th trial}\}.$$

It will be convenient to define

(2.2)
$$f_0 = 0, \qquad u_0 = 1,$$

and to introduce the generating functions

(2.3)
$$F(s) = \sum_{k=1}^{\infty} f_k s^k, \qquad U(s) = \sum_{k=0}^{\infty} u_k s^k.$$

Observe that $\{u_k\}$ is not a probability distribution; in fact, in representative cases we shall have $\sum u_k = \infty$. However, the events "$\mathcal{E}$ occurs for the first time at the nth trial" are mutually exclusive, and therefore

$$(2.4) \qquad\qquad f = \sum_{n=1}^{\infty} f_n \leq 1.$$

It is clear that $1 - f$ should be interpreted as *the probaiblity that $\mathcal{E}$ does not occur in an indefinitely prolonged sequence of trials.* If $f = 1$ we may introduce a random variable $\mathbf{T}$ with distribution

$$(2.5) \qquad\qquad \mathbf{P}\{\mathbf{T} = n\} = f_n.$$

We shall use the same notation (2.5) even if $f < 1$. Then $\mathbf{T}$ *is an improper, or defective random variable, which with probability* $1 - f$ *does not assume a numerical value.* (For our purposes we could assign to $\mathbf{T}$ the symbol ∞, and it should be clear that no new rules are required.)

The *waiting time for* $\mathcal{E}$, that is, the number of trials up to and including the first occurrence of $\mathcal{E}$, is a random variable with the distribution (2.5); however, this random variable is really defined only in the space of infinite sequences $(E_{j_1}, E_{j_2}, \ldots)$.

By the definition of recurrent events the probability that $\mathcal{E}$ occurs for the first time at trial number k and for the *second* time at the nth trial equals $f_k f_{n-k}$. Therefore the probability $f_n^{(2)}$ that $\mathcal{E}$ occurs for the second time at the nth trial equals

$$(2.6) \qquad\qquad f_n^{(2)} = f_1 f_{n-1} + f_2 f_{n-2} + \cdots + f_{n-1} f_1.$$

The right side is the convolution of $\{f_n\}$ with itself and therefore $\{f_n^{(2)}\}$ represents the probability distribution of the sum of two independent random variables each having the distribution (2.5). More generally, if $f_n^{(r)}$ is the probability that the rth occurrence of $\mathcal{E}$ takes place at the nth trial we have

$$(2.7) \qquad\qquad f_n^{(r)} = f_1 f_{n-1}^{(r-1)} + f_2 f_{n-2}^{(r-1)} + \cdots + f_{n-1} f_1^{(r-1)}.$$

This simple fact is expressed in the

Theorem. *Let $f_n^{(r)}$ be the probability that the rth occurrence of $\mathcal{E}$ takes place at the nth trial. Then $\{f_n^{(r)}\}$ is the probability distribution of the sum*

$$(2.8) \qquad\qquad \mathbf{T}^{(r)} = \mathbf{T}_1 + \mathbf{T}_2 + \cdots + \mathbf{T}_r$$

of r independent random variables $\mathbf{T}_1, \ldots, \mathbf{T}_r$ each having the distribution (2.5). *In other words: For fixed r the sequence $\{f_n^{(r)}\}$ has the generating function $F^r(s)$.*

It follows in particular that

(2.9)
$$\sum_{n=1}^{\infty} f_n^{(r)} = F^r(1) = f^r.$$

In words: *the probability that $\mathcal{E}$ occurs at least r   times equals f^r* (a fact which could have been anticipated). We now introduce

Definition 2.   *A recurrent event $\mathcal{E}$ will be called persistent[3] if f = 1 and transient if f < 1.*

For a transient $\mathcal{E}$ the probability f^r that it occurs at least r times tends to zero, whereas for a persistent $\mathcal{E}$ this probability remains unity. This can be described by saying *with probability one a persistent $\mathcal{E}$ is bound to occur infinitely often whereas a transient $\mathcal{E}$ occurs only a finite number of times.* (This statement not only is a description but is formally correct if interpreted in the sample space of infinite sequences $E_{j_1}, E_{j_2}, \ldots$.)

We require one more definition. In Bernoulli trials a return to equilibrium [example (1.*a*)] can occur only at an *even*-numbered trial. In this case $f_{2n+1} = u_{2n+1} = 0$, and the generating functions $F(s)$ and $U(s)$ are power series in s^2 rather than s. Similarly, in example (1.*c*) if a is an integer, $\mathcal{E}$ can occur at the *n*th trial only if n is a multiple of a. We express this by saying that $\mathcal{E}$ is periodic. In essence periodic recurrent events differ only notationally from non-periodic ones, but every theorem requires a special mention of the exceptional periodic case. In other words, periodic recurrent events are a great nuisance without redeeming features of interest.

Definition 3.   *The recurrent event $\mathcal{E}$ is called periodic if there exists an integer $\lambda > 1$ such that $\mathcal{E}$ can occur only at trials number $\lambda, 2\lambda, 3\lambda, \ldots$ (i.e., $u_n = 0$ whenever n is not divisible by λ). The greatest λ with this property is called the period of $\mathcal{E}$.*

In conclusion let us remark that in the sample space of infinite sequences $E_{j_1}, E_{j_2}, \ldots$ the number of trials between the (r−1)st and the rth occurrence of $\mathcal{E}$ is a well-defined random variable (possibly a defective one), having the probability distribution of our $\mathbf{T}_r$. In other words, our variables $\mathbf{T}_r$ really stand for the *waiting times between the successive occurrences of $\mathcal{E}$ (the recurrence times)*. We have defined the $\mathbf{T}_r$ analytically in order not to refer to sample spaces beyond the scope of this volume, but it is hoped that the probabilistic background appears in all its intuitive simplicity. The notion of recurrent events is designed to

---

[3] In the first edition the terms certain and uncertain were used, but the present terminology is preferable in applications to Markov chains.

reduce a fairly general situation to sums of independent random variables. Conversely, *an arbitrary probability distribution* $\{f_n\}$, $n = 1, 2, \ldots$ *may be used to define a recurrent event*. We prove this assertion by the

Example. *Self-renewing aggregates.* Consider an electric bulb, fuse, or other piece of equipment with a finite life span. As soon as the piece fails, it is replaced by a new piece of like kind, which in due time is replaced by a third piece, and so on. We assume that the life span is a random variable which ranges only over multiples of a unit time interval (year, day, or second). Each time unit then represents a trial with possible outcomes "replacement" and "no replacement." The successive replacements may be treated as recurrent events. If f_n is the probability that a new piece will serve for exactly n time units, then $\{f_n\}$ is the distribution of the recurrence times. When it is certain that the life span is finite, then $\sum f_n = 1$ and the recurrent event is persistent. Usually it is known that the life span cannot exceed a fixed number m, in which case the generating function $F(s)$ is a polynomial of a degree not exceeding m. In applications we desire the probability u_n that a replacement takes place at time n. This u_n may be calculated from (3.1). Here we have a class of recurrent events defined solely in terms of an arbitrary distribution $\{f_n\}$. The case $f < 1$ is not excluded, $1 - f$ being the probability of an eternal life of our piece of equipment. ▶

3. THE BASIC RELATIONS

We adhere to the notations (2.1)–(2.4) and propose to investigate the connection between the $\{f_n\}$ and the $\{u_n\}$. The probability that $\mathcal{E}$ occurs for the first time at trial number ν and then again at a later trial $n > \nu$ is, by definition, $f_\nu u_{n-\nu}$. The probability that $\mathcal{E}$ occurs at the nth trial for the first time is $f_n = f_n u_0$. Since these cases are mutually exclusive we have

$$(3.1) \qquad u_n = f_1 u_{n-1} + f_2 u_{n-2} + \cdots + f_n u_0, \qquad n \geq 1.$$

At the right we recognize the convolution $\{f_k\} * \{u_k\}$ with the generating function $F(s) U(s)$. At the left we find the sequence $\{u_n\}$ with the term u_0 missing, so that its generating function is $U(s) - 1$. Thus $U(s) - 1 = = F(s) U(s)$, and we have proved

Theorem 1. *The generating functions of $\{u_n\}$ and $\{f_n\}$ are related by*

$$(3.2) \qquad U(s) = \frac{1}{1 - F(s)}.$$

Note. The right side in (3.2) can be expanded into a geometric series $\sum F^r(s)$ converging for $|s| < 1$. The coefficient $f_n^{(r)}$ of s^n in $F^r(s)$ being the probability that the rth occurrence of $\mathcal{E}$ takes place at the nth trial, (3.2) is equivalent to

$$(3.3) \qquad u_n = f_n^{(1)} + f_n^{(2)} + \cdots ;$$

this expresses the obvious fact that if $\mathcal{E}$ occurs at the nth trial, it has previously occurred $0, 1, 2, \ldots, n-1$ times. (Clearly $f_n^{(r)} = 0$ for $r > n$.)

Theorem 2. *For $\mathcal{E}$ to be transient, it is necessary and sufficient that*

$$(3.4) \qquad u = \sum_{j=0}^{\infty} u_j$$

is finite. In this case the probability f that $\mathcal{E}$ ever occurs is given by

$$(3.5) \qquad f = \frac{u-1}{u}.$$

Note. We can interpret u_j as the expectation of a random variable which equals 1 or 0 according to whether $\mathcal{E}$ does or does not occur at the jth trial. Hence $u_1 + u_2 + \cdots + u_n$ *is the expected number of occurrences of $\mathcal{E}$ in n trials,* and $u - 1$ can be interpreted as the expected number of occurrences of $\mathcal{E}$ in infinitely many trials.

Proof. The coefficients u_k being non-negative, it is clear that $U(s)$ increases monotonically as $s \to 1$ and that for each N

$$\sum_{n=0}^{N} u_n \le \lim_{s \to 1} U(s) \le \sum_{n=0}^{\infty} u_n = u.$$

Since $U(s) \to (1-f)^{-1}$ when $f < 1$ and $U(s) \to \infty$ when $f = 1$, the theorem follows. ▶

The next theorem is of particular importance.[4] The proof is of an

---

[4] Special cases are easily proved (see problem 1) and were known for a long time. A huge literature tried to improve on the conditions, but it was generally believed that some restrictions were necessary. In full generality theorem 3 was proved by P. Erdös, W. Feller, and H. Pollard, A theorem on power series, Bull. Amer. Math. Soc. vol. 55 (1949), pp. 201–204. After the appearance of the first edition it was observed by K. L. Chung that the theorem could be derived from Kolmogorov's results about the asymptotic behavior of Markov chains. Many prominent mathematicians proved various extensions of the theorem to different classes of probability distributions. These investigations contributed to the methodology of modern probability theory. Eventually it turned out that an analogue to theorem 3 holds for arbitrary probability distributions. For an elementary (if not simple) proof see XI,9 of volume 2.

elementary nature, but since it does not contribute to a probabilistic understanding we defer it to the end of the chapter.

Theorem 3. *Let* ϵ *be persistent and not periodic and denote by* μ *the mean of the recurrence times* $\mathbf{T}_\nu$, *that is,*

$$(3.6) \qquad\qquad \mu = \sum jf_j = F'(1)$$

(possibly $\mu = \infty$*). Then*

$$(3.7) \qquad\qquad u_n \to \mu^{-1}$$

as $n \to \infty$ *(*$u_n \to 0$ *if the mean recurrence time is infinite).*

The restriction to non-periodic $\mathcal{E}$ is easily removed. In fact, when $\mathcal{E}$ has period λ the series $\sum f_n s^n$ contains only powers of s^λ. Let us call a power series honest if this is not the case for any integer $\lambda > 1$. Theorem 3 may then be restated to the effect, that *if* F *is an honest probability generating function and* U *is defined by* (3.2), *then* $u_n \to 1/F'(1)$. Now if $\mathcal{E}$ has period λ then $F(s^{1/\lambda})$ is an honest probability generating function, and hence the coefficients of $U(s^{1/\lambda})$ converge to $\lambda/F'(1)$. We have thus

Theorem 4. *If* $\mathcal{E}$ *is persistent and has period* λ *then*

$$(3.8) \qquad\qquad u_{n\lambda} \to \lambda/\mu$$

while $u_k = 0$ *for every* k *not divisible by* λ.

4. EXAMPLES

(*a*) *Successes in Bernoulli trials.* For a trite example let $\mathcal{E}$ stand for "success" in a sequence of Bernoulli trials. Then $u_n = p$ for $n \geq 1$, whence

$$(4.1) \qquad U(s) = \frac{1 - qs}{1 - s} \quad \text{and therefore} \quad F(s) = \frac{ps}{1 - qs}$$

by virtue of (3.2). In this special case theorem 2 merely confirms the obvious fact that the waiting times between consecutive successes have a geometric distribution with expectation $1/p$.

(*b*) *Returns to equilibrium* [*example* (1.a)]. At the kth trial the accumulated numbers of heads and tails can be equal only if $k = 2n$ is even, and in this case the probability of an equalization equals

$$(4.2) \qquad\qquad u_{2n} = \binom{2n}{n} p^n q^n = \binom{-\tfrac{1}{2}}{n}(-4pq)^n.$$

From the binomial expansion II, (8.7) it follows therefore that

(4.3)
$$U(s) = \frac{1}{\sqrt{1 - 4pqs^2}}$$

and hence from (3.2)

(4.4)
$$F(s) = 1 - \sqrt{1 - 4pqs^2}.$$

A second application of the binomial expansion leads to an explicit expression for f_{2n}. (Explicit expressions for u_{2n} and f_{2n} when $p = \frac{1}{2}$ were derived by combinatorial methods in III,3; the generating functions U and F were found by other methods in XI,3. It will be noticed that only the present method requires no artifice.)

For $s = 1$ the square root in (4.4) equals $|p - q|$ and so

(4.5)
$$f = 1 - |p - q|.$$

Thus *returns to equilibrium represent a recurrent event with period 2 which is transient when $p \neq q$, and persistent in the symmetric case $p = q$.* The probability of at least r returns to equilibrium equals f^r.

When $p = q = \frac{1}{2}$ the waiting time for the first return to equilibrium is a proper random variable, but $F'(1) = \infty$ and so *the mean recurrence time μ is infinite.* (This follows also from theorem 4 and the fact that $u_n \to 0$.) The fact that the mean recurrence time is infinite implies that the chance fluctuations in an individual prolonged coin-tossing game are far removed from the familiar pattern governed by the normal distribution. The rather paradoxical true nature of these fluctuations was discussed in chapter III.

(c) *Return to equilibrium through negative values.* In example (1.b) the return to equilibrium was subject to the restriction that no preceding partial sum S_j was positive. The distribution of the recurrence times for this recurrent event is defined by

(4.6)
$$f_{2n}^- = P\{S_{2n} = 0, S_1 < 0, \ldots, S_{2n-1} < 0\}$$

and, of course, $f_{2n-1}^- = 0$. It does not seem possible to find these probabilities by a direct argument, but they follow easily from the preceding example. Indeed, a sample sequence $(X_1, \ldots, X_{2n})$ satisfying the condition in (4.6) contains n plus ones and n minus ones, and hence it has the same probability as $(-X_1, \ldots, -X_{2n})$. Now a *first* return to equilibrium occurs either through positive or through negative values, and we conclude that these two contingencies have the same probability. Thus $f_{2n}^- = \frac{1}{2}f_{2n}$ where $\{f_n\}$ is the distribution for the returns to equilibrium found in the preceding example. The generating function for our recurrence times is therefore given by

(4.7) $$F^-(s) = \tfrac{1}{2} - \tfrac{1}{2}\sqrt{1 - 4pqs^2},$$

and hence

(4.8) $$U^-(s) = \frac{2}{1 + \sqrt{1 - 4pqs^2}} = \frac{1 - \sqrt{1 - 4pqs^2}}{2pqs^2}.$$

The event $\mathcal{E}$ is transient, the probability that it ever occurs being $\tfrac{1}{2} - \tfrac{1}{2}|p - q|$.

   (d) *Ladder variables.* The first positive partial sum can occur at the kth trial only if $k = 2n + 1$ is odd. For the corresponding probabilities we write

(4.9) $$\phi_{2n+1} = P\{S_1 < 0, \ldots, S_{2n} = 0, S_{2n+1} = 1\}.$$

Thus $\{\phi_k\}$ is the distribution of the recurrent event of example $(1.d)$. Now the condition in (4.9) requires that $X_{2n+1} = +1$, and that the recurrent event of the preceding example occurs at the $2n$th trial. It follows that $\phi_{2n+1} = p \cdot u_{2n}^-$. With obvious notations therefore

(4.10) $$\Phi(s) = psU^-(s) = \frac{1 - \sqrt{1 - 4pqs^2}}{2qs}.$$

This is the generating function for the first-passage times found in XI,(3.6). An explicit expression for ϕ_{2n+1} follows from (4.10) using the binomial expansion II,(8.7). This expression for ϕ_{2n+1} agrees with that found by combinatorial methods in theorem 2 of III,7.

   (e) *Geiger counters.* In example $(1.g)$ the counter remains free if no registration takes place at epoch 1. Otherwise it becomes locked and is freed again at epoch $r + 1$ if no particle arrives at that epoch; the counter is freed at epoch $2r + 1$ if a particle appears at epoch $r + 1$, but none at epoch $2r + 1$, and so on. The generating function of the recurrence times is therefore given by

(4.11) $$qs + qps^{r+1} + qp^2s^{2r+1} + \cdots = \frac{qs}{1 - ps^r}.$$

(See also problems 7–9.)

   (f) *The simplest queuing problem* [example $(1.h)$]. Here the server remains free if no customer arrives at epoch 1. If a customer arrives there follows a so-called "busy period" which terminates at the epoch when the counter first becomes free. The generating function $\rho(s)$ for the busy period was derived in example XII,$(5.c)$ using the methods of branching processes.

It follows that in the present case the generating function of the recurrence times is given by $qs + ps\rho(s)$, in agreement with XII,(5.7).

(g) *Ties in multiple coin games.* We conclude with a simple example showing the possibility of certain conclusions without explicit knowledge of the generating functions. Let $r \geq 2$ be an arbitrary integer and consider a sequence of simultaneous independent tosses of r coins. Let $\mathcal{E}$ stand for the recurrent event that *all r coins are in the same phase* (that is, the accumulated numbers of heads are the same for all r coins). The probability that this occurs at the nth trial is

$$(4.12) \qquad u_n = 2^{-rn}\left[\binom{n}{0}^r + \binom{n}{1}^r + \cdots + \binom{n}{n}^r\right].$$

On the right we recognize the terms of the binomial distribution with $p = \frac{1}{2}$, and from the normal approximation to the latter we conclude easily that for each fixed r as $n \to \infty$

$$(4.13) \qquad u_n \sim \left(\frac{2}{\pi n}\right)^{\frac{1}{2}r} \sum_j e^{-2rj^2/n}$$

(the summation extending over all integers j between $-\frac{1}{2}n$ and $\frac{1}{2}n$). But by the very definition of the integral

$$(4.14) \qquad 2\sqrt{\frac{r}{n}} \sum_j e^{-2rj^2/n} \to \int_{-\infty}^{+\infty} e^{-\frac{1}{2}x^2}\, dx = \sqrt{2\pi}$$

and hence we conclude that

$$(4.15) \qquad u_n \sim \frac{1}{\sqrt{r}}\left(\frac{2}{\pi n}\right)^{\frac{1}{2}(r-1)}.$$

This implies that $\sum u_n$ diverges when $r \leq 3$, but converges when $r \geq 4$. It follows that $\mathcal{E}$ *is persistent when $r \leq 3$ but transient if $r \geq 4$.* Since $u_n \to 0$ the mean recurrence time is infinite when $r \leq 3$. (Compare problems 2 and 3.) ▶

5. DELAYED RECURRENT EVENTS.
A GENERAL LIMIT THEOREM

We shall now introduce a slight extension of the notion of recurrent events which is so obvious that it could pass without special mention, except that it is convenient to have a term for it and to have the basic equations on record.

Perhaps the best informal description of delayed recurrent events is to say that they refer to trials where we have "missed the beginning and start in the middle." The waiting time up to the *first* occurrence of $\mathcal{E}$ has a distribution $\{b_n\}$ different from the distribution $\{f_n\}$ of the recurrence times between the following occurrences of $\mathcal{E}$. The theory applies without change except that the trials following each occurrence of $\mathcal{E}$ are exact replicas of a fixed sample space which is not identical with the original one.

The situation being so simple, we shall forego formalities and agree to speak of a *delayed recurrent $\mathcal{E}$ when the definition of recurrent events applies only if the trials leading up to the first occurrence of $\mathcal{E}$ are disregarded; it is understood that the waiting time up to the first appearance of $\mathcal{E}$ is a random variable independent of the following recurrence times, although its distribution $\{b_n\}$ may be different from the common distribution $\{f_n\}$ of the recurrence times.*

We denote by v_n the probability of the occurrence of $\mathcal{E}$ at the nth trial. To derive an expression for v_n we argue as follows. Suppose that $\mathcal{E}$ occurs at trial number $k < n$. Relative to the subsequent trials $\mathcal{E}$ becomes an ordinary recurrent event and so the (conditional) probability of a renewed occurrence at the nth trial equals u_{n-k}. Now if $\mathcal{E}$ occurs at the nth trial this is either its first occurrence, or else the first occurrence took place at the kth trial for some $k < n$. Summing over all possibilities we get

$$(5.1) \qquad v_n = b_n + b_{n-1}u_1 + b_{n-2}u_2 + \cdots + b_1 u_{n-1} + b_0 u_n.$$

We are thus in possession of an explicit expression for v_n. [For an alternative proof see example (10.a).] The relations (5.1) may be rewritten in the compact form of a convolution equation:

$$(5.2) \qquad\qquad \{v_n\} = \{b_n\} * \{u_n\}.$$

This implies that the corresponding generating functions satisfy the identity

$$(5.3) \qquad\qquad V(s) = B(s)U(s) = \frac{B(s)}{1 - F(s)}.$$

Example. (a) In the Bernoulli trials considered in examples (4.a)–(4.d) the event $S_n = 1$ is a delayed recurrent event. The waiting time for its first occurrence has the generating function Φ of (4.10); the recurrence times between successive occurrences of $\{S_n = 1\}$ have the generating function F of the returns to equilibrium [see (4.4)]. Thus in the present case $V = \Phi/(1-F)$. ▶

It is easy to show that the asymptotic behavior of the probabilities v_n is essentially the same as that of u_n. To avoid trivialities we assume that $\mathcal{E}$ is not periodic.[5] We know from section 3 that in this case u_n approaches a finite limit, and that $\sum u_n < \infty$ if, and only if, $\mathcal{E}$ is transient.

Theorem 1. *If* $u_n \to \omega$ *then*

$$(5.4) \qquad\qquad v_n \to b\omega \qquad where \quad b = \sum b_k = B(1).$$

If $\sum u_n = u < \infty$ *then*

$$(5.5) \qquad\qquad \sum v_n = bu.$$

In particular, $v_n \to \mu^{-1}$ *if* $\mathcal{E}$ *is persistent.*

Proof. Let $r_k = b_{k+1} + b_{k+2} + \cdots$. Since $u_n \le 1$ it is obvious from (5.1) that for $n > k$

$$(5.6) \quad b_0 u_n + \cdots + b_k u_{n-k} \le v_n \le b_0 u_n + \cdots + b_k u_{n-k} + r_k.$$

Choose k so large that $r_k < \epsilon$. For n sufficiently large the leftmost member in (5.6) is then greater than $b\omega - 2\epsilon$, whereas the rightmost member is less than $b\omega + 2\epsilon$. Thus (5.4) is true. The assertion (5.5) follows either by summing (5.1) over n, or else from (5.3) on letting $s = 1$. ▶

We turn to a general limit theorem of wide applicability. Suppose that there are denumerably many possible states $E_0, E_1, \ldots$ for a certain system, and that the transitions from one state to another depend on a chance mechanism of some sort. For example, in the simple queuing process (1.h) we say that the system is in state E_k if there are k customers in the queue, including the customer being served. A problem involving seventeen servers may require eighteen numbers to specify the state of the system, but all imaginable states can still be ordered in a sequence $E_0, E_1, \ldots$. We need not consider how this is best done, because the following theorem does not lead to practical methods for evaluating probabilities. It is a pure existence theorem showing that a steady state exists under most circumstances encountered in practice. This is of conceptual interest, but also of practical value because, as a rule, mathematical analysis of a steady state is much simpler than the study of the time-dependent process.

We suppose that for $n = 1, 2, \ldots$ and every n-tuple $(r_1, \ldots, r_n)$ there exists a well-defined probability that the states of the system at epochs

---

[5] Periodic recurrent events are covered by theorem 10.2. For a different proof of theorem 1 see example (10.a).

$0, 1, \ldots, n - 1$ are represented by $(E_{r_1}, \ldots, E_{r_n})$. We shall not introduce any particular assumptions concerning the mutual dependence of these events or the probabilities for the transitions from one state to another. For simplicity we consider only *the probabilities $p_n^{(r)}$ that at epoch n the system is in state E_r.* (It will be obvious how the theorem generalizes to pairs, triples, etc.) The crucial assumption is that there exists some recurrent event $\mathcal{E}$ connected with our process. For example, in the queuing process $(1.h)$ the state E_0 represents such a recurrent event. In this case, if $\mathcal{E}$ were transient there would exist a positive probability that the queue does not terminate. This would imply that sooner or later we would encounter an unending queue, that is, a queue of indefinitely increasing size. This is a limit theorem of some sort showing that such servers are impossible in practice. This example should explain the role of the condition that $\mathcal{E}$ be persistent. (The non-periodicity is introduced only to avoid trivialities).

Theorem 2. *Assume that there exists a non-periodic persistent (possibly delayed) recurrent event $\mathcal{E}$ associated with our process. Then as $n \to \infty$*

$$(5.7) \qquad p_n^{(r)} \to p^{(r)}$$

where

$$(5.8) \qquad \sum p^{(r)} = 1$$

if the mean recurrence time μ is finite, and $p^{(r)} = 0$ otherwise.

Proof. Every time when $\mathcal{E}$ occurs the process starts from scratch. There exists therefore a well-defined conditional probability $g_n^{(r)}$ that if $\mathcal{E}$ occurs at some epoch, the state E_r occurs n time units later and *before* the next occurrence of $\mathcal{E}$ (here $n = 0, 1, \ldots$). For delayed recurrent events we require also the probability $\gamma_n^{(r)}$ that E_r occurs at epoch n *before* the first occurrence of $\mathcal{E}$. (Clearly $\gamma_n^{(r)} = g_n^{(r)}$ if $\mathcal{E}$ is not delayed.)

Let us now classify the ways in which E_r can occur at epoch n according to the last occurrence of $\mathcal{E}$ before epoch n. First, it is possible that $\mathcal{E}$ did not yet occur. The probability for this is $\gamma_n^{(r)}$. Or else there exists a $k \leq n$ such that $\mathcal{E}$ occurred at epoch k but not between k and n. The probability for this is $v_k g_{n-k}^{(r)}$. Summing over all mutually exclusive cases we find

$$(5.9) \qquad p_n^{(r)} = \gamma_n^{(r)} + g_{n-1}^{(r)} v_1 + g_{n-2}^{(r)} v_2 + \cdots + g_0^{(r)} v_n.$$

(Here we adhere to the notations of theorem 1. For delayed events $v_0 = 0$; for non-delayed events $v_k = u_k$ and $\gamma_n^{(r)} = g_n^{(r)}$.)

The relation (5.9) is analogous to (5.1) except for the appearance of the term $\gamma_n^{(r)}$ on the right. This quantity is obviously smaller than the probability that $\mathcal{E}$ did not occur before epoch n, and $\mathcal{E}$ being persistent it follows that $\gamma_n^{(r)} \to 0$ as $n \to \infty$. For the remaining terms we can apply theorem 1 with the notational change that u_k is replaced by v_k and b_k by $g_n^{(r)}$. Since $\mathcal{E}$ is persistent $v_n \to \mu^{-1}$ and it follows that

$$(5.10) \qquad\qquad p_n^{(r)} \to \mu^{-1} \sum_{k=0}^{\infty} g_k^{(r)}.$$

This proves the existence of the limits (5.7). To prove that they add to unity note that at any epoch the system is in some state and hence

$$(5.11) \qquad\qquad \sum_{r=0}^{\infty} g_n^{(r)} = g_n$$

is the probability that a recurrence time is $\geq n$, that is,

$$g_n = f_n + f_{n+1} + \cdots .$$

Thus

$$(5.12) \qquad\qquad \sum_{r=0}^{\infty} p^{(r)} = \frac{1}{\mu} \sum_{n=0}^{\infty} g_n = 1$$

by theorem XI,1.2.   ▶

[The limit theorem in example (10.b) may be treated as a special case of the present theorem.]

6. THE NUMBER OF OCCURRENCES OF $\mathcal{E}$

Up to now we have studied a recurrent event $\mathcal{E}$ in terms of the waiting times between its successive occurrences. Often it is preferable to consider the number n of trials as given and to take *the number N_n of occurrences of $\mathcal{E}$* in the first n trials as basic variable. We shall now investigate the asymptotic behavior of the distribution of N_n for large n. For simplicity we assume that $\mathcal{E}$ is not delayed.

As in (2.8) let $T^{(r)}$ stand for the number of trials up to and including the rth occurrence of $\mathcal{E}$. The probability distributions of $T^{(r)}$ and N_n are related by the obvious identity

$$(6.1) \qquad\qquad P\{N_n \geq r\} = P\{T^{(r)} \leq n\}.$$

We begin with the simple case where $\mathcal{E}$ is persistent and the distribution $\{f_n\}$ of its recurrence times has finite mean μ and variance σ^2. Since $T^{(r)}$ is the sum of r independent variables, the central limit theorem of

X,1 asserts that for each fixed x as $r \to \infty$

$$(6.2) \qquad \mathbf{P}\left\{\frac{\mathbf{T}^{(r)} - r\mu}{\sigma\sqrt{r}} < x\right\} \to \mathfrak{N}(x)$$

where $\mathfrak{N}(x)$ is the normal distribution function. Now let $n \to \infty$ and $r \to \infty$ in such a way that

$$(6.3) \qquad \frac{n - r\mu}{\sigma\sqrt{r}} \to x;$$

then (6.1) and (6.2) together lead to

$$(6.4) \qquad \mathbf{P}\{\mathbf{N}_n \geq r\} \to \mathfrak{N}(x).$$

To write this relation in a more familiar form we introduce the *reduced variable*

$$(6.5) \qquad \mathbf{N}_n^* = (\mu\mathbf{N}_n - n)\sqrt{\frac{\mu}{\sigma^2 n}}.$$

The inequality $\mathbf{N}_n \geq r$ is identical with

$$(6.6) \qquad \mathbf{N}_n^* \geq \frac{r\mu - n}{\sigma\sqrt{r}} \cdot \sqrt{\frac{r\mu}{n}} = -x\sqrt{\frac{r\mu}{n}}.$$

On dividing (6.3) by r it is seen that $n/r \to \mu$, and hence the right side in (6.6) tends to $-x$. Since $\mathfrak{N}(-x) = 1 - \mathfrak{N}(x)$ it follows that

$$(6.7) \quad \mathbf{P}\{\mathbf{N}_n^* \geq -x\} \to \mathfrak{N}(x) \qquad or \qquad \mathbf{P}\{\mathbf{N}_n^* < -x\} \to 1 - \mathfrak{N}(x),$$

and we have proved the

Theorem. *Normal approximation. If the recurrent event $\mathcal{E}$ is persistent and its recurrence times have finite mean μ and variance σ^2, then both the number $\mathbf{T}^{(r)}$ of trials up to the rth occurrence of $\mathcal{E}$ and the number $\mathbf{N}_n$ of occurrences of $\mathcal{E}$ in the first n trials are asymptotically normally distributed as indicated in (6.2) and (6.7).*

Note that in (6.7) we have the central limit theorem applied to a sequence of *dependent* variables $\mathbf{N}_n$. Its usefulness will be illustrated in the next section by an application to the theory of runs.

The relations (6.7) make it plausible that

$$(6.8) \qquad \mathbf{E}(\mathbf{N}_n) \sim n/\mu, \qquad \mathrm{Var}\,(\mathbf{N}_n) \sim n\sigma^2/\mu^3$$

where the sign $\sim$ indicates that the ratio of the two sides tends to unity. To prove (6.8) we note that $\mathbf{N}_n$ is the sum of n (dependent) variables $\mathbf{Y}_k$

such that Y_k equals one or zero according as $\mathcal{E}$ does or does not occur at the kth trial. Thus $E(Y_k) = u_k$ and

$$(6.9) \qquad\qquad E(N_n) = u_1 + u_2 + \cdots + u_n.$$

Since $u_n \to \mu$ this implies the first relation in (6.8). The second follows by a similar argument (see problem 20).

Unfortunately surprisingly many recurrence times occurring in various stochastic processes and in applications have *infinite expectations*. In such cases the normal approximation is replaced by more general limit theorems of an entirely different character,[6] and the chance fluctuations exhibit unexpected features. For example, one expects intuitively that $E(N_n)$ should increase linearly with n "because on the average $\mathcal{E}$ must occur twice as often in twice as many trials." Yet *this is not so*. An infinite mean recurrence time implies that $u_n \to 0$, and then $E(N_n)/n \to 0$ by virtue of (6.9). This means that in the long run the occurrences of $\mathcal{E}$ become rarer and rarer, and this is possible only if some recurrence times are fantastically large. Two examples may show how pronounced this phenomenon is apt to be.

Examples. (*a*) When $\mathcal{E}$ stands for a return to equilibrium in a coin-tossing game [example (1.*b*) with $p = \frac{1}{2}$] we have $u_{2n} \sim 1/\sqrt{\pi n}$, and it is easily seen from (6.9) that this implies $E(N_{2n}) \sim 2\sqrt{n/\pi}$. Thus the *average* recurrence time up to epoch n is likely to increase as $\sqrt{n}$. The curious consequences of this were discussed at length in chapter III.

(*b*) Returning to example (4.*g*) consider repeated tosses of $r = 3$ dice and let $\mathcal{E}$ stand for the event that all three coins are in the same phase. We saw that $\mathcal{E}$ is a persistent recurrent event, and that $u_n \sim \dfrac{2}{\sqrt{3} \cdot \pi n}$. Thus $E(N_n)$ *increases roughly* as $\log n$ and so the *average* of the recurrence times up to epoch n is likely to be of the fantastic magnitude $n/\log n$. ▶

*7. APPLICATION TO THE THEORY OF SUCCESS RUNS

In the sequel r will denote a fixed positive integer and $\mathcal{E}$ will stand for the occurrence of a success run of length r in a sequence of Bernoulli trials. It is important that the length of a run be defined as stated in

---

* Sections 7 and 8 treat a special topic and may be omitted.

[6] W. Feller, *Fluctuation theory of recurrent events*, Trans. Amer. Math. Soc., vol. 67 (1949), pp. 98–119.

example (1.*e*), for otherwise runs are not recurrent events, and the calculations become more involved. As in (2.1) and (2.2), u_n *is the probability of* $\mathcal{E}$ *at the nth trial, and* f_n *is the probability that the first run of length* r *occurs at the nth trial.*

The probability that the r trials number $n, n-1, n-2, \ldots, n-r+1$ result in success is obviously p^r. In this case $\mathcal{E}$ occurs at one among these r trials; the probability that $\mathcal{E}$ occurs at the trial number $n-k$ ($k = 0, 1, \ldots, r-1$) and the following k trials result in k successes equals $u_{n-k}p^k$. Since these r possibilities are mutually exclusive, we get the recurrence relation[7]

$$(7.1) \qquad u_n + u_{n-1}p + \cdots + u_{n-r+1}p^{r-1} = p^r$$

valid for $n \geq r$. Clearly

$$(7.2) \qquad u_1 = u_2 = \cdots = u_{r-1} = 0, \qquad u_0 = 1.$$

On multiplying (7.1) by s^n and summing over $n = r, r+1, r+2, \ldots,$ we get on the left side

$$(7.3) \qquad \{U(s) - 1\}(1+ps+p^2s^2+ \cdots +p^{r-1}s^{r-1})$$

and on the right side $p^r(s^r+s^{r+1}+ \cdots)$. The two series are geometric, and we find that

$$(7.4) \qquad \{U(s) - 1\} \cdot \frac{1 - (ps)^r}{1 - ps} = \frac{p^r s^r}{1 - s}$$

or

$$(7.5) \qquad U(s) = \frac{1 - s + qp^r s^{r+1}}{(1-s)(1-p^r s^r)}.$$

From (3.2), we get now *the generating function of the recurrence times:*

$$(7.6) \quad F(s) = \frac{p^r s^r(1-ps)}{1 - s + qp^r s^{r+1}} = \frac{p^r s^r}{1 - qs(1+ps+ \cdots +p^{r-1}s^{r-1})}.$$

The fact that $F(1) = 1$ shows that in a prolonged sequence of trials the number of runs of any length is certain to increase over all bounds. The mean recurrence time μ could be obtained directly from (7.1) since we know that $u_n \to \mu^{-1}$. Since we require also the variance, it is preferable

---

[7] The classical approach consists in deriving a recurrence relation for f_n. This method is more complicated and does not apply to, say, runs of either kind or patterns like *SSFFSS*, to which our method applies without change [cf. example (8.*c*)].

to calculate the derivatives of $F(s)$. This is best done by implicit differentiation after clearing (7.6) of the denominator. An easy calculation then shows that *the mean and variance of the recurrence times of runs of length r are*

$$(7.7) \qquad \mu = \frac{1-p^r}{qp^r}, \qquad \sigma^2 = \frac{1}{(qp^r)^2} - \frac{2r+1}{qp^r} - \frac{p}{q^2},$$

respectively. By the theorem of the last section for large n *the number N_n of runs of length r produced in n trials is approximately normally*

TABLE 2

MEAN RECURRENCE TIMES FOR SUCCESS RUNS IF TRIALS
ARE PERFORMED AT THE RATE OF ONE PER SECOND

Length of Run	$p = 0.6$	$p = 0.5$ (Coins)	$p = \frac{1}{6}$ (Dice)
$r = 5$	30.7 seconds	1 minute	2.6 hours
10	6.9 minutes	34.1 minutes	28.0 months
15	1.5 hours	18.2 hours	18,098 years
20	19 hours	24.3 days	140.7 million years

distributed, that is, for fixed $\alpha < \beta$ the probability that

$$(7.8) \qquad \frac{n}{\mu} + \alpha\sigma\sqrt{\frac{n}{\mu^3}} < N_n < \frac{n}{\mu} + \beta\sigma\sqrt{\frac{n}{\mu^3}}$$

tends to $\mathfrak{N}(\beta) - \mathfrak{N}(\alpha)$. This fact was first proved by von Mises, by rather lengthy calculations. Table 2 gives a few typical means of recurrence times.

The method of partial fractions of XI, 4, permits us to derive excellent approximations. The second representation in (7.6) shows clearly that the denominator has a unique *positive root* $s = x$. For every real or complex number s with $|s| \leq x$ we have

$$(7.9) \quad |qs(1+ps+ \cdots +p^{r-1}s^{r-1})| \leq qx(1+px+ \cdots +p^{r-1}x^{r-1}) = 1$$

where the equality sign is possible only if all terms on the left have the same argument, that is, if $s = x$. Hence x is smaller in absolute value than any other root of the denominator in (7.6). We can, therefore, apply formulas (4.5) and (4.9) of chapter XI with $s_1 = x$, letting $U(s) = = p^r s^r(1-ps)$ and $V(s) = 1 - s + qp^r s^{r+1}$. We find, using that $V(x) = 0$,

$$(7.10) \qquad f_n \sim \frac{(x-1)(1-px)}{(r+1-rx)q} \cdot \frac{1}{x^{n+1}}.$$

The probability of no run in n trials is $q_n = f_{n+1} + f_{n+2} + f_{n+3} + \cdots$ and summing the geometric series in (7.10) we get

$$(7.11) \qquad q_n \sim \frac{1-px}{(r+1-rx)q} \cdot \frac{1}{x^{n+1}}.$$

We have thus found that *the probability of no success run of length* r *in* n *trials satisfies* (7.11). Table 3 shows that the right side gives surprisingly good approximations even for very small n, and the approximation improves rapidly with n. This illustrates the power of the method of generating function and partial fractions.

TABLE 3

PROBABILITY OF HAVING NO SUCCESS RUN OF LENGTH
$r = 2$ IN n TRIALS WITH $p = \frac{1}{2}$

n	q_n Exact	From (7.11)	Error
2	0.75	0.76631	0.0163
3	0.625	0.61996	0.0080
4	0.500	0.50156	0.0016
5	0.40625	0.40577	0.0005

Numerical Calculations. For the benefit of the practical-minded reader we use this occasion to show that the numerical calculations involved in partial fraction expansions are often less formidable than they appear at first sight, and that excellent estimates of the error can be obtained.

The asymptotic expansion (7.11) raises two questions: First, the contribution of the $r - 1$ neglected roots must be estimated, and second, the dominant root x must be evaluated.

The first representation in (7.6) shows that all roots of the denominator of $F(s)$ satisfy the equation

$$(7.12) \qquad s = 1 + qp^r s^{r+1},$$

but (7.12) has the additional extraneous root $s = p^{-1}$. For positive s the graph of $f(s) = 1 + qp^r s^{r+1}$ is convex; it intersects the bisector $y = s$ at x and p^{-1} and in the interval between x and p^{-1} the graph lies *below* the bisector. Furthermore, $f'(p^{-1}) = (r+1)q$. If this quantity exceeds unity, the graph of $f(s)$ crosses the bisector at $s = p$ from below, and hence $p^{-1} > x$. To fix ideas we shall assume that

$$(7.13) \qquad (r+1)q > 1;$$

in this case $x < p^{-1}$, and $f(s) < s$ for $x < s < p^{-1}$. It follows that for all complex numbers s such that $x < |s| < p^{-1}$ we have $|f(s)| \leq f(|s|) < |s|$ so that no root s_k can lie in the annulus $x < |s| < p^{-1}$. Since x was chosen as the root smallest in absolute value, this implies that

(7.14) $|s_k| > p^{-1}$ *when* $s_k \neq x.$

By differentiation of (7.12) it is now seen that all roots are simple.

The contribution of each root to q_n is of the same form as the contribution (7.11) of the dominant root x, and therefore the $r - 1$ terms neglected in (7.11) are of the form

(7.15) $$A_k = \frac{ps_k - 1}{rs_k - (r + 1)} \cdot \frac{1}{qs_k^{n+1}}.$$

We require an upper bound for the first fraction on the right. For that purpose note that for fixed $s > p^{-1} > (r + 1)r^{-1}$

(7.16) $$\left| \frac{pse^{i\theta} - 1}{rse^{i\theta} - (r + 1)} \right| \leq \frac{ps + 1}{rs + r + 1};$$

in fact, the quantity on the left obviously assumes its maximum and minimum for $\theta = 0$ and $\theta = \pi$, and a direct substitution shows that 0 corresponds to a minimum, π to a maximum. In view of (7.13) and (7.14) we have then

(7.17) $$|A_k| < \frac{2p^{n+1}}{(r + 1 + rp^{-1})q} < \frac{2p^{n+2}}{rq(1 + p)}.$$

We conclude that in (7.11) *the error committed by neglecting the* $r - 1$ *roots different from* x *is less in absolute value than*

(7.18) $$\frac{2(r - 1)p}{rq(1 + p)}.$$

The root x is easily calculated from (7.12) by successive approximations putting $x_0 = 1$ and $x_{v+1} = f(x_v)$. The sequence will converge monotonically to x, and each term provides a lower bound for x, whereas any value s such that $s > f(s)$ provides an upper bound. It is easily seen that

(7.19) $$x = 1 + qp^r + (r + 1)(qp^r)^2 + \cdots.$$

*8. MORE GENERAL PATTERNS

Our method is applicable to more general problems which have been considered as considerably more difficult than simple runs.

Examples. (a) *Runs of either kind.* Let $\mathcal{E}$ stand for "*either a success run of length* r *or a failure run of length* ρ" [see example (1.f)]. We are dealing with *two* recurrent events $\mathcal{E}_1$ and $\mathcal{E}_2$, where $\mathcal{E}_1$ stands for "success run of length r" and $\mathcal{E}_2$ for "failure run of length ρ" and $\mathcal{E}$ means "either $\mathcal{E}_1$ or $\mathcal{E}_2$." To $\mathcal{E}_1$ there corresponds the generating function (7.5) which will now be denoted by $U_1(s)$. The corresponding generating function

---

* This section treats a special topic and may be omitted.

$U_2(s)$ for $\mathcal{E}_2$ is obtained from (7.5) by interchanging p and q and replacing r by ρ. The probability u_n that $\mathcal{E}$ occurs at the nth trial is the sum of the corresponding probabilities for $\mathcal{E}_1$ and $\mathcal{E}_2$, except that $u_0 = 1$. It follows that

$$(8.1) \qquad\qquad U(s) = U_1(s) + U_2(s) - 1.$$

The generating function $F(s)$ of the recurrence times of $\mathcal{E}$ is again $F(s) = 1 - U^{-1}(s)$ or

$$(8.2) \qquad F(s) = \frac{(1-ps)p^r s^r(1-q^\rho s^\rho) + (1-qs)q^\rho s^\rho(1-p^r s^r)}{1 - s + qp^r s^{r+1} + pq^\rho s^{\rho+1} - p^r q^\rho s^{r+\rho}}.$$

The *mean recurrence time* follows by differentiation

$$(8.3) \qquad\qquad \mu = \frac{(1-p^r)(1-q)^\rho}{qp^r + pq^\rho - p^r q^\rho}.$$

As $\rho \to \infty$, this expression tends to the mean recurrence time of success runs as given in (7.7).

(b) In VIII,1, we calculated the probability x that a *success run of length r occurs before a failure run of length ρ.* Define two recurrent events $\mathcal{E}_1$ and $\mathcal{E}_2$ as in example (a). Let $x_n =$ probability that $\mathcal{E}_1$ occurs for the first time at the nth trial and no $\mathcal{E}_2$ precedes it; $f_n =$ probability that $\mathcal{E}_1$ occurs for the first time at the nth trial (with no condition on $\mathcal{E}_2$). Define y_n and g_n as x_n and f_n, respectively, but with $\mathcal{E}_1$ and $\mathcal{E}_2$ interchanged.

The generating function for f_n is given in (7.6), and $G(s)$ is obtained by interchanging p and q and replacing r by ρ. For x_n and y_n we have the obvious recurrence relations

$$(8.4) \qquad x_n = f_n - (y_1 f_{n-1} + y_2 f_{n-2} + \cdots + y_{n-1} 1 f)$$

$$y_n = g_n - (x_1 g_{n-1} + x_2 g_{n-2} + \cdots + x_{n-1} g_1).$$

They are of the convolution type, and for the corresponding generating functions we have, therefore,

$$(8.5) \qquad\qquad X(s) = F(s) - Y(s)F(s)$$

$$Y(s) = G(s) - X(s)G(s).$$

From these two linear equations we get

$$(8.6) \qquad X(s) = \frac{F(s)\{1 - G(s)\}}{1 - F(s)G(s)}, \qquad Y(s) = \frac{G(s)\{1 - F(s)\}}{1 - F(s)G(s)}.$$

Expressions for x_n and y_n can again be obtained by the method of partial fractions. For $s = 1$ we get $X(1) = \sum x_n = x$, the probability of $\mathcal{E}_1$ occurring before $\mathcal{E}_2$. Both numerator and denominator vanish, and $X(1)$ is obtained from L'Hospital's rule differentiating numerator and denominator: $X(1) = G'(1)/\{F'(1) + G'(1)\}$. Using the values $F'(1) = (1-p^r)/qp^r$ and $G'(1) = (1-q^\rho)/pq^\rho$ from (7.7), we find $X(1)$ as given in VIII,(1.3).

(c) Consider the recurrent event defined by the pattern *SSFFSS*. Repeating the argument of section 7, we easily find that

(8.7) $$p^4q^2 = u_n + p^2q^2u_{n-4} + p^3q^2u_{n-5}.$$

Since we know that $u_n \to \mu^{-1}$ we get for the mean recurrence time $\mu = p^{-4}q^{-2} + p^{-2} + p^{-1}$. For $p = q = \frac{1}{2}$ we find $\mu = 70$, whereas the mean recurrence time for a success run of length 6 is 126. This shows that, contrary to expectation, *there is an essential difference in coin tossing between head runs and other patterns of the same length.*   ▶

9. LACK OF MEMORY OF GEOMETRIC WAITING TIMES

The geometric distribution for waiting times has an interesting and important property not shared by any other distribution. Consider a sequence of Bernoulli trials and let **T** be the number of trials up to and including the first success. Then $\mathbf{P}\{\mathbf{T} > k\} = q^k$. Suppose we know that no success has occurred during the first m trials; the waiting time **T** from this mth failure to the first success has exactly the same distribution $\{q^k\}$ and is independent of the number of preceding failures. In other words, the probability that the waiting time will be prolonged by k always equals the initial probability of the total length exceeding k. If the life span of an atom or a piece of equipment has a geometric distribution, then *no aging* takes place; as long as it lives, the atom has the same probability of decaying at the next trial. Radioactive atoms actually have this property (except that in the case of a continuous time the exponential distribution plays the role of the geometric distribution). Conversely, if it is known that a phenomenon is characterized by a complete lack of memory or aging, then the probability distribution of the duration must be geometric or exponential. Typical is a well-known type of telephone conversation often cited as the model of incoherence and depending entirely on momentary impulses; a possible termination is an instantaneous chance effect without relation to the past chatter. By contrast, the knowledge that no streetcar has passed for five minutes increases our expectation that it will come soon. In coin tossing, the probability that the cumulative numbers of heads and tails will equalize at the second trial is $\frac{1}{2}$. However, given that they did not, the probability that they equalize after two additional trials is only $\frac{1}{4}$. These are examples for aftereffect.

For a rigorous formulation of the assertion, suppose that a waiting time T assumes the values $0, 1, 2, \ldots$ with probabilities $p_0, p_1, p_2, \ldots$. Let the distribution of T have the following property: *The conditional probability that the waiting time terminates at the kth trial, assuming that it has not terminated before, equals p_0 (the probability at the first trial).* We claim that $p_k = (1-p_0)^k p_0$, so that T has a geometric distribution.

For a proof we introduce again the "tails"

$$q_k = p_{k+1} + p_{k+2} + p_{k+3} + \cdots = \mathbf{P}\{T > k\}.$$

Our hypothesis is $T > k - 1$, and its probability is q_{k-1}. The conditional probability of $T = k$ is therefore p_k/q_{k-1}, and the assumption is that for all $k \geq 1$

$$(9.1) \qquad\qquad \frac{p_k}{q_{k-1}} = p_0.$$

Now $p_k = q_{k-1} - q_k$, and hence (9.1) reduces to

$$(9.2) \qquad\qquad \frac{q_k}{q_{k-1}} = 1 - p_0.$$

Since $q_0 = p_1 + p_2 + \cdots = 1 - p_0$, it follows that $q_k = (1-p_0)^{k+1}$, and hence $p_k = q_{k-1} - q_k = (1 - p_0)^k p_0$, as asserted. ▶

In the theory of stochastic processes the described lack of memory is connected with the *Markovian property;* we shall return to it in XV,13.

10. RENEWAL THEORY

The convolution equations which served as a basis for the theory of recurrent events are of much wider applicability than appears in the foregoing sections. We shall therefore restate their analytic content in somewhat greater generality and describe the typical probabilistic renewal argument as well as applications to the study of populations of various sorts.

We start from two arbitrary sequences[8] $f_1, f_2, \ldots$ and $b_0, b_1, \ldots$ of real numbers. A new sequence $v_0, v_1, \ldots$ may then be defined by the

---

[8] We put $f_0 = 0$. It is clear from (10.1) that the case $f_0 \neq 0$ involves only a change of notations, provided that $f_0 \neq 1$.

convolution equations

(10.1) $$v_n = b_n + f_1 v_{n-1} + f_2 v_{n-2} + \cdots + f_n v_0.$$

These define recursively $v_0, v_1, v_2, \ldots$ and so the v_n are uniquely defined under any circumstances. We shall, however, consider only sequences satisfying the conditions[9]

(10.2) $$f_n \geq 0, \qquad f = \sum_{n=1}^{\infty} f_n < \infty; \qquad b_n \geq 0, \qquad b = \sum_{n=1}^{\infty} b_n < \infty.$$

In this case the v_n are non-negative and the corresponding generating functions must satisfy the identity

(10.3) $$V(s) = \frac{B(s)}{1 - F(s)}.$$

The generating functions F and B converge at least for $0 \leq s < 1$, and so (10.3) defines a power series converging as long as $F(s) < 1$. Relations (10.1) and (10.3) are fully equivalent. In section 3 we considered the special case $B(s) = 1$ (with $v_n = u_n$ for all n). Section 5 covered the general situation under the restriction $f \leq 1$. In view of applications to population theory we shall now permit that $f > 1$; fortunately this case is easily reduced to the standard case $f = 1$.

We shall say that *the sequence* $\{f_n\}$ *has period* $\lambda > 1$ if $f_n = 0$ except when $n = k\lambda$ is a multiple of λ, and λ is the greatest integer with this property. This amounts to saying that $F(s) = F_1(s^\lambda)$ is a power series in s^λ, but not in $s^{r\lambda}$ for any $r > 1$. We put again

(10.4) $$\mu = \sum n f_n \leq \infty$$

and adhere to the convention that μ^{-1} is to be interpreted as 0 if $\mu = \infty$.

Theorem 1. (*Renewal theorem.*) *Suppose* (10.2) *and that* $\{f_n\}$ *is not periodic.*

(i) *If* $f < 1$ *then* $v_n \to 0$ *and*

(10.5) $$\sum_{n=0}^{\infty} v_n = \frac{b}{1 - f}.$$

(ii) *If* $f = 1$

(10.6) $$v_n \to b\mu^{-1}.$$

---

[9] The positivity of f_n is essential, but the convergence of the two series is imposed only for convenience. No general conclusion can be drawn if $b = \infty$ *and* $\mu = \infty$. The assertion (10.7) remains true when $f = \infty$ except that in this case $F'(\xi)$ is not necessarily finite, and (10.7) is meaningless if $b = \infty$ *and* $F'(\xi) = \infty$.

(iii) *If $f > 1$ there exists a unique positive root of the equation $f(\xi) = 1$,* and

(10.7)
$$\xi^n v_n \to \frac{B(\xi)}{\xi F'(\xi)}.$$

Obviously $\xi < 1$ and hence the derivative $F'(\xi)$ is finite; (10.7) shows that the sequence $\{v_n\}$ behaves ultimately like a geometric sequence with ratio $\xi^{-1} > 1$.

Proof. The assertions (i) and (ii) were proved in section 5. To prove (iii) it suffices to apply the result (ii) to the sequences $\{f_n\xi^n\}$, $\{b_n\xi^n\}$, and $\{v_n\xi^n\}$ with generating functions given by $F(\xi s)$, $B(\xi s)$, and $V(\xi s)$, respectively. ▶

We have excluded periodic sequences $\{f_n\}$ because they are of secondary interest. Actually they present nothing new. Indeed, if $\{b_n\}$ and $\{f_n\}$ have the same period λ then both $B(s)$ and $F(s)$ are power series in s^λ, and hence the same is true of $V(s)$. Theorem 1 then applies to the sequences $\{f_{n\lambda}\}$, $\{b_{n\lambda}\}$, and $\{v_{n\lambda}\}$ with generating functions $F(s^{1/\lambda})$, $B(s^{1/\lambda})$, and $V(s^{1/\lambda})$. When $F(1) = 1$ it follows that $v_{n\lambda} \to b\lambda/\mu$. Now the most general power series B can be written as a linear combination

(10.8)
$$B(s) = B_0(s) + sB_1(s) + \cdots + s^{\lambda-1}B_{\lambda-1}(s)$$

of λ power series B_j each of which involves only powers of s^λ. Introducing this into (10.3) and applying the result just stated shows the validity of

Theorem 2. *Let (10.2) hold and suppose that $\{f_n\}$ has period $\lambda > 1$.*

(i) *If $f < 1$ then (10.5) holds.*
(ii) *If $f = 1$ then for $j = 0, 1, \ldots, \lambda - 1$ as $n \to \infty$*

(10.9)
$$u_{n\lambda+j} \to \lambda B_j(1)/\mu.$$

(iii) *If $f > 1$ then for $j = 0, 1, \ldots, \lambda - 1$ as $n \to \infty$*

(10.10)
$$\xi^{n\lambda} u_{n\lambda+j} \to \lambda B_j(\xi)/(\xi\mu).$$

In a great variety of stochastic processes it is possible to adapt the argument used for recurrent events to show that certain probabilities satisfy an equation of the convolution type like (10.1). Many important limit theorems appear in this way as simple corollaries of theorem 1. This approach has now generally supplanted clumsier older methods and has become known as *renewal argument.* Its full power appears only when used for processes with a continuous time parameter, but the first two examples may serve as an illustration. For further examples see problems 8–9. An application of theorem 1 to a non-probabilistic limit theorem is contained in example (c). The last two examples are devoted to practical applications.

Examples. (*a*) *Delayed recurrent events.* We give a new derivation of the result in section 5 for a delayed recurrent event $\mathcal{E}$ with the distribution $\{f_j\}$ for the recurrence times, and the distribution $\{b_j\}$ for the *first* occurrence of $\mathcal{E}$. Let v_n stand for the probability that $\mathcal{E}$ occurs at the nth trial. We show that (10.1) holds. There are two ways in which $\mathcal{E}$ can occur at the nth trial. The occurrence may be the first, and the probability for this is b_n. Otherwise there was a last occurrence of $\mathcal{E}$ before the nth trial, and so there exists a number $1 \leq j < n$ such that $\mathcal{E}$ did occur at the jth trial and the *next* time at the nth trial. The probability for this is $v_j f_{n-j}$. The cases are mutually exclusive, and so

$$(10.11) \qquad v_n = b_n + v_1 f_{n-1} + v_2 f_{n-2} + \cdots + v_{n-1} f_1,$$

which is the same as (10.1). The generating function V is therefore given by (10.3) in agreement with the result in section 5. (Though the results agree even formally, the arguments are different: in section 5 the enumeration proceeded according to the first appearance of $\mathcal{E}$ whereas the present argument uses the last appearance. Both procedures are used in other circumstances and sometimes lead to formally different equations.)

(*b*) *Hitting probabilities.* Consider a sequence of trials with a proper (not delayed) persistent recurrent event $\mathcal{E}$. Let $\nu \geq 0$ be an integer. Suppose that we start to observe the process only after the νth trial and that we are interested in the waiting time for the next occurrence of $\mathcal{E}$. More formally, for $r = 1, 2, \ldots$ denote by $w_\nu(r)$ the probability that *the first occurrence of $\mathcal{E}$ after the νth trial* takes place at the $(\nu+r)$th trial. For consistency we put $w_\nu(0) = 0$. [The $w_\nu(r)$ are called hitting probabilities because of their meaning in random walks. In other contexts it is more natural to speak of the distribution of the residual waiting time commencing at the νth trial. Cf. example XV,(2.k).]

To determine these probabilities we use the standard renewal argument as follows. It is possible that $\mathcal{E}$ occurs for the very first time at the $(\nu+r)$th trial. The probability for this is $f_{\nu+r}$. Otherwise there exists an integer $k \leq \nu$ such that $\mathcal{E}$ occurred for the first time at the kth trial. The continuation of the process after the kth trial is a probabilistic replica of the whole process, except that the original νth trial now becomes the $(\nu-k)$th trial. The probability of our event is therefore $f_k w_{\nu-k}(r)$, and hence for each $r > 0$

$$(10.12) \qquad w_\nu(r) = f_{\nu+r} + \sum_{k=1}^{\nu} f_k w_{\nu-k}(r).$$

This equation is of the standard type (10.1) with $b_n = f_{n+r}$. We are not interested in the generating function but wish to describe the asymptotic behavior of the hitting probabilities for very large ν. This is achieved by theorem 1. Put

$$(10.13) \qquad \rho_k = f_{k+1} + f_{k+2} + \cdots$$

and recall from XI,(1.8) that the mean recurrence time satisfies

$$(10.14) \qquad \mu = \rho_1 + \rho_2 + \cdots.$$

If $\mathcal{E}$ is not periodic we conclude from theorem 1 that as $\nu \to \infty$

$$(10.15) \qquad w_\nu(r) \to \begin{cases} \dfrac{\rho_r/\mu} & \text{if } \mu < \infty \\[2mm] 0 & \text{if } \mu = \infty. \end{cases}$$

This result is of great interest. In the case of a finite mean recurrence time (10.14) implies that $\{\rho_r/\mu\}$ is a probability distribution, and hence we have a limit theorem of a standard type. If, however, $\mu = \infty$ *the probability tends to 1 that the waiting time will exceed any given integer r.* In other words, our waiting times behave much worse than the recurrence times themselves. This unexpected phenomenon has significant consequences discussed in detail in volume 2. (See also problem 10.)

(c) *Repeated averaging.* The following problem is of an analytic character and was treated in various contexts by much more intricate methods. Suppose that $f_1 + \cdots + f_r = 1$ with $f_j \geq 0$. Given any r numbers $v_1, \ldots, v_r$ we define $f_1 v_r + \cdots + f_r v_1$ as their *weighted average.* We now define an infinite sequence $v_1, v_2, \ldots$ starting with the given r-tuple and defining v_n as the weighted average of the preceding r terms. In other words, for $n > r$ we define

$$(10.16) \qquad v_n = f_1 v_{n-1} + \cdots + f_r v_{n-r}.$$

Since the sequence $f_1, f_2, \ldots$ terminates with the rth term these equations are of the form (10.1). We now define the b_k so that (10.1) will be true for all n. This means that we put $b_0 = v_0 = 0$ and

$$(10.17) \qquad b_k = v_k - f_1 v_{k-1} - \cdots - f_{k-1} v_1 \qquad\qquad k \leq r.$$

(For $k > r$, by definition $b_k = 0$.) Without any calculations it follows from theorem 1 that with this repeated averaging the v_n *tend to a finite limit.* To calculate the limit we have to evaluate $b = b_1 + \cdots + b_r$. With the notation (10.13) for the remainders of $\sum f_k$ it is obvious from (10.17) and (10.6) that

$$(10.18) \qquad v_n \to \frac{v_1 \rho_{r-1} + \cdots + v_r \rho_0}{f_1 + 2f_2 + \cdots + rf_r}.$$

For example, if $r = 3$ and one takes *arithmetic means*, then $f_1 = f_2 = = f_3 = \frac{1}{3}$ and

$$(10.19) \qquad\qquad v_n \to \tfrac{1}{6}(v_1 + 2v_2 + 3v_3).$$

The ease with which we derived this result should not obscure the fact that the problem is difficult when taken out the present context. (For an alternative treatment see problem 15 of XV,14.)

TABLE 1

ILLUSTRATING THE DEVELOPMENT OF THE AGE DISTRIBUTION
IN A POPULATION DESCRIBED IN EXAMPLE (10.d)

n:	0	1	2	3	4	5	6	7	∞
$k = 0$	500	397	411.4	412	423.8	414.3	417.0	416.0	416.7
1	320	400	317.6	329.1	329.6	339.0	331.5	333.6	333.3
2	74	148	185	146.9	152.2	152.4	156.8	153.3	154.2
3	100	40	80	100	79.4	82.3	82.4	84.8	83.3
4	6	15	6	12	15	11.9	12.3	12.4	12.5

The columns give the age distribution of a population of $N = 1000$ elements at epochs $n = 0, 1, \ldots, 7$ together with the limiting distribution. The assumed mortalities are [10]

$$f_1 = 0.20; \qquad f_2 = 0.43; \qquad f_3 = 0.17; \qquad f_4 = 0.17; \qquad f_5 = 0.03,$$

so that no piece effectively attains age 5.

(d) *Self-renewing aggregates.* We return to the example of section 2 where a piece of equipment installed at epoch n has a lifetime with probability distribution $\{f_n\}$. When it expires it is immediately replaced by a new piece of the same character, and so the successive replacements constitute a persistent recurrent event in a sequence of dependent trials (whose outcomes decide whether or not a replacement takes place).

Suppose now that the piece of equipment installed at epoch 0 has an age k rather than being new. This affects only the first waiting time, and so $\mathcal{E}$ becomes a *delayed* recurrent event. To obtain the distribution $\{b_n\}$ of the first waiting time note that b_n is the (conditional) expectation that a piece will expire at age $n + k$ given that it has attained age k. Thus for $k \geq 1$

$$(10.20) \qquad\qquad b_n = f_{n+k}/r_k \qquad \text{where} \quad r_k = f_{k+1} + f_{k+2} + \cdots .$$

In practice one is not interested in a single piece of equipment but in a whole population (say the street lamps in a town). Suppose then that *the initial population* (at epoch 0) *consists of N pieces, among which β_k have*

---

[10] The roots of the equation $1 - F(s) = 0$ are 1, $-\frac{5}{3}$, -5, and $\pm 2i$. The mean recurrence time is 2.40.

age k (where $\sum \beta_k = N$). Each piece originates a line of descendants which may require a replacement at epoch n. *The expected number* v_n *of all replacements at epoch* n *obviously satisfies the basic equations* (10.1) *with*

$$(10.21) \qquad b_n = \sum \beta_k f_{n+k} / r_k.$$

We have here the first example where v_n is an *expectation* rather than a probability; we know only that $v_n < N$.

An easy calculation shows that $b = \sum b_n = N$, and so theorem 1 shows that $v_n \to N/\mu$ provided that the replacements are not periodic. This result implies the existence of a *stable limit for the age distribution*. In fact, for a piece to be of age k at epoch n it is necessary and sufficient that it was installed at epoch $n - k$ and that it survived age k. The expected number of such pieces is therefore $v_{n-k} r_k$ and tends to $N r_k / \mu$ as $n \to \infty$. In other words, as time goes on the *fraction of the population of age* k *tends to* r_k/μ. Thus *the limiting age distribution is independent of the initial age distribution* and depends only on the mortalities f_n. A similar result holds under much wider conditions. For a numerical illustration see table 1. It reveals the noteworthy fact that the approach to the limit is not monotone. (See also problems 16–18.)

(*e*) *Human populations.* For an example where $f = \sum f_n > 1$ we use the simplest model of a human population. It is analogous to the model in the preceding example except that the population size is now variable and female births take over the role of replacements. The novel feature is that a mother may have any number of daughters, and hence her line may become extinct, but it may also increase in numbers. We now define f_n the probability, at birth, that a mother will (survive and) at age n give birth to a female child. (The dependence on the number and the ages of previous children is neglected.) Then $f = \sum f_n$ is the expected number of daughters and so in a healthy population $f > 1$. Theorem 1 then promises a population size that increases roughly at the constant rate ξ, and the age distribution of the population tends to a limit as described in the preceding example. The model is admittedly crude but presents nevertheless some practical interest. The curious dependence of the limiting behavior ξ was certainly not predictable without a proper mathematical analysis.   ▶

*11. PROOF OF THE BASIC LIMIT THEOREM

In section 3 we omitted the proof of theorem 3 which we now restate as follows: *Let* $f_1, f_2, \ldots$ *be a sequence of numbers* $f_n \geq 0$ *such that*

---

* This section is not used in the sequel.

$\sum f_n = 1$ *and* 1 *is the greatest common divisor of those* n *for which* $f_n > 0$. *Let* $u_0 = 1$ *and*

$$(11.1) \qquad u_n = f_1 u_{n-1} + f_2 u_{n-2} + \cdots + f_n u_0, \qquad n \geq 1.$$

Then

$$(11.2) \qquad u_n \to \mu^{-1} \qquad where \quad \mu = \sum_{n=1}^{\infty} n f_n$$

(μ^{-1} *being interpreted as* 0 *when* $\mu = \infty$).

In order not to interrupt the argument we preface the proof by two well-known lemmas that are widely used outside probability.

Let A be the set of all integers n for which $f_n > 0$, and denote by A^+ the set of all positive linear combinations

$$(11.3) \qquad p_1 a_1 + \cdots + p_r a_r$$

of numbers $a_1, \ldots, a_r$ in A (the p_j are positive integers).

Lemma 1. *There exists an integer* N *such that* A^+ *contains all integers* $n > N$.

Proof. As is known from Euclid, the fact that 1 is the greatest common divisor of the numbers in A means that it is possible to choose integers $a_1, \ldots, a_r$ in A and (not necessarily positive) integers c_j such that

$$(11.4) \qquad c_1 a_1 + \cdots + c_r a_r = 1.$$

Put $s = a_1 + \cdots + a_r$. *Every* integer n admits of a unique representation $n = xs + y$ where x and y are integers and $0 \leq y < s$. Then

$$(11.5) \qquad n = \sum_{k=1}^{r} (x + c_k y) a_k$$

and all the coefficients will be positive as soon as x exceeds y times the largest among the numbers $|c_k|$. ▶

Lemma 2. (*Selection principle.*) *Suppose that for every integer* $\nu > 0$ *we are given a sequence of numbers* $z_1^{(\nu)}, z_2^{(\nu)}, \ldots$ *such that* $0 \leq z_k^{(\nu)} \leq 1$. *Then there exists a sequence* $\nu^{(1)}, \nu^{(2)}, \ldots \to \infty$ *such that as* ν *runs through it,* $z_k^{(\nu)}$ *tends to a limit for every fixed* k.

Proof[11] Choose an increasing sequence $\nu_1^{(1)}, \nu_2^{(1)}, \ldots$ such that as ν runs through it $z_1^{(\nu)}$ converges to a limit z_1. Out of this sequence choose

---

[11] The proof is based on the so-called *diagonal method* due to G. Cantor (1845–1918). It has become a standard tool but was shockingly new in Cantor's time.

a *subsequence* $v_1^{(2)}, v_2^{(2)}, \ldots$ such that as v runs through it $z_2^{(v)} \to z_2$. Continuing in this way we get for each n a sequence of integers $v_j^{(n)} \to \infty$ such that as v runs through it $z_n^{(v)} \to z_n$, and each $v_j^{(n)}$ is an element of the preceding sequence $\{v_j^{(n-1)}\}$. Finally, put $v^{(r)} = v_r^{(r)}$. Let $r > n$. Except for the first n terms every element $v^{(r)}$ appears in the sequence $v_1^{(n)}, v_2^{(n)}, \ldots$, and hence $z_n^{(v)} \to z_n$ as v runs through the sequence $v^{(1)}, v^{(2)}, \ldots$. ▶

Lemma 3. *Let* $\{w_n\}$ $(n = 0, \pm 1, \pm 2, \ldots)$ *be a doubly infinite sequence of numbers such that* $0 \leq w_n \leq 1$ *and*

$$(11.6) \qquad w_n = \sum_{k=1}^{\infty} f_k w_{n-k}$$

for each n. *If* $w_0 = 1$ *then* $w_n = 1$ *for all* n.

Proof. Since

$$(11.7) \qquad w_0 = \sum_{k=1}^{\infty} f_k w_{-k} \leq \sum_{k=1}^{\infty} f_k = 1$$

the condition $w_0 = 1$ requires that the two series agree termwise, and so for each k either $f_k = 0$ or else $w_{-k} = 1$. This means that $w_{-a} = 1$ for every integer a of A. But then the argument used for $n = 0$ applies also with $n = -a$, and we conclude that $w_{-a-b} = 1$ whenever the integers a and b are in A. Proceeding by induction we conclude that $w_{-m} = 1$ for every integer in A^+, and hence $w_{-m} = 1$ for every $m > N$. But this implies that for $n = -N$ the right side in (11.6) equals 1 and so $w_{-N} = 1$. Letting $n = -N + 1$ we find in like manner $w_{-N+1} = 1$, and proceeding in this way we find by induction that $w_n = 0$ for all n. ▶

Proof of the theorem. Let

$$(11.8) \qquad \eta = \limsup_{n \to \infty} u_n.$$

It is obvious from (11.1) that $0 \leq \eta \leq 1$, and there exists a sequence $r_1, r_2, \ldots$ tending to infinity such that as $v \to \infty$

$$(11.9) \qquad u_{r_v} \to \eta.$$

For each positive integer v we define a doubly infinite sequence $\{u_n^{(v)}\}$ by

$$(11.10) \qquad u_n^{(v)} = \begin{array}{ll} u_{r_v+n} & \text{for } n \geq -r_v \\ 0 & \text{for } n < -r_v. \end{array}$$

For simplicity of expression lemma 2 was formulated for simple sequences, but it obviously applies to double sequences also. Accordingly, it is possible to choose an increasing sequence of integers $v_1, v_2, \ldots$ such that when v runs through it $u_n^{(v)}$ tends to a limit w_n for each n. From the construction $0 \leq w_n \leq \eta$ and $w_0 = \eta$. Furthermore, for each v and $n > -v$ the definition (11.1) reads

$$(11.11) \qquad u_n^{(v)} = \sum_{v=1}^{\infty} f_k u_{n-k}^{(v)},$$

and in the limit we find the relation (11.6). By lemma 3 therefore $w_n = \eta$ for all n.

We are now ready for the final argument. As before we put

$$(11.12) \qquad \rho_k = f_{k+1} + f_{k+2} + \cdots$$

so that $r_0 = 1$ and $\sum \rho_k = \mu$ [see XI, (1.8)]. Summing the defining relations (11.1) over $n = 1, 2, \ldots, N$ and collecting terms we get the identity

$$(11.13) \qquad \rho_0 u_N + \rho_1 u_{N-1} + \cdots + \rho_N u_0 = 1.$$

We use this relation successively for $N = v_1, v_2, \ldots$. As N runs through this sequence $u_{N-k} \to w_{-k} = \eta$ for each k. If $\sum \rho_k = \infty$ it follows that $\eta = 0$ and so $u_n \to 0$ as asserted. When $\mu = \sum \rho_k < \infty$ it follows that $\eta = \mu^{-1}$, and it remains to show that this implies $u_N \to \eta$ for any approach $N \to \infty$. By the definition of the upper limit we have $u_{N-k} < < \eta + \epsilon$ for each fixed k and N sufficiently large. Furthermore $u_n \leq 1$ for all n. Suppose then that N approaches infinity in such a manner that $u_N \to \eta_0$. From (11.13) it is clear that ultimately

$$(11.14) \quad \rho_0 \eta_0 + (\rho_1 + \cdots + \rho_r)(\eta + \epsilon) + (\rho_{r+1} + \rho_{r+2} + \cdots) \geq 1,$$

and hence

$$(11.15) \qquad \rho_0(\eta_0 - \eta) + \mu(\eta + \epsilon) \geq 1.$$

But $\mu\eta = 1$ and $\eta_0 \leq \eta$ by the definition of η. Since (11.15) is true for arbitrary $\epsilon > 0$ it follows that $\eta_0 = \eta$ and so $u_N \to \mu^{-1}$ for any approach $N \to \infty$.   ▶

12. PROBLEMS FOR SOLUTION

1. Suppose that $F(s)$ is a polynomial. Prove for this case all theorems of section 3, using the partial fraction method of XI, 4.

2. Let r coins be tossed repeatedly and let $\mathcal{E}$ be the recurrent event that for each of the r coins the accumulated number of heads and tails are equal. Is $\mathcal{E}$ persistent or transient? For the smallest r for which $\mathcal{E}$ is transient, estimate the probability that $\mathcal{E}$ ever occurs.

3. In a sequence of independent throws of a perfect die let $\mathcal{E}$ stand for the event that the accumulated numbers of ones, twos, . . . , sixes are equal. Show that $\mathcal{E}$ is a transient (periodic) recurrent event and estimate the probability f that $\mathcal{E}$ will ever occur.

4. In a sequence of Bernoulli trials let $\mathcal{E}$ occur when the accumulated number of successes equals λ times the accumulated number of failures; here λ is a positive integer. [See example (1.c).] Show that $\mathcal{E}$ is recurrent if, and only if, $p/q = \lambda$, that is, $p = \lambda/(\lambda+1)$. *Hint:* Use the normal approximation.

5. In a sequence of Bernoulli trials we say that $\mathcal{E}$ occurs when the accumulated number of successes is twice the accumulated number of failures and the ratio has never exceeded 2. Show that $\mathcal{E}$ is transient and periodic. Furthermore, show that $f_n = p^2 q u_{n-3}$, and derive the generating function $F(s)$ from this relation.

6. Let the X_j be independent integral-valued random variables with a common distribution. Assume that these variables assume both positive and negative values. Prove that the event defined by $S_n = 0, S_1 \leq 0, \ldots, S_{n-1} \leq 0$ is recurrent and transient.

7. *Geiger counters.* [See examples (1.g) and (4.e).] Denote by N_n and Z_n, respectively, the number of occurrences of $\mathcal{E}$ and the number of registrations up to and including epoch n. Discuss the relationship between these variables and find asymptotic expressions for $E(Z_n)$ and $\mathrm{Var}\,(Z_n)$.

8. In *Geiger counters of type* II every arriving particle (whether registered or not) locks the counter for exactly r time units (that is, at the $r-1$ trials following the arrival). The duration of the locked time following a registration is therefore a random variable. Find its generating function G. If $\mathcal{E}$ is again the recurrent event that the counter is free, express the generating function F of the recurrence times in terms of G. Finally, find the mean recurrence time.

9. *A more general type of Geiger counters.* As in problem 8 we assume that every arriving particle completely obliterates the effect of the preceding ones, but we assume now that the time for which a particle locks the counter is a random variable with a given generating function $B(s)$. [In the preceding problem $B(s) = s^r$.] Do problem 8 under these more general conditions.

10. For a delayed recurrent event $\mathcal{E}$ the probabilities v_n are constant only when the generating function of the first occurrence of $\mathcal{E}$ is given by $B(s) = = [1-F(s)]/\mu(1-s)$, that is, when $b_n = f_{n+1} + f_{n+2} + \cdots$. Discuss the relation with the limit theorem for hitting probabilities in example (10.b).

11. Find an approximation to the probability that in 10,000 tossings of a coin the number of head runs of length 3 will lie between 700 and 730.

12. In a sequence of tossings of a coin let $\mathcal{E}$ stand for the pattern HTH. Let r_n be the probability that $\mathcal{E}$ does not occur in n trials. Find the generating function and use the partial fraction method to obtain an asymptotic expansion.

13. In example (8.b) show that the expected duration of the game is

$$\mu_1\mu_2/(\mu_1+\mu_2),$$

where μ_1 and μ_2 are the mean recurrence times for success runs of length r and failure runs of length ρ, respectively.

14. The possible outcomes of each trial are A, B, and C; the corresponding probabilities are α, β, γ ($\alpha + \beta + \gamma = 1$). Find the generating function of the probability that in n trials there is no run of length r: (a) of A's, (b) of A's or B's, (c) of any kind.

15. *Continuation.* Find the probability that the first A-run of length r precedes the first B-run of length ρ and terminates at the nth trial. [Note that this problem does *not* reduce to that of example (8.b) with $p = \alpha/(\alpha+\beta)$, $q = \beta/(\alpha+\beta)$.]

16. *Self-renewing aggregates.* In example (10.d) find the limiting age distribution assuming that the lifetime distribution is geometric: $f_k = q^{k-1}p$.

17. *Continuation.* The initial *age distribution* $\{\beta_k\}$ *is called stationary if it* perpetuates itself for all times. Show (without computation) that this is the case only when $\beta_k = r_k/\mu$.

18. *Continuation.* Denote by $w_k(n)$ the expected number of elements at epoch n that are of age k. Find the determining equations and verify from them that the population size remains constant. Furthermore, show that the expected number $w_0(n)$ satisfies

$$w_0(n) = w_0(n-1)f_1/r_0 + w_1(n-1)f_2/r_1 + \cdots.$$

---

19. Let $\mathcal{E}$ be a persistent aperiodic recurrent event. Assume that the recurrence time has finite mean μ and variance σ^2. Put $q_n = f_{n+1} + f_{n+2} + \cdots$ and $r_n = q_{n+1} + q_{n+2} + \cdots$. Show that the generating functions $Q(s)$ and $R(s)$ converge for $s = 1$. Prove that

$$(12.1) \qquad \sum \left(u_n - \frac{1}{\mu} \right) s^n = \frac{R(s)}{\mu Q(s)}$$

and hence that

$$(12.2) \qquad \sum \left(u_n - \frac{1}{\mu} \right) = \frac{\sigma^2 - \mu + \mu^2}{2\mu^2}.$$

20. Let $\mathcal{E}$ be a persistent recurrent event and $\mathbf{N}_r$ the number of occurrences of $\mathcal{E}$ in r trials. Prove that

$$(12.3) \qquad \mathbf{E}(\mathbf{N}_r^2) = u_1 + \cdots + u_r + 2 \sum_{j=1}^{r-1} u_j(u_1 + \cdots + u_{r-j})$$

and hence that $\mathbf{E}(\mathbf{N}_r^2)$ is the coefficient of s^r in

$$(12.4) \qquad \frac{F^2(s) + F(s)}{(1-s)\{1-F(s)\}^2}$$

(Note that this may be reformulated more elegantly using bivariate generating functions.)

21. Let $q_{k,n} = \mathbf{P}\{\mathbf{N}_k = n\}$. Show that $q_{k,n}$ is the coefficient of s^k in

$$(12.5) \qquad F^n(s) \frac{\{1-F(s)\}}{1 - s}.$$

Deduce that $E(N_r)$ and $E(N_r^2)$ are the coefficients of s^r in

(12.6) $$\frac{F(s)}{(1-s)\{1-F(s)\}}$$

and (12.4), respectively.

22. Using the notations of problem 19, show that

(12.7) $$\frac{F(s)}{(1-s)\{1-F(s)\}} = -\frac{1}{1-s} + \frac{1}{\mu(1-s)^2} + \frac{R(s)}{\mu\{1-F(s)\}}.$$

Hence, using the last problem, conclude that

(12.8) $$E(N_r) = \frac{r+1}{\mu} + \frac{\sigma^2 - \mu - \mu^2}{2\mu^2} + \epsilon_r$$

with $\epsilon_r \to 0$.

23. *Continuation.* Using a similar argument, show that

(12.9) $$E(N_r^2) = \frac{(r+2)(r+1)}{\mu^2} + \frac{2\sigma^2 - 2\mu - \mu^2}{\mu^3} r + \alpha_r,$$

where $\alpha_r/r \to 0$. Hence

(12.10) $$\text{Var}\,(N_r) \sim \frac{\sigma^2}{\mu^3} r.$$

25. In a sequence of Bernoulli trials let $q_{k,n}$ be the probability that exactly n success runs of length r occur in k trials. Using problem 22, show that the generating function $Q_k(x) = \sum q_{k,n}x^n$ is the coefficient of s^k in

$$\frac{1 - p^r s^r}{1 - s + qp^r s^{r+1} - (1-ps)p^r s^r x}.$$

Show, furthermore, that the root of the denominator which is smallest in absolute value is $s_1 \approx 1 + qp^r(1-x)$.

26. *Continuation. The Poisson distribution of long runs.*[12] If the number k of trials and the length r of runs both tend to infinity, so that $kqp^r \to \lambda$, then the probability of having exactly n runs of length r tends to $e^{-\lambda}\lambda^n/n!$.

Hint: Using the preceding problem, show that the generating function is asymptotically $\{1 + qp^r(1-x)\}^{-k} \sim e^{-\lambda(1-r)}$. Use the *continuity theorem* of XI, 6.

———————

[12] The theorem was proved by von Mises, but the present method is considerably simpler.

CHAPTER XIV

Random Walk and Ruin Problems

1. GENERAL ORIENTATION

The first part of this chapter is devoted to Bernoulli trials, and once more the picturesque language of betting and random walks is used to simplify and enliven the formulations.

Consider the familiar gambler who wins or loses a dollar with probabilities p and q, respectively. Let his initial capital be z and let him play against an adversary with initial capital $a - z$, so that the combined capital is a. The game continues until the gambler's capital either is reduced to zero or has increased to a, that is, until one of the two players is ruined. We are interested in the probability of the gambler's ruin and the probability distribution of the duration of the game. This is *the classical ruin problem*.

Physical applications and analogies suggest the more flexible interpretation in terms of the notion of a variable point or "*particle*" on the x-axis. This particle starts from the *initial position z*, and moves at regular time intervals a unit step in the positive or negative direction, depending on whether the corresponding trial resulted in success or failure. The position of the particle after n steps represents the gambler's capital at the conclusion of the nth trial. The trials terminate when the particle for the first time reaches either 0 or a, and we describe this by saying that the particle performs *a random walk with absorbing barriers at 0 and a*. This random walk is *restricted* to the possible positions $1, 2, \ldots, a - 1$; in the absence of absorbing barriers the random walk is called *unrestricted*. Physicists use the random-walk model as a crude approximation to one-dimensional diffusion or Brownian motion, where a physical particle is exposed to a great number of molecular collisions which impart to it a random motion. The case $p > q$ corresponds to a *drift* to the right when shocks from the left are more probable; when $p = q = \frac{1}{2}$, the random walk is called *symmetric*.

342

In the limiting case $a \to \infty$ we get a random walk on a semi-infinite line: A particle starting at $z > 0$ performs a random walk up to the moment when it for the first time reaches the origin. In this formulation we recognize the *first-passage time problem;* it was solved by elementary methods in chapter III (at least for the symmetric case) and by the use of generating functions in XI,3. We shall encounter formulas previously obtained, but the present derivation is self-contained.

In this chapter we shall use the method of *difference equations* which serves as an introduction to the differential equations of diffusion theory. This analogy leads in a natural way to various modifications and generalizations of the classical ruin problem, a typical and instructive example being the replacing of absorbing barriers by *reflecting* and *elastic* barriers. To describe a reflecting barrier, consider a random walk in a finite interval as defined before except that whenever the particle is at point 1 it has probability p of moving to position 2 and probability q to stay at 1. In gambling terminology this corresponds to a convention that whenever the gambler loses his last dollar it is generously replaced by his adversary so that the game can continue. The physicist imagines a wall placed at the point $\frac{1}{2}$ of the x-axis with the property that a particle moving from 1 toward 0 is reflected at the wall and returns to 1 instead of reaching 0. Both the absorbing and the reflecting barriers are special cases of the so-called elastic barrier. We define an *elastic barrier at the origin by the rule that from position* 1 *the particle moves with probability* p *to position* 2; *with probability* δq *it stays at* 1; *and with probability* $(1-\delta)q$ *it moves to* 0 *and is absorbed* (i.e., the process terminates). For $\delta = 0$ we have the classical ruin problem or absorbing barriers, for $\delta = 1$ reflecting barriers. As δ runs from 0 to 1 we have a family of intermediate cases. The greater δ is, the more likely is the process to continue, and with two reflecting barriers the process can never terminate.

Sections 2 and 3 are devoted to an elementary discussion of the classical ruin problem and its implications. The next three sections are more technical (and may be omitted); in 4 and 5 we derive the relevant generating functions and from them explicit expressions for the distribution of the duration of the game, etc. Section 6 contains an outline of the passage to the limit to the diffusion equation (the formal solutions of the latter being the limiting distributions for the random walk).

In section 7 the discussion again turns elementary and is devoted to *random walks in two or more dimensions* where new phenomena are encountered. Section 8 treats a generalization of an entirely different type, namely a random walk in one dimension where the particle is no longer restricted to move in unit steps but is permitted to change its position in jumps which are arbitrary multiples of unity. Such generalized random walks have attracted widespread interest in connection with Wald's theory of *sequential sampling*.

The problem section contains essential complements to the text and outlines of alternative approaches. It is hoped that a comparison of the methods used will prove highly instructive.

In conclusion it must be emphasized that each random walk represents a special Markov chain, and so the present chapter serves partly as an introduction to the next where several random-walk problems (e.g., elastic barriers) will be reformulated.

2. THE CLASSICAL RUIN PROBLEM

We shall consider the problem stated at the opening of the present chapter. Let q_z be the probability of the gambler's ultimate[1] ruin and p_z the probability of his winning. In random-walk terminology q_z and p_z are the probabilities that a particle starting at z will be absorbed at 0 and a, respectively. We shall show that $p_z + q_z = 1$, so that we need not consider the possibility of an unending game.

After the first trial the gambler's fortune is either $z - 1$ or $z + 1$, and therefore we must have

$$(2.1) \qquad\qquad q_z = pq_{z+1} + qq_{z-1}$$

provided $1 < z < a - 1$. For $z = 1$ the first trial may lead to ruin, and (2.1) is to be replaced by $q_1 = pq_2 + q$. Similarly, for $z = a - 1$ the first trial may result in victory, and therefore $q_{a-1} = qq_{a-2}$. To unify our equations we define

$$(2.2) \qquad\qquad q_0 = 1, \qquad q_a = 0.$$

With this convention the probability q_z of ruin satisfies (2.1) for $z = 1, 2, \ldots, a - 1$.

Systems of the form (2.1) are known as *difference equations*, and (2.2) represents the *boundary conditions* on q_z. We shall derive an explicit expression for q_z by the *method of particular solutions*, which will also be used in more general cases.

Suppose first that $p \neq q$. It is easily verified that the difference

---

[1] Strictly speaking, the probability of ruin is defined in a sample space of infinitely prolonged games, but we can work with the sample space of n trials. The probability of ruin in less than n trials increases with n and has therefore a limit. We call this *limit* "the probability of ruin." All probabilities in this chapter may be interpreted in this way without reference to infinite spaces (cf. VIII,1).

equations (2.1) admit of the two particular solutions $q_z = 1$ and $q_z = (q/p)^z$. It follows that for arbitrary constants A and B the sequence

$$(2.3) \qquad\qquad q_z = A + B \left(\frac{q}{p}\right)^z$$

represents a formal solution of (2.1). The boundary conditions (2.2) will hold if, and only if, A and B satisfy the two linear equations $A + B = 1$ and $A + B(q/p)^a = 0$. Thus

$$(2.4) \qquad\qquad q_z = \frac{(q/p)^a - (q/p)^z}{(q/p)^a - 1}$$

is a formal solution of the difference equation (2.1), satisfying the boundary conditions (2.2). In order to prove that (2.4) is the required probability of ruin it remains to show that the solution is unique, that is, that *all* solutions of (2.1) are of the form (2.3). Now, given an arbitrary solution of (2.1), the two constants A and B can be chosen so that (2.3) will agree with it for $z = 0$ and $z = 1$. From these two values all other values can be found by substituting in (2.1) successively $z = 1, 2, 3, \ldots$. Therefore two solutions which agree for $z = 0$ and $z = 1$ are identical, and hence every solution is of the form (2.3).

Our argument breaks down if $p = q = \frac{1}{2}$, for then (2.4) is meaningless because in this case the two formal particular solutions $q_z = 1$ and $q_z = (q/p)^z$ are identical. However, when $p = q = \frac{1}{2}$ we have a second solution in $q_z = z$, and therefore $q_z = A + Bz$ is a solution of (2.1) depending on two constants. In order to satisfy the boundary conditions (2.2) we must put $A = 1$ and $A + Ba = 0$. Hence

$$(2.5) \qquad\qquad q_z = 1 - \frac{z}{a} .$$

(The same numerical value can be obtained formally from (2.4) by finding the limit as $p \to \frac{1}{2}$, using L'Hospital's rule.)

We have thus proved that the required *probability of the gambler's ruin is given by* (2.4) *if* $p \neq q$, *and by* (2.5) *if* $p = q = \frac{1}{2}$. The probability p_z of the gambler's winning the game equals the probability of his adversary's ruin and is therefore obtained from our formulas on replacing p, q, and z by q, p, and $a - z$, respectively. It is readily seen that $p_z + q_z = 1$, as stated previously.

We can reformulate our result as follows: *Let a gambler with an initial capital* z *play against an infinitely rich adversary who is always willing to play, although the gambler has the privilege of stopping at his pleasure. The gambler adopts the strategy of playing until he either loses his capital or increases it to* a *(with a net gain* $a - z$*). Then* q_z *is the probability of his losing and* $1 - q_z$ *the probability of his winning.*

Under this system the gambler's ultimate gain or loss is a random variable **G** which assumes the values $a - z$ and $-z$ with probabilities $1 - q_z$ and q_z, respectively. The expected gain is

$$(2.6) \qquad\qquad \mathbf{E(G)} = a(1 - q_z) - z.$$

Clearly $\mathbf{E(G)} = 0$ if, and only if, $p = q$. This means that, with the system described, *a "fair" game remains fair, and no "unfair" game can be changed into a "fair" one.*

From (2.5) we see that in the case $p = q$ a player with initial capital $z = 999$ has a probability 0.999 to win a dollar before losing his capital. With $q = 0.6$, $p = 0.4$ the game is unfavorable indeed, but still the probability (2.4) of winning a dollar before losing the capital is about $\frac{2}{3}$. In general, a gambler with a relatively large initial capital z has a reasonable chance to win a small amount $a - z$ before being ruined.[2]

[For a surprising consequence of our result see problem 4.]

Let us now investigate the effect of *changing stakes.* Changing the unit from a dollar to a half-dollar is equivalent to doubling the initial capitals. The corresponding probability of ruin q_z^* is obtained from (2.4) on replacing z by $2z$ and a by $2a$:

$$(2.7) \qquad q_z^* = \frac{(q/p)^{2a} - (q/p)^{2z}}{(q/p)^{2a} - 1} = q_z \cdot \frac{(q/p)^a + (q/p)^z}{(q/p)^a + 1}.$$

For $q > p$ the last fraction is greater than unity and $q_z^* > q_z$. We restate this conclusion as follows: *if the stakes are doubled while the initial capitals remain unchanged, the probability of ruin decreases for the player whose probability of success is* $p < \frac{1}{2}$ *and increases for the adversary (for whom the game is advantageous).*[3] Suppose, for example, that Peter owns 90 dollars and Paul 10, and let $p = 0.45$, the game being unfavorable to Peter. If at each trial the stake is one dollar, table 1 shows the probability

---

[2] A certain man used to visit Monte Carlo year after year and was always successful in recovering the cost of his vacations. He firmly believed in a magic power over chance. Actually his experience is not surprising. Assuming that he started with ten times the ultimate gain, the chances of success in any year are nearly 0.9. The probability of an unbroken sequence of ten successes is about $(1 - \frac{1}{10})^{10} \approx e^{-1} \approx 0.37$. Thus continued success is by no means improbable. Moreover, *one* failure would, of course, be blamed on an oversight or momentary indisposition.

[3] A detailed analysis of other possible strategies will be found in the (not elementary) book by L. E. Dubbins and L. J. Savage, *How to gamble if you must* (which has a more informative subtitle: *Inequalities for stochastic processes*), New York (McGraw-Hill), 1965.

of Peter's ruin to be 0.866, approximately. If the same game is played for
a stake of 10 dollars, the probability of Peter's ruin drops to less than one
fourth, namely about 0.210. Thus the effect of increasing stakes is more
pronounced than might be expected. In general, if k dollars are staked
at each trial, we find the probability of ruin from (2.4), replacing z by
z/k and a by a/k; the probability of ruin decreases as k increases. In
a game with constant stakes the gambler therefore minimizes the probability
of ruin by selecting the stake as large as consistent with his goal of gaining
an amount fixed in advance. The empirical validity of this conclusion has

TABLE 1

ILLUSTRATING THE CLASSICAL RUIN PROBLEM

p	q	z	a	Probability of Ruin	Probability of Success	Expected Gain	Expected Duration
0.5	0.5	9	10	0.1	0.9	0	9
0.5	0.5	90	100	0.1	0.9	0	900
0.5	0.5	900	1,000	0.1	0.9	0	90,000
0.5	0.5	950	1,000	0.05	0.95	0	47,500
0.5	0.5	8,000	10,000	0.2	0.8	0	16,000,000
0.45	0.55	9	10	0.210	0.790	−1.1	11
0.45	0.55	90	100	0.866	0.134	−76.6	765.6
0.45	0.55	99	100	0.182	0.818	−17.2	171.8
0.4	0.6	90	100	0.983	0.017	−88.3	441.3
0.4	0.6	99	100	0.333	0.667	−32.3	161.7

The initial capital is z. The game terminates with ruin (loss z) or capital a (gain $a - z$).

been challenged, usually by people who contended that every "unfair" bet
is unreasonable. If this were to be taken seriously, it would mean the end
of all insurance business, for the careful driver who insures against
liability obviously plays a game that is technically "unfair." Actually,
there exists no theorem in probability to discourage such a driver from
taking insurance.

The limiting case $a = \infty$ corresponds to a game against an infinitely
rich adversary. Letting $a \to \infty$ in (2.4) and (2.5) we get

$$(2.8) \qquad q_z = \begin{cases} 1 & \text{if } p \le q \\ (q/p)^z & \text{if } p > q. \end{cases}$$

We interpret q_z as the probability of ultimate ruin of a gambler with initial
capital z playing against an infinitely rich adversary.[4] In random walk

---

[4] It is easily seen that the q_z represent a solution of the difference equations (2.1)
satisfying the (now unique) boundary condition $q_0 = 1$. When $p > q$ the solution
is not unique. Actually our result is contained in XI,(3.9) and will be derived independently (in a strengthened form) in section 4.

terminology q_z is the probability that a particle starting at $z > 0$ will ever reach the origin. It is more natural to rephrase this result as follows: *In a random walk starting at the origin the probability of ever reaching the position $z > 0$ equals 1 if $p \geq q$ and equals $(p/q)^z$ when $p < q$.*

3. EXPECTED DURATION OF THE GAME

The probability distribution of the duration of the game will be deduced in the following sections. However, its expected value can be derived by a much simpler method which is of such wide applicability that it will now be explained at the cost of a slight duplication.

We are still concerned with the classical ruin problem formulated at the beginning of this chapter. We shall assume as known the fact that the duration of the game has a finite expectation D_z. A rigorous proof will be given in the next section.

If the first trial results in success the game continues as if the initial position had been $z + 1$. The conditional expectation of the duration assuming success at the first trial is therefore $D_{z+1} + 1$. This argument shows that the expected duration D_z satisfies the difference equation

$$(3.1) \qquad D_z = pD_{z+1} + qD_{z-1} + 1, \qquad 0 < z < a$$

with the boundary conditions

$$(3.2) \qquad D_0 = 0, \qquad D_a = 0.$$

The appearance of the term 1 makes the difference equation (3.1) non-homogeneous. If $p \neq q$, then $D_z = z/(q-p)$ is a formal solution of (3.1). The difference Δ_z of any two solutions of (3.1) satisfies the homogeneous equations $\Delta_z = p\Delta_{z+1} + q\Delta_{z-1}$, and we know already that all solutions of this equation are of the form $A + B(q/p)^z$. It follows that when $p \neq q$ all solutions of (3.1) are of the form

$$(3.3) \qquad D_z = \frac{z}{q - p} + A + B\left(\frac{q}{p}\right)^z.$$

The boundary conditions (3.2) require that

$$A + B = 0, \qquad A + B(q/p)^a = -a/(q-p).$$

Solving for A and B, we find

$$(3.4) \qquad D_z = \frac{z}{q - p} - \frac{a}{q - p} \cdot \frac{1 - (q/p)^z}{1 - (q/p)^a}.$$

Again the method breaks down if $q = p = \frac{1}{2}$. In this case we replace $z/(q-p)$ by $-z^2$, which is now a solution of (3.1). It follows that when $p = q = \frac{1}{2}$ all solutions of (3.1) are of the form $D_z = -z^2 + A + Bz$. The required solution D_z satisfying the boundary conditions (3.2) is

$$(3.5) \qquad\qquad D_z = z(a-z).$$

The expected duration of the game in the classical ruin problem is given by (3.4) or (3.5), according as $p \neq q$ or $p = q = \frac{1}{2}$.

It should be noted that this duration is considerably longer than we would naively expect. If two players with 500 dollars each toss a coin until one is ruined, the average duration of the game is 250,000 trials. If a gambler has only one dollar and his adversary 1000, the average duration is 1000 trials. Further examples are found in table 1.

As indicated at the end of the preceding section, we may pass to the limit $a \to \infty$ and consider a game against an infinitely rich adversary. When $p > q$ the game may go on forever, and in this case it makes no sense to talk about its expected duration. When $p < q$ we get for the expected duration $z(q-p)^{-1}$, but when $p = q$ the expected duration is infinite. (The same result was established in XI,3 and will be proved independently in the next section.)

*4. GENERATING FUNCTIONS FOR THE DURATION OF THE GAME AND FOR THE FIRST-PASSAGE TIMES

We shall use the method of generating functions to study the duration of the game in the classical ruin problem, that is, the restricted random walk with absorbing barriers at 0 and a. The initial position is z (with $0 < z < a$). Let $u_{z,n}$ denote the probability that the process ends with the nth step at the barrier 0 (gambler's ruin at the nth trial). After the first step the position is $z + 1$ or $z - 1$, and we conclude that for $1 < z < a - 1$ and $n \geq 1$

$$(4.1) \qquad\qquad u_{z,n+1} = pu_{z+1,n} + qu_{z-1,n}.$$

This is a difference equation analogous to (2.1), but depending on the two variables z and n. In analogy with the procedure of section 2 we wish to define boundary values $u_{0,n}$, $u_{a,n}$, and $u_{z,0}$ so that (4.1) becomes valid also for $z = 1$, $z = a - 1$, and $n = 0$. For this purpose we put

$$(4.2) \qquad\qquad u_{0,n} = u_{a,n} = 0 \qquad\qquad \textit{when} \quad n \geq 1$$

---

* This section together with the related section 5 may be omitted at first reading.

and

(4.3) $u_{0,0} = 1,   u_{z,0} = 0$ *when $z > 0$.*

Then (4.1) holds for all z with $0 < z < a$ and all $n \geq 0$.
    We now introduce the generating functions

(4.4) $$U_z(s) = \sum_{n=0}^{\infty} u_{z,n} s^n.$$

Multiplying (4.1) by s^{n+1} and adding for $n = 0, 1, 2, \ldots$, we find

(4.5) $U_z(s) = ps U_{z+1}(s) + qs U_{z-1}(s),$ $0 < z < a;$

the boundary conditions (4.2) and (4.3) lead to

(4.6) $U_0(s) = 1,   U_a(s) = 0.$

The system (4.5) represents difference equations analogous to (2.1), and the boundary conditions (4.6) correspond to (2.2). The novelty lies in the circumstance that the coefficients and the unknown $U_z(s)$ now depend on the variable s, but as far as the difference equation is concerned, s is merely an arbitrary constant. We can again apply the method of section 2 provided we succeed in finding two particular solutions of (4.5). It is natural to inquire whether there exist two solutions $U_z(s)$ of the form $U_z(s) = \lambda^z(s)$. Substituting this expression into (4.5), we find that $\lambda(s)$ must satisfy the quadratic equation

(4.7) $\lambda(s) = ps\lambda^2(s) + qs,$

which has the two roots

(4.8) $\lambda_1(s) = \dfrac{1 + \sqrt{1-4pqs^2}}{2ps},$ $\lambda_2(s) = \dfrac{1 - \sqrt{1-4pqs^2}}{2ps}$

(we take $0 < s < 1$ and the positive square root).
    We are now in possession of two particular solutions of (4.5) and conclude as in section 2 that for arbitrary functions $A(s)$ and $B(s)$

(4.9) $U_z(s) = A(s)\lambda_1^z(s) + B(s)\lambda_2^z(s)$

is a solution of (4.5). To satisfy the boundary conditions (4.6), we must have $A(s) + B(s) = 1$ and $A(s)\lambda_1^a(s) + B(s)\lambda_2^a(s) = 0$, whence

(4.10) $$U_z(s) = \frac{\lambda_1^a(s)\lambda_2^z(s) - \lambda_1^z(s)\lambda_2^a(s)}{\lambda_1^a(s) - \lambda_2^a(s)}.$$

Using the obvious relation $\lambda_1(s)\lambda_2(s) = q/p$, this simplifies to

$$(4.11) \qquad U_z(s) = \left(\frac{q}{p}\right)^z \frac{\lambda_1^{a-z}(s) - \lambda_2^{a-z}(s)}{\lambda_1^a(s) - \lambda_2^a(s)}.$$

This is *the required generating function of the probability of ruin (absorption at 0) at the nth trial.* The same method shows that the generating function for the probabilities of absorption at a is given by

$$(4.12) \qquad \frac{\lambda_1^z(s) - \lambda_2^z(s)}{\lambda_1^a(s) - \lambda_2^a(s)}.$$

The generating function for *the duration of the game* is, of course, the sum of the generating functions (4.11) and (4.12).

Infinite Intervals and First Passages

The preceding considerations apply equally to random walks on the interval $(0, \infty)$ with an absorbing barrier at 0. A particle starting from the position $z > 0$ is eventually absorbed at the origin or else the random walk continues forever. Absorption corresponds to the ruin of a gambler with initial capital z playing against an infinitely rich adversary. The generating function $U_z(s)$ of the probabilities $u_{z,n}$ that absorption takes place exactly at the nth trial satisfies again the difference equations (4.5) and is therefore of the form (4.9), but this solution is unbounded at infinity unless $A(s) = 0$. The unique boundary condition is now $U_0(s) = 1$, and hence

$$(4.13) \qquad U_z(s) = \lambda_2^z(s).$$

[The same result can be obtained by letting $a \to \infty$ in (4.11), and remembering that $\lambda_1(s)\lambda_2(s) = q/p$.]

It follows from (4.13) for $s = 1$ that an ultimate absorption is certain if $p \leq q$, and has probability q/p otherwise. The same conclusion was reached in section 2.

Our absorption at the origin admits of an important alternative interpretation as a first passage in an *unrestricted* random walk. Indeed, on moving the origin to the position z it is seen that in a random walk on the entire line and starting from the origin $u_{z,n}$ *is the probability that the first visit to the point* $-z < 0$ *takes place at the nth trial.* That the corresponding generating function (4.13) is the zth power of λ_2 reflects the obvious fact that the waiting time for the first passage through $-z$ is the sum of z independent waiting times between the successive first passages through $-1, -2, \ldots, -z$.

An explicit formula for $u_{z,n}$ in the special case $p = \frac{1}{2}$ was derived by elementary methods in III,(7.5). Considering that $(n+z)/2$ steps must lead to the left, and $(n-z)/2$ to the right, one concludes easily that in general the same formula holds except that the individual paths have now probability $p^{(n-z)/2}q^{(n+z)/2}$ rather than 2^{-n}. Thus

$$(4.14) \qquad u_{z,n} = \frac{z}{n}\binom{n}{(n+z)/2} p^{(n-z)/2}q^{(n+z)/2},$$

where the binomial coefficient is to be interpreted as zero if n and z are not of the same parity. (Concerning the derivation of this formula from the generating function see the end of XI,3. An alternative explicit formula of an entirely different appearance is contained in problem 13.)

*5. EXPLICIT EXPRESSIONS

The generating function U_z of (4.11) depends formally on a square root but is actually a rational function. In fact, an application of the binomial theorem reduces the denominator to the form

$$(5.1) \qquad \lambda_1^a(s) - \lambda_2^a(s) = s^{-a}\sqrt{1-4pqs^2}\, P_a(s)$$

where P_a is an even polynomial of degree $a - 1$ when a is odd, and of degree $a - 2$ when a is even. The numerator is of the same form except that a is replaced by $a - z$. Thus U_z is the ratio of two polynomials whose degrees differ at most by 1. Consequently it is possible to derive an explicit expression for the ruin probabilities $u_{z,n}$ by the method of partial fractions described in XI,4. The result is interesting because of its connection with diffusion theory, and the derivation as such provides an excellent illustration for the techniques involved in the practical use of partial fractions.

The calculations simplify greatly by the use of an auxiliary variable ϕ defined by

$$(5.2) \qquad \cos \phi = \frac{1}{2\sqrt{pq} \cdot s}.$$

(To $0 < s < 1$ there correspond complex values of ϕ, but this has no effect on the formal calculations.) From (4.8)

$$(5.3) \qquad \lambda_1(s) = \sqrt{q/p}\,[\cos \phi + i \sin \phi] = \sqrt{q/p}\, e^{i\phi}$$

while $\lambda_2(s)$ equals the right side with i replaced by $-i$. Accordingly

$$(5.4) \qquad U_z(s) = \left(\sqrt{q/p}\right)^z \frac{\sin (a-z)\phi}{\sin a\phi}.$$

The roots $s_1, s_2, \ldots$ of the denominator are simple and hence there exists a partial fraction expansion of the form

$$(5.5) \quad \left(\sqrt{q/p}\right)^z \cdot \frac{\sin(a-z)\phi}{\sin a\phi} = A + Bs + \frac{\rho_1}{s_1 - s} + \cdots + \frac{\rho_{a-1}}{s_{a-1} - s}.$$

In principle we should consider only the roots s_ν which are not roots of the numerator also, but if s_ν is such a root then $U_z(s)$ is continuous at $s = s_\nu$ and hence $\rho_\nu = 0$. Such canceling roots do therefore not contribute to the right side and hence it is not necessary to treat them separately.

The roots $s_1, \ldots, s_{a-1}$ correspond obviously to $\phi_\nu = \pi\nu/a$ with $\nu = 1, \ldots, a - 1$, and so

$$(5.6) \qquad\qquad s_\nu = \frac{1}{2\sqrt{pq} \cos \pi\nu/a}.$$

This expression makes no sense when $\nu = a/2$ and a is even, but then ϕ_ν is a root of the numerator also and this root should be discarded. The corresponding term in the final result vanishes, as is proper.

To calculate ρ_ν we multiply both sides in (5.5) by $s_\nu - s$ and let $s \to s_\nu$. Remembering that $\sin a\phi_\nu = 0$ and $\cos a\phi_\nu = 1$ we get

$$\rho_\nu = \left(\sqrt{q/p}\right)^z \sin z\phi_\nu \cdot \lim_{s \to s_\nu} \frac{s - s_\nu}{\sin a\phi}.$$

The last limit is determined by L'Hospital's rule using implicit differentiation in (5.2). The result is

$$\rho_\nu = a^{-1} \cdot 2\sqrt{pq} \left(\sqrt{q/p}\right)^z \sin z\phi_\nu \cdot \sin \phi_\nu \cdot s_\nu^2.$$

From the expansion of the right side in (5.5) into geometric series we get for $n > 1$

$$u_{z,n} = \sum_{\nu=1}^{a-1} \rho_\nu s_\nu^{-n-1} = a^{-1} 2\sqrt{pq} \left(\sqrt{q/p}\right)^z \sum_{\nu=1}^{a-1} s_\nu^{-n+1} \cdot \sin \phi_\nu \cdot \sin z\phi_\nu$$

and hence finally

$$(5.7) \quad u_{z,n} = a^{-1} 2^n p^{(n-z)/2} q^{(n+z)/2} \sum_{\nu=1}^{a-1} \cos^{n-1} \frac{\pi\nu}{a} \sin \frac{\pi\nu}{a} \sin \frac{\pi z\nu}{a}.$$

This, then, is an explicit formula for *the probability of ruin at the nth trial.* It goes back to Lagrange and has been derived by classical authors in various ways,[5] but it continues to be rediscovered in the modern literature.

---

[5] For an elementary derivation based on trigonometric interpolation see R. E. Ellis, Cambridge Math. J., vol. 4 (1844), or his *Collected works*, Cambridge and London 1863.

It is interesting that the method of images (or of repeated reflections) leads to another explicit expression for $u_{z,n}$ in terms of binomial coefficients (problem 21). An alternative method for deriving (5.7) is described in XVI,3.

Passing to the limit as $a \to \infty$ we get the probability that in a game against an infinitely rich adversary a player with initial capital z will be ruined at the nth trial. (See problem 13.)

A glance at the sum in (5.7) shows that the terms corresponding to the summation indices $v = k$ and $v = a - k$ are of the same absolute value; they are of the same sign when n and z are of the same parity and cancel otherwise. Accordingly $u_{z,n} = 0$ *when $n - z$ is odd while for even $n - z$ and $n > 1$*

$$(5.8) \qquad u_{z,n} = a^{-1}2^{n+1}p^{(n-z)/2}q^{(n+z)/2} \sum_{v < a/2} \cos^{n-1}\frac{\pi v}{a} \sin\frac{\pi v}{a} \sin\frac{\pi z v}{a}$$

the summation extending over the positive integers $< a/2$. This form is more natural than (5.7) because now the coefficients $\cos \pi v/a$ form a decreasing sequence and so for large n it is essentially only the first term that counts.

6. CONNECTION WITH DIFFUSION PROCESSES

This section is devoted to an informal discussion of random walks in which the length δ of the individual steps is small but the steps are spaced so close in time that the resultant change appears practically as a continuous motion. A passage to the limit leads to the Wiener process (Brownian motion) and other diffusion processes. The intimate connection between such processes and random walks greatly contributes to the understanding of both.[6] The problem may be formulated in mathematical as well as in physical terms.

It is best to begin with an *unrestricted random walk* starting at the origin. The nth step takes the particle to the position S_n where $S_n = X_1 + \cdots + X_n$ is the sum of n independent random variables each assuming the values $+1$ and -1 with probabilities p and q, respectively. Thus

$$(6.1) \qquad E(S_n) = (p-q)n, \qquad Var(S_n) = 4pqn.$$

Figure 4 of III,7 presents the first 10,000 steps of such a random walk with $p = q = \frac{1}{2}$; to fit the graph to a printed page it was necessary to choose

---

[6] This approach was also fruitful historically. It was fully exploited (though in a heuristic manner) by L. Bachelier, whose work has inspired A. Kolmogorov to develop the formal foundations of Markov processes. See, in particular, L. Bachelier, *Calcul des probabilités*, Paris (Gauthier-Villars), 1912.

appropriate scales for the two axes. Let us now go a step further and contemplate a motion picture of the random walk. Suppose that it is to take 1000 seconds (between 16 and 17 minutes). To present one million steps it is necessary that the random walk proceeds at the rate of one step per millisecond, and this fixes the time scale. What units are we to choose to be reasonably sure that the record will fit a screen of a given height? For this question we use a fixed unit of measurement, say inches or feet, both for the screen and the length of the individual steps. We are then no longer concerned with the variables S_n, but with δS_n, where δ stands for the length of the individual steps. Now

$$(6.2) \qquad E(\delta S_n) = (p-q)\,\delta n, \qquad \text{Var}\,(\delta S_n) = 4pq\,\delta^2 n,$$

and it is clear from the central limit theorem that the contemplated film is possible only if for $n = 1,000,000$ both quantities in (6.2) are smaller than the width of the screen. But if $p \neq q$ and δn is comparable to the width of the screen, $\delta^2 n$ will be indistinguishable from 0 and the film will show linear motion without visible chance fluctuations. The character of the random walk can be discerned only when $\delta^2 n$ is of a moderate positive magnitude, and this is possible only when $p - q$ is of a magnitude comparable to δ.

If the question were purely mathematical we should conclude that the desired graphical presentation is impossible unless $p = q$, but the situation is entirely different when viewed from a physical point of view. In Brownian motion we see particles suspended in a liquid moving in random fashion, and the question arises naturally whether the motion can be interpreted as the result of a tremendous number of collisions with smaller particles in the liquid. It is, of course, an over-simplification to assume that the collisions are spaced uniformly in time and that each collision causes a displacement precisely equal to $\pm\delta$. Anyhow, for a first orientation we treat the impacts as governed by Bernoulli trials and ask whether the observed motion of the particles is compatible with this picture. From actual observations we find the average displacement c and the variance D for a unit time interval. Denote by r the (unknown) number of collisions per time unit. Then we must have, approximately,

$$(6.3) \qquad (p-q)\,\delta r = c, \qquad 4pq\,\delta^2 r = D.$$

In a simulated experiment no chance fluctuations would be observable unless the two conditions (6.3) are satisfied with $D > 0$. An experiment with $p = 0.6$ and $\delta r = 1$ is imaginable, but in it the variance would be so small that the motion would appear deterministic: A clump of particles initially close together would remain together as if it were a rigid body.

Essentially the same consideration applies to many other phenomena in physics, economics, learning theory, evolution theory, etc., when slow fluctuations of the state of a system are interpreted as the result of a huge number of successive small changes due to random impacts. The simple random-walk model does not appear realistic in any particular case, but fortunately the situation is similar to that in the central limit theorem. Under surprisingly mild conditions the nature of the individual changes is not important, because the observable effect depends only on their expectation and variance. In such circumstances it is natural to take the simple random-walk model as universal prototype.

To summarize, as a preparation for a more profound study of various stochastic processes it is natural to consider random walks in which the length δ of the individual steps is small, the number r of steps per time unit is large, and $p - q$ is small, the balance being such that (6.3) holds (where c and $D > 0$ are given constants). The words large and small are vague and must remain flexible for practical applications.[7]

The analytical formulation of the problem is as follows. To every choice of δ, r, and p there corresponds a random walk. *We ask what happens in the limit when $\delta \to 0$, $r \to \infty$, and $p \to \frac{1}{2}$ in such a manner that*

$$(6.4) \qquad (p-q)\delta r \to c, \qquad 4pq\delta^2 r \to D.$$

Two procedures are available. Whenever we are in possession of an explicit expression for relevant probabilities we can pass to the limit directly. We shall illustrate this method because it sheds new light on the normal approximation and the limit theorems derived in chapter III. This method is of limited scope, however, because it does not lend itself to generalizations. More fruitful is the start from the difference equations governing the random walks and the derivation of the limiting differential equations. It turns out that these differential equations govern well defined stochastic processes depending on a continuous time parameter. The same is true of various obvious generalizations of these differential equations, and so the second method leads to the important general class of diffusion processes.

---

[7] The number of molecular shocks per time unit is beyond imagination. At the other extreme, in evolution theory one considers small changes from one generation to the next, and the time separating two generations is not small by everyday standards. The number of generations considered is not fantastic either, but may go into many thousands. The point is that the process proceeds on a scale where the changes appear in practice continuous and a diffusion model with continuous time is preferable to the random-walk model.

To describe the direct method in the simplest case we continue to denote by $\{S_n\}$ the standard random walk with unit steps and put

$$(6.5) \qquad\qquad v_{k,n} = \mathbf{P}\{S_n = k\}.$$

In our accelerated random walk the nth step takes place at epoch n/r, and the position is $S_n\delta = k\delta$. We are interested in the probability of finding the particle at a given epoch t in the neighborhood of a given point x, and so we must investigate the asymptotic behavior of $v_{k,n}$ when $k \to \infty$ and $n \to \infty$ in such a manner that $n/r \to t$ and $k\delta \to x$. The event $\{S_n = k\}$ requires that n and k be of the same parity and takes place when exactly $(n+k)/2$ among the first n steps lead to the right. From the de Moivre-Laplace approximation we conclude therefore that in our passage to the limit

$$(6.6) \quad v_{k,n} \sim \frac{1}{\sqrt{2\pi npq}} e^{-[\frac{1}{2}(n+k)-np]^2/(2npq)} = \frac{1}{\sqrt{2\pi npq}} e^{-[k-n(p-q)]^2/(8npq)}$$

$$\sim \frac{2\delta}{\sqrt{2\pi Dt}} e^{-(x-ct)^2/(2Dt)}$$

where the sign $\sim$ indicates that the ratio of the two sides tends to unity. Now $v_{k,n}$ is the probability of finding $S_n\delta$ between $k\delta$ and $(k+2)\delta$, and since this interval has length 2δ we can say that the ratio $v_{k,n}/(2\delta)$ measures locally the probability per unit length, that is the probability *density*. The second relation in (6.6) implies that the ratio $v_{k,n}/(2\delta)$ tends to

$$(6.7) \qquad\qquad v(t, x) = \frac{1}{\sqrt{2\pi Dt}} e^{-\frac{1}{2}(x-ct)^2/Dt}.$$

It follows that sums of the probabilities $v_{k,n}$ can be approximated by integrals over $v(t, x)$, and our result may be restated to the effect that with our passage to the limit

$$(6.8) \qquad \mathbf{P}\{\alpha < S_n\delta < \beta\} \to \frac{1}{\sqrt{2\pi Dt}} \int_\alpha^\beta e^{-\frac{1}{2}(x-ct)^2/Dt}\, dx.$$

The integral on the right can be expressed in terms of the normal distribution function $\mathfrak{N}$ and (6.8) is in fact only a notational variant of the de Moivre-Laplace limit theorem for the binomial distribution.

The approach based on the appropriate difference equations is more interesting. Considering the position of the particle at the nth and the $(n+1)$st trial it is obvious that the probabilities $v_{k,n}$ satisfy the difference equations

$$(6.9) \qquad\qquad v_{k,n+1} = pv_{k-1,n} + qv_{k+1,n}.$$

On multiplying by 2δ it follows from our preceding result that the limit $v(t, x)$ should be an *approximate* solution of the difference equation

(6.10) $v(t+r^{-1}, x) = pv(t, x-\delta) + qv(t, x+\delta)$.

Since v has continuous derivatives we can expand the terms according to Taylor's theorem. Using the first-order approximation on the left and second-order approximation on the right we get (after canceling the leading terms)

(6.11) $$\frac{\partial v(t, x)}{\partial t} = (q-p)\,\delta r \cdot \frac{\partial v(t, x)}{\partial x} + \frac{1}{2}\delta^2 r\,\frac{\partial^2 v(t, x)}{\partial x^2} + \cdots .$$

In our passage to the limit the omitted terms tend to zero and (6.11) becomes in the limit

(6.12) $$\frac{\partial v(t, x)}{\partial t} = -c\,\frac{\partial v(t, x)}{\partial x} + \frac{1}{2}\,D\,\frac{\partial^2 v(t, x)}{\partial x^2} .$$

This is a special *diffusion equation* also known as the *Fokker-Planck* equation for diffusion. Our calculations were purely formal and heuristic, but it will not come as a surprise that the function v of (6.7) indeed satisfies the differential equation (6.12). Furthermore, it can be shown that (6.7) represents the only solution of the diffusion equation having the obvious properties required by the probabilistic interpretation.

The diffusion equation (6.12) can be generalized by permitting the coefficients c and D to depend on x and t. Furthermore, it possesses obvious analogues in higher dimensions, and all these generalizations can be derived directly from general probabilistic postulates. This topic will be taken up in chapter X of volume 2; here we must be satisfied by these brief and heuristic indications of the connections between random walks and general diffusion theory.

As a second example we take the ruin probabilities $u_{z,n}$ discussed in the preceding two sections. The underlying difference equations (4.2) differ from (6.9) in that the coefficients p and q are interchanged.[8] The formal calculations indicated in (6.11) now lead to a diffusion equation obtained from (6.12) on replacing $-c$ by c. Our limiting procedure leads from the probabilities $u_{z,n}$ to a function $u(t, \xi)$ which satisfies this modified diffusion equation and which has probabilistic significance

---

[8] The reason is that in $u_{z,n}$ the variable z stands for the *initial* position whereas the probability $v_{k,n}$ refers to the position at the running time. In the terminology to be introduced in volume 2 probabilities depending on the initial position satisfy *backward* (retrospective) equations, the others *forward* (or Fokker-Planck) equations. In physics the latter are sometimes called *continuity* equations. The same situation will be encountered in chapter XVII.

similar to $u_{z,n}$: In a diffusion process starting at the point $\xi > 0$ the probability that the particle reaches the point $\alpha > \xi$ *before* reaching the origin and that this event occurs in the time interval $t_1 < t < t_2$ is given by the integral of $u(t, \xi)$ over this interval.

The formal calculations are as follows. For $u_{z,n}$ we have the explicit expression (5.8). Since z and n must be of the same parity $u_{z,n}$ corresponds to the interval between n/r and $(n+2)/r$, and we have to calculate the limit of the ratio $u_{z,n}r/2$ when $r \to \infty$ and $\delta \to 0$ in accordance with (6.4). The length a of the interval and the initial position z must be adjusted so as to obtain the limits α and ξ. Thus $z \sim \xi/\delta$ and $a \sim \alpha/\delta$. It is now easy to find the limits for the individual factors in (5.8).

From the first relation in (6.4) we get $2p \sim 1 + c\delta/D$, and

$$2q \sim 1 - c\delta/D;$$

from the second relation in (6.4) we see that $\delta^2 r \to D$. Therefore

(6.13)
$$(4pq)^{\frac{1}{2}n}(q/p)^{\frac{1}{2}z} \sim (1-c^2\delta^2/D^2)^{\frac{1}{2}(rt)}(1-2c\delta/D)^{\frac{1}{2}\xi/\delta}$$
$$\sim e^{-\frac{1}{2}c^2t/D} \cdot e^{-c\xi/D}$$

Similarly for fixed ν

(6.14)
$$\left(\cos\frac{\nu\pi\delta}{\alpha}\right)^n \sim \left(1 - \frac{\nu^2\pi^2\delta^2}{2\alpha^2}\right)^{tr} \sim e^{-\frac{1}{2}\nu^2\pi^2Dt/\alpha^2}.$$

Finally $\sin \nu\pi\delta/\alpha \sim \nu\pi\delta/\alpha$. Substitution into (5.8) leads formally to

(6.15)
$$v(t, \xi) = \pi D\alpha^{-2}e^{-\frac{1}{2}(ct+2\xi)c/D}\sum_{\nu=1}^{\infty}\nu e^{-\frac{1}{2}\nu^2\pi^2Dt/\alpha^2}\sin\frac{\pi\xi\nu}{\alpha}.$$

(Since the series converges uniformly it is not difficult to justify the formal calculations.) In physical diffusion theory (6.15) is known as *Fürth's formula for first passages*. [For the limiting case $\alpha = \infty$ see problem 14. For an alternative form of (6.15) see problem 22.]

*7. RANDOM WALKS IN THE PLANE AND SPACE

In a two-dimensional random walk the particle moves in unit steps in one of the four directions parallel to the x- and y-axes. For a particle starting at the origin the possible positions are all points of the plane with integral-valued coordinates. Each position has four *neighbors*. Similarly, in three dimensions each position has six neighbors. The random walk is defined by specifying the corresponding four or six probabilities. For

---

* This section treats a special topic and may be omitted at first reading.

simplicity we shall consider only the *symmetric* case where all directions have the same probability. The complexity of problems is considerably greater than in one dimension, for now the domains to which the particle is restricted may have arbitrary shapes and complicated boundaries take the place of the single-point barriers in the one-dimensional case.

We begin with an interesting theorem due to Polya.[9]

Theorem. *In the symmetric random walks in one and two dimensions there is probability one that the particle will sooner or later (and therefore infinitely often) return to its initial position. In three dimensions, however, this probability is only about* 0.35. (The expected number of returns is then $0.65 \sum k(0.35)^k = 0.35/0.65 \approx 0.53$.)

Before proving the theorem let us give two alternative formulations, both due to Polya. First, it is almost obvious that the theorem implies that in *one and two dimensions there is probability* 1 *that the particle will pass infinitely often through every possible point*; in three dimensions this is not true, however. Thus the statement "all roads lead to Rome" is, in a way, justified in two dimensions.

Alternatively, consider *two* particles performing independent symmetric random walks, the steps occurring simultaneously. Will they ever meet? To simplify language let us define the *distance* of two possible positions as the smallest number of steps leading from one position to the other. (This distance equals the sum of absolute differences of the coordinates.) If the two particles move one step each, their mutual distance either remains the same or changes by two units, and so their distance either is even at all times or else is always odd. In the second case the two particles can never occupy the same position. In the first case it is readily seen that the probability of their meeting at the nth step equals the probability that the first particle reaches in $2n$ steps the initial position of the second particle. Hence our theorem states that in two, but not in three, dimensions the two particles are sure infinitely often to occupy the same position. If the initial distance of the two particles is odd, a similar argument shows that they will infinitely often occupy neighboring positions. If this is called meeting, then our theorem asserts that *in one and two dimensions the two particles are certain to meet infinitely often, but in three dimensions there is a positive probability that they never meet.*

---

[9] G. Polya, *Über eine Aufgabe der Wahrscheinlichkeitsrechnung betreffend die Irrfahrt im Strassennetz*, Mathematische Annalen, vol. 84 (1921), pp. 149–160. The numerical value 0.35 was calculated by W. H. McCrea and F. J. W. Whipple, *Random paths in two and three dimensions*, Proceedings of the Royal Society of Edinburgh, vol. 60 (1940), pp. 281–298.

Proof. For one dimension the theorem has been proved in example XIII,(4.b) by the method of recurrent events. The proof for two and three dimensions proceeds along the same lines. Let u_n be the probability that the nth trial takes the particle to the initial position. According to theorem 2 of XIII,3, we have to prove that in the case of two dimensions $\sum u_n$ diverges, whereas in the case of three dimensions $\sum u_n \approx 0.53$. In two dimensions a return to the initial position is possible only if the numbers of steps in the positive x- and y-directions equal those in the negative x- and y-directions, respectively. Hence $u_n = 0$ if n is odd and [using the multinomial distribution VI,(9.2)]

$$(7.1) \qquad u_{2n} = \frac{1}{4^{2n}} \sum_{k=0}^{n} \frac{(2n)!}{k!\,k!\,(n-k)!\,(n-k)!} = \frac{1}{4^{2n}} \binom{2n}{n} \sum_{k=0}^{n} \binom{n}{k}^2$$

By III,(12.11) the right side equals $4^{-2n} \binom{2n}{n}^2$. Stirling's formula now shows that u_{2n} is of the order of magnitude $1/n$, so that $\sum u_{2n}$ diverges as asserted.

In three dimensions we find similarly

$$(7.2) \qquad u_{2n} = 6^{-2n} \sum_{j,k} \frac{(2n)!}{j!\,j!\,k!\,k!\,(n-j-k)!\,(n-j-k)!} ,$$

the summation extending over all j, k with $j + k \leq n$. It is easily verified that

$$(7.3) \qquad u_{2n} = \frac{1}{2^{2n}} \binom{2n}{n} \sum_{j,k} \left\{ \frac{1}{3^n} \frac{n!}{j!\,k!\,(n-j-k)!} \right\}^2 .$$

Within the braces we have the terms of a trinomial distribution, and we know that they add to unity. Hence the sum of the squares is smaller than the maximum term within braces, and the latter is attained when both j and k are about $n/3$. Stirling's formula shows that this maximum is of the order of magnitude n^{-1}, and therefore u_{2n} is of the magnitude $1/\sqrt{n^3}$ so that $\sum u_{2n}$ converges as asserted. ▶

We conclude this section with another problem which generalizes the concept of *absorbing barriers*. Consider the case of two dimensions where instead of the interval $0 \leq x \leq a$ we have a plane domain D, that is, a collection of points with integral-valued coordinates. Each point has four neighbors, but for some points of D one or more of the neighbors lie outside D. Such points form the boundary of D, and all other points are called interior points. In the one-dimensional case the two barriers form the boundary, and our problem consisted in finding the probability that, starting from z, the particle will reach the boundary point 0 before reaching a. By analogy, we now ask for the probability that the particle will reach a certain section of the boundary before reaching any boundary point that is not in this section. This means that we divide all boundary points into two sets B' and B''. If (x, y) is an interior point, we seek the probability $u(x, y)$ that, starting from (x, y), the particle will reach a point of B' before reaching a point of B''. In particular, if B' consists of a single point, then $u(x, y)$ is the probability that the particle will, sooner or later, be absorbed at the particular point.

Let (x, y) be an interior point. The first step takes the particle from (x, y) to one of the four neighbors $(x \pm 1, y)$, $(x, y \pm 1)$, and if all four of them are interior points, we have obviously

$$(7.4) \quad u(x, y) = \tfrac{1}{4}[u(x+1, y) + u(x-1, y) + u(x, y+1) + u(x, y-1)].$$

This is a partial difference equation which takes the place of (2.1) (with $p = q = \tfrac{1}{2}$). If $(x+1, y)$ is a boundary point, then its contribution $u(x+1, y)$ must be replaced by 1 or 0, according to whether $(x+1, y)$ belongs to B' or B''. *Hence (7.4) will be valid for all interior points if we agree that for a boundary point (ξ, η) in B' we put $u(\xi, \eta) = 1$ whereas $u(\xi, \eta) = 0$ if (ξ, η) is in B''. This convention takes the place of the boundary conditions (2.2).*

In (7.4) we have a system of linear equations for the unknowns $u(x, y)$; to each interior point there correspond one unknown and one equation. The system is non-homogeneous, since in it there appears at least one boundary point (ξ, η) of B' and it gives rise to a contribution $\tfrac{1}{4}$ on the right side. If the domain D is finite, there are as many equations as unknowns, and it is well known that the system has a unique solution if, and only if, the corresponding homogeneous system (with $u(\xi, \eta) = 0$ for all boundary points) has no non-vanishing solution. Now $u(x, y)$ is the mean of the four neighboring values $u(x \pm 1, y)$, $u(x, y \pm 1)$ and cannot exceed all four. In other words, in the interior $u(x, y)$ has neither a maximum nor a minimum in the strict sense, and the greatest and the smallest value occur at boundary points. Hence, if all boundary values vanish, so does $u(x, y)$ at all interior points, which proves the existence and uniqueness of the solution of (7.4). Since the boundary values are 0 and 1, all values $u(x, y)$ lie between 0 and 1, as is required for probabilities. These statements are true also for the case of infinite domains, as will be seen from a general theorem on infinite Markov chains.[10]

---

[10] Explicit solutions are known in only a few cases and are always very complicated. Solutions for the case of rectangular domains, infinite strips, etc., will be found in the paper by McCrea and Whipple cited in the preceding footnote.

*8. THE GENERALIZED ONE-DIMENSIONAL
RANDOM WALK (SEQUENTIAL SAMPLING)

We now return to one dimension but abandon the restriction that the particle moves in unit steps. Instead, *at each step the particle shall have probability* p_k *to move from any point* x *to* $x + k$, where the integer k may be zero, positive, or negative. We shall investigate the following *ruin problem: The particle starts from a position* z *such that* $0 < z < a$; *we seek the probability* u_z *that the particle will arrive at some position* ≤ 0 *before reaching any position* $\geq a$. In other words, the position of the particle following the nth trial is the point $z + X_1 + X_2 + \cdots + X_n$ of the x-axis, where the $\{X_k\}$ are mutually independent random variables with the common distribution $\{p_v\}$; the process stops when for the first time either $X_1 + \cdots X_n \leq -z$ or $X_1 + \cdots X_n \geq a - z$.

This problem has attracted widespread interest in connection with *sequential sampling*. There the X_k represent certain characteristics of samples or observations. Measurements are taken until a sum $X_1 + \cdots + X_k$ falls outside two preassigned limits (our $-z$ and $a - z$). In the first case the procedure leads to what is technically known as *rejection*, in the second case to *acceptance*.[11]

Example. (*a*) As an illustration, take Bartky's double-sampling inspection scheme. To test a consignment of items, samples of size N are taken and subjected to complete inspection. It is assumed that the samples are stochastically independent and that the number of defectives in each has the same binomial distribution. Allowance is made for one defective item per sample, and so we let $X_k + 1$ equal the number of defectives in the kth sample. Then for $k \geq 0$

$$p_k = \binom{N}{k+1} p^{k+1} q^{N-k-1}$$

and $p_{-1} = q^N$, $p_x = 0$ for $x < -1$. The procedural rule is as follows: A preliminary sample is drawn and, if it contains no defective, the whole consignment is accepted; if the number of defectives exceeds a, the whole lot is rejected. In either of these cases the process stops. If, however, the number z of defectives lies in the range $1 \leq z \leq a$, the sampling

---

* This section is not used later on.

[11] The general theory of sequential statistical procedures was developed by Abraham Wald during the Second World War in connection with important practical problems. Modern treatments can be found in many textbooks on mathematical statistics. Bartky's scheme described in the example dates from 1943 and seems to have been the very first sequential sampling procedure proposed in the literature.

continues in the described way as long as the sum is contained between 1 and a. Sooner or later it will become either 0, in which case the consignment is accepted, or $\geq a$, in which case the consignment is rejected. ▶

Without loss of generality we shall suppose that steps are possible in both the positive and negative directions. Otherwise we would have either $u_z = 0$ or $u_z = 1$ for all z. The probability of ruin at the *first* step is obviously

(8.1) $$r_z = p_{-z} + p_{-z-1} + p_{-z-2} + \cdots$$

(a quantity which may be zero). The random walk continues only if the particle moved to a position x with $0 < x < a$; the probability of a jump from z to x is p_{x-z}, and the probability of subsequent ruin is then u_x. Therefore

(8.2) $$u_z = \sum_{x=1}^{a-1} u_x p_{x-z} + r_z.$$

Once more we have here $a - 1$ linear equations for $a - 1$ unknowns u_z. The system is non-homogeneous, since at least for $z = 1$ the probability r_1 is different from zero (because steps in the negative direction are possible). To show that the linear system (8.2) possesses a unique solution we must show that the associated homogeneous system

(8.3) $$u_z = \sum_{x=1}^{a-1} u_x p_{x-z}$$

has no solution except zero. To reduce the number of subscripts appearing in the proof we assume that $p_{-1} \neq 0$ (but the argument applies equally to other positive terms with negative index). Suppose, then, that u_z satisfies (8.3) and denote by M the maximum of the values u_z. Let $u_r = M$. Since the coefficients p_{x-z} in (8.3) add to unity this equation is possible for $z = r$ only if those u_x that actually appear on the right side (with positive coefficients) equal M and if their coefficients add to unity. Hence $u_{r-1} = M$ and, arguing in the same way, $u_{r-2} = u_{r-3} = \cdots = = u_1 = M$. However, for $z = 1$ the coefficients p_{x-r} in (8.3) add to less than unity, so that M must be zero.

It follows that (8.2) has a unique solution, and thus our problem is determined. Again we simplify the writing by introducing the boundary conditions

(8.4)
$$u_x = 1 \qquad\qquad \text{if } x \leq 0$$
$$u_x = 0 \qquad\qquad \text{if } x \geq a.$$

Then (8.2) can be written in the form

$$(8.5) \qquad u_z = \sum u_x p_{x-z},$$

the summation now extending over all x [for $x \geq a$ we have no contribution owing to the second condition (8.4); the contributions for $x \leq 0$ add to r_z owing to the first condition].

For large a it is cumbersome to solve $a - 1$ linear equations directly, and it is preferable to use the *method of particular solutions* analogous to the procedure of section 2. It works whenever the probability distribution $\{p_k\}$ has relatively few positive terms. Suppose that only the p_k with $-\nu \leq k \leq \mu$ are different from zero, so that the largest possible jumps in the positive and negative directions are μ and ν, respectively. The *characteristic equation*

$$(8.6) \qquad \sum p_k \sigma^k = 1$$

is equivalent to an algebraic equation of degree $\nu + \mu$. If σ is a root of (8.6), then $u_z = \sigma^z$ is a formal solution of (8.5) for all z, but this solution does not satisfy the boundary conditions (8.4). If (8.6) has $\mu + \nu$ distinct roots $\sigma_1, \sigma_2, \ldots$, then the linear combination

$$(8.7) \qquad u_z = \sum A_k \sigma_k^z$$

is again a formal solution of (8.5) for all z, and we must adjust the constants A_k to satisfy the boundary conditions. Now for $0 < z < a$ only values x with $-\nu + 1 \leq x \leq a + \mu - 1$ appear in (8.5). It suffices therefore to satisfy the boundary conditions (8.4) for $x = 0, -1, -2, \ldots, -\nu + 1$, and $x = a, a + 1, \ldots, a + \mu - 1$, so that we have $\mu + \nu$ conditions in all. If σ_k is a double root of (8.5), we lose one constant, but in this case it is easily seen that $u_z = z\sigma_k^z$ is another formal solution. In every case the $\mu + \nu$ boundary conditions determine the $\mu + \nu$ arbitrary constants.

Example. (*b*) Suppose that each individual step takes the particle to one of the four nearest positions, and we let $p_{-2} = p_{-1} = p_1 = p_2 = \frac{1}{4}$. The characteristic equation (8.6) is $\sigma^{-2} + \sigma^{-1} + \sigma + \sigma^2 = 4$. To solve it we put $t = \sigma + \sigma^{-1}$: with this substitution our equation becomes $t^2 + t = 6$, which has the roots $t = 2, -3$. Solving $t = \sigma + \sigma^{-1}$ for σ we find the four roots

$$(8.8) \quad \sigma_1 = \sigma_2 = 1, \qquad \sigma_3 = \frac{-3 + \sqrt{5}}{2} = \sigma_4^{-1}, \qquad \sigma_4 = \frac{-3 - \sqrt{5}}{2} = \sigma_3^{-1}.$$

Since σ_1 is a double root, the general solution of (8.5) in our case is

(8.9) $u_z = A_1 + A_2 z + A_3 \sigma_3^z + A_4 \sigma_4^z.$

The boundary conditions $u_0 = u_{-1} = 1$ and $u_a = u_{a+1} = 0$ lead to four linear equations for the coefficients A_j and to the final solution

(8.10) $u_z = 1 - \dfrac{z}{a} + \dfrac{(2z-a)(\sigma_3^a - \sigma_4^a) - a(\sigma_3^{2z-a} - \sigma_4^{2z-a})}{a\{(a+2)(\sigma_3^a - \sigma_4^a) - a(\sigma_3^{a+2} - \sigma_4^{a+2})\}}.$ ▶

Let $m = \Sigma k p_k$ be the *expected gain* in a single trial (or expected length of a single step). It is easily seen from (8.6) that $\sigma_1 > 1$ or $\sigma_1 < 1$ according to whether $m < 0$ or $m > 0$. Letting $a \to \infty$, we conclude from our theorem that *in a game against an infinitely rich adversary the probability of an ultimate ruin is one if and only if $m \leq 0$.* The *duration of game* can be discussed by similar methods (cf. problem 9).

Numerical Approximations. Usually it is cumbersome to find all the roots, but rather satisfactory approximations can be obtained in a surprisingly simple way. Consider first the case where the probability distribution $\{p_k\}$ has mean zero. Then the characteristic equation (8.6) has a double root at $\sigma = 1$, and $A + Bz$ is a formal solution of (8.5). Of course, the two constants A and B do not suffice to satisfy the $\mu + \nu$ boundary conditions (8.4). However, if we determine A and B so that $A + Bz$ vanishes for $z = a + \mu - 1$ and equals 1 for $z = 0$, then $A + Bx \geq 1$ for $x \leq 0$ and $A + Bx \geq 0$ for $a \leq x < a + \mu$ so that $A + Bz$ satisfies the boundary conditions (8.4) with the equality sign replaced by $\geq$. Hence the difference $A + Bz - u_z$ is a formal solution of (8.5) with non-negative boundary values, and therefore $A + Bz - u_z \geq 0$. In like manner we can get a lower bound for u_z by determining A and B so that $A + Bz$ vanishes for $z = a$ and equals 1 for $z = -\nu + 1$. Hence

(8.11) $\dfrac{a - z}{a + \nu - 1} \leq u_z \leq \dfrac{a + \mu - z - 1}{a + \mu - 1}.$

This estimate is excellent when a is large as compared to $\mu + \nu$. [Of course, $u_z \approx (1 - z/a)$ is a better approximation but does not give precise bounds.]

Next, consider the general case where the mean of the distribution $\{p_k\}$ is not zero. The characteristic equation (8.6) has then a simple root at $\sigma = 1$. The left side of (8.6) approaches ∞ as $\sigma \to 0$ and as $\sigma \to \infty$. For positive σ the curve $y = \Sigma p_k \sigma^k$ is continuous and convex, and since it intersects the line $y = 1$ at $\sigma = 1$, there exists exactly one more intersection. Therefore, the characteristic equation (8.6) has exactly two positive roots, 1 and σ_1. As before, we see that $A + B\sigma_1^z$ is a formal solution of (8.5), and we can apply our previous argument to this solution instead of $A + Bz$. We find in this case

(8.12) $\dfrac{\sigma_1^a - \sigma_1^z}{\sigma_1^a - \sigma_1^{-\nu+1}} \leq u_z \leq \dfrac{\sigma_1^{a+\mu-1} - \sigma_1^z}{\sigma_1^{a+\mu-1} - 1},$

and have the

Theorem. *The solution of our ruin problem satisfies the inequalities (8.11) if $\{p_k\}$ has zero mean, and (8.12) otherwise. Here σ_1 is the unique positive root different from 1 of (8.6), and μ and $-\nu$ are defined, respectively, as the largest and smallest subscript for which $p_k \neq 0$.*

9. PROBLEMS FOR SOLUTION

Note: *Problems 1–4 refer only to section 2 and require no calculations.*

1. In a random walk starting at the origin find the probability that the point $a > 0$ will be reached before the point $-b < 0$.

2. Prove that with the notations of section 2:

(*a*) In a random walk starting at the origin the probability to reach the point $a > 0$ before returning to the origin equals $p(1 - q_1)$.

(*b*) In a random walk starting at $a > 0$ the probability to reach the origin before returning to the starting point equals qq_{a-1}.

3. If $q \geq p$, conclude from the preceding problem: In a random walk starting at the origin the number of visits to the point $a > 0$ that take place before the first return to the origin has a geometric distribution with ratio $1 - qq_{a-1}$. (Why is the condition $q \geq p$ necessary?)

4. Using the preceding two problems prove the theorem[12]: *The number of visits to the point $a > 0$ that take place prior to the first return to the origin has expectation $(p/q)^a$ when $p < q$ and 1 when $p = q$.*

5. Consider the ruin problem of sections 2 and 3 for the case of a modified random walk in which the particle moves a unit step to the right or left, or stays at its present position with probabilities α, β, γ, respectively ($\alpha + \beta + \gamma = 1$). (In gambling terminology, the bet may result in a tie.)

6. Consider the ruin problem of sections 2 and 3 for the case where the origin is an *elastic* barrier (as defined in section 1). The difference equations for the probability of ruin (absorption at the origin) and for the expected duration are the same, but with new boundary conditions.

7. A particle moves at each step *two* units to the right or *one* unit to the left, with corresponding probabilities p and q ($p + q = 1$). If the starting position is $z > 0$, find the probability a_z that the particle will ever reach the origin. (This is the ruin problem against an infinitely rich adversary.)

Hint: The equation corresponding to (2.1) has the particular solution $q_z = 1$ and two particular solutions of the form λ^z, where λ satisfies a quadratic equation.

8. *Continuation.*[13] Show that a_1 equals the probability that in a sequence of Bernoulli trials the accumulated number of failures will ever exceed twice the accumulated number of successes.

[When $p = q$ this probability equals $(\sqrt{5} - 1)/2$.]

---

[12] The truly amazing implications of this result appear best in the language of fair games. A perfect coin is tossed until the first equalization of the accumulated numbers of heads and tails. The gambler receives one penny for every time that the accumulated number of heads exceeds the accumulated number of tails by m. The *"fair entrance fee"* equals 1 *independently of m.*

For a different (elementary) proof see problems 1–2 of XII,10 in volume 2.

[13] This problem was formulated by D. J. Newman. That its solution is a simple corollary to the preceding problem (in the second edition) was observed by W. A. O'N. Waugh. The reader may try the same approach for the more general problem when the factor 2 is replaced by some other rational. A solution along different lines was devised by J. S. Frame. See *Solution to problem 4864*, Amer. Math. Monthly, vol. 67 (1960), pp. 700–702.

9. In the generalized random-walk problem of section 8 put [in analogy with (8.1)] $p_z = p_{a-z} + p_{a+1-z} + p_{a+2-z} + \cdots$, and let $d_{z,n}$ be the probability that the game lasts for exactly n steps. Show that for $n \geq 1$

$$d_{z,n+1} = \sum_{x=1}^{a-1} d_{x,n} p_{x-z}$$

with $d_{z,1} = r_z + \rho_z$. Hence prove that the generating function $d_z(\sigma) = \Sigma d_{z,n} \sigma^n$ is the solution of the system of linear equations

$$\sigma^{-1} d_z(\sigma) - \sum_{x=1}^{a-1} d_x(\sigma) p_{x-z} = r_z + \rho_z.$$

By differentiation it follows that the expected duration e_z is the solution of

$$e_z - \sum_{x=1}^{a-1} e_x p_{x-z} = 1.$$

10. In the random walk with *absorbing* barriers at the points 0 and a and with initial position z, let $w_{z,n}(x)$ be the probability that the nth step takes the particle to the position x. Find the difference equations and boundary conditions which determine $w_{z,n}(x)$.

11. *Continuation.* Modify the boundary conditions for the case of two *reflecting barriers* (i.e., elastic barriers with $\delta = 1$).

12. A symmetric random walk $(p = q)$ has possible positions $1, 2, \ldots, a - 1$. There is an absorbing barrier at the origin and a reflecting barrier at the other end. Find the generating function for the waiting time for absorption.

13. *An alternative form for the first-passage probabilities.* In the explicit formula (5.7) for the ruin probabilities let $a \to \infty$. Show that the result is

$$u_{z,n} = 2^n p^{(n-z)/2} q^{(n+z)/2} \int_0^1 \cos^{n-1} \pi x \cdot \sin \pi x \cdot \sin \pi x z \cdot dx.$$

Consequently, this formula must be equivalent to (4.14). Verify this by showing that the appropriate difference equations and boundary conditions are satisfied.

14. *Continuation: First passages in diffusion.* Show that the passage to the limit described in section 6 leads from the last formula to the expression

$$\frac{z}{\sqrt{2\pi Dt^3}} e^{-(z+ct)^2/(2Dt)}$$

for the probability density for the waiting time for absorption at the origin in a diffusion starting at the point $z > 0$. When $p = q$ this result is equivalent to the limit theorem 3 of III,7.

Note: *In the following problems* $v_{x,n}$ *is the probability* (6.1) *that in an unrestricted random walk starting at the origin the nth step takes the particle to the position* x.

15. *Method of images.*[14] Let $p = q = \frac{1}{2}$. In a random walk in $(0, \infty)$ with an absorbing barrier at the origin and initial position at $z > 0$, let $u_{z,n}(x)$ be the probability that the nth step takes the particle to the position $x > 0$. Show that $u_{z,n}(x) = v_{x-z,n} - v_{x+z,n}$. [*Hint:* Show that a difference equation corresponding to (4.1) and the appropriate boundary conditions are satisfied.]

16. *Continuation.* If the origin is a *reflecting barrier*, then

$$u_{z,n}(x) = v_{x-z,n} + v_{x+z-1,n}.$$

17. *Continuation.* If the random walk is restricted to $(0, a)$ and both barriers are *absorbing*, then

(9.1) $$u_{z,n}(x) = \sum_k \{v_{k-z-2ka,n} - v_{x+z-2ka,n}\},$$

the summation extending over all k, positive or negative (only finitely many terms are different from zero). If both barriers are *reflecting*, equation (9.1) holds with *minus* replaced by *plus* and $x + z$ replaced by $x + z - 1$.

18. *Distribution of maxima.* In a symmetric unrestricted random walk starting at the origin let $\mathbf{M}_n$ be the maximum abscissa of the particle in n steps. Using problem 15, show that

(9.2) $$\mathbf{P}\{\mathbf{M}_n = z\} = v_{z,n} + v_{z+1,n}.$$

19. Let $V_x(s) = \sum v_{x,n}s^n$ (cf. the note preceding problem 15). Prove that $V_x(s) = V_0(x)\lambda_2^{-x}(s)$ when $x \leq 0$ and $V_x(s) = V_0(s)\lambda_1^{-x}(s)$ when $x \geq 0$, where $\lambda_1(s)$ and $\lambda_2(s)$ are defined in (4.8). Moreover, $V_0(s) = (1-4pqs^2)^{-\frac{1}{2}}$.

Note: These relations follow *directly* from the fact that $\lambda_1(s)$ and $\lambda_2(s)$ are generating functions of first-passage times as explained at the conclusion of section 4.

20. In a random walk in $(0, \infty)$ with an absorbing barrier at the origin and initial position at z, let $u_{z,n}(x)$ be the probability that the nth step takes the particle to the position x, and let

(9.3) $$U_z(s; x) = \sum_{n=0}^{\infty} u_{z,n}(x)s^n.$$

Using problem 19, show that $U_z(s; x) = V_{x-z}(s) - \lambda_2^z(s)V_x(s)$. Conclude

(9.4) $$u_{z,n}(x) = v_{x-z,n} - (q/p)^z \cdot v_{x+z,n}.$$

Compare with the result of problem 15 and derive (9.4) from the latter by combinatorial methods.

---

[14] Problems 15–17 are examples of the *method of images.* The term $v_{x-z,n}$ corresponds to a particle in an unrestricted random walk, and $v_{x+z,n}$ to an "image point." In (9.1) we find image points starting from various positions, obtained by repeated reflections at both boundaries. In problems 20–21 we get the general result for the unsymmetric random walk using generating functions. In the theory of differential equations the method of images is always ascribed to Lord Kelvin. In the probabilistic literature the equivalent reflection principle is usually attributed to D. André. See footnote 5 of III,1.

21. *Alternative formula for the probability of ruin* (5.7). Expanding (4.11) into a geometric series, prove that

$$u_{z,n} = \sum_{k=0}^{\infty} \left(\frac{p}{q}\right)^{ka} w_{z+2ka,n} - \sum_{k=1}^{\infty} \left(\frac{p}{q}\right)^{ka-z} w_{2ka-z,n}$$

where $w_{z,n}$ denotes the first-passage probability of (4.14).

22. If the passage to the limit of section 6 is applied to the expression for $u_{z,n}$ given in the preceding problem, show that the probability density of the absorption time equals[15]

$$\frac{1}{\sqrt{2\pi Dt^3}} e^{-(ct+2\xi)c/(2D)} \sum_{k=-\infty}^{\infty} (\xi + 2k\alpha)e^{-(\xi+2k\alpha)^2/(2Dt)}$$

(*Hint:* Apply the normal approximation to the binomial distribution.)

23. *Renewal method for the ruin problem.*[16] In the random walk with two absorbing barriers let $u_{z,n}$ and $u^*_{z,n}$ be, respectively, the probabilities of absorption at the left and the right barriers. By a proper interpretation prove the truth of the following two equations:

$$V_{-z}(s) = U_z(s)V_0(s) = U^*_z(s)V_{-a}(s),$$

$$V_{a-z}(s) = U_z(s)V_a(s) + U^*_z(s)V_0(s).$$

Derive (4.11) by solving this system for $U_z(s)$.

24. Let $u_{z,n}(x)$ be the probability that the particle, starting from z, will at the nth step be at x without having previously touched the absorbing barriers. Using the notations of problem 23, show that for the corresponding generating function $U_z(s; x) = \Sigma u_{z,n}(x)s^n$ we have

$$U_z(s; x) = V_{x-z}(s) - U_z(s)V_x(s) - U^*_z(s)V_{x-a}(s).$$

(No calculations are required.)

25. *Continuation.* The generating function $U_z(s; x)$ of the preceding problem can be obtained by putting $U_z(s; x) = V_{x-z}(s) - A\lambda_1^z(s) - B\lambda_2^z(s)$ and determining the constants so that the boundary conditions $U_z(s; x) = 0$ for $z = 0$ and $z = a$ are satisfied. With *reflecting barriers* the boundary conditions are $U_0(s; x) = U_1(s; x)$ and $U_a(s; x) = U_{a-1}(s; x)$.

26. Prove the formula

$$v_{x,n} = (2\pi)^{-1}2^n p^{(n+x)/2}q^{(n-x)/2} \int_{-\pi}^{\pi} \cos^n t \cdot \cos tx \cdot dt$$

by showing that the appropriate difference equation is satisfied. Conclude that

$$V_x(s) = (2\pi)^{-1} \left(\frac{p}{q}\right)^{x/2} \int_{-\pi}^{\pi} \frac{\cos tx}{1 - 2\sqrt{pq} \cdot s \cdot \cos t} dt.$$

---

[15] The agreement of the new formula with the limiting form (6.15) is a well-known fact of the theory of theta functions. See XIX, (5.8) of volume 2.

[16] Problems 23–25 contain a new and independent derivation of the main results concerning random walks in one dimension.

27. In a three-dimensional symmetric random walk the particle has probability one to pass infinitely often through any particular line $x = m$, $y = n$.
(*Hint:* Cf. problem 5.)

28. In a two-dimensional symmetric random walk starting at the origin
the probability that the nth step takes the particle to (x, y) is

$$(2\pi)^{-2}2^{-n} \int_{-\pi}^{\pi} \int_{-\pi}^{\pi} (\cos \alpha + \cos \beta)^n \cdot \cos x\alpha \cdot \cos y\beta \cdot d\alpha \, d\beta.$$

Verify this formula and find the analogue for three dimensions. (*Hint:* Check
that the expression satisfies the proper difference equation.)

29. In a two-dimensional symmetric random walk let $\mathbf{D}_n^2 = x^2 + y^2$ be
the square of the distance of the particle from the origin at time n. Prove
$\mathbf{E}(\mathbf{D}_n^2) = n$. [*Hint:* Calculate $\mathbf{E}(\mathbf{D}_{n-1}^2 - \mathbf{D}_n^2)$.]

30. In a symmetric random walk in d dimensions the particle has probability
1 to return infinitely often to a position already previously occupied. *Hint:*
At each step the probability of moving to a new position is at most $(2d-1)/(2d)$.

31. Show that the method described in section 8 works also for the generating
function $U_z(s)$ of the waiting time for ruin.

CHAPTER XV

Markov Chains

1. DEFINITION

Up to now we have been concerned mostly with independent trials which can be described as follows. A set of possible outcomes $E_1, E_2, \ldots$, (finite or infinite in number) is given, and with each there is associated a probability p_k; the probabilities of sample sequences are defined by the multiplicative property $\mathbf{P}\{(E_{j_0}, E_{j_1}, \ldots, E_{j_n})\} = p_{j_0} p_{j_1} \cdots p_{j_n}$. In the theory of Markov chains we consider the simplest generalization which consists in permitting the outcome of any trial to depend on the outcome of the directly preceding trial (and only on it). The outcome E_k is no longer associated with a fixed probability p_k, but to every pair (E_j, E_k) there corresponds a *conditional probability* p_{jk}; given that E_j has occurred at some trial, the probability of E_k at the next trial is p_{jk}. In addition to the p_{jk} we must be given the probability a_k of the outcome E_k at the *initial* trial. For p_{jk} to have the meaning attributed to them, the probabilities of sample sequences corresponding to two, three, or four trials must be defined by

$$\mathbf{P}\{(E_j, E_k)\} = a_j p_{jk}, \qquad \mathbf{P}\{(E_j, E_k, E_r)\} = a_j p_{jk} p_{kr},$$

$$\mathbf{P}\{(E_j, E_k, E_r, E_s)\} = a_j p_{jk} p_{kr} p_{rs},$$

and generally

(1.1) $\qquad \mathbf{P}\{(E_{j_0}, E_{j_1}, \ldots, E_{j_n})\} = a_{j_0} p_{j_0 j_1} p_{j_1 j_2} \cdots p_{j_{n-2} j_{n-1}} p_{j_{n-1} j_n}.$

Here the initial trial is numbered zero, so that trial number one is the second trial. (This convention is convenient and has been introduced tacitly in the preceding chapter.)

Several processes treated in the preceding chapters are Markov chains, but in special cases it is often preferable to use different notations and modes of description. The principal results of the present chapter concern the existence of certain limits and equilibrium distributions; they are, of course, independent of notations and apply to all Markov chains.

Examples. (*a*) *Random walks.* A random walk on the line is a Markov chain, but it is natural to order the possible positions in a doubly infinite sequence $\ldots, -2, -1, 0, 1, 0, \ldots$. With this order transitions are possibly only between neighboring positions, that is, $p_{jk} = 0$ unless $k = j \pm 1$. With our present notations we would be compelled to order the integers in a simple sequence, say $0, 1, -1, 2, -2, \ldots$ and this would lead to clumsy formulas for the probabilities p_{jk}. The same remark applies to random walks in higher dimensions: For actual calculations it is preferable to specify the points by their coordinates, but the symbolism of the present chapter can be used for theoretical purposes.

(*b*) *Branching processes.* Instead of saying that the nth trial results in E_k we said in XII,3 that the nth generation is of size k. Otherwise, we were concerned with a standard Markov chain whose transition probability p_{jk} is the coefficient of a s^k in the jth power $p^j(s)$ of the given generating function.

(*c*) *Urn models.* It is obvious that several urn models of V.2 represent Markov chains. Conversely, every Markov chain is equivalent to an urn model as follows. Each occurring subscript is represented by an urn, and each urn contains balls marked $E_1, E_2, \ldots$. The composition of the urns remains fixed, but varies from urn to urn; in the jth urn the probability to draw a ball marked E_k is p_{jk}. At the *initial*, or zero-th, trial an urn is chosen in accordance with the probability distribution $\{a_i\}$. From that urn a ball is drawn at random, and if it is marked E_j, the next drawing is made from the jth urn, etc. Obviously with this procedure the probability of a sequence $(E_{j_0}, \ldots, E_{j_n})$ is given by (1.1). We see that the notion of a Markov chain is not more general than urn models, but the new symbolism will prove more practical and more intuitive.   ▶

If a_k is the probability of E_k at the initial (or zero-th) trial, we must have $a_k \geq 0$ and $\sum a_k = 1$. Moreover, whenever E_j occurs it must be followed by some E_k, and it is therefore necessary that for all j and k

$$(1.2) \qquad\qquad p_{j1} + p_{j2} + p_{j3} + \cdots = 1, \qquad\qquad p_{jk} \geq 0.$$

We now show that for any numbers a_k and p_{jk} satisfying these conditions, the assignment (1.1) is a permissible definition of probabilities in the sample space corresponding to $n + 1$ trials. The numbers defined in (1.1) being non-negative, we need only prove that they add to unity. Fix first $j_0, j_1, \ldots, j_{n-1}$ and add the numbers (1.1) for all possible j_n. Using (1.2) with $j = j_{n-1}$, we see immediately that the sum equals $a_{j_0} p_{j_0 j_1} \cdots p_{j_{n-2} j_{n-1}}$. Thus the sum over all numbers (1.1) does not depend on n, and since $\sum a_{j_0} = 1$, the sum equals unity for all n.

The definition (1.1) depends formally on the number of trials, but our argument proves the mutual consistency of the definitions (1.1) for all n.

For example, to obtain the probability of the event "the first two trials result in (E_j, E_k)," we have to fix $j_0 = j$ and $j_1 = k$, and add the probabilities (1.1) for all possible $j_2, j_3, \ldots, j_n$. We have just shown that the sum is $a_j p_{jk}$ and is thus independent of n. This means that it is usually not necessary explicitly to refer to the number of trials; the event $(E_{j_0}, \ldots, E_{j_r})$ has the same probability in all sample spaces of more than r trials. In connection with independent trials it has been pointed out repeatedly that. from a mathematical point of view, it is most satisfactory to introduce only the unique sample space of unending sequences of trials and to consider the result of finitely many trials as the beginning of an infinite sequence. This statement holds true also for Markov chains. Unfortunately, sample spaces of infinitely many trials lead beyond the theory of discrete probabilities to which we are restricted in the present volume.

To summarize, our starting point is the following

Definition. *A sequence of trials with possible outcomes* $E_1, E_2, \ldots$ *is called a Markov chain[1] if the probabilities of sample sequences are defined by* (1.1) *in terms of a probability distribution* $\{a_k\}$ *for* E_k *at the initial (or zero-th) trial and fixed conditional probabilities* p_{jk} *of* E_k *given that* E_j *has occurred at the preceding trial.*

A slightly modified terminology is better adapted for applications of Markov chains. The possible outcomes E_k are usually referred to as possible *states of the system*; instead of saying that the nth trial results in E_k one says that the nth *step leads to* E_k, or that E_k is entered at the nth step. Finally, p_{jk} is called the probability of a *transition from* E_j *to* E_k. As usual we imagine the trials performed at a uniform rate so that the number of the step serves as time parameter.

The transition probabilities p_{jk} will be arranged in a *matrix of transition probabilities*

(1.3)
$$P = \begin{bmatrix} p_{11} & p_{12} & p_{13} & \cdots \\ p_{21} & p_{22} & p_{23} & \cdots \\ p_{31} & p_{32} & p_{33} & \cdots \\ \cdot & \cdot & \cdot & \cdots \\ \cdot & \cdot & \cdot & \cdots \\ \cdot & \cdot & \cdot & \cdots \end{bmatrix}$$

---

[1] This is not the standard terminology. We are here considering only a special class of Markov chains, and, strictly speaking, here and in the following sections the term Markov chain should always be qualified by adding the clause "with stationary transition probabilities." Actually, the general type of Markov chain is rarely studied. It will be defined in section 13, where the Markov property will be discussed in relation to general stochastic processes. There the reader will also find examples of dependent trials that do not form Markov chains.

where the first subscript stands for row, the second for column. Clearly P is a square matrix with non-negative elements and unit row sums. Such a matrix (finite or infinite) is called a *stochastic matrix*. *Any stochastic matrix can serve as a matrix of transition probabilities; together with our initial distribution* $\{a_k\}$ *it completely defines a Markov chain with states* $E_1, E_2, \ldots$.

In some special cases it is convenient to number the states starting with 0 rather than with 1. A zero row and zero column are then to be added to P.

Historical Note. Various problems treated in the classical literature by urn models now appear as special Markov chains, but the original methods were entirely different. Furthermore, many urn models are of a different character because they involve aftereffects, and this essential difference was not properly understood. In fact, the confusion persisted long after Markov's pioneer work. A. A. Markov (1856–1922) laid the foundations of the theory of finite Markov chains, but concrete applications remained confined largely to card-shuffling and linguistic problems. The theoretical treatment was usually by algebraic methods related to those described in the next chapter. This approach is outlined in M. Fréchet's monograph.[2]

The theory of chains with infinitely many states was introduced by A. Kolmogorov.[3] The new approach in the first edition of this book made the theory accessible to a wider public and drew attention to the variety of possible applications. Since then Markov chains have become a standard topic in probability and a familiar tool in many applications. For more recent theoretical developments see the notes to sections 11 and 12.

2. ILLUSTRATIVE EXAMPLES

(For applications to the classical problem of card-shuffling see section 10.)

(a) When there are only two possible states E_1 and E_2 the matrix of transition probabilities is necessarily of the form

$$P = \begin{bmatrix} 1 - p & p \\ \alpha & 1 - \alpha \end{bmatrix}.$$

Such a chain could be realized by the following conceptual experiment. A particle moves along the x-axis in such a way that its absolute speed remains constant but the direction of the motion can be reversed. The system is said to be in state E_1 if the particle moves in the positive direction, and in state E_2 if the motion is to the left. Then p is the probability

---

[2] *Recherches théoriques modernes sur le calcul des probabilités*, vol. 2 (Théorie des événements en chaine dans le cas d'un nombre fini d'états possibles), Paris, 1938.

[3] *Anfangsgründe der Theorie der Markoffschen Ketten mit unendlich vielen möglichen Zuständen*, Matematičeskii Sbornik, N.S., vol. 1 (1936), pp. 607–610. This paper contains no proofs. A complete exposition was given only in Russian, in Bulletin de l'Université d'État à Moscou, Sect. A., vol. 1 (1937), pp. 1–15.

of a reversal when the particle moves to the right, and α the probability of a reversal when it moves to the left. [For a complete analysis of this chain see example XVI,(2.a).]

(*b*) *Random walk with absorbing barriers.* Let the possible states be $E_0, E_1, \ldots, E_\rho$ and consider the matrix of transition probabilities

$$
P = \begin{bmatrix}
1 & 0 & 0 & 0 & \cdots & 0 & 0 & 0 \\
q & 0 & p & 0 & \cdots & 0 & 0 & 0 \\
0 & q & 0 & p & \cdots & 0 & 0 & 0 \\
\cdot & \cdot & \cdot & \cdot & \cdots & \cdot & \cdot & \cdot \\
\cdot & \cdot & \cdot & \cdot & \cdots & \cdot & \cdot & \cdot \\
0 & 0 & 0 & 0 & \cdots & q & 0 & p \\
0 & 0 & 0 & 0 & \cdots & 0 & 0 & 1
\end{bmatrix} .
$$

From each of the "interior" states $E_1, \ldots, E_{\rho-1}$ transitions are possible to the right and the left neighbors (with $p_{i,i+1} = p$ and $p_{i,i-1} = q$). However, no transition is possible from either E_0 or E_ρ to any other state; the system may move from one state to another, but once E_0 or E_ρ is reached, the system stays there fixed forever. Clearly this Markov chain differs only terminologically from the model of a random walk with absorbing barriers at 0 and ρ discussed in the last chapter. There the random walk started from a fixed point z of the interval. In Markov chain terminology this amounts to choosing the initial distribution so that $a_z = 1$ (and hence $a_x = 0$ for $x \neq z$). To a randomly chosen initial state there corresponds the initial distribution $a_k = 1/(\rho+1)$.

(*c*) *Reflecting barriers.* An interesting variant of the preceding example is represented by the chain with possible states $E_1, \ldots, E_\rho$ and transition probabilities

$$
P = \begin{bmatrix}
q & p & 0 & 0 & \cdots & 0 & 0 & 0 \\
q & 0 & p & 0 & \cdots & 0 & 0 & 0 \\
0 & q & 0 & p & \cdots & 0 & 0 & 0 \\
\cdot & \cdot & \cdot & \cdot & \cdots & \cdot & \cdot & \cdot \\
\cdot & \cdot & \cdot & \cdot & \cdots & \cdot & \cdot & \cdot \\
\cdot & \cdot & \cdot & \cdot & \cdots & \cdot & \cdot & \cdot \\
0 & 0 & 0 & 0 & \cdots & q & 0 & p \\
0 & 0 & 0 & 0 & \cdots & 0 & q & p
\end{bmatrix}
$$

This chain may be interpreted in gambling language by considering two players playing for unit stakes with the agreement that every time a player loses his last dollar his adversay returns it so that the game can continue forever. We suppose that the players own between them $\rho + 1$ dollars and say that the system is in state E_k if the two capitals are k and $\rho - k + 1$, respectively. The transition probabilities are then given by our matrix P. In the terminology introduced in XIV,1 our chain represents a random walk with reflecting barriers at the points $\frac{1}{2}$ and $\rho + \frac{1}{2}$. Random walks with elastic barriers can be treated in the same way. A complete analysis of the reflecting barrier chain will be found in XVI,3. [See also example (7.c).]

(d) *Cyclical random walks.* Again let the possible states be E_1, E_2, ..., E_ρ but order them cyclically so that E_ρ has the neighbors $E_{\rho-1}$ and E_1. If, as before, the system always passes either to the right or to the left neighbor, the rows of the matrix P are as in example (b), except that the first row is $(0, p, 0, 0, \ldots, 0, q)$ and the last $(p, 0, 0, 0, \ldots, 0, q, 0)$.

More generally, we may permit transitions between any two states. Let $q_0, q_1, \ldots, q_{\rho-1}$ be, respectively, the probability of staying fixed or moving $1, 2, \ldots, \rho - 1$ units to the right (where k units to the right is the same as $\rho - k$ units to the left). Then P is the cyclical matrix

$$P = \begin{bmatrix} q_0 & q_1 & q_2 & \cdots & q_{\rho-2} & q_{\rho-1} \\ q_{\rho-1} & q_0 & q_1 & \cdots & q_{\rho-3} & q_{\rho-2} \\ q_{\rho-2} & q_{\rho-1} & q_0 & \cdots & q_{\rho-4} & q_{\rho-3} \\ \cdot & \cdot & \cdot & \cdots & \cdot & \cdot \\ \cdot & \cdot & \cdot & \cdots & \cdot & \cdot \\ q_1 & q_2 & q_3 & \cdots & q_{\rho-1} & q_0 \end{bmatrix}.$$

For an analysis of this chain see example XVI,(2.d).

(e) *The Ehrenfest model of diffusion.* Once more we consider a chain with the $\rho + 1$ states $E_0, E_1, \ldots, E_\rho$ and transitions possible only to the right and to the left neighbor; this time we put $p_{j,j+1} = 1 - j/\rho$ and $p_{j,j-1} = j/\rho$, so that

$$P = \begin{bmatrix} 0 & 1 & 0 & 0 & \cdots & 0 & 0 \\ \rho^{-1} & 0 & 1 - \rho^{-1} & 0 & \cdots & 0 & 0 \\ 0 & 2\rho^{-1} & 0 & 1 - 2\rho^{-1} & \cdots & 0 & 0 \\ \cdot & \cdot & \cdot & \cdot & \cdots & \cdot & \cdot \\ \cdot & \cdot & \cdot & \cdot & \cdots & \cdot & \cdot \\ 0 & 0 & 0 & 0 & \cdots & 0 & \rho^{-1} \\ 0 & 0 & 0 & 0 & \cdots & 1 & 0 \end{bmatrix}.$$

This chain has two interesting physical interpretations. For a discussion of various recurrence problems in statistical mechanics, P. and T. Ehrenfest[4] described a conceptual urn experiment where ρ molecules are distributed in two containers A and B. At each trial a molecule is chosen at random and moved from its container to the other. The state of the system is determined by the number of molecules in A. Suppose that at a certain moment there are exactly k molecules in the container A. At the next trial the system passes into E_{k-1} or E_{k+1} according to whether a molecule in A or B is chosen; the corresponding probabilities are k/ρ and $(\rho-k)/\rho$, and therefore our chain describes Ehrenfest's experiment. However, our chain can also be interpreted as *diffusion with a central force*, that is, a random walk in which the probability of a step to the right varies with the position. From $x = j$ the particle is more likely to move to the right or to the left according as $j < \rho/2$ or $j > \rho/2$; this means that the particle has a tendency to move toward $x = \rho/2$, which corresponds to an attractive elastic force increasing in direct proportion to the distance. [The Ehrenfest model has been described in example V(2.c); see also example (7.d) and problem 12.]

(f) *The Bernoulli-Laplace model of diffusion.*[5] A model similar to the Ehrenfest model was proposed by D. Bernoulli as a probabilistic analogue for the flow of two incompressible liquids between two containers. This time we have a total of 2ρ particles among which ρ are black and ρ white. Since these particles are supposed to represent incompressible liquids the densities must not change, and so the number ρ of particles in each urn remains constant. We say that the system is in state E_k ($k = 0, 1, \ldots, \rho$) if the first urn contains k white particles. (This implies that it contains $\rho - k$ black particles while the second urn contains $\rho - k$ white and k black particles). At each trial one particle is chosen from each urn, and these two particles are interchanged. The transition probabilities are then given by

$$(2.1) \qquad p_{j,j-1} = \left(\frac{j}{\rho}\right)^2, \qquad p_{j,j+1} = \left(\frac{\rho-j}{\rho}\right)^2, \qquad p_{jj} = 2\,\frac{j(\rho-j)}{\rho^2}$$

---

[4] P. and T. Ehrenfest, *Über zwei bekannte Einwände gegen das Boltzmannsche H-Theorem*, Physikalische Zeitschrift, vol. 8 (1907), pp. 311–314. Ming Chen Wang and G. E. Uhlenbeck, *On the theory of the Brownian motion II*, Reviews of Modern Physics, vol. 17 (1945), pp. 323–342. For a more complete discussion see M. Kac, *Random walk and the theory of Brownian motion*, Amer. Math. Monthly, vol. 54 (1947), pp. 369–391. These authors do not mention Markov chains, but Kac uses methods closely related to those described in the next chapter. See also B. Friedman, *A simple urn model*, Communications on Pure and Applied Mathematics, vol. 2 (1949), pp. 59–70.

[5] In the form of an urn model this problem was treated by Daniel Bernoulli in 1769, criticized by Malfatti in 1782, and analyzed by Laplace in 1812. See I. Todhunter, *A history of the mathematical theory of probability*, Cambridge, 1865.

and $p_{jk} = 0$ whenever $|j - k| > 1$ (here $j = 0, \ldots, \rho$). [For the steady state distribution see example (7.e); for a generalization of the model see problem 10.]

(g) *Random placements of balls.* Consider a sequence of independent trials each consisting in placing a ball at random in one of ρ given cells (or urns). We say that the system is in state E_k if exactly k cells are occupied. This determines a Markov chain with states $E_0, \ldots, E_\rho$ and transition probabilities such that

$$(2.2) \qquad p_{jj} = \frac{j}{\rho}, \qquad p_{j,j+1} = \frac{\rho - j}{\rho}$$

and, of course, $p_{jk} = 0$ for all other combinations of j and k. If initially all cells are empty, the distribution $\{a_k\}$ is determined by $a_0 = 1$ and $a_k = 0$ for $k > 0$. [This chain is further analyzed in example XVI,(2.e). Random placements of balls were treated from different points of view in II,5 and IV,2.]

(h) *An example from cell genetics.*[6] A Markov chain with states E_0, $\ldots, E_N$ and transition probabilities

$$(2.3) \qquad p_{jk} = \binom{2j}{k}\binom{2N-2j}{N-k} \Big/ \binom{2N}{N}$$

occurs in a biological problem which may be described roughly as follows. Each cell of a certain organism contains N particles, some of which are of type A, the others of type B. The cell is said to be in state E_j if it contains exactly j particles of type A. Daughter cells are formed by cell division, but prior to the division each particle replicates itself; the daughter cell inherits N particles chosen at random from the $2j$ particles of type A and $2N - 2j$ particles of type B present in the parental cell. The probability that a daughter cell is in state E_k is then given by the hypergeometric distribution (2.3).

It will be shown in example (8.b) that *after sufficiently many generations the entire population will be (and remain) in one of the pure states E_0 or E_N; the probabilities of these two contingencies are $1 - j/N$ and j/N,* respectively, where E_j stands for the initial state.

---

[6] I. V. Schensted, *Model of subnuclear segregation in the macronucleus of ciliates,* The Amer. Naturalist, vol. 92 (1958), pp. 161–170. This author uses essentially the methods of chapter XVI, but does not mention Markov chains. Our formulation of the problem is mathematically equivalent, but oversimplified biologically.

(*i*) *Examples from population genetics.*[7] Consider the successive generations of a population (such as the plants in a corn field) which is kept constant in size by the selection of N individuals in each generation. A particular gene assuming the forms A and a has $2N$ representatives; if in the nth generation A occurs j times, then a occurs $2N - j$ times. In this case we say that the population is in state E_j $(0 \leq j \leq 2N)$. Assuming random mating, the composition of the following generation is determined by $2N$ Bernoulli trials in which the A-gene has probability $j/2N$. We have therefore a Markov chain with

$$(2.4) \qquad p_{jk} = \binom{2N}{k} \left(\frac{j}{2N}\right)^k \left(1 - \frac{j}{2N}\right)^{2N-k}.$$

In the states E_0 and E_{2N} all genes are of the same type, and no exit from these states is possible. (They are called homozygous.) It will be shown in example (8.*b*) that *ultimately the population will be fixed at one of the homozygous states* E_0 *or* E_{2N}. If the population starts from the initial state E_j the corresponding probabilities are $1 - j/(2N)$ and $j/(2N)$.

This model can be modified so as to take into account possible mutations and selective advantages of the genes.

(*j*) *A breeding problem.* In the so-called brother-sister mating two individuals are mated, and among their direct descendants two individuals of opposite sex are selected at random. These are again mated, and the process continues indefinitely. With three genotypes AA, Aa, aa for each parent, we have to distinguish six combinations of parents which we label as follows: $E_1 = AA \times AA$, $E_2 = AA \times Aa$, $E_3 = Aa \times Aa$, $E_4 = Aa \times aa$, $E_5 = aa \times aa$, $E_6 = AA \times aa$. Using the rules of V,5 it is easily seen that the matrix of transition probabilities is in this case

$$\begin{bmatrix} 1 & 0 & 0 & 0 & 0 & 0 \\ \frac{1}{4} & \frac{1}{2} & \frac{1}{4} & 0 & 0 & 0 \\ \frac{1}{16} & \frac{1}{4} & \frac{1}{4} & \frac{1}{4} & \frac{1}{16} & \frac{1}{8} \\ 0 & 0 & \frac{1}{4} & \frac{1}{2} & \frac{1}{4} & 0 \\ 0 & 0 & 0 & 0 & 1 & 0 \\ 0 & 0 & 1 & 0 & 0 & 0 \end{bmatrix}.$$

---

[7] This problem was discussed by different methods by R. A. Fisher and S. Wright. The formulation in terms of Markov chains is due to G. Malécot, *Sur un problème de probabilités en chaine que pose la génétique*, Comptes rendus de l'Académie des Sciences, vol. 219 (1944), pp. 379–381.

[The discussion is continued in problem 4; a complete treatment is given in example XVI,(4.b).]

(k) *Recurrent events and residual waiting times.* The chain with states E_0, $E_1, \ldots$ and transition probabilities

$$P = \begin{bmatrix} f_1 & f_2 & f_3 & f_4 & \cdots \\ 1 & 0 & 0 & 0 & \cdots \\ 0 & 1 & 0 & 0 & \cdots \\ 0 & 0 & 1 & 0 & \cdots \\ 0 & 0 & 0 & 1 & \cdots \\ \cdot & \cdot & \cdot & \cdot & \cdots \\ \cdot & \cdot & \cdot & \cdot & \cdots \end{bmatrix}$$

will be used repeatedly for purposes of illustration; the probabilities f_k are arbitrary except that they must add to unity. To visualize the process suppose that it starts from the initial state E_0. If the first step leads to E_{k-1} the system is bound to pass successively through $E_{k-2}, E_{k-3}, \ldots$, and at the kth step the system returns to E_0, whence the process starts from scratch. The successive returns to E_0 thus represent a persistent recurrent event $\mathcal{E}$ with the distribution $\{f_k\}$ for the recurrence times. The state of the system at any time is determined by the waiting time to the *next* passage through E_0. In most concrete realizations of recurrent events the waiting time for the next occurrence depends on future developments and our Markov chain is then without operational meaning. But the chain is meaningful when it is possible to imagine that simultaneously with each occurrence of $\mathcal{E}$ there occurs a random experiment whose outcome decides on the length of the next waiting time. Such situations occur in practice although they are the exception rather than the rule. For example, in the theory of self-renewing aggregates [example XIII,(10.d)] it is sometimes assumed that the lifetime of a newly installed piece of equipment depends on the choice of this piece but is completely determined once the choice is made. Again, in the theory of queues at servers or telephone trunk lines the successive departures of customers usually correspond to recurrent events. Suppose now that there are many types of customers but that each type requires service of a known duration. The waiting time between two successive departures is then uniquely determined from the moment when the corresponding customer joins the waiting line. [See example (7.g).]

(*l*) *Another chain connected with recurrent events.* Consider again a chain with possible states $E_0, E_1, \ldots$ and transition probabilities

$$P = \begin{bmatrix} q_1 & p_1 & 0 & 0 & 0 & \cdots \\ q_2 & 0 & p_2 & 0 & 0 & \cdots \\ q_3 & 0 & 0 & p_3 & 0 & \cdots \\ q_4 & 0 & 0 & 0 & p_4 & \cdots \\ \cdot & \cdot & \cdot & \cdot & \cdot & \cdots \\ \cdot & \cdot & \cdot & \cdot & \cdot & \cdots \end{bmatrix}$$

where $p_k + q_k = 1$. For a picturesque description we may interpret the state E_k as representing the "age" of the system. When the system reaches age k the aging process continues with probability p_{k+1}, but with probability q_{k+1} it rejuvenates and starts afresh with age zero. The successive passages through the state E_0 again represent a recurrent event and the probability that a recurrence time equals k is given by the product $p_1 p_2 \cdots p_{k-1} q_k$. It is possible to choose the p_k in such a way as to obtain a prescribed distribution $\{f_k\}$ for the recurrence times; it suffices to put $q_1 = f_1$, then $q_2 = f_2/p_1$, and so on. Generally

$$(2.5) \qquad\qquad p_k = \frac{1 - f_1 - \cdots - f_k}{1 - f_1 - \cdots - f_{k-1}}.$$

In this way an arbitrary recurrent event $\mathcal{E}$ with recurrence time distribution $\{f_k\}$ corresponds to a Markov chain with matrix P determined by (2.5). At the nth trial the system is in state E_k if, and only if, the trial number $n - k$ was the last at which $\mathcal{E}$ occurred (here $k = 0, 1, \ldots$). This state is frequently called "the spent waiting time." [The discussion is continued in examples (5.*b*), (7.*f*), and (8.*e*).]

(*m*) *Success runs.* As a special case of the preceding example consider a sequence of Bernoulli trials and let us agree that at the nth trial the system is in the state E_k if the last *failure* occurred at the trial number $n - k$. Here $k = 0, 1, \ldots$ and the zeroth trial counts as failure. In other words, the index k equals the length of the uninterrupted block of successes ending at the nth trial. The transition probabilities are those of the preceding example with $p_k = p$ and $q_k = q$ for all k.

3. HIGHER TRANSITION PROBABILITIES

We shall denote by $p_{jk}^{(n)}$ *the probability of a transition from* E_j *to* E_k *in exactly* n *steps.* In other words, $p_{jk}^{(n)}$ is the conditional probability of entering E_k at the nth step given the initial state E_j; this is the sum of the probabilities of all possible paths $E_j E_{j_1} \cdots E_{j_{n-1}} E_k$ of length n starting at E_j and ending at E_k. In particular $p_{jk}^{(1)} = p_{jk}$ and

$$(3.1) \qquad p_{jk}^{(2)} = \sum_v p_{jv} p_{vk}.$$

By induction we get *the general recursion formula*

$$(3.2) \qquad p_{jk}^{(n+1)} = \sum_v p_{jv} p_{vk}^{(n)};$$

a further induction on m leads to *the basic identity*

$$(3.3) \qquad p_{jk}^{(m+n)} = \sum_v p_{jv}^{(m)} p_{vk}^{(n)}$$

(which is a special case of the Chapman-Kolmogorov identity). It reflects the simple fact that the first m steps lead from E_j to some intermediate state E_v, and that the probability of a subsequent passage from E_v to E_k does not depend on the manner in which E_v was reached.[8]

In the same way as the p_{jk} form the matrix P, *we arrange the* $p_{jk}^{(n)}$ *in a matrix to be denoted by* P^n. Then (3.2) states that to obtain the element $p_{jk}^{(n+1)}$ of P^{n+1} we have to multiply the elements of the jth row of P by the corresponding elements of the kth column of P^n and add all products. This operation is called row-into-column multiplication of the matrices P and P^n and is expressed symbolically by the equation $P^{n+1} = PP^n$. This suggests calling P^n the nth power of P; equation (3.3) expresses the familiar law $P^{m+n} = P^m P^n$.

In order to have (3.3) true for all $n \geq 0$ we define $p_{jk}^{(0)}$ by $p_{jj}^{(0)} = 1$ and $p_{jk}^{(0)} = 0$ for $j \neq k$ as is natural.

Examples. (*a*) *Independent trials.* Explicit expressions for the higher-order transition probabilities are usually hard to come by, but fortunately they are only of minor interest. As an important, if trivial, exception we note the special case of independent trials. This case arises when all rows of P are identical with a given probability distribution, and it is clear without calculations that this implies $P^n = P$ for all n.

(*b*) *Success runs.* In example (2.*m*) it is easy to see [either from the recursion formula (3.2) or directly from the definition of the process] that

$$p_{jk}^{(n)} = \begin{cases} qp^k & \text{for} \quad k = 0, 1, \ldots, j+n-1 \\ p^k & \text{for} \quad k = j+n \\ 0 & \text{otherwise.} \end{cases}$$

---

[8] The latter property is characteristic of Markov processes to be defined in section 13. It has been assumed for a long time that (3.3) could be used for a definition of Markov chains but, surprisingly, this is not so [see example (13.*f*)].

In this case it is clear that P^n converges to a matrix such that all elements in the column number k equal qp^k.   ▶

Absolute Probabilities

Let again a_j stand for the probability of the state E_j at the initial (or zeroth) trial. The (unconditional) probability of entering E_k at the nth step is then

$$(3.4) \qquad a_k^{(n)} = \sum_j a_j p_{jk}^{(n)}.$$

Usually we let the process start from a fixed state E_i, that is, we put $a_i = 1$. In this case $a_k^{(n)} = p_{ik}^{(n)}$.

We feel intuitively that the influence of the initial state should gradually wear off so that for large n the distribution (3.4) should be nearly independent of the initial distribution $\{a_j\}$. This is the case if (as in the last example) $p_{jk}^{(n)}$ converges to a limit independent of j, that is, if P^n converges to a matrix with identical rows. We shall see that this is usually so, but once more we shall have to take into account the annoying exception caused by periodicities.

4. CLOSURES AND CLOSED SETS

We shall say that E_k *can be reached from* E_j if there exists some $n \geq 0$ such that $p_{jk}^{(n)} > 0$ (i.e., if there is a positive probability of reaching E_k from E_j including the case $E_k = E_j$). For example, in an unrestricted random walk each state can be reached from every other state, but from an absorbing barrier no other state can be reached.

Definition. *A set C of states is closed if no state outside C can be reached from any state E_j in C. For an arbitrary set C of states the smallest closed set containing C is called the closure of C.*

A single state E_k forming a closed set will be called absorbing.

A Markov chain is irreducible if there exists no closed set other than the set of all states.

Clearly C is closed if, and only if, $p_{jk} = 0$ whenever j is in C and k outside C, for in this case we see from (3.2) that $p_{jk}^{(n)} = 0$ for every n. We have thus the obvious

Theorem. *If in the matrices P^n all rows and all columns corresponding to states outside the closed set C are deleted, there remain stochastic matrices for which the fundamental relations (3.2) and (3.3) again hold.*

This means that we have a Markov chain defined on C, and this *subchain can be studied independently of all other states.*

The state E_k is absorbing if, and only if, $p_{kk} = 1$; in this case the matrix of the last theorem reduces to a single element. In general it is clear that the totality of all states E_k that can be reached from a given state E_j forms a closed set. (Since the closure of E_j cannot be smaller it coincides with this set.) An irreducible chain contains no proper closed subsets, and so we have the simple but useful

Criterion. *A chain is irreducible if, and only if, every state can be reached from every other state.*

Examples. (*a*) In order to find all closed sets it suffices to know which p_{jk} vanish and which are positive. Accordingly, we use a $*$ to denote positive elements and consider a typical matrix, say

$$P = \begin{bmatrix} 0 & 0 & 0 & * & 0 & 0 & 0 & 0 & * \\ 0 & * & * & 0 & * & 0 & 0 & 0 & * \\ 0 & 0 & 0 & 0 & 0 & 0 & 0 & * & 0 \\ * & 0 & 0 & 0 & 0 & 0 & 0 & 0 & 0 \\ 0 & 0 & 0 & 0 & * & 0 & 0 & 0 & 0 \\ 0 & * & 0 & 0 & 0 & 0 & 0 & 0 & 0 \\ 0 & * & 0 & 0 & 0 & * & * & 0 & 0 \\ 0 & 0 & * & 0 & 0 & 0 & 0 & 0 & 0 \\ 0 & 0 & 0 & * & 0 & 0 & 0 & 0 & * \end{bmatrix}$$

We number the states from 1 to 9. In the fifth row a $*$ appears only at the fifth place, and therefore $p_{55} = 1$: the state E_5 is *absorbing*. The third and the eighth row contain only one positive element each, and it is clear that E_3 and E_8 form a *closed* set. From E_1 passages are possible into E_4 and E_9, and from there only to E_1, E_4, E_9. Accordingly the three states E_1, E_4, E_9 form another *closed* set.

From E_2 direct transitions are possible to itself and to E_3, E_5, and E_8. The pair (E_3, E_8) forms a closed set while E_5 is asorbing; accordingly, the closure of E_2 consists of the set E_2, E_3, E_5, E_8. The closures of the remaining states E_6 and E_7 are easily seen to consist of all nine states.

The appearance of our matrix and the determination of the closed sets can be simplified by renumbering the states in the order

$$E_5 E_3 E_8 E_1 E_4 E_9 E_2 E_6 E_7.$$

The closed sets then contain only adjacent states and a glance at the new matrix reveals the grouping of the states.

(b) In the matrix of example (2.j) the states E_1 and E_5 are absorbing and there exist no other closed sets.

(c) In the genetics example (2.i) the states E_0 and E_{2N} are absorbing. When $0 < j < 2N$ the closure of E_j contains all states. In example (2.h) the states E_0 and E_N are absorbing. ▶

Consider a chain with states $E_1, \ldots, E_\rho$ such that $E_1, \ldots, E_r$ form a closed set $(r < \rho)$. The r by r submatrix of P appearing in the left upper corner is then stochastic, and we can exhibit P in the form of a partitioned matrix

$$(4.1) \qquad P = \begin{bmatrix} Q & 0 \\ U & V \end{bmatrix}.$$

The matrix in the upper right corner has r rows and $\rho - r$ columns and only zero entries. Similarly, U stands for a matrix with $\rho - r$ rows and r columns while V is a square matrix. We shall use the symbolic partitioning (4.1) also when the closed set C and its complement C' contain infinitely many states; the partitioning indicates merely the grouping of the states and the fact that $p_{jk} = 0$ whenever E_j is in C and E_k in the complement C'. From the recursion formula (3.2) it is obvious that the higher-order transition probabilities admit of a similar partitioning:

$$(4.2) \qquad P^n = \begin{bmatrix} Q^n & 0 \\ U_n & V^n \end{bmatrix}.$$

We are not at present interested in the form of the elements of the matrix U_n appearing in the left lower corner. The point of interest is that (4.2) reveals three obvious, but important, facts. First, $p_{jk}^{(n)} = 0$ whenever $E_j \in C$ but $E_k \in C'$. Second, the appearance of the power Q^n indicates that when both E_j and E_k are in C the transition probabilities $p_{jk}^{(n)}$ are obtained from the recursion formula (3.2) with the summation restricted to the states of the closed set C. Finally, the appearance of V^n indicates that the last statement remains true when C is replaced by its complement C'. As a consequence it will be possible to simplify the further study of Markov chains by considering separately the states of the closed set C and those of the complement C'.

Note that we have not assumed Q to be irreducible. If C decomposes into several closed subsets then Q admits of a further partitioning. There exist chains with infinitely many closed subsets.

Example. (d) As was mentioned before, a random walk in the plane represents a special Markov chain even though an ordering of the states in a simple sequence would be inconvenient for practical purposes. Suppose now that we modify the random walk by the rule that on reaching the

x-axis the particle continues a random walk along this axis without ever leaving it. The points of the x-axis then form an infinite closed set. On the other hand, if we stipulate that on reaching the x-axis the particle remains forever fixed at the hitting point, then every point of the x-axis becomes an absorbing state.   ▶

5. CLASSIFICATION OF STATES

In a process starting from the initial state E_j the successive returns to E_j constitute a recurrent event, while the successive passages through any other state constitute a delayed recurrent event (as defined in XIII,5). The theory of Markov chains therefore boils down to a simultaneous study of many recurrent events. The general theory of recurrent events is applicable without modifications, but to avoid excessive references to chapter XIII we shall now restate the basic definitions. The present chapter thus becomes essentially self-contained and independent of chapter XIII except that the difficult proof of (5.8) will not be repeated in full.

The states of a Markov chain will be classified independently from two viewpoints. The classification into persistent and transient states is fundamental, whereas the classification into periodic and aperiodic states concerns a technical detail. It represents a nuisance in that it requires constant references to trivialities; the beginner should concentrate his attention on chains without periodic states. All definitions in this section involve only the matrix of transition probabilities and are independent of the initial distribution $\{a_j\}$.

Definition 1. *The state* E_j *has period* $t > 1$ *if* $p_{jj}^{(n)} = 0$ *unless* $n = vt$ *is a multiple of* t, *and* t *is the largest integer with this property. The state* E_j *is aperiodic if no such* $t > 1$ *exists.*[9]

To deal with a periodic E_j it suffices to consider the chain at the trials number $t, 2t, 3t, \ldots$. In this way we obtain a new Markov chain with transition probabilities $p_{ik}^{(t)}$, and in this new chain E_j is aperiodic. In this way results concerning aperiodic states can be transferred to periodic states. The details will be discussed in section 9 and (excepting the following example) we shall now concentrate our attention on aperiodic chains.

Example. (*a*) In an unrestricted random walk all states have period 2. In the random walk with absorbing barriers at 0 and ρ [example (2.*b*)] the interior states have period 2, but the absorbing states E_0 and E_ρ are, of course, aperiodic. If at least one of the barriers is made reflecting [example (2.*c*)], all states become aperiodic.   ▶

---

[9] A state E_j to which no return is possible (for which $p_{jj}^{(n)} = 0$ for all $n > 0$) will be considered aperiodic.

Notation. *Throughout this chapter $f_{jk}^{(n)}$ stands for the probability that in a process starting from E_j the first entry to E_k occurs at the nth step. We put $f_{jk}^{(0)} = 0$ and*

$$(5.1) \qquad f_{jk} = \sum_{n=1}^{\infty} f_{jk}^{(n)}$$

$$(5.2) \qquad \mu_j = \sum_{n=1}^{\infty} n f_{jj}^{(n)}.$$

Obviously f_{jk} is the probability that, starting from E_j, the system will ever pass through E_k. Thus $f_{jk} \leq 1$. When $f_{jk} = 1$ the $\{f_{jk}^{(n)}\}$ is a proper probability distribution and we shall refer to it as the *first-passage distribution for E_k*. In particular, $\{f_{jj}^{(n)}\}$ represents the distribution of *the recurrence times for E_j*. The definition (5.2) is meaningful only when $f_{jj} = 1$, that is, when a return to E_j is certain. In this case $\mu_j \leq \infty$ is the *mean recurrence time for E_j*.

No actual calculation of the probabilities $f_{jk}^{(n)}$ is required for our present purposes, but for conceptual clarity we indicate how the $f_{jk}^{(n)}$ can be determined (by the standard renewal argument). If the first passage through E_k occurs at the νth trial $(1 \leq \nu \leq n - 1)$ the (conditional) probability of E_k at the nth trial equals $p_{kk}^{(n-\nu)}$. Remembering the convention that $p_{kk}^{(0)} = 1$ we conclude that

$$(5.3) \qquad p_{jk}^{(n)} = \sum_{\nu=1}^{n} f_{jk}^{(\nu)} p_{kk}^{(n-\nu)}.$$

Letting successively $n = 1, 2, \ldots$ we get recursively $f_{jk}^{(1)}$, $f_{jk}^{(2)}, \ldots$. Conversely, if the $f_{jk}^{(n)}$ are known for the pair j, k then (5.3) determines all the transition probabilities $p_{jk}^{(n)}$.

The first question concerning any state E_j is whether a return to it is certain. If it is certain, the question arises whether the mean recurrence time μ_j is finite or infinite. The following definition agrees with the terminology of chapter XIII.

Definition 2. *The state E_j is persistent if $f_{jj} = 1$ and transient if $f_{jj} < 1$.*

A persistent state E_j is called null state if its mean recurrence time $\mu_j = \infty$.

This definition applies also to periodic states. It classifies all persistent states into null states and non-null states. The latter are of special interest, and since we usually focus our attention on aperiodic states it is convenient to use the term ergodic for aperiodic, persistent non-null states.[10] This leads us to

Definition 3. *An aperiodic persistent state* E_j *with* $\mu_j < \infty$ *is called ergodic.*

The next theorem expresses the conditions for the different types in terms of the transition probabilities $p_{jj}^{(n)}$. It is of great importance even though the criterion contained in it is usually too difficult to be useful. Better criteria will be found in sections 7 and 8, but unfortunately there exists no simple universal criterion.

Theorem. (i) E_j *is transient if, and only if,*

$$(5.4) \qquad \sum_{n=0}^{\infty} p_{jj}^{(n)} < \infty.$$

In this case

$$(5.5) \qquad \sum_{n=1}^{\infty} p_{ij}^{(n)} < \infty$$

for all i.

(ii) E_j *is a (persistent) null state if, and only if,*

$$(5.6) \qquad \sum_{n=0}^{\infty} p_{jj}^{(n)} = \infty, \quad but \quad p_{jj}^{(n)} \to 0$$

as $n \to \infty$. *In this case*

$$(5.7) \qquad p_{ij}^{(n)} \to 0$$

for all i.

(iii) *An aperiodic (persistent) state* E_j *is ergodic if, and only if,* $\mu_j < \infty$. *In this case as* $n \to \infty$

$$(5.8) \qquad p_{ij}^{(n)} \to f_{ij}\mu_j^{-1}.$$

Corollary. *If* E_j *is aperiodic,* $p_{ij}^{(n)}$ *tends either to 0 or to the limit given by (5.8).*

---

[10] Unfortunately this terminology is not generally accepted. In Kolmogorov's terminology transient states are called *"unessential,"* but this chapter was meant to show that the theoretical and practical interest often centers on transient states. (Modern potential theory supports this view.) Ergodic states are sometimes called *"positive,"* and sometimes the term "ergodic" is used in the sense of our persistent. (In the first edition of this book persistent E_j were regrettably called recurrent.)

Proof. The assertion (5.4) is contained in theorem 2 of XIII,3. The assertion (5.5) is an immediate consequence of this and (5.3), but it is also contained in theorem 1 of XIII,5.

For an aperiodic persistent state E_j theorem 3 of XIII, 3 asserts that $p_{jj}^{(n)} \to \mu_j^{-1}$, where the right side is to be interpreted as zero if $\mu_j = \infty$. The assertions (5.7) and (5.8) follow again immediately from this and (5.3), or else from theorem 1 of XIII,5.

Let E_j be persistent and $\mu_j = \infty$. By theorem 4 of XIII,3 in this case $p_{jj}^{(n)} \to 0$, and this again implies (5.7). $\blacktriangleright$

Examples. (b) Consider the state E_0 of the chain of example (2.l). The peculiar nature of the matrix of transition probabilities shows that a first return at the nth trial can occur only through the sequence

$$E_0 \to E_1 \to E_2 \to \cdots \to E_{n-1} \to E_0,$$

and so for $n \geq 1$

$$(5.9) \qquad\qquad f_{00}^{(n)} = p_1 p_2 \cdots p_{n-1} q_n$$

and $f_{00}^{(1)} = q_1$. In the special case that the p_k are defined by (2.5) this reduces to $f_{00}^{(n)} = f_n$. Thus E_0 is transient if $\sum f_n < 1$. For a persistent E_0 the mean recurrence time μ_0 of E_0 coincides with the expectation of the distribution $\{f_n\}$. Finally, if E_0 has period t then $f_n = 0$ except when n is a multiple of t. In short, as could be expected, E_0 is under any circumstances of the same type as the recurrent event $\mathcal{E}$ associated with our Markov chain.

(c) In example (4.a) no return to E_2 is possible once the system leaves this state, and so E_2 is transient. A slight refinement of this argument shows that E_6 and E_7 are transient. From theorem 6.4 it follows easily that all other states are ergodic. $\blacktriangleright$

6. IRREDUCIBLE CHAINS. DECOMPOSITIONS

For brevity we say that *two states are of the same type* if they agree in all characteristics defined in the preceding section. In other words, two states of the same type have the same period or they are both aperiodic; both are transient or else both are persistent; in the latter case either both mean recurrence times are infinite, or else both are finite.

The usefulness of our classification depends largely on the fact that for all practical purposes it is always possible to restrict the attention to states of one particular type. The next theorem shows that this is strictly true for irreducible chains.

Theorem 1. *All states of an irreducible chain are of the same type*

Proof. Let E_j and E_k be two arbitrary states of an irreducible chain. In view of the criterion of section 4 every state can be reached from every other state, and so there exist integers r and s such that $p_{jk}^{(r)} = \alpha > 0$ and $p_{kj}^{(s)} = \beta > 0$. Obviously

$$(6.1) \qquad p_{jj}^{(n+r+s)} \geq p_{jk}^{(r)} p_{kk}^{(n)} p_{kj}^{(s)} = \alpha\beta p_{kk}^{(n)}.$$

Here j, k, r, and s are fixed while n is arbitrary. For a transient E_j the left side is the term of a convergent series, and therefore the same is true of $p_{kk}^{(n)}$. Furthermore, if $p_{jj}^{(n)} \to 0$ then also $p_{kk}^{(n)} \to 0$. The same statements remain true when the roles of j and k are interchanged, and so either both E_j and E_k are transient, or neither is; if one is a null state, so is the other.

Finally, suppose that E_j has period t. For $n = 0$ the right side in (6.1) is positive, and hence $r + s$ is a multiple of t. But then the left side vanishes unless n is a multiple of t, and so E_k has a period which is a multiple of t. Interchanging the roles of j and k we see that these states have the same period.   ▶

The importance of theorem 1 becomes apparent in conjunction with

Theorem 2. *For a persistent E_j there exists a unique irreducible closed set C containing E_j and such that for every pair E_i, E_k of states in C*

$$(6.2) \qquad f_{ik} = 1 \qquad and \qquad f_{ki} = 1.$$

In other words: Starting from an arbitrary state E_i in C the system is certain to pass through every other state of C; by the definition of closure no exit from C is possible.

Proof. Let E_k be a state that can be reached from E_j. It is then obviously possible to reach E_k without previously returning to E_j, and we denote the probability of this event by α. Once E_k is reached, the probability of never returning to E_j is $1 - f_{kj}$. The probability that, starting from E_j, the system never returns to E_j is therefore at least $\alpha(1 - f_{kj})$. But for a persistent E_j the probability of no return is zero, and so $f_{kj} = 1$ for every E_k that can be reached from E_j.

Denote by C the aggregate of all states that can be reached from E_j. If E_i and E_k are in C we saw that E_j can be reached from E_k, and hence also E_i can be reached from E_k. Thus every state in C can be reached from every other state in C, and so C is irreducible by the criterion of section 4. It follows that all states in C are persistent, and so every E_i can be assigned the role of E_j in the first part of the argument. This means that $f_{ki} = 1$ for all E_k in C, and so (6.2) is true.   ▶

The preceding theorem implies that the closure of a persistent state is irreducible. This is not necessarily true of transient states.

Example. Suppose that $p_{jk} = 0$ whenever $k \leq j$, but $p_{j,j+1} > 0$. Transitions take place only to higher states, and so no return to any state is possible. Every E_j is transient, and the closure of E_j consists of the states $E_j, E_{j+1}, E_{j+2}, \ldots$, but contains the closed subset obtained by deleting E_j. It follows that there exist no irreducible sets. ▶

The last theorem implies in particular that no transient state can ever be reached from a persistent state. If the chain contains both types of states, this means that the matrix P can be partitioned symbolically in the form (4.1) where the matrix Q corresponds to the persistent states. Needless to say, Q may be further decomposable. But every persistent state belongs to a unique *irreducible* subset, and no transition between these subsets is possible. We recapitulate this in

Theorem 3. *The states of a Markov chain can be divided, in a unique manner, into non-overlapping sets* T, C_1, C_2, ... *such that*
(i) *T consists of all transient states.*
(ii) *If E_j is in C_v then $f_{jk} = 1$ for all E_k in C_v while $f_{jk} = 0$ for all E_k outside C_v.*

This implies that C_v is irreducible and contains only persistent states of the same type. The example above shows that all states can be transient, while example (4.*d*) proves the possibility of infinitely many C_v.

We derive the following theorem as a simple corollary to theorem 2, but it can be proved in other simple ways (see problems 18–20).

Theorem 4. *In a finite chain there exist no null states, and it is impossible that all states are transient.*

Proof. The rows of the matrix P^n add to unity, and as they contain a fixed number of elements it is impossible that $p_{jk}^{(n)} \to 0$ for all pairs j, k. Thus not all states are transient. But a persistent state belongs to an irreducible set C. All states of C are of the same type. The fact that C contains a persistent state and at least one non-null state therefore implies that it contains no null state. ▶

7. INVARIANT DISTRIBUTIONS

Since every persistent state belongs to an irreducible set whose asymptotic behavior can be studied independently of the remaining states, we shall now concentrate on irreducible chains. All states of such a chain are of the same type and we begin with the simplest case, namely chains with finite mean recurrence times μ_j. To avoid trivialities we postpone the discussion of periodic chains to section 9. In other words, we consider now chains whose states are aperiodic and persistent with finite mean recurrence times. Such chains are called *ergodic* (definition 5.3).

Theorem. *In an irreducible ergodic chain the limits*

$$(7.1) \qquad u_k = \lim_{n \to \infty} p_{jk}^{(n)}$$

exist and are independent of the initial state j. *Furthermore* $u_k > 0$,

$$(7.2) \qquad \sum u_k = 1$$

and[11]

$$(7.3) \qquad u_j = \sum_i u_i p_{ij}.$$

Conversely, suppose that the chain is irreducible and aperiodic, and that there exist numbers $u_k \geq 0$ *satisfying* (7.2)–(7.3). *Then the chain is ergodic, the* u_k *are given by* (7.1), *and*

$$(7.4) \qquad u_k = 1/\mu_k$$

where μ_k *is the mean recurrence time of* E_k.

Proof. (*i*) Suppose the chain irreducible and ergodic, and define u_k by (7.4). Theorem 6.2 guarantees that $f_{ij} = 1$ for every pair of states, and so the assertion (7.1) reduces to (5.8). Now

$$(7.5) \qquad p_{ik}^{(n+1)} = \sum_j p_{ij}^{(n)} p_{jk}.$$

As $n \to \infty$ the left side approaches u_k, while the general term of the sum on the right tends to $u_j p_{jk}$. Taking only finitely many terms we infer that

$$(7.6) \qquad u_k \geq \sum_j u_j p_{jk}.$$

For fixed i and n the left sides in (7.5) add to unity, and hence

$$(7.7) \qquad s = \sum u_k \leq 1.$$

Summing over k in (7.6) we get the relation $s \geq s$ in which the inequality sign is impossible. We conclude that in (7.6) the equality sign holds for all k, and so the first part of the theorem is true.

---

[11] If we conceive of $\{u_j\}$ as a row vector, (7.3) can be written in the matrix form $u = uP$.

(ii) Assume $u_k \geq 0$ and (7.2)–(7.3). By induction

$$(7.8) \qquad u_k = \sum_i u_i p_{ik}^{(n)}$$

for every $n > 1$. Since the chain is assumed irreducible all states are of the same type. If they were transient or null states, the right side in (7.8) would tend to 0 as $n \to \infty$, and this cannot be true for all k because the u_k add to unity. Periodic chains being excluded, this means that the chain is ergodic and so the first part of the theorem applies. Thus, letting $n \to \infty$,

$$(7.9) \qquad u_k = \sum_i u_i \mu_k^{-1}.$$

Accordingly, the probability distribution $\{u_k\}$ is proportional to the probability distribution $\{\mu_k^{-1}\}$, and so $u_k = \mu_k^{-1}$ as asserted.   ▶

To appreciate the meaning of the theorem consider the development of the process from an initial distribution $\{a_j\}$. The probability of the state E_k at the nth step is given by

$$(7.10) \qquad a_k^{(n)} = \sum_j a_j p_{jk}^{(n)}$$

[see (3.4)]. In view of (7.1) therefore as $n \to \infty$

$$(7.11) \qquad a_k^{(n)} \to u_k.$$

In other words, whatever the initial distribution, the probability of E_k tends to u_k. On the other hand, when $\{u_k\}$ is the initial distribution (that is, when $a_k = u_k$), then (7.3) implies $a_k^{(1)} = u_k$, and by induction $a_k^{(n)} = u_k$ for all n. Thus an initial distribution satisfying (7.3) perpetuates itself for all times. For this reason it is called invariant.

Definition. *A probability distribution* $\{u_k\}$ *satisfying* (7.3) *is called invariant or stationary (for the given Markov chain).*

The main part of the preceding theorem may now be reformulated as follows.

An irreducible aperiodic chain possesses an invariant probability distribution $\{u_k\}$ *if, and only if, it is ergodic. In this case* $u_k > 0$ *for all* k, *and the absolute probabilities* $a_k^{(n)}$ *tend to* u_k *irrespective of the initial distribution.*

The physical significance of stationarity becomes apparent if we imagine a large number of processes going on simultaneously. To be specific, consider N particles performing independently the same type of random walk. At the nth step the expected number of particles in state E_k equals $Na_k^{(n)}$ which tends to Nu_k. After a sufficiently long time the distribution will be approximately invariant, and the physicist would say that he observes the particles in equilibrium. The distribution $\{u_k\}$ is therefore also called *equilibrium distribution*. Unfortunately this term distracts attention from the important circumstance that it refers to a so-called *macroscopic equilibrium*, that is, an equilibrium maintained by a large number of transitions in opposite directions. The individual particle exhibits no tendency to equilibrium, and our limit theorem has no implications for the individual process. Typical in this respect is the symmetric random walk discussed in chapter III. If a large number of particles perform independently such random walks starting at the origin, then at any time roughly half of them will be to the right, the other half to the left of the origin. But this does not mean that the majority of the particles spends half their time on the positive side. On the contrary, the arc sine laws show that the majority of the particles spend a disproportionately large part of their time on the same side of the origin, and in this sense *the majority is not representative of the ensemble*. This example is radical in that it involves infinite mean recurrence times. With ergodic chains the chance fluctuations are milder, but for practical purposes they will exhibit the same character whenever the recurrence times have very large (or infinite) variances. Many protracted discussions and erroneous conclusions could be avoided by a proper understanding of the statistical nature of the "tendency toward equilibrium."

In the preceding theorem we assumed the chain irreducible and aperiodic, and it is pertinent to ask to what extent these assumptions are essential. A perusal of the proof will show that we have really proved more than is stated in the theorem. In particular we have, in passing, obtained the following criterion applicable to arbitrary chains (including periodic and reducible chains).

Criterion. *If a chain possesses an invariant probability distribution $\{u_k\}$, then $u_k = 0$ for each E_k that is either transient or a persistent null state.*

In other words, $u_k > 0$ implies that E_k is persistent and has a finite mean recurrence time, but E_k may be periodic.

Proof. We saw that the stationarity of $\{u_k\}$ implies (7.8). If k is either transient or a null state, then $p_{jk}^{(n)} \to 0$ for all j, and so $u_k = 0$ as asserted. ▶

As for periodic chains, we anticipate the result proved in section 9 that *a unique invariant probability distribution $\{u_k\}$ exists for every irreducible chain whose states have finite mean recurrence times*. Periodic chains were excluded from the theorems only because the simple limit relations (7.1) and (7.11) take on a less attractive form which detracts from the essential point without really affecting it.

Examples. (*a*) Chains with several irreducible components may admit of several stationary solutions. A trite, but typical, example is presented by the random walk with two absorbing states E_0 and E_ρ [example (2.*b*)]. Every probability distribution of the form $(\alpha, 0, 0, \ldots, 0, 1 - \alpha)$, attributing positive weights only to E_0 and E_ρ, is stationary.

(*b*) Given a matrix of transition probabilities p_{jk} it is not always easy to decide whether an invariant distribution $\{u_k\}$ exists. A notable exception occurs when

$$(7.12) \qquad p_{jk} = 0 \qquad for \qquad |k - j| > 1,$$

that is, when all non-zero elements of the matrix are on the main diagonal or on a line directly adjacent to it. With the states numbered starting with 0 the defining relations (7.3) take on the form

$$(7.13) \qquad \begin{aligned} u_0 &= p_{00}u_0 + p_{10}u_1 \\ u_1 &= p_{01}u_0 + p_{11}u_1 + p_{21}u_2, \end{aligned}$$

and so on. To avoid trivialities we assume that $p_{j,j+1} > 0$ and $p_{j,j-1} > 0$ for all j, but nothing is assumed about the diagonal elements p_{jj}. The equations (7.13) can be solved successively for $u_1, u_2, \ldots$. Remembering that the row sums of the matrix P add to unity we get

$$(7.14) \qquad u_1 = \frac{p_{01}}{p_{10}} u_0, \qquad u_2 = \frac{p_{01}p_{12}}{p_{10}p_{21}} u_0, \qquad u_3 = \frac{p_{01}p_{12}p_{23}}{p_{10}p_{21}p_{32}} u_0,$$

and so on. The resulting (finite or infinite) sequence $u_0, u_1, \ldots$ represents the unique solution of (7.13). To make it a probability distribution the norming factor u_0 must be chosen so that $\sum u_k = 1$. Such a choice is possible if, and only if,

$$(7.15) \qquad \sum \frac{p_{01}p_{12}p_{23} \cdots p_{k-1,k}}{p_{10}p_{21}p_{32} \cdots p_{k,k-1}} < \infty.$$

This, then, is the necessary and sufficient condition for the existence of an invariant probability distribution; if it exists, it is necessarily unique. [If (7.15) is false, (7.12) is a so-called invariant measure. See section 11.]

In example (8.*d*) we shall derive a similar criterion to test whether the states are persistent. The following three examples illustrate the applicability of our criterion.

(c) *Reflecting barriers.* The example (2.c) (with $\rho \leq \infty$) represents the special case of the preceding example with $p_{j,j+1} = p$ for all $j < \rho$ and $p_{j,j-1} = q$ for all $j > 0$. When the number of states is finite there exists an invariant distribution with u_k proportional to $(q/p)^k$. With infinitely many states the convergence of (7.15) requires that $p < q$, and in this case $u_0 = (1 - p/q)(p/q)^k$. From the general theory of random walks it is clear that the states are transient when $p > q$, and persistent null states when $p = q$. This will follow also from the criterion in example (8.d).

(d) *The Ehrenfest model of diffusion.* For the matrix of example (2.e) the solution (7.14) reduces to

$$(7.16) \qquad\qquad u_k = \binom{\rho}{k} u_0, \qquad\qquad k = 0, \ldots, \rho.$$

The binomial coefficients are the terms in the binomial expansion for $(1+1)^\rho$, and to obtain a probability distribution we must therefore put $u_0 = 2^{-\rho}$. The chain has period 2, the states have finite mean recurrence times, and *the binomial distribution with $p = \frac{1}{2}$ is invariant.*

This result can be interpreted as follows: Whatever the initial number of molecules in the first container, after a long time the probability of finding k molecules in it is nearly the same as if the a molecules had been distributed at random, each molecule having probability $\frac{1}{2}$ to be in the first container. This is a typical example of how our result gains physical significance.

For large a the normal approximation to the binomial distribution shows that, once the limiting distribution is approximately established, we are practically certain to find about one-half the molecules in each container. To the physicist $a = 10^6$ is a small number, indeed. But even with $a = 10^6$ molecules the probability of finding more than 505,000 molecules in one container (density fluctuation of about 1 per cent) is of the order of magnitude 10^{-23}. With $a = 10^8$ a density fluctuation of one in a thousand has the same negligible probability. It is true that the system will occasionally pass into very improbable states, but their recurrence times are fantastically large as compared to the recurrence times of states near the equilibrium. Physical irreversibility manifests itself in the fact that, whenever the system is in a state far removed from equilibrium, it is much more likely to move toward equilibrium than in the opposite direction.

(e) *The Bernoulli-Laplace model of diffusion.* For the matrix with elements (2.1) we get from (7.14)

$$(7.17) \qquad\qquad u_k = \binom{\rho}{k}^2 u_0, \qquad\qquad k = 0, \ldots, \rho.$$

The binomial coefficients add to $\binom{2\rho}{\rho}$ [see II,(12.11)], and hence

(7.18)
$$u_k = \binom{\rho}{k}^2 \Big/ \binom{2\rho}{\rho}$$

represents *an invariant distribution*. It is a hypergeometric distribution (see II,6). This means that in the state of equilibrium the distribution of colors in each container is the same as if the ρ particles in it had been chosen at random from a collection of ρ black and ρ white particles.

(f) In example (2.l) the defining relations for an invariant probability distribution are

(7.19a)
$$u_k = p_k u_{k-1} \qquad\qquad k = 1, 2, \ldots$$

(7.19b)
$$u_0 = q_1 u_0 + q_2 u_1 + q_3 u_2 + \cdots .$$

From (7.19a) we get

(7.20)
$$u_k = p_1 \cdots p_k u_0,$$

and it is now easily seen that the first k terms on the right in (7.19b) add to $u_0 - u_k$. Thus (7.19a) is automatically satisfied whenever $u_k \to 0$, and *an invariant probability distribution exists if, and only if,*

(7.21)
$$\sum_k p_1 p_2 \cdots p_k < \infty .$$

[See also examples (8.e) and (11.c).]

(g) *Recurrent events.* In example (2.k) the conditions for an invariant probability distribution reduce to

(7.22)
$$u_k = u_{k+1} + f_{k+1} u_0 \qquad\qquad k = 0, 1, \ldots .$$

Adding over $k = 0, 1, \ldots$ we get

(7.23)
$$u_n = r_n u_0, \qquad \text{where} \quad r_n = f_{n+1} + f_{n+2} + \cdots .$$

Now $r_0 + r_1 \cdots = \mu$ is the expectation of the distributions. *An invariant probability distribution is given by* $u_n = r_n/\mu$ *if* $\mu < \infty$; no such probability distribution exists when $\mu = \infty$.

It will be recalled that our Markov chain is connected with a recurrent event $\mathcal{E}$ with recurrence time distribution $\{f_k\}$. In the special case $p_r = r_r/r_{k-1}$ the chain of the preceding example is connected with the same recurrent event $\mathcal{E}$ and in this case (7.20) and (7.23) are equivalent. Hence *the invariant distributions are the same.* In the language of queuing theory one should say that the *spent waiting time and the residual waiting time tend to the same distribution*, namely $\{r_n/\mu\}$.

We derived the basic limit theorems for Markov chains from the theory of recurrent events. We now see that, conversely, recurrent events could be treated as special Markov chains. [See also example (11.*d*).]

(*h*) *Doubly stochastic matrices.* A stochastic matrix P is called doubly stochastic if not only the row sums but also the column sums are unity. If such a chain contains only a finite number, a, of states then $u_k = a^{-1}$ represents an invariant distribution. This means that in macroscopic equilibrium all states are equally probable.   ▶

8. TRANSIENT STATES

We saw in section 6 that the persistent states of any Markov chain may be divided into non-overlapping closed irreducible sets $C_1, C_2, \ldots$. In general there exists also a non-empty class T of transient states. When the system starts from a transient state two contingencies arise: Either the system ultimately passes into one of the closed sets C_v and stays there forever, or else the system remains forever in the transient set T. Our main problem consists in determining the corresponding probabilities. Its solution will supply a criterion for deciding whether a state is persistent or transient.

Examples. (*a*) *Martingales.* A chain is called a martingale if for every j the expectation of the probability distribution $\{p_{jk}\}$ equals j, that is, if

$$(8.1) \qquad \sum_k p_{jk} k = j.$$

Consider a finite chain with states $E_0, \ldots, E_a$. Letting $j = 0$ and $j = a$ in (8.1) we see that $p_{00} = p_{aa} = 1$, and so E_0 and E_a are absorbing. To avoid trivialities we assume that the chain contains no further closed sets. It follows that the interior states $E_1, \ldots, E_{a-1}$ are transient, and so the process will ultimately terminate either at E_0 or at E_a. From (8.1) we infer by induction that for all n

$$(8.2) \qquad \sum_{k=0}^{a} p_{ik}^{(n)} k = i.$$

But $p_{ik}^{(n)} \to 0$ for every transient E_k, and so (8.2) implies that for all $i > 0$

$$(8.3) \qquad p_{ia}^{(n)} \to i/a.$$

In other words, if the process starts with E_i *the probabilities of ultimate absorption at E_0 and E_a are $1 - i/a$ and i/a, respectively.*

(b) *Special cases.* The chains of the examples from genetics (2.*h*) and (2.*i*) are of the form discussed in the preceding example with $a = N$ and $a = 2N$, respectively. Given the initial state E_i, the probability of ultimate fixation at E_0 is therefore $1 - i/a$.

(c) Consider a chain with states $E_0, E_1, \ldots$ such that E_0 is absorbing while from other states E_j transitions are possible to the right neighbor E_{j+1} and to E_0, but to no other state. For $j \geq 1$ we put

$$(8.4) \qquad p_{j0} = \epsilon_j, \qquad p_{j,j+1} = 1 - \epsilon_j$$

where $\epsilon_j > 0$. With the initial state E_j the probability of no absorption at E_0 in n trials equals

$$(8.5) \qquad (1-\epsilon_j)(1-\epsilon_{j+1}) \cdots (1-\epsilon_{j+n-1}).$$

This product decreases with increasing n and hence it approaches a limit λ_j. We infer that the probability of ultimate absorption equals $1 - \lambda_j$ while with probability λ_j the system remains forever at transient states. In order that $\lambda_j > 0$ it is necessary and sufficient that $\sum \epsilon_k < \infty$. ▶

The study of the transient states depends on the submatrix of P obtained by deleting all rows and columns corresponding to persistent states and retaining only the elements p_{jk} for which both E_j and E_k are transient. The row sums of this submatrix are no longer unity, and it is convenient to introduce the

Definition. *A matrix Q with elements q_{ik} is substochastic if $q_{ik} \geq 0$ and all row sums are ≤ 1.*

In the sense of this definition every stochastic matrix is substochastic and, conversely, every substochastic matrix can be enlarged to a stochastic matrix by adding an absorbing state E_0. (In other words, we add a top row $1, 0, 0, \ldots$ and a column whose elements are the defects of the rows of Q.) It is therefore obvious that what was said about stochastic matrices applies without essential change also to substochastic matrices. In particular, the recursion relation (3.2) defines the nth power Q^n as the matrix with elements

$$(8.6) \qquad q_{ik}^{(n+1)} = \sum_{\nu} q_{i\nu} q_{\nu k}^{(n)}.$$

Denote by $\sigma_i^{(n)}$ the sum of the elements in the ith row of Q^n. Then for $n \geq 1$

$$(8.7) \qquad \sigma_i^{(n+1)} = \sum_{\nu} q_{i\nu} \sigma_{\nu}^{(n)},$$

and this relation remains valid also for $n = 0$ provided we put $\sigma_v^{(0)} = 1$ for all v. The fact that Q is substochastic means that $\sigma_i^{(1)} \leq \sigma_i^{(0)}$, and from (8.7) we see now by induction that $\sigma_i^{(n+1)} \leq \sigma_i^{(n)}$. For fixed i therefore the sequence $\{\sigma_i^{(n)}\}$ decreases monotonically to a limit $\sigma_i \geq 0$, and clearly

$$(8.8) \qquad\qquad \sigma_i = \sum_v q_{iv}\sigma_v.$$

The whole theory of the transient states depends on the solutions of this system of equations. In some cases there exists no non-zero solution (that is, we have $\sigma_i = 0$ for all i). In others, there may exist infinitely many linearly independent solutions, that is, different sequences of numbers satisfying

$$(8.9) \qquad\qquad x_i = \sum_v q_{iv}x_v.$$

Our first problem is to characterize the particular solution $\{\sigma_i\}$. We are interested only in solutions $\{x_i\}$ such that $0 \leq x_i \leq 1$ for all i. This can be rewritten in the form $0 \leq x_i \leq \sigma_i^{(0)}$; comparing (8.9) with (8.7) we see inductively that $x_i \leq \sigma_i^{(n)}$ for all n, and so

$$(8.10) \qquad 0 \leq x_i \leq 1 \qquad implies \qquad x_i \leq \sigma_i \leq 1.$$

The solution $\{\sigma_i\}$ will be called *maximal*, but it must be borne in mind that in many cases $\sigma_i = 0$ for all i. We summarize this result in the following

Lemma. *For a substochastic matrix Q the linear system (8.9) possesses a maximal solution $\{\sigma_i\}$ with the property (8.10). These σ_i represent the limits of the row sums of Q^n.*

We now identify Q with the submatrix of P obtained by retaining only the elements p_{jk} for which E_j and E_k are transient. The linear system (8.9) may then be written in the form

$$(8.11) \qquad\qquad x_i = \sum_T p_{iv}x_v, \qquad\qquad E_i \in T,$$

the summation extending only over those v for which E_v belongs to the class T of transient states. With this identification $\sigma_i^{(n)}$ is the probability that, with the initial state E_i, no transition to a persistent state occurs during the first n trials. Hence the limit σ_i equals the probability that no such transition ever occurs. We have thus

Theorem 1. *The probabilities that the system stays forever among the transient states are given by the maximal solution of (8.11).*

The same argument leads to the

Criterion. *In an irreducible[12] Markov chain with states* $E_0, E_1, \ldots$ *the state* E_0 *is persistent if, and only if, the linear system*

$$(8.12) \qquad\qquad x_i = \sum_{v=1}^{\infty} p_{iv} x_v, \qquad\qquad i \geq 1$$

admits of no solution with $0 \leq x_i \leq 1$ *except* $x_i = 0$ *for all* i.

Proof. We identify the matrix Q of the lemma with the submatrix of P obtained by deleting the row and column corresponding to E_0. The argument used for theorem 1 shows that σ_i is the probability that (with E_i as initial state) the system remains forever among the states $E_1, E_2, \ldots$. But if E_0 is persistent the probability f_{i0} of reaching E_0 equals 1, and hence $\sigma_i = 0$ for all i. ▶

Examples. (*d*) As in example (7.*b*) we consider a chain with states $E_0, E_1, \ldots$ such that

$$(8.13) \qquad\qquad p_{jk} = 0 \qquad when \qquad |k - j| > 1.$$

To avoid trivialities we assume that $p_{j,j+1} \neq 0$ and $p_{j,j-1} \neq 0$. The chain is irreducible because every state can be reached from every other state. Thus all states are of the same type, and it suffices to test the character of E_0. The equations (8.12) reduce to the recursive system

$$(8.14) \qquad\qquad x_1 = p_{11} x_1 + p_{12} x_2$$

$$p_{j,j-1}(x_j - x_{j-1}) = p_{j,j+1}(x_j - x_{j+1}), \qquad\qquad j \geq 2.$$

Thus

$$(8.15) \qquad\qquad x_j - x_{j+1} = \frac{p_{21} p_{32} \cdots p_{j,j-1}}{p_{23} p_{34} \cdots p_{j,j+1}}(x_1 - x_2).$$

Since $p_{10} > 0$ we have $x_1 - x_2 > 0$, and so a bounded non-negative solution $\{x_j\}$ exists if, and only if,

$$(8.16) \qquad\qquad \sum \frac{p_{21} \cdots p_{j,j-1}}{p_{23} \cdots p_{j,j+1}} < \infty.$$

The chain is persistent if, and only if, the series diverges. In the special case of random walks we have $p_{j,j+1} = p$ and $p_{j,j-1} = q$ for all $j > 1$, and we see again that the states are persistent if, and only if, $p \leq q$.

---

[12] Irreducibility is assumed only to avoid notational complications. It represents no restriction because it suffices to consider the closure of E_0. Incidentally, the criterion applies also to periodic chains.

(This chain may be interpreted as a random walk on the line with probabilities varying from place to place.)

(e) For the matrix of example (2.l) the equations (8.12) reduce to

$$(8.17) \qquad\qquad x_j = p_{j+1}x_{j+1}$$

and a bounded positive solution exists if, and only if, the infinite product $p_1 p_2 \cdots$ converges. If the chain is associated with a recurrent event $\mathcal{E}$, the p_k are given by (2.5) and the product converges if, and only if, $\sum f_i < \infty$. Thus (as could be anticipated) the chain and $\mathcal{E}$ are either both transient, or both persistent.   ▶

To answer the last question proposed at the beginning of this section, denote again by T the class of transient states and let C be any *closed* set of persistent states. (It is not required that C be irreducible.) Denote by y_i *the probability of ultimate absorption in* C, given the initial state E_i. We propose to show that the y_i satisfy the system of inhomogeneous equations

$$(8.18) \qquad\qquad y_i = \sum_T p_{iv}y_v + \sum_C p_{iv}, \qquad\qquad E_i \in T,$$

the summations extending over those v for which $E_v \in T$ and $E_v \in C$, respectively. The system (8.18) may admit of several independent solutions, but the following proof will show that among them there exists a *minimal* solution defined in the obvious manner by analogy with (8.10).

Theorem 2. *The probabilities y_i of ultimate absorption in the closed persistent set C are given by the minimal non-negative solution of* (8.18).

Proof. Denote by $y_i^{(n)}$ the probability that an absorption in C takes place at or before the nth step. Then for $n \geq 1$ clearly

$$(8.19) \qquad\qquad y_i^{(n+1)} = \sum_T p_{iv}y_v^{(n)} + \sum_C p_{iv}$$

and this is true also for $n = 0$ provided we put $y_v^{(0)} = 0$ for all v. For fixed i the sequence $\{y_i^{(n)}\}$ is non-decreasing, but it remains bounded by 1. The limits obviously satisfy (8.18). Conversely, if $\{y_i\}$ is any non-negative solution of (8.18) we have $y_i \geq y_i^{(1)}$ because the second sum in (8.18) equals $y_i^{(1)}$. By induction $y_i \geq y_i^{(n)}$ for all n, and so the limits of $y_i^{(n)}$ represent a minimal solution.   ▶

For an illustration see example (c).

9. PERIODIC CHAINS

Periodic chains present no difficulties and no unexpected new features. They were excluded in the formulation of the main theorem in section 7 only because they are of secondary interest and their description requires disproportionately many words. The discussion of this section is given for the sake of completeness rather than for its intrinsic interest. The results of this section will not be used in the sequel.

The simplest example of a chain with period 3 is a chain with three states in which only the transitions $E_1 \to E_2 \to E_3 \to E_1$ are possible. Then

$$P = \begin{pmatrix} 0 & 1 & 0 \\ 0 & 0 & 1 \\ 1 & 0 & 0 \end{pmatrix}, \qquad P^2 = \begin{pmatrix} 0 & 0 & 1 \\ 1 & 0 & 0 \\ 0 & 1 & 0 \end{pmatrix}, \qquad P^3 = \begin{pmatrix} 1 & 0 & 0 \\ 0 & 1 & 0 \\ 0 & 0 & 1 \end{pmatrix}.$$

We shall now show that this example is in many respects typical.

Consider an irreducible chain with finitely or infinitely many states $E_1, E_2, \ldots$. By theorem 6.1 all states have the same period t (we assume $t > 1$). Since in an irreducible chain every state can be reached from every other state there exist for every state E_k two integers a and b such that $p_{1k}^{(a)} > 0$ and $p_{k1}^{(b)} > 0$. But $p_{11}^{(a+b)} \geq p_{1k}^{(a)} p_{k1}^{(b)}$ and so $a + b$ must be divisible by the period t. Keeping b fixed we conclude that each integer a for which $p_{1k}^{(a)} > 0$ is of the form $\alpha + \nu t$ where α is a fixed integer with $0 \leq \alpha < t$. The integer α is characteristic of the state E_k and so all states can be divided into t mutually exclusive classes $G_0, \ldots, G_{t-1}$ such that

(9.1)   if $E_k \in G_\alpha$ then $p_{1k}^{(n)} = 0$ unless $n = \alpha + \nu t$.

We imagine the classes $G_0, \ldots, G_{t-1}$ ordered cyclically so that G_{t-1} is the left neighbor of G_0.

It is now obvious that *one-step* transitions are possible only to a state in the neighboring class to the right, and hence a path of t steps leads always to a state of the same class. This implies that in the Markov chain with transition matrix P^t each class G_α forms a closed set.[13] This

---

[13] When $t = 3$ there are three classes and with the symbolic partitioning introduced in section 4 the matrix P takes on the form

$$\begin{pmatrix} 0 & A & 0 \\ 0 & 0 & B \\ C & 0 & 0 \end{pmatrix}$$

where A represents the matrix of transition probabilities from G_0 to G_1, and so on.

set is irreducible because in the original chain every state can be reached from any other state and within the same class the required number of steps is necessarily divisible by t. We have thus proved the

Theorem. *In an irreducible chain with period t the states can be divided into t mutually exclusive classes $G_0, \ldots, G_{t-1}$ such that (9.1) holds and a one-step transition always leads to a state in the right neighboring class (in particular, from G_{t-1} to G_0). In the chain with matrix P^t each class G_α corresponds to an irreducible closed set.*

Using this theorem it is now easy to describe the asymptotic behavior of the transition probabilities $p_{jk}^{(n)}$. We know that $p_{jk}^{(n)} \to 0$ if E_k is either transient or a persistent null state, and also that all states are of the same type (section 6). We need therefore consider only the case where each state E_k has a finite mean recurrence time μ_k. Relative to the chain with matrix P^t the state E_k has the mean recurrence time μ_k/t, and relative to this chain each class G_α is ergodic. Thus, if E_j belongs to G_α

$$(9.2) \qquad \lim_{n \to \infty} p_{jk}^{(nt)} = \begin{cases} t/\mu_k & \text{if } E_k \in G_\alpha \\ 0 & \text{otherwise} \end{cases}$$

and the weights t/μ_k define a probability distribution on the states of the class G_α (see the theorem of section 7). Since there are t such classes *the numbers $u_k = 1/\mu_k$ define a probability distribution on the integers* as was the case for aperiodic chains. We show that this distribution is invariant. For this purpose we need relations corresponding to (9.2) when the exponent is not divisible by the period t.

We start from the fundamental relation

$$(9.3) \qquad p_{jk}^{(nt+\beta)} = \sum_v p_{jv}^{(\beta)} p_{vk}^{(nt)}.$$

The factor $p_{jv}^{(\beta)}$ vanishes except when E_v is in $G_{\alpha+\beta}$. (When $\alpha + \beta \geq t$ read $G_{\alpha+\beta-t}$ for $G_{\alpha+\beta}$.) In this case $p_{vk}^{(nt)}$ vanishes unless E_k is in $G_{\alpha+\beta}$, and hence for fixed β and E_j in G_α

$$(9.4) \qquad \lim_{n \to \infty} p_{jk}^{(nt+\beta)} = \begin{cases} t/\mu_k & \text{if } E_k \in G_{\alpha+\beta} \\ 0 & \text{otherwise.} \end{cases}$$

We now rewrite (9.3) in the form

$$(9.5) \qquad p_{ik}^{(nt+1)} = \sum_v p_{iv}^{(nt)} p_{vk}.$$

Consider an arbitrary state E_k and let G_ρ be the class to which it belongs. Then $p_{vk} = 0$ unless $E_v \in G_{\rho-1}$, and so both sides in (9.5) vanish unless

$E_i \in G_{\rho-1}$. In this case $p_{ik}^{(nt+1)} \to tu_k$ whence

(9.6) $$u_k = \sum_v u_v p_{vk}.$$

Since E_k is an arbitrary state we have proved that *the probability distribution* $\{u_k\}$ *is invariant.*

10. APPLICATION TO CARD SHUFFLING

A deck of N cards numbered $1, 2, \ldots, N$ can be arranged in $N!$ different orders, and each represents a possible state of the system. Every particular shuffling operation effects a transition from the existing state into some other state. For example, "cutting" will change the order $(1, 2, \ldots, N)$ into one of the N cyclically equivalent orders $(r, r+1, \ldots, N, 1, 2, \ldots, r - 1)$. The same operation applied to the inverse order $(N, N - 1, \ldots, 1)$ will produce $(N - r + 1, N - r, \ldots, 1, N, N - 1, \ldots, N - r + 2)$. In other words, we conceive of each particular shuffling operation as a transformation $E_j \to E_k$. If *exactly* the same operation is repeated, the system will pass (starting from the given state E_j) through a well-defined succession of states, and after a finite number of steps the original order will be re-established. From then on the same succession of states will recur periodically. For most operations the period will be rather small, and in *no* case can all states be reached by this procedure.[14] For example, a perfect "lacing" would change a deck of $2m$ cards from $(1, \ldots, 2m)$ into $(1, m+1, 2, m+2, \ldots, m, 2m)$. With six cards four applications of this operation will re-establish the original order. With ten cards the initial order will reappear after six operations, so that repeated perfect lacing of a deck of ten cards can produce only six out of the $10! = 3,628,800$ possible orders.

In practice the player may wish to vary the operation, and at any rate, accidental variations will be introduced by chance. We shall assume that we can account for the player's habits and the influence of chance variations by assuming that every particular operation has a certain probability (possibly zero). We need assume nothing about the numerical values of these probabilities but shall suppose that the player operates without regard to the past and does not know the order of the cards.[15] This implies that the successive operations correspond to independent trials with fixed probabilities; for the actual deck of cards we then have a Markov chain.

---

[14] In the language of group theory this amounts to saying that the permutation group is not cyclic and can therefore not be generated by a single operation.

[15] This assumption corresponds to the usual situation at bridge. It is easy to devise more complicated shuffling techniques in which the operations depend on previous operations and the final outcome is not a Markov chain [cf. example (13.e)].

We now show that the matrix P of transition probabilities is *doubly stochastic* [example (7.*h*)]. In fact, if an operation changes a state (order of cards) E_j to E_k, then there exists another state E_r which it will change into E_j. This means that the elements of the *j*th column of P are identical with the elements of the *j*th row, except that they appear in a different order. All column sums are therefore unity.

It follows that no state can be transient. *If the chain is irreducible and aperiodic, then in the limit all states become equally probable.* In other words, *any* kind of shuffling will do, provided only that it produces an irreducible and aperiodic chain. It is safe to assume that this is usually the case. Suppose, however, that the deck contains an even number of cards and the procedure consists in dividing them equally into two parts and shuffling them separately by any method. If the two parts are put together in their original order, then the Markov chain is reducible (since not every state can be reached from every other state). If the order of the two parts is inverted, the chain will have period 2. Thus both contingencies can arise in theory, but hardly in practice, since chance precludes perfect regularity.

It is seen that continued shuffling may reasonably be expected to produce perfect "randomness" and to eliminate all traces of the original order. It should be noted, however, that the number of operations required for this purpose is extremely large.[16]

*11. INVARIANT MEASURES.   RATIO LIMIT THEOREMS

In this section we consider an irreducible chain with persistent null states. Our main objective is to derive analogues to the results obtained in section 7 for chains whose states have finite mean recurrence times. An outstanding property of such chains is the existence of an invariant (or stationary) probability distribution defined by

$$(11.1) \qquad u_k = \sum_v u_v p_{vk}.$$

We know that no such invariant probability distribution exists when the mean recurrence times are infinite, but we shall show that the linear

---

* The next two sections treat topics playing an important role in contemporary research, but the results will not be used in this book.

[16] For an analysis of unbelievably poor results of shuffling in records of extrasensory perception experiments, see W. Feller, *Statistical aspects of ESP*, Journal of Parapsychology, vol. 4 (1940), pp. 271–298. In their amazing *A review of Dr. Feller's critique, ibid.*, pp. 299–319, J. A. Greenwood and C. E. Stuart try to show that these results are due to chance. Both their arithmetic and their experiments have a distinct tinge of the supernatural.

system (11.1) still admits of a positive solution $\{u_k\}$ such that $\sum u_k = \infty$. Such $\{u_k\}$ is called *an invariant (or stationary) measure.* If the chain is irreducible and persistent, the invariant measure is unique up to an arbitrary norming constant.

Examples. (*a*) Suppose that the matrix P of transition probabilities is doubly stochastic, that is, the column sums as well as the row sums are unity. Then (11.1) holds with $u_k = 1$ for all k. This fact is expressed by saying that the *uniform measure is invariant.*

(*b*) *Random walks.* An interesting special case is provided by the unrestricted random walk on the line. We number the states in their natural order from $-\infty$ to ∞. This precludes exhibiting the transition probabilities in the standard form of a matrix, but the necessary changes of notation are obvious. If the transitions to the right and left neighbors have probabilities p and q, respectively, the system (11.1) takes on the form

$$u_k = pu_{k-1} + qu_{k+1}, \qquad -\infty < k < \infty.$$

The states are persistent only if $p = q = \frac{1}{2}$, and in this case $u_k = 1$ represents the only positive solution. This solution remains valid if $p \neq q$, except that it is no longer unique; a second non-negative solution is represented by $u_k = (p/q)^k$. This example proves that an invariant measure may exist also for transient chains, but it need not be unique. We shall return to this interesting point in the next section.

The invariant $\{u_j\}$ measure can be interpreted intuitively if one considers simultaneously infinitely many processes subject to the same matrix P of transition probabilities. For each j define a random variable $\mathbf{N}_j$ with a Poisson distribution with mean u_j, and consider $\mathbf{N}_j$ independent processes starting from E_j. We do this simultaneously for all states, assuming that all these processes are mutually independent. It is not difficult to show that at any given time with probability one only finitely many processes will be found in any given state E_k. The number of processes found at the nth step in state E_k is therefore a random variable $\mathbf{X}_k^{(n)}$ and *the invariance of $\{u_k\}$ implies that* $\mathbf{E}\{\mathbf{X}_k^{(n)}\} = u_k$ *for all* n. (Cf. problem 29.)

(*c*) In example (7.*f*) we found that an invariant probability distribution exists only if the series (7.21) converges. In case of divergence (7.20) still represents an invariant measure provided only that $u_k \to 0$, which is the same as $p_1 p_2 \cdots p_k \to 0$. No invariant measure exists when the product $p_1 \cdots p_k$ remains bounded away from 0, for example, when $p_k = 1 - (k+1)^{-1}$. In this case the chain is transient.

(*d*) In example (7.*g*) the relations (7.23) define an invariant measure even when $\mu = \infty$. ▶

In ergodic chains the probabilities $p_{jk}^{(n)}$ tend to the term u_k of the invariant probability distribution. For persistent null chains we shall prove a weaker version of this result, namely that as $N \to \infty$ for all E_α and E_β

$$\text{(11.2)} \qquad \frac{\sum_{n=0}^{N} p_{\alpha i}^{(n)}}{\sum_{n=0}^{N} p_{\beta j}^{(n)}} \to \frac{u_i}{u_j}.$$

The sums on the left represent the expected numbers of passages, in the first N trials, through E_i and E_j. Roughly speaking (11.2) states that these expectations are asymptotically independent of the initial states E_α and E_β, and stand in the same proportion as the corresponding terms of the invariant measures. Thus the salient facts are the same as in the case of ergodic chains, although the situation is more complicated. On the other hand, periodic chains now require no special consideration. [In fact (11.2) covers *all* persistent chains. For an ergodic chain the numerator on the left is $\sim N u_i$.]

Relations of the form (11.2) are called *ratio limit theorems*. We shall derive (11.2) from a stronger result which was until recently considered a more complicated refinement. Our proofs will be based on considering only paths avoiding a particular state E_r. Following Chung we call the forbidden state E_r *taboo*, and the transition probabilities to it are *taboo probabilities*.

Definition. *Let E_r be an arbitrary, but fixed, state. For $E_k \neq E_r$ and $n \geq 1$ we define $_r p_{jk}^{(n)}$ as the probability that, starting from E_j, the state E_k is entered at the nth step without a previous passage through E_r.*

Here E_j is allowed to coincide with E_r. We extend this definition to $E_k = E_r$ and $n = 0$ in the natural way by

$$\text{(11.3)} \qquad\qquad _r p_{jr}^{(n)} = 0 \qquad\qquad n \geq 1$$

and

$$\text{(11.4)} \qquad\qquad _r p_{jk}^{(0)} = \begin{cases} 1 & \text{if } E_j = E_k \\ 0 & \text{otherwise.} \end{cases}$$

In analytical terms we have for $n \geq 0$ and $E_k \neq E_r$

$$\text{(11.5)} \qquad\qquad _r p_{jk}^{(n+1)} = \sum_v {_r p_{jv}^{(n)}} p_{vk}.$$

In fact, for $n = 0$ the sum on the right reduces to a single term, namely p_{jk}. When $n \geq 1$ the term corresponding to $v = r$ vanishes by virtue of (11.3), and so (11.5) is equivalent to the original definition.

Introducing E_r as taboo state amounts to considering the original Markov process only until E_r is entered for the first time. In an irreducible persistent chain the state E_r is entered with probability one from any initial state E_j. It follows that in the chain with taboo E_r the successive passages through the initial state E_j form a *transient* recurrent event; and the passages through any other state $E_k \neq E_r$ form a delayed transient recurrent event. Thus for $E_k \neq E_r$

$$(11.6) \qquad \sum_{n=0}^{\infty} {}_r p_{jk}^{(n)} = {}_r \pi_{jk} < \infty$$

by the basic theorem 2 of XIII,3. For $E_k = E_r$ the summands with $n \geq 1$ vanish and the sum reduces to 1 or 0 according as $j = r$ or $j \neq r$.

We are now in a position to prove the existence of an invariant measure, that is, of numbers u_k satisfying (11.1). This will not be used in the proof of theorem 2.

Theorem 1. *If the chain is irreducible and persistent, the numbers*

$$(11.7) \qquad u_k = {}_r \pi_{rk}$$

represent an invariant measure; furthermore $u_k > 0$ for all k and $u_r = 1$.
Conversely, if $u_k \geq 0$ for all k and (11.1) holds, then there exists a constant λ such that $u_k = \lambda \cdot {}_r \pi_{rk}$.

Here E_r is arbitrary, but the asserted uniqueness implies that the sequences $\{u_k\}$ obtained by varying r differ only by proportionality factors. Note that the theorem and its proof cover also chains with finite mean recurrence times.

Proof. If $k \neq r$ we use (11.5) with $j = r$. Summing over $n = 0$, 1, ... we get

$$(11.8) \qquad {}_r \pi_{rk} = \sum_v {}_r \pi_{rv} p_{vk},$$

and so the numbers (11.7) satisfy the defining equations (11.1) at least when $k \neq r$. For $j = k = r$ it is clear that

$$(11.9) \qquad \sum_v {}_r p_{rv}^{(n)} p_{vr} = f_{rr}^{(n+1)}$$

equals the probability that (in the original chain) the first return to E_r occurs at the $(n+1)$st step. Since the chain is irreducible and persistent these probabilities add to unity. Summing (11.9) over $n = 0, 1, \ldots$ we get therefore

(11.10) $$\sum_v {}_r\pi_{rv}p_{vr} = 1.$$

But by definition ${}_r\pi_{rr} = 1$, and so (11.8) is true also for $k = r$. Accordingly (11.7) represents an invariant measure.

Next consider an arbitrary non-negative invariant measure $\{u_k\}$. It is clear from the definition (11.1) that if $u_k = 0$ for some k, then $u_v = 0$ for all v such that $p_{vk} > 0$. By induction it follows that $u_v = 0$ for every v such that E_k can be reached from E_v. As the chain is irreducible this implies that $u_v = 0$ for all v. Thus an invariant measure is strictly positive (or identically zero).

For the converse part of the theorem we may therefore assume that the given invariant measure is normed by the condition $u_r = 1$ for some prescribed r. Then

(11.11) $$u_k = p_{kr} + \sum_{j \neq r} u_j p_{jk}.$$

Suppose $k \neq r$. We express the u_j inside the sum by means of the defining relation (11.1) and separate again the term involving u_r in the double sum. The result is

(11.12) $$u_k = p_{rk} + {}_rp_{rk}^{(2)} + \sum_{v \neq r} u_v \cdot {}_rp_{vk}^{(2)}.$$

Proceeding in like manner we get for every n

(11.13) $$u_k = p_{rk} + {}_rp_{rk}^{(2)} + \cdots + {}_rp_{rk}^{(n)} + \sum_{v \neq r} u_v \cdot {}_rp_{vk}^{(n)}.$$

Letting $n \to \infty$ we see that $u_k \geq {}_r\pi_{rk}$. It follows that $\{u_k - {}_r\pi_{rk}\}$ defines an invariant measure vanishing for the particular value $k = r$. But such a measure vanishes identically, and so (11.7) is true.   ▶

It will be seen presently that the following theorem represents a sharpening of the ratio limit theorem.

Theorem 2. *In an irreducible persistent chain*

(11.14) $$0 \leq \sum_{n=0}^{N} p_{kk}^{(n)} - \sum_{n=0}^{N} p_{ak}^{(n)} \leq {}_a\pi_{kk}$$

and

(11.15) $$-1 \leq \frac{1}{{}_j\pi_{ii}} \sum_{n=0}^{N} p_{ii}^{(n)} - \frac{1}{{}_i\pi_{jj}} \sum_{n=0}^{N} p_{jj}^{(n)} \leq 1$$

for all N.

Proof of (11.14). Consider the first entry to E_k; it is clear that for $\alpha \neq k$

$$(11.16) \qquad p_{\alpha k}^{(n)} = \sum_{v=1}^{n} f_{\alpha k}^{(v)} p_{kk}^{(n-v)}.$$

[This is the same as (5.3).] Summing over n we get

$$(11.17) \qquad \sum_{n=0}^{N} p_{\alpha k}^{(n)} \leq \sum_{n=0}^{N} p_{kk}^{(n)} \cdot \sum_{v=1}^{\infty} f_{\alpha k}^{(v)} = \sum_{n=0}^{N} p_{kk}^{(n)}$$

which proves the first inequality in (11.14).

Next we note that, starting from E_k, a return to E_k may occur without intermediate passage through E_α, or else, a first entry to E_α occurs at the vth step with $1 \leq v < n$. This means that

$$(11.18) \qquad p_{kk}^{(n)} = {}_\alpha p_{kk}^{(n)} + \sum_{v=1}^{n} f_{k\alpha}^{(v)} p_{\alpha k}^{(n-v)}.$$

Summation over n leads to the second inequality in (11.14).

Proof of (11.15). On account of the obvious symmetry in i and j it suffices to prove the second inequality. We start from the identity

$$(11.19) \qquad p_{ii}^{(n)} = {}_j p_{ii}^{(n)} + \sum_{v=1}^{n-1} p_{ij}^{(n-v)} \cdot {}_j p_{ji}^{(v)}$$

which expresses the fact that a return from E_i to E_i occurs either without intermediate passage through E_j, or else the *last* entry to E_j occurs at the $(n-v)$th step and the next v steps lead from E_j to E_i without further return to E_j. Summing over n we get

$$(11.20) \qquad \begin{aligned} \sum_{n=0}^{N} p_{ii}^{(n)} &\leq {}_j\pi_{ii} + {}_j\pi_{ji} \sum_{n=0}^{N} p_{ij}^{(n)} \\ &\leq {}_j\pi_{ii} + {}_j\pi_{ji} \sum_{n=0}^{N} p_{jj}^{(n)} \end{aligned}$$

by virtue of (11.14). To put this inequality into the symmetric form of (11.15) it suffices to note that

$$(11.21) \qquad {}_j\pi_{ji} = \frac{{}_j\pi_{ii}}{{}_i\pi_{jj}}.$$

In fact, by analogy with (11.16) we have

$$(11.22) \qquad {}_j\pi_{ji} = {}_jf_{ji} \cdot {}_j\pi_{ii}$$

where $_jf_{ji}$ is the probability of reaching E_i from E_j without a previous return to E_j. The alternative to this event is that a return to E_j occurs before an entry to E_i, and hence

$$(11.23) \qquad _jf_{ji} = 1 - _if_{jj} = \frac{1}{_i\pi_{jj}}.$$

(The last equation is the basic identity for the transient recurrent event which consists in a return to E_j without an intermediate passage through E_i.) Substituting from (11.23) into (11.22) we get the assertion (11.21), and this accomplishes the proof. ▶

The relation (11.21) leads to the interesting

Corollary 1. *If* $\{u_k\}$ *is an invariant measure, then*

$$(11.24) \qquad \frac{_j\pi_{ii}}{_i\pi_{jj}} = \frac{u_i}{u_j}.$$

Proof. The invariant measure is determined up to a multiplicative constant, and so the right side in (11.24) is uniquely determined. We may therefore suppose that $\{u_k\}$ is the invariant measure defined by (11.7) when the taboo state E_r is identified with E_j. But then $u_j = 1$ and $_j\pi_{ji} = u_i$, and so (11.21) reduces to (11.24). ▶

Corollary 2. (*Ratio limit theorem.*) *In an irreducible persistent chain the ratio limit theorem* (11.2) *holds.*

Proof. The sums of theorem 2 tend to ∞ as $N \to \infty$. The ratio of the two sums in (11.14) therefore tends to unity, and so it suffices to prove (11.2) for the special choice $\alpha = i$ and $\beta = j$. But with this choice (11.2) is an immediate consequence of (11.15) and (11.24). ▶

The existence of an invariant measure for persistent chains was first proved by C. Derman (1954). The existence of a limit in (11.2) was demonstrated by A. Doblin (1938). Taboo probabilities as a powerful tool in the theory of Markov chains were introduced by Chung (1953). Further details are given in the first part of his basic treatise.[17] The boundedness of the partial sums $\sum_0^N (p_{kk}^{(n)} - p_{ii}^{(n)})$ was proved by S. Orey, who considered also the problem of convergence.[18]

---

[17] *Markov chains with stationary transition probabilities*, Berlin (Springer), 1960. A revised edition covering boundary theory is in preparation. (Our notations are not identical with his.)

[18] *Sums arising in the theory of Markov chains*, Proc. Amer. Math. Soc., vol. 12 (1961), pp. 847–856.

*12. REVERSED CHAINS. BOUNDARIES

When studying the development of a system we are usually interested in the probabilities of possible future events, but occasionally it is necessary to study the past. In the special case of a Markov chain we may ask for the (conditional) probability that at some time in the past the system was in state E_i given that the present state is E_j.

Consider first a chain with a strictly positive invariant probability distribution $\{u_k\}$; that is, we assume that $u_k > 0$ and $\sum u_k = 1$ where

$$(12.1) \qquad u_k = \sum_v u_v p_{vk}.$$

[Recall from the theorem in section 7 that the invariant probability distribution of an irreducible chain is automatically strictly positive.]

If the process starts from $\{u_k\}$ as initial distribution, the probability of finding the system at any time in state E_i equals u_i. Given this event, the conditional probability that n time units earlier the system was in state E_j equals

$$(12.2) \qquad q_{ij}^{(n)} = \frac{u_j p_{ji}^{(n)}}{u_i}.$$

For $n = 1$ we get

$$(12.3) \qquad q_{ij} = \frac{u_j p_{ji}}{u_i}.$$

In view of (12.1) it is clear that the q_{ij} are the elements of a *stochastic* matrix Q. Furthermore, the probabilities $q_{ij}^{(n)}$ are simply the elements of the nth power Q^n (in other words, the $q_{ij}^{(n)}$ can be calculated from the q_{ij} in the same manner as the $p_{ji}^{(n)}$ are calculated from the p_{ji}). It is now apparent that *the study of the past development of our Markov chain reduces to the study of a Markov chain with transition probabilities q_{ij}.* The absolute probabilities of the new chain coincide, of course, with the invariant probability distribution $\{u_k\}$. The probabilities q_{ij} are called *inverse probabilities* (relative to the original chain) and the procedure leading from one chain to the other is called *reversal of the time*. In the special case where $q_{ij} = p_{ij}$ one says that the chain is *reversible*; the probability relations for such a chain are symmetric in time.

We know that an irreducible chain possesses an invariant probability distribution only if the states have finite mean recurrence times. If the states are persistent null states there exists an invariant measure which is unique except for an arbitrary multiplicative constant. For a transient chain all contingencies are possible: some chains have no invariant measure, others infinitely many. [Examples (11.b) and (11.c).] Under these circumstances it is remarkable that the transformation (12.3) *defines a stochastic matrix Q whenever $\{u_k\}$ is a strictly positive invariant measure.* The powers of Q are given by (12.2). In this sense *every strictly positive invariant measure defines a reversed Markov chain.* Unfortunately the new transition probabilities q_{ij} cannot be interpreted directly as conditional probabilities in the old process.[19]

A glance at (12.3) shows that $\{u_j\}$ is an invariant measure also for the reversed chain. Furthermore it is clear from (12.2) that either both series $\sum_n q_{ij}^{(n)}$ and $\sum_n p_{ji}^{(n)}$ converge or both diverge. It follows that *the states of the two chains are of the same type*: if one chain is transient, or persistent, so is the other.

Examples. (*a*) The invariant probability distribution corresponding to the *Ehrenfest model* [example (2.e)] was found in (7.16). A simple calculation shows that *the Ehrenfest model is reversible* in the sense that $q_{ii} = p_{ij}$.

(*b*) In example (11.b) we found the invariant measures corresponding to a random walk on the line in which the transitions to the right and left neighbor have probabilities p and q, respectively. If we choose $u_k = 1$ for $k = 0, \pm 1, \pm 2, \ldots$, we get $q_{ij} = p_{ji}$, and we are led to a new random walk in which the roles of p and q are interchanged. On the other hand, the invariant measure with $u_k = (p/q)^k$ yields a reversed random walk identical with the original one.

(*c*) In examples (2.k) and (2.l) we introduced two Markov chains related to a recurrent event $\mathcal{E}$. For a persistent $\mathcal{E}$ with finite mean recurrence time μ we saw in example (7.h) that the two chains have the same invariant probability distribution defined by (7.23). When $\mu = \infty$ these relations define an invariant measure common to the two chains [see examples (11.c) and (11.d)]. A simple calculation now shows that *the two chains are obtained from each other by reversing the time.* This is not surprising seeing that the chain of (2.k) concerns the waiting time to the next occurrence of $\mathcal{E}$ while (2.l) refers to the time elapsed from the last occurrence. ▶

Consider now an arbitrary irreducible transient chain with an invariant measure $\{u_k\}$. The equations (12.1) defining an invariant measure may admit of other solutions, and the question of uniqueness is closely related

---

[19] For an operational interpretation of the q_{ij} it is necessary to consider infinitely many simultaneous processes, as indicated in example (11.b).

with the question of uniqueness of the adjoint system of linear equations,[20]

$$(12.4) \qquad\qquad \xi_i = \sum_v p_{iv}\xi_v,$$

which played an important role in section 8. This system admits of the trivial solution $\xi_i = c$ for all i. Any non-negative solution is automatically strictly positive. (Indeed, $\xi_i = 0$ would imply $\xi_v = 0$ for all v such that $p_{iv} > 0$. This in turn would imply $\xi_v = 0$ whenever $p_{iv}^{(2)} > 0$, and generally $\xi_v = 0$ for every state E_v that can be reached from E_i. Thus $\xi_v = 0$ for all v because the chain is irreducible.) If $\{\xi_i\}$ is a non-constant solution then a glance at (12.3) shows that

$$(12.5) \qquad\qquad v_i = u_i\xi_i$$

defines an invariant measure for the reverse matrix Q. Conversely, if $\{v_i\}$ stands for such a measure then (12.5) defines a positive solution of (12.4). In other words, *the positive solutions of* (12.4) *stand in one-to-one correspondence with the invariant measures of the reversed chain*[21] with matrix Q.

In the modern theory of Markov chains and potentials the positive solutions $\{\xi_i\}$ and $\{u_k\}$ are used to define boundaries. It is beyond the scope of this book to describe how this is done, but the following examples may give some idea of what is meant by an *exit boundary*.

Examples. (*a*) Consider a random walk on the infinite line such that from the position $j \neq 0$ the particle moves with probability p a unit step away from the origin, and with probability q a unit step toward the origin. From the origin the particle moves with equal probabilities to $+1$ or -1. We assume $p > q$.

---

[20] If ξ stands for the column vector with components ξ_i the system (12.4) reduces to the matrix equation $\xi = P\xi$. The system (12.1) corresponds to $u = uP$ where u is a row vector.

[21] For an irreducible persistent chain the invariant measure is unique up to a multiplicative constant. Since the chains with matrices P and Q are of the same type we have proved the

Theorem. *For an irreducible persistent chain the only non-negative solution of* (12.4) *is given by* $\xi_i = $ const.

This can be proved also by repeating almost verbatim the last part of the proof of theorem 11.1. Indeed, by induction we find that for arbitrary i, r, and n

$$\xi_i = [f_{ir}^{(1)} + \cdots + f_{ir}^{(n)}]\xi_r + \sum_v {}_r p_{iv}^{(n)}\xi_v.$$

For a persistent chain the expression within brackets tends to 1 while the series tends to 0. Hence $\xi_i = \xi_r$ as asserted.

In the Markov chain the states are numbered from $-\infty$ to ∞, and the equations (12.4) take on the form

$$\xi_i = p\xi_{i+1} + q\xi_{i-1} \qquad\qquad i > 0,$$

(12.6) $$\xi_0 = \tfrac{1}{2}\xi_1 + \tfrac{1}{2}\xi_{-1}$$

$$\xi_i = q\xi_{i+1} + p\xi_{i-1} \qquad\qquad i < 0.$$

Put

(12.7) $$\eta_i = 1 - \frac{1}{2}\left(\frac{q}{p}\right)^i \quad for \quad i \ge 0, \qquad \eta_i = \frac{1}{2}\left(\frac{q}{p}\right)^{-i} \quad for \quad i \le 0.$$

It is easily seen that $\xi_i = \eta_i$ and $\xi_i = 1 - \eta_i$ defines two[22] non-trivial solutions of the system (12.6). It follows that our chain is transient, and so the position of the particle necessarily tends either to $+\infty$ or to $-\infty$.

This conclusion can be reached directly from the theory of random walks. In fact, we know from XIV,2 that when the particle starts from a position $i > 0$ the probability of ever reaching the origin equals $(q/p)^i$. For reasons of symmetry a particle starting from the origin has equal probabilities to drift toward $+\infty$ or $-\infty$, and so the probability of an ultimate drift to $-\infty$ equals $\tfrac{1}{2}(q/p)^i$. We conclude that η_i *is the probability that, starting from an arbitrary position i, the particle ultimately drifts to $+\infty$.* The drift to $-\infty$ has probability $1 - \eta_i$. In the modern theory the situation would be described by introducing the "exit boundary points" $+\infty$ and $-\infty$.

(b) The preceding example is somewhat misleading by its simplicity, and it may therefore be useful to have an example of *a boundary consisting of infinitely many points.* For this purpose we consider a random walk in the x,y-plane as follows. The x-coordinate performs an ordinary random walk in which the steps $+1$ and -1 have probabilities p and $q < p$. The y-coordinate remains fixed except when the x-coordinate is zero, in which case the y-coordinate decreases by 1. More explicitly, when $j \ne 0$ only the transitions $(j, k) \rightarrow (j + 1, k)$ and $(j-1, k)$ are possible, and they have probabilities p and $q < p$, respectively. From $(0, k)$ the particle moves with probability p to $(1, k-1)$ and with probability q to $(-1, k-1)$.

From the theory of random walks we know that the x-coordinate is bound to tend to $+\infty$, and that (with probability one) it will pass only finitely often through 0. It follows that (excepting an event of zero probability) the y-coordinate will change only finitely often. This means that

---

[22] The most general solution is given by $\xi_i = A + B\eta_i$ where A and B are arbitrary constants. Indeed, these constants can be chosen so as to yield prescribed values for ξ_1 and ξ_{-1}, and it is obvious from (12.6) that the values for ξ_1 and ξ_{-1} uniquely determine all ξ_i.

after finitely many changes of the y-coordinate the particle will remain on a line $y = r$. In this sense there are infinitely many "escape routes to infinity," and for each initial position (j, k) we may calculate[23] the probability $\xi_{j,k}^{(r)}$ that the particle ultimately settles on the line $y = r$. It is easily seen that for fixed r the probabilities $\xi_{j,k}^{(r)}$ represent a solution of the system corresponding to (12.4), and that the most general solution is a linear combination of these particular solutions. Furthermore, the particular solution $\xi_{j,k}^{(r)}$ is characterized by the intuitively obvious "boundary condition" that $\xi_{j,k}^{(r)} \to 0$ as $j \to \infty$ except when $k = r$, in which case $\xi_{j,r}^{(r)} \to 1$.   ▶

These examples are typical in the following sense. Given an irreducible transient Markov chain it is always possible to define a "boundary" such that with probability one the state of the system tends to some point of the boundary. Given a set Γ on the boundary we can ask for the probability η_i that, starting from the initial state E_i, the system converges to a point of Γ. We refer to $\{\eta_i\}$ as the *absorption probabilities for* Γ. It turns out that such absorption probabilities are always solutions of the linear system (12.4) and, conversely, that all bounded solutions of (12.4) are linear combinations of absorption probabilities. Furthermore, the absorption probabilities $\{\eta_i\}$ for Γ are given by the unique solution of (12.4) which assumes the boundary values 1 on Γ and the boundary values 0 on the complement of Γ on the boundary. We may now form a new stochastic matrix $\hat{P}$ with elements

$$(12.8) \qquad\qquad \hat{p}_{ik} = p_{ik}\frac{\eta_k}{\eta_i}.$$

This is the conditional probability of a transition from E_i to E_k given that the state ultimately tends to a point of Γ. The Markov process with matrix $\hat{P}$ may be described as obtained from the original process by conditioning on the hypothesis of an ultimate absorption in Γ. Since the

---

[23] An explicit expression for $\xi_{j,k}^{(r)}$ can be obtained from the results in XIV,2 concerning one-dimensional random walks. From an initial position $i \leq 0$ the probability that the origin will be touched exactly $\rho > 0$ times equals $(2q)^{\rho-1}(p-q)$; when $i \geq 0$ this probability equals $(q/p)^i(2q)^{\rho-1}(p-q)$. The probability that the origin is never touched equals 0 for $i \leq 0$ and $1 - (q/p)^i$ for $i \geq 0$. It follows easily that for $i \leq 0$

$$\xi_{i,k}^{(r)} = (2q)^{k-r-1}(p-q) \qquad\qquad\qquad k > r$$

while for $i > 0$

$$\xi_{i,k}^{(r)} = (q/p)^i(2q)^{k-r-1}(p-q) \qquad\qquad k > r$$

$$\xi_{i,r}^{(r)} = 1 - (q/p)^i$$

and, of course, $\xi_{i,r}^{(k)} = 0$ when $k < r$.

future development can never be known in advance such a conditioning appears at first sight meaningless. It is nevertheless a powerful analytic tool and has even an operational meaning for processes that have been going on for a very long time.

A boundary can be defined also for the matrix Q obtained by a reversal of the time. In general therefore there are two distinct boundaries corresponding to a given chain. They are called *exit* and *entrance* boundaries, respectively. Roughly speaking, the former refers to the remote future, the latter to the remote past.

Time-reversed Markov chains were first considered by A. Kolmogorov.[24] The role of the solutions of (12.4) was stressed in the earlier editions of this book. Exit and entrance boundaries were introduced by W. Feller.[25] His construction is satisfactory when there are only finitely many boundary points, but in general it is simpler to adapt the construction introduced by R. S. Martin in the theory of harmonic functions. This was pointed out by J. L. Doob.[26] The relativization (12.8) was introduced by Feller;[26] an analogous transformation in the theory of classical harmonic functions was defined at the same time by M. Brelot.[27]

13. THE GENERAL MARKOV PROCESS

In applications it is usually convenient to describe Markov chains in terms of random variables. This can be done by the simple device of replacing in the preceding sections the symbol E_k by the integer k. The state of the system at time n then is a random variable $\mathbf{X}^{(n)}$, which assumes the value k with probability $a_k^{(n)}$; the joint distribution of $\mathbf{X}^{(n)}$ and $\mathbf{X}^{(n+1)}$ is given by $\mathbf{P}\{\mathbf{X}^{(n)} = j, \mathbf{X}^{(n+1)} = k\} = a_j^{(n)}p_{jk}$, and the joint distribution of $(\mathbf{X}^{(0)}, \ldots, \mathbf{X}^{(n)})$ is given by (1.1). It is also possible, and sometimes preferable, to assign to E_k a numerical value e_k different from k. With this notation a Markov chain becomes a special stochastic process,[28] or in other words, a sequence of (dependent) random variables[29]

---

[24] *Zur Theorie der Markoffschen Ketten,* Mathematische Annalen, vol. 112(1935), pp. 155–160.

[25] *Boundaries induced by positive matrices,* Trans. Amer. Math. Soc., vol. 83(1956), pp. 19–54.

[26] *Discrete potential theory and boundaries,* J. Math. Mechanics, vol. 8(1959), pp. 433–458.

[27] *Le problème de Dirichlet. Axiomatique et frontière de Martin,* J. Math. Pures Appl., vol. 35(1956), pp. 297–335.

[28] The terms "stochastic process" and "random process" are synonyms and cover practically all the theory of probability from coin tossing to harmonic analysis. In practice, the term "stochastic process" is used mostly when a time parameter is introduced.

[29] This formulation refers to an infinite product space, but in reality we are concerned only with joint distributions of finite collections of the variables.

$(\mathbf{X}^{(0)}, \mathbf{X}^{(1)}, \ldots)$. The superscript n plays the role of time. In chapter XVII we shall get a glimpse of more general stochastic processes in which the time parameter is permitted to vary continuously. The term "Markov process" is applied to a very large and important class of stochastic processes (with both discrete and continuous time parameters). Even in the discrete case there exist more general Markov processes than the simple chains we have studied so far. It will, therefore, be useful to give a definition of the Markov property, to point out the special condition characterizing our Markov chains, and, finally, to give a few examples of non-Markovian processes.

Conceptually, a Markov process is the probabilistic analogue of the processes of classical mechanics, where the future development is completely determined by the present state and is independent of the way in which the present state has developed. These processes differ essentially from processes with aftereffect (or hereditary processes), such as occur in the theory of plasticity, where the whole past history of the system influences its future. In stochastic processes the future is not uniquely determined, but we have at least probability relations enabling us to make predictions. For the Markov chains studied in this chapter it is clear that probability relations relating to the future depend on the present state, but not on the manner in which the present state has emerged from the past. In other words, if two independent systems subject to the same transition probabilities happen to be in the same state, then all probabilities relating to their future developments are identical. This is a rather vague description which is formalized in the following

Definition. *A sequence of discrete-valued random variables is a Markov process if, corresponding to every finite collection of integers $n_1 < n_2 < < \cdots < n_r < n$, the joint distribution of $(\mathbf{X}^{(n_1)}, \mathbf{X}^{(n_2)}, \ldots, \mathbf{X}^{(n_r)}, \mathbf{X}^{(n)})$ is defined in such a way that the conditional probability of the relation $\mathbf{X}^{(n)} = x$ on the hypothesis $\mathbf{X}^{(n_1)} = x_1, \ldots, \mathbf{X}^{(n_r)} = x_r$ is identical with the conditional probability of $\mathbf{X}^{(n)} = x$ on the single hypothesis $\mathbf{X}^{(n_r)} = x_r$. Here $x_1, \ldots, x_r$, are arbitrary numbers for which the hypothesis has a positive probability.*

Reduced to simpler terms, this definition states that, given the present state x_r, no additional data concerning states of the system in the past can alter the (conditional) probability of the state x at a future time.

The Markov chains studied so far in this chapter are obviously Markov processes, but they have the additional property that their *transition probabilities* $p_{jk} = \mathbf{P}\{\mathbf{X}^{(m+1)} = k \mid \mathbf{X}^{(m)} = j\}$ *are independent of* m. The more general transition probabilities

$$(13.1) \qquad\qquad p_{jk}^{(n-m)} = \mathbf{P}\{\mathbf{X}^{(n)} = k \mid \mathbf{X}^{(m)} = j\} \qquad\qquad (m < n)$$

then depend only on the difference $n - m$. Such transition probabilities are called *stationary* (*or time-homogeneous*). For a general integral-valued Markov chain the right side in (13.1) depends on m and n. We shall denote it by $p_{jk}(m, n)$ so that $p_{jk}(n, n + 1)$ define the one-step transition probabilities. Instead of (1.1) we get now for the probability of the path $(j_0, j_1, \ldots, j_n)$ the expression

$$(13.2) \qquad a^{(0)}_{j_0} p_{j_0 j_1}(0, 1) p_{j_1 j_2}(1, 2) \cdots p_{j_{n-1} j_n}(n-1, n).$$

The proper generalization of (3.3) is obviously the identity

$$(13.3) \qquad p_{jk}(m, n) = \sum_{v} p_{jv}(m, r) p_{vk}(r, n)$$

which is valid for all r with $m < r < n$. This identity follows directly from the definition of a Markov process and also from (13.2); it is called the *Chapman-Kolmogorov* equation. [Transition probabilities $p_{jk}(m, n)$ are defined also for non-Markovian discrete processes, but for them the factor $p_{vk}(r, n)$ in (13.3) must be replaced by an expression depending not only on v and k, but also on j.]

The Markov chains studied in this chapter represent the general time-homogeneous discrete Markov process. We shall not dwell on the time-inhomogeneous Markov process. The following examples may be helpful for an understanding of the Markov property and will illustrate situations when the Chapman-Kolmogorov equation (13.3) does not hold.

Examples of Non-Markovian Processes

(a) *The Polya urn scheme* [example V,(2.c)]. Let $X^{(n)}$ equal 1 or 0 according to whether the nth drawing results in a black or red ball. The sequence $\{X^{(n)}\}$ is *not* a Markov process. For example,

$$\mathbf{P}\{X^{(3)} = 1 \mid X^{(2)} = 1\} = (b+c)/(b+r+c),$$

but

$$\mathbf{P}\{X^{(3)} = 1 \mid X^{(2)} = 1, X^{(1)} = 1\} = (b+2c)/(b+r+2c).$$

(Cf. problems V, 19–20.) On the other hand, if $Y^{(n)}$ is the number of black balls in the urn a time n, then $\{Y^{(n)}\}$ is an ordinary Markov chain with constant transition probabilities.

(b) *Higher sums.* Let $Y_0, Y_1, \ldots$ be mutually independent random variables, and put $S_n = Y_0 + \cdots + Y_n$. The difference $S_n - S_m$ (with $m < n$) depends only on $Y_{m+1}, \ldots, Y_n$, and it is therefore easily seen that the sequence $\{S_n\}$ is a Markov process. Now let us go one step further and define a new sequence of random variables U_n by

$$U_n = S_0 + S_1 + \cdots + S_n = Y_n + 2Y_{n-1} + 3Y_{n-2} + \cdots + (n+1) Y_0.$$

The sequence $\{U_n\}$ forms a stochastic process whose probability relations can, in principle, be expressed in terms of the distributions of the Y_k. The $\{U_n\}$ process is in general not of the Markov type, since there is no reason why, for example, $P\{U_n = 0 \mid U_{n-1} = a\}$ should be the same as $P\{U_n = 0 \mid U_{n-1} = a, U_{n-2} = b\}$; the knowledge of U_{n-1} and U_{n-2} permits better predictions than the sole knowledge of U_{n-1}.

In the case of a continuous time parameter the preceding summations are replaced by integrations. In diffusion theory the Y_n play the role of accelerations; the S_n are then velocities, and the U_n positions. If only positions can be measured, we are compelled to study a non-Markovian process, even though it is indirectly defined in terms of a Markov process.

(c) *Moving averages.* Again let $\{Y_n\}$ be a sequence of mutually independent random variables. Moving averages of order r are defined by $X^{(n)} = (Y_n + Y_{n+1} + \cdots + Y_{n+r-1})/r$. It is easily seen that the $X^{(n)}$ are not a Markov process. Processes of this type are common in many applications (cf. problem 25).

(d) *A traffic problem.* For an empirical example of a non-Markovian process R. Fürth[30] made extensive observations on the number of pedestrians on a certain segment of a street. An idealized mathematical model of this process can be obtained in the following way. For simplicity we assume that all pedestrians have the same speed v and consider only pedestrians moving in one direction. We partition the x-axis into segments $I_1, I_2, \ldots$ of a fixed length d and observe the configuration of pedestrians regularly at moments d/v time units apart. Define the random variable Y_k as the number of pedestrians initially in I_k. At the nth observation these same pedestrians will be found in I_{k-n}, whereas the interval I_k will contain Y_{k+n} pedestrians. The total number of pedestrians within the interval $0 < x < Nd$ is therefore given by $X^{(n)} = Y_{n+1} + \cdots + Y_{n+N}$, and so our process is essentially a moving average process. The simplest model for the random variables Y_k is represented by Bernoulli trials. In the limit as $d \to 0$ they lead to a continuous model, in which a Poisson distribution takes over the role of the binomial distribution.

(e) *Superposition of Markov processes* (*composite shuffling*). There exist many technical devices (such as groups of selectors in telephone exchanges, counters, filters) whose action can be described as a superposition of two Markov processes with an output which is non-Markovian. A fair idea

---

[30] R. Fürth, *Schwankungserscheinungen in der Physik*, Sammlung Vieweg, Braunschweig, 1920, pp. 17ff. The original observations appeared in Physikalische Zeitschrift, vols. 19 (1918) and 20 (1919).

of such mechanisms may be obtained from the study of the following method of card shuffling.

In addition to the target deck of N cards we have an equivalent auxiliary deck, and the usual shuffling technique is applied to this auxiliary deck. If its cards appear in the order $(a_1, a_2, \ldots, a_N)$, we permute the cards of the target deck so that the first, second, ..., Nth cards are transferred to the places number $a_1, a_2, \ldots, a_N$. Thus the shuffling of the auxiliary deck indirectly determines the successive orderings of the target deck. The latter form *a stochastic process which is not of the Markov type.* To prove this, it suffices to show that the knowledge of two successive orderings of the target deck conveys in general more clues to the future than the sole knowledge of the last ordering. We show this in a simple special case.

Let $N = 4$, and suppose that the auxiliary deck is initially in the order (2431). Suppose, furthermore, that the shuffling operation always consists of a true "cutting," that is, the ordering (a_1, a_2, a_3, a_4) is changed into one of the three orderings (a_2, a_3, a_4, a_1), (a_3, a_4, a_1, a_2), (a_4, a_1, a_2, a_3); we attribute to each of these three possibilities probability $\frac{1}{3}$. With these conventions the auxiliary deck will at any time be in one of the four orderings (2431), (4312), (3124), (1243). On the other hand, a little experimentation will show that the target deck will gradually pass through all 24 possible orderings and that each of them will appear in combination with each of the four possible orderings of the auxiliary deck. This means that the ordering (1234) of the target deck will recur infinitely often, and it will always be succeeded by one of the four orderings (2431), (4312), (3124), (1243). Now the auxiliary deck can never remain in the same ordering, and hence the target deck cannot twice in succession undergo the same permutation. Hence, if at trials number $n - 1$ and n the orderings are (1234) and (1243), respectively, then at the next trial the state (1234) is impossible. Thus two consecutive observations convey more information than does one single observation.

(*f*) *A non-Markovian process satisfying the Chapman-Kolmogorov equation.* The identity (3.3) was derived from the assumption that a transition from E_v to E_k does not depend on the manner in which the state E_v was reached. Originally it seemed therefore intuitively clear that no non-Markovian process should satisfy this identity; this conjecture seemed supported by the fact that the n-step transition probabilities of such a process must satisfy a host of curious identities. It turned out nevertheless that exceptions exist (at least in theory). In fact, in IX,1 we encountered an infinite sequence of pairwise independent identically distributed random variables assuming the values 1, 2, and 3 each with probability $\frac{1}{3}$. We have thus a process with possible states 1, 2, 3 and such that $p_{jk} = \frac{1}{3}$ for all combinations of j and k. The indentity (3.3) is therefore trivially satisfied with $p_{jk}^{(n)} = \frac{1}{3}$. The process is nonetheless non-Markovian. To see this suppose that the first step takes the system to the state 2. A transition to 3 at the next step is then possible if, and only if, the initial state was 1. Thus the transitions following the first step depend not only on the present state but also on the initial state. (For various modifications see the note and footnote 3 in IX,1.)

14. PROBLEMS FOR SOLUTION

1. In a sequence of Bernoulli trials we say that at time n the state E_1 is observed if the trials number $n - 1$ and n resulted in SS. Similarly E_2, E_3, E_4 stand for SF, FS, FF. Find the matrix P and all its powers. Generalize the scheme.

2. Classify the states for the four chains whose matrices P have the rows given below. Find in each case P^2 and the asymptotic behavior of $p_{jk}^{(0)}$.
(a) $(0, \frac{1}{2}, \frac{1}{2}), (\frac{1}{2}, 0, \frac{1}{2}), (\frac{1}{2}, \frac{1}{2}, 0)$;
(b) $(0, 0, 0, 1), (0, 0, 0, 1), (\frac{1}{2}, \frac{1}{2}, 0, 0), (0, 0, 1, 0)$;
(c) $(\frac{1}{2}, 0, \frac{1}{2}, 0, 0), (\frac{1}{4}, \frac{1}{4}, \frac{1}{4}, 0, 0), (\frac{1}{2}, 0, \frac{1}{2}, 0, 0), (0, 0, 0, \frac{1}{2}, \frac{1}{2}), (0, 0, 0, \frac{1}{2}, \frac{1}{2})$;
(d) $(0, \frac{1}{2}, \frac{1}{2}, 0, 0, 0), (0, 0, 0, \frac{1}{3}, \frac{1}{3}, \frac{1}{3}), (0, 0, 0, \frac{1}{3}, \frac{1}{3}, \frac{1}{3}), (1, 0, 0, 0, 0, 0),$
$(1, 0, 0, 0, 0, 0), (1, 0, 0, 0, 0, 0)$.

3. We consider throws of a true die and agree to say that at epoch n the system is in state E_j if j is the highest number appearing in the first n throws. Find the matrix P^n and verify that (3.3) holds.

4. In example (2.j) find the (absorption) probabilities x_k and y_k that, starting from E_k, the system will end in E_1 or E_5, respectively ($k = 2, 3, 4, 6$). (Do this problem from the basic definitions without referring to section 8.)

5. Treat example I, (5.b) as a Markov chain. Calculate the probability of winning for each player.

6. Let E_0 be absorbing (that is, put $p_{00} = 1$). For $j > 0$ let $p_{jj} = p$ and $p_{j,j-1} = q$, where $p + q = 1$. Find the probability $f_{j0}^{(n)}$ that absorption at E_0 takes place exactly at the nth step. Find also the expectation of this distribution.

7. The first row of the matrix P is given by $v_0, v_1, \ldots$. For $j > 0$ we have (as in the preceding problem) $p_{jj} = p$ and $p_{j,j-1} = q$. Find the distribution of the recurrence time for E_0.

8. For $j = 0, 1, \ldots$ let $p_{j,j+2} = v_j$ and $p_{j0} = 1 - v_j$. Discuss the character of the states.

9. *Two reflecting barriers.* A chain with states $1, 2, \ldots, \rho$ has a matrix whose first and last rows are $(q, p, 0, \ldots, 0)$ and $(0, \ldots, 0, q, p)$. In all other rows $p_{k,k+1} = p, p_{k,k-1} = q$. Find the stationary distribution. Can the chain be periodic?

10. Generalize the *Bernoulli-Laplace model of diffusion* [example (2.f)] by assuming that there are $b \geq \rho$ black particles and $w = 2\rho - b$ white ones. The number of particles in each container remains $= \rho$.

11. A chain with states $E_0, E_1, \ldots$ has transition probabilities

$$p_{jk} = e^{-\lambda} \sum_{\nu=0}^{j} \binom{j}{\nu} p^\nu q^{j-\nu} \frac{\lambda^{k-\nu}}{(k-\nu)!}$$

where the terms in the sum should be replaced by zero if $\nu > k$. Show that

$$p_{jk}^{(n)} \to e^{-\lambda/q} \frac{(\lambda/q)^k}{k!} .$$

Note: This chain occurs in statistical mechanics[31] and can be interpreted as follows. The state of the system is defined by the number of particles in a certain region of space. During each time interval of unit length each particle has probability q to leave the volume, and the particles are stochastically independent. Moreover, new particles may enter the volume, and the probability of r entrants is given by the Poisson expression $e^{-\lambda}\lambda^r/r!$. The stationary distribution is then a Poisson distribution with parameter λ/q.

12. *Ehrenfest model.* In example (2.e) let there initially be j molecules in the first container, and let $\mathbf{X}^{(n)} = 2k - a$ if at the nth step the system is in state k (so that $\mathbf{X}^{(n)}$ is the difference of the number of molecules in the two containers). Let $e_n = \mathbf{E}(\mathbf{X}^{(n)})$. Prove that $e_{n+1} = (a-2)e_n/a$, whence $e_n = (1-2/a)^n(2j-a)$. (Note that $e_n \to 0$ as $n \to \infty$.)

13. Treat the counter problem, example XIII, (1.g), as a Markov chain.

14. *Plane random walk with reflecting barriers.* Consider a *symmetric* random walk in a bounded region of the plane. The boundary is reflecting in the sense that, whenever in a unrestricted random walk the particle would leave the region, it is forced to return to the last position. Show that, if every point of the region can be reached from every other point, there exists a stationary distribution and that $u_k = 1/a$, where a is the number of positions in the region. (If the region is unbounded the states are persistent null states and $u_k = 1$ represents an invariant measure.)

15. *Repeated averaging.* Let $\{x_1, x_2, \ldots\}$ be a bounded sequence of numbers and P the matrix of an ergodic chain. Prove that $\sum_j p_{ij}^{(n)}x_j \to \Sigma u_j x_j$. Show that the repeated averaging procedure of example XIII, (10.c) is a special case.

16. In the theory of *waiting lines* we ecounter the chain matrix

$$\begin{bmatrix} p_0 & p_1 & p_2 & p_3 & \cdots \\ p_0 & p_1 & p_2 & p_3 & \cdots \\ 0 & p_0 & p_1 & p_2 & \cdots \\ 0 & 0 & p_0 & p_1 & \cdots \end{bmatrix}$$

where $\{p_k\}$ is a probability distribution. Using generating functions, discuss the character of the states. Find the generating function of the stationary distribution, if any.

17. *Waiting time to absorption.* For transient E_j let $\mathbf{Y}_j$ be the time when the system for *the first time* passes into a persistent state. Assuming that the probability of staying forever in transient states is zero, prove that $d_j = \mathbf{E}(\mathbf{Y}_j)$ is uniquely determined as the solution of the system of linear equations

$$d_j = \sum_T p_{j\nu}d_\nu + 1,$$

the summation extending over all ν such that E_ν is transient. However, d_ν need not be finite.

---

[31] S. Chandrasekhar, *Stochastic problems in physics and astronomy*, Reviews of Modern Physics, vol. 15 (1943), pp. 1–89, in particular p. 45.

18. If the number of states is $a < \infty$ and if E_k can be reached from E_j, then it can be reached in a steps or less.

19. Let the chain contain a states and let E_j be persistent. There exists a number $q < 1$ such that for $n \geq a$ the probability of the recurrence time of E_j exceeding n is smaller than q^n. (*Hint:* Use problem 18.)

20. In a finite chain E_j is transient if and only if there exists an E_k such that E_k can be reached from E_j but not E_j from E_k. (For infinite chains this is false, as shown by random walks.)

21. An irreducible chain for which *one* diagonal element p_{jj} is positive cannot be periodic.

22. A finite irreducible chain is non-periodic if and only if there exists an n such that $p_{jk}^{(n)} > 0$ for all j and k.

23. In a chain with a states let $(x_1, \ldots, x_a)$ be a solution of the system of linear equations $x_j = \Sigma p_{jv} x_v$. Prove: (a) If $x_j \leq 1$ for all j then the states for which $x_r = 1$ form a closed set. (b) If E_j and E_k belong to the same irreducible set then $x_j = x_k$. (c) In a finite irreducible chain the solution $\{x_j\}$ reduces to a constant. *Hint:* Consider the restriction of the equations to a closed set.

24. *Continuation.* If $(x_1, \ldots, x_a)$ is a (complex valued) solution of $x_j = = s \sum p_{jv} x_v$ with $|s| = 1$ but $s \neq 1$, then there exists an integer $t > 1$ such that $s^t = 1$. If the chain is irreducible, then the smallest integer of this kind is the period of the chain.

Hint: Without loss of generality assume $x_1 = 1$. Consider successively the states for which x_j equals $s^{-1}, s^{-2}, \ldots$.

25. *Moving averages.* Let $\{\mathbf{Y}_k\}$ be a sequence of mutually independent random variables, each assuming the values ± 1 with probability $\frac{1}{2}$. Put $\mathbf{X}^{(n)} = (\mathbf{Y}_n + \mathbf{Y}_{n+1})/2$. Find the transition probabilities

$$p_{jk}(m, n) = \mathbf{P}\{\mathbf{X}^{(n)} = k \mid \mathbf{X}^{(m)} = j\},$$

where $m < n$ and $j, k = -1, 0, 1$. Conclude that $\{\mathbf{X}^{(n)}\}$ is not a Markov process and that (13.3) does not hold.

26. In a sequence of Bernoulli trials say that the state E_1 is observed at time n if the trials number $n - 1$ and n resulted in success; otherwise the system is in E_2. Find the n-step transition probabilities and discuss the non-Markovian character.

Note: This process is obtained from the chain of problem 1 by lumping together three states. Such a *grouping* can be applied to any Markov chain and destroys the Markovian character. Processes of this type were studied by Harris.[32]

27. *Mixing of Markov chains.* Given two Markov chains with the same number of states, and matrices P_1 and P_2. A new process is defined by an initial distribution and n-step transition probabilities $\frac{1}{2}P_1^n + \frac{1}{2}P_2^n$. Discuss the non-Markovian character and the relation to the urn models of V, 2.

[32] T. E. Harris, *On chains of infinite order*, Pacific Journal of Mathematics, vol. 5 (1955), Supplement 1, pp. 707–724.

28. Let **N** be a Poisson variable with expectation λ. Consider **N** independent Markov processes starting at E_0 and having the same matrix P. Denote by $\mathbf{Z}_k^{(n)}$ the number among them after n steps are found in state E_k. Show that $\mathbf{Z}_k^{(n)}$ has a Poisson distribution with expectation $\lambda \cdot p_{0k}^{(n)}$.

Hint: Use the result of example XII,(1.b).

29. Using the preceding problem show that the variable $\mathbf{X}_k^{(n)}$ of example (11.b) has a Poisson distribution with expectation $\sum_j u_j p_{jk}^{(n)} = u_k$.

CHAPTER XVI

Algebraic Treatment
of Finite Markov Chains

In this chapter we consider a Markov chain with finitely many states $E_1, \ldots, E_\rho$ and a given matrix of transition probabilities p_{jk}. Our main aim is to derive explicit formulas for the n-step transition probabilities $p_{jk}^{(n)}$. We shall not require the results of the preceding chapter, except the general concepts and notations of section 3.

We shall make use of the method of generating functions and shall obtain the desired results from the partial fraction expansions of XI,4. Our results can also be obtained directly from the theory of canonical decompositions of matrices (which in turn can be derived from our results). Moreover, for *finite* chains the ergodic properties proved in chapter XV follow from the results of the present chapter. However, for simplicity, we shall slightly restrict the generality and disregard exceptional cases which complicate the general theory and hardly occur in practical examples.

The general method is outlined in section 1 and illustrated in sections 2 and 3. In section 4 special attention is paid to transient states and absorption probabilities. In section 5 the theory is applied to finding the variances of the recurrence times of the states E_j.

1. GENERAL THEORY

For fixed j and k we introduce the generating function[1]

$$(1.1) \qquad P_{jk}(s) = \sum_{n=0}^{\infty} p_{jk}^{(n)} s^n.$$

---

* This chapter treats a special topic and may be omitted.

[1] Recall that $p_{jk}^{(0)}$ equals 0 or 1 according as $j \neq k$ or $j = k$. (The $p_{jk}^{(0)}$ are known as Kronecker symbols.)

Multiplying by sp_{ij} and adding over $j = 1, \ldots, \rho$ we get

$$(1.2) \qquad s\sum_{j=1}^{\rho} p_{ij}P_{jk}(s) = P_{ik}(s) - p_{ik}^{(0)}.$$

This means that for fixed k and s the quantities $z_j = P_{jk}(s)$ satisfy a system of a linear equations of the form

$$(1.3) \qquad z_i - s\sum_{j=1}^{\rho} p_{ij}z_j = b_i.$$

The solutions z_j of (1.3) are obviously rational functions of s with a common denominator $D(s)$, the determinant of the system. To conform with the standard notations of linear algebra we put $s = t^{-1}$. Then $t^\rho D(t^{-1})$ is a polynomial of degree ρ (called the characteristic polynomial of the matrix P of transition probabilities p_{jk}). Its roots $t_1, \ldots, t_\rho$ are called the *characteristic roots* (or eigenvalues) of the matrix P.

We now introduce the *simplifying assumptions that the characteristic roots $t_1, \ldots, t_\rho$ are simple* (distinct) *and*[2] $\neq 0$. This is a slight restriction of generality, but the theory will cover most cases of practical interest.

As already stated, for fixed k the ρ quantities $P_{jk}(s)$ are rational functions of s with the common denominator $D(s)$. The roots of $D(s)$ are given by the reciprocals of the non-vanishing characteristic roots t_ν. It follows therefore from the results of XI,4 that there exist constants $b_{jk}^{(\nu)}$ such that[3]

$$(1.4) \qquad P_{jk}(s) = \frac{b_{jk}^{(1)}}{1 - st_1} + \cdots + \frac{b_{jk}^{(\rho)}}{1 - st_\rho}.$$

Expanding the fractions into geometric series we get the equivalent relations

$$(1.5) \qquad p_{jk}^{(n)} = b_{jk}^{(1)}t_1^n + \cdots + b_{jk}^{(\rho)}t_\rho^n$$

valid for all integers $n \geq 0$. We proceed to show that the coefficients $b_{jk}^{(\nu)}$ are uniquely determined as solutions of certain systems of linear equations. The quantity $p_{ik}^{(n+1)}$ can be obtained from (1.5) by changing n into $n + 1$, but also by multiplying (1.5) by p_{ji} and summing over

---

[2] The condition $t_r \neq 0$ will be discarded presently. A chain with multiple roots is treated numerically in example (4.b).

[3] In theory we should omit those roots t_r that cancel against a root of the numerator. For such roots we put $b_{jk}^{(\nu)} = 0$ and so (1.4) and (1.5) remain valid under any circumstances.

$j = 1, \ldots, \rho$. Equating the two expressions we get an identity of the form

$$(1.6) \qquad C_1 t_1^n + \cdots + C_\rho t_\rho^n = 0$$

valid for all n. This is manifestly impossible unless all coefficients vanish, and we conclude that

$$(1.7) \qquad \sum_{j=1}^{\rho} p_{ij} b_{jk}^{(v)} = t_v b_{ik}^{(v)}$$

for all combinations i, k, and v. On multiplying (1.5) by p_{kr} and summing over k we get in like manner

$$(1.8) \qquad \sum_{k=1}^{\rho} b_{jk}^{(v)} p_{kr} = t_v b_{jr}^{(v)}.$$

Consider the ρ by ρ matrix $b^{(v)}$ with elements $b_{ik}^{(v)}$. The relations[4] (1.7) assert that its kth column represents a solution of the ρ linear equations

$$(1.9) \qquad \sum_{j=1}^{\rho} p_{ij} x_j - t x_i = 0$$

with $t = t_v$; similarly (1.8) states that the jth row satisfies

$$(1.10) \qquad \sum_{k=1}^{\rho} y_k p_{kr} - t y_r = 0$$

with $t = t_v$. The system (1.10) is obtained from (1.9) by interchanging rows and columns, and so the determinants are the same. The determinant of (1.9) vanishes only if t coincides with one of the distinct characteristic values $t_1, \ldots, t_\rho$. In other words, the two systems (1.9) and (1.10) admit of a non-trivial solution if, and only if, $t = t_v$ for some v. We denote a pair of corresponding solutions by $(x_1^{(v)}, \ldots, x_\rho^{(v)})$ and $(y_1^{(v)}, \ldots, y_\rho^{(v)})$. They are determined up to multiplicative constants, and so

$$(1.11) \qquad b_{jk}^{(v)} = c^{(v)} x_j^{(v)} y_k^{(v)},$$

where $c^{(v)}$ is a constant (independent of j and k). To find this unknown constant we note that (1.9) implies by induction that

$$(1.12) \qquad \sum_{j=1}^{\rho} p_{ij}^{(n)} x_j = t^n x_i$$

for all n. We use this relation for $t = t_\lambda$, where λ is an arbitrary integer between 1 and ρ. When $p_{ij}^{(n)}$ is expressed in accordance with (1.5) we

---

[4] The two systems (1.7) and (1.8) may be written in the compact matrix form $P b^{(v)} = t_v b^{(v)}$ and $b^{(v)} P = t_v b^{(v)}$.

find

$$(1.13) \qquad t_\lambda^n x_i = t_1^n c^{(1)} x_i^{(1)} \sum_{k=1}^{\rho} y_k^{(1)} x_k^{(\lambda)} + \cdots + t_\rho^n c^{(\rho)} x_i^{(\rho)} \sum_{k=1}^{\rho} y_k^{(\rho)} x_k^{(\lambda)} .$$

This represents an identity of the form (1.6) which can hold only if all coefficients vanish. Equating the coefficients of t_λ^n on both sides we get finally[5]

$$(1.14) \qquad c^{(\lambda)} \sum_{k=1}^{\rho} y_k^{(\lambda)} x_k^{(\lambda)} = 1.$$

This relation determines the coefficient $b_{jk}^{(\lambda)}$ in (1.11). It is true that the $x_j^{(\lambda)}$ and $y_k^{(\lambda)}$ are determined only up to a multiplicative constant, but replacing $x_j^{(\lambda)}$ by $A x_j^{(\lambda)}$ and $y_k^{(\lambda)}$ by $B y_k^{(\lambda)}$ changes $c^{(\lambda)}$ into $c^{(\lambda)}/AB$, and the coefficient $b_{jk}^{(\lambda)}$ remains unchanged.

We summarize this result as follows. The two systems of linear equations (1.9) and (1.10) admit of non-trivial solutions only for at most ρ distinct values of t (the same for both systems). We suppose that there are exactly ρ such values $t_1, \ldots, t_\rho$, all different from 0. *To each* t_λ *choose a non-zero solution* $(x_1^{(\lambda)}, \ldots, x_\rho^{(\lambda)})$ *of* (1.9) *and a non-zero solution* $(y_1^{(\lambda)}, \ldots, y_\rho^{(\lambda)})$ *of* (1.10). *With* $c^{(\lambda)}$ *given by* (1.14) *we have then for* $n = 0, 1, \ldots$

$$(1.15) \qquad p_{jk}^{(n)} = \sum_{\lambda=1}^{\rho} c^{(\lambda)} x_j^{(\lambda)} y_k^{(\lambda)} t_\lambda^n .$$

We have thus found an explicit expression for all the transition probabilities.[6]

The assumption that the characteristic roots are distinct is satisfied in most practical cases, except for decomposable chains, and these require only minor changes in the setup (see section 4). Not infrequently, however, 0 is among the characteristic roots. In this case we put $t_\rho = 0$. The novel feature derives from the fact that the determinant $D(s)$ of the system (1.3) now has only the $\rho - 1$ roots $t_1^{-1}, \ldots, t_{\rho-1}^{-1}$, and so the generating function $P_{jk}(s)$ is the ratio of two polynomials of degree $\rho - 1$. The

---

[5] The vanishing of the other coefficients implies that $\sum_{k=1}^{\rho} y_k^{(\lambda)} x_k^{(\nu)} = 0$ whenever $\lambda \neq \nu$.

[6] The final formula (1.15) becomes more elegant in matrix form. Let $X^{(\lambda)}$ be the *column* vector (or ρ by 1 matrix) with elements $x_j^{(\lambda)}$, and $Y^{(\lambda)}$ the *row* vector (or 1 by ρ matrix) with elements $y_k^{(\lambda)}$. Then (1.15) takes on the form

$$P^n = \sum_{\lambda=1}^{\rho} c^{(\lambda)} X^{(\lambda)} Y^{(\lambda)} t_\lambda^n$$

and $c^{(\lambda)}$ is defined by the scalar equation $c^{(\lambda)} Y^{(\lambda)} X^{(\lambda)} = 1$.

partial fraction expansions require that the degree of the numerator be smaller than the degree of the denominator, and to achieve this we must first subtract an appropriate constant from $P_{jk}(s)$. In this way we obtain for $P_{jk}(s)$ a partial fraction expansion differing from (1.4) in that the last term is replaced by a constant. A glance at (1.15) shows that this affects the right side only when $n = 0$. In other words, *the explicit representation* (1.15) *of* $p_{jk}^{(n)}$ *remains valid for* $n \geq 1$ *even if* $t_\rho = 0$ (provided the roots $t_1, \ldots, t_{\rho-1}$ are distinct and different from zero).

The left side in (1.15) can remain bounded for all n only if $|t_\lambda| \leq 1$ for all λ. For $t = 1$ the equations (1.9) have the solution $x_j = 1$ and so one characteristic root equals 1. Without loss of generality we may put $t_1 = 1$. If the chain is aperiodic we have $|t_\lambda| < 1$ for all other roots and one sees from (1.15) that as $n \to \infty$

$$(1.16) \qquad p_{jk}^{(n)} \to c^{(1)} y_k^{(1)} .$$

In other words, *the invariant probability distribution is characterized as a solution of* (1.10) *with* $t = 1$.

2. EXAMPLES

(*a*) Consider first a chain with only two states. The matrix of transition probabilities assumes the simple form

$$P = \begin{pmatrix} 1-p & p \\ \alpha & 1-\alpha \end{pmatrix}$$

where $0 < p < 1$ and $0 < \alpha < 1$. The calculations are trivial since they involve only systems of two equations. The characteristic roots are $t_1 = 1$ and $t_2 = (1-\alpha-p)$. The explicit representation (1.15) for $p_{jk}^{(n)}$ may be exhibited in matrix form

$$P^n = \frac{1}{\alpha + p} \begin{pmatrix} \alpha & p \\ \alpha & p \end{pmatrix} + \frac{(1-\alpha-p)^n}{\alpha + p} \begin{pmatrix} p & -p \\ -\alpha & \alpha \end{pmatrix}$$

(where factors common to all four elements have been taken out as factors to the matrices). This formula is valid for $n \geq 0$.

(*b*) Let

$$(2.1) \qquad P = \begin{bmatrix} 0 & 0 & 0 & 1 \\ 0 & 0 & 0 & 1 \\ \frac{1}{2} & \frac{1}{2} & 0 & 0 \\ 0 & 0 & 1 & 0 \end{bmatrix}$$

[this is the matrix of problem (2.b) in XV,14]. The system (1.9) reduces to

$$(2.2) \qquad x_4 = tx_1, \qquad x_4 = tx_2, \qquad \tfrac{1}{2}(x_1+x_2) = tx_3, \qquad x_3 = tx_4.$$

To $t = 0$ there corresponds the solution $(1, -1, 0, 0)$, but we saw that the characteristic root 0 is not required for the explicit representation of $p_{jk}^{(n)}$ for $n \geq 1$. The standard procedure of eliminating variables shows that the other characteristic roots satisfy the cubic equation $t^3 = 1$. If we put for abbreviation

$$(2.3) \qquad\qquad \theta = e^{\frac{2}{3}\pi i} = \cos \tfrac{2}{3}\pi + i \sin \tfrac{2}{3}\pi$$

(where $i^2 = -1$) the three characteristic roots are $t_1 = 1$, $t_2 = \theta$, and $t_3 = \theta^2$ (which is the same as $t_3 = \theta^{-1}$). We have now to solve the systems (1.9) and (1.10) with these values for t. Since a multiplicative constant remains arbitrary we may put $x_1^{(\nu)} = y_1^{(\nu)} = 1$. The solutions then coincide, respectively, with the first columns and first rows of the three matrices in the final explicit representation

(2.4)

$$P^n = \frac{1}{6}\begin{bmatrix} 1 & 1 & 2 & 2 \\ 1 & 1 & 2 & 2 \\ 1 & 1 & 2 & 2 \\ 1 & 1 & 2 & 2 \end{bmatrix} + \frac{\theta^n}{6}\begin{bmatrix} 1 & 1 & 2\theta & 2\theta^2 \\ 1 & 1 & 2\theta & 2\theta^2 \\ \theta^2 & \theta^2 & 2 & 2\theta \\ \theta & \theta & 2\theta^2 & 2 \end{bmatrix} + \frac{\theta^{2n}}{6}\begin{bmatrix} 1 & 1 & 2\theta^2 & 2\theta \\ 1 & 1 & 2\theta^2 & 2\theta \\ \theta & \theta & 2 & 2\theta^2 \\ \theta^2 & \theta^2 & 2\theta & 2 \end{bmatrix}.$$

Since we have discarded the characteristic root $t = 0$ this formula is valid only for $n \geq 1$.

It is obvious from (2.4) that the chain has period 3. To see the asymptotic behavior of P^n we note that $1 + \theta + \theta^2 = 0$. Using this it is easily verified that when $n \to \infty$ through numbers of the form $n = 3k$ the rows of P^n tend to $(\tfrac{1}{2}, \tfrac{1}{2}, 0, 0)$. For $n = 3k + 1$ and $n = 3k + 2$ the corresponding limits are $(0, 0, 0, 1)$ and $(0, 0, 1, 0)$. It follows that the invariant probability distribution is given by $(\tfrac{1}{6}, \tfrac{1}{6}, \tfrac{1}{3}, \tfrac{1}{3})$.

(c) Let $p + q = 1$, and

$$(2.5) \qquad\qquad P = \begin{bmatrix} 0 & p & 0 & q \\ q & 0 & p & 0 \\ 0 & q & 0 & p \\ p & 0 & q & 0 \end{bmatrix}.$$

This chain represents a special case of the next example but is treated separately because of its simplicity. It is easily seen that the system (1.9) reduces to two linear equations for the two unknowns $x_1 + x_3$ and

$x_2 + x_4$, and hence that the four characteristic roots are given by

(2.6) $t_1 = 1,$ $t_2 = -1,$ $t_3 = i(q-p),$ $t_4 = -i(q-p).$

The corresponding solutions are $(1, 1, 1, 1)$, $(-1, 1, -1, 1)$, $(-i, -1, i, 1)$, and $(i, -1, -i, 1)$. [It will be noted that they are of the form $(\theta, \theta^2, \theta^3, \theta^4)$ where θ is a fourth root of unity.] The system (1.10) differs from (1.9) only in that the roles of p and q are interchanged, and we get therefore without further calculations

(2.7) $p_{jk}^{(n)} = \tfrac{1}{4}\{1 + (q-p)^n i^{j-k-n}\}\{1 + (-1)^{k+j-n}\}.$

(d) In the *general cyclical random walk* of example XV, (2.d) the first row of the matrix P is given by $q_0, \ldots, q_{\rho-1}$ and the other rows are obtained by cyclical permutations. In the special case $\rho = 4$ it was shown in the preceding example that $x_j^{(v)}$ and $y_k^{(v)}$ are expressible as powers of the fourth roots of unity. It is therefore natural to try a similar procedure in terms of the ρth root of unity, namely

(2.8) $$\theta = e^{2i\pi/\rho}.$$

All ρth roots of unity are given by $1, \theta, \theta^2, \ldots, \theta^{\rho-1}$. For $r = 1, \ldots,$ we put

(2.9) $$t_r = \sum_{v=0}^{\rho-1} q_v \theta^{vr}.$$

It is easily verified that for $t = t_r$ the systems (1.9) and (1.10) have the solutions

(2.10) $$x_j^{(r)} = \theta^{rj}, \qquad y_k^{(r)} = \theta^{-rk}$$

and for the corresponding coefficients $c^{(r)}$ we have in all cases $c^{(r)} = 1/\rho$. Thus finally[7]

(2.11) $$p_{jk}^{(n)} = \rho^{-1} \sum_{r=1}^{\rho-1} \theta^{r(j-k)} t_r^n.$$

---

[7] For $n = 0$ the right side in (2.11) is defined only when no t_r vanishes. Actually we have proved the validity of (2.11) for $n \geq 1$ assuming that the roots t_r are distinct, and this is not necessarily true in the present situation. For example, if $q_k = \rho^{-1}$ for all k then $t_0 = 1$, but $t_1 = \cdots = t_{\rho-1} = 0$. Even in this extreme case (2.11) remains valid since the right side yields for all j, k, and $n \geq 1$. Fortunately it is not difficult to verify (2.11) directly by induction on n. In particular, when $n = 1$ the factor of q_v in (2.9) reduces to

$$\sum_{r=0}^{\rho-1} \theta^{r(j-k+v)}.$$

This sum is zero except when $j - k + v = 0$ or ρ, in which case each term equals one. Hence $p_{jk}^{(1)}$ reduces to q_{k-j} if $k \geq j$ and to $q_{\rho+k-j}$ if $k < j$, and this is the given matrix (p_{jk}).

(e) *The occupancy problem.* Example XV, (2.g) shows that the classical occupancy problem can be treated by the method of Markov chains. The system is in state j if there are j occupied and $\rho - j$ empty cells. If this is the initial situation and n additional balls are placed at random, then $p_{jk}^{(n)}$ is the probability that there will be k occupied and $\rho - k$ empty cells (so that $p_{jk}^{(n)} = 0$ if $k < j$). For $j = 0$ this probability follows from II, (11.7). We now derive a formula for $p_{jk}^{(n)}$, thus generalizing the result of chapter II.

Since $p_{jj} = j/\rho$ and $p_{j,j+1} = (\rho-j)/\rho$ the system (1.9) reduces to

$$(2.12) \qquad\qquad (\rho t - j)x_j = (\rho - j)x_{j+1}.$$

For $t = 1$ this implies $x_j = 1$ for all j. When $t \neq 1$ it is necessary that $x_\rho = 0$, and hence there exists some index r such that $x_{r+1} = 0$ but $x_r \neq 0$; from (2.12) it follows then that $\rho\, t = r$. The characteristic roots are therefore given by

$$(2.13) \qquad\qquad t_r = r/\rho, \qquad\qquad r = 1, \ldots, \rho.$$

The corresponding solutions of (2.12) are given by

$$(2.14) \qquad\qquad x_j^{(r)} = \binom{r}{j} \Big/ \binom{\rho}{j}$$

so that $x_j^{(r)} = 0$ when $j > r$. For $t = t_r$ the system (1.10) reduces to

$$(2.15) \qquad\qquad (r-j)y_j^{(r)} = (\rho-j+1)y_{j-1}^{(r)}$$

and has the solution

$$(2.16) \qquad\qquad y_j^{(r)} = \binom{\rho-r}{j-r}(-1)^{j-r}$$

where, of course, $y_j^{(r)} = 0$ if $j < r$. Since $x_j^{(r)} = 0$ for $j > r$ and $y_j^{(r)} = 0$ for $j < r$ we get

$$1/c^{(r)} = x_r^{(r)}y_r^{(r)} = \binom{\rho}{r}$$

and hence

$$(2.17) \qquad p_{jk}^{(n)} = \sum_{r=j}^{k} \left(\frac{r}{\rho}\right)^n \binom{\rho}{r}\binom{r}{j}\binom{\rho-r}{k-r}(-1)^{k-r} \Big/ \binom{\rho}{j}.$$

On expressing the binomial coefficients in terms of factorials, this formula simplifies to

$$(2.18) \qquad p_{jk}^{(n)} = \binom{\rho-j}{\rho-k}\sum_{v=0}^{k-j} \left(\frac{v+j}{\rho}\right)^n (-1)^{k-j-v}\binom{k-j}{v},$$

with $p_{jk}^{(n)} = 0$ if $k < j$.   ▶

[For a numerical illustration see example (4.b).]

3. RANDOM WALK WITH REFLECTING BARRIERS

The application of Markov chains will now be illustrated by a complete discussion of a random walk with states $1, 2, \ldots, \rho$ and two reflecting barriers.[8] The matrix P is displayed in example XV, $(2.c)$. For $2 \leq k \leq$ $\leq \rho - 1$ we have $p_{k,k+1} = p$ and $p_{k,k-1} = q$; the first and the last rows are defined by $(q, p, 0, \ldots, 0)$ $(0, \ldots, 0, q, p)$.

For convenience of comparisons with the developments in chapter XIV we now discard the variable $t = s^{-1}$ and write the characteristic roots in the form s_r^{-1} (rather than t_r); it will be convenient to number them from 0 to $\rho - 1$. In terms of the variable s the linear system (1.9) becomes

$$x_1 = s(qx_1 + px_2)$$

(3.1) $$x_j = s(qx_{j-1} + px_{j+1}) \qquad (j = 2, 3, \ldots, \rho - 1)$$

$$x_\rho = s(qx_{\rho-1} + px_\rho).$$

This system admits the solution $x_j = 1$ corresponding to the root $s = 1$. To find all other solutions we apply the method of particular solutions (which we have used for similar equations in XIV, 4). The middle equation in (3.1) is satisfied by $x_j = \lambda^j$ provided that λ is a root of the quadratic equation $\lambda = qs + \lambda^2 ps$. The two roots of this equation are

(3.2) $$\lambda_1(s) = \frac{1 + \sqrt{1 - 4pqs^2}}{2ps}, \qquad \lambda_2(s) = \frac{1 - \sqrt{1 - 4pqs^2}}{2ps},$$

and the most general solution of the middle equation in (3.1) is therefore

(3.3) $$x_j = A(s)\lambda_1^j(s) + B(s)\lambda_2^j(s),$$

where $A(s)$ and $B(s)$ are arbitrary. The first and the last equation in (3.1) will be satisfied by (3.3) if, and only if, $x_0 = x_1$ and $x_\rho = x_{\rho+1}$. This requires that $A(s)$ and $B(s)$ satisfy the conditions

(3.4)
$$A(s)\{1 - \lambda_1(s)\} + B(s)\{1 - \lambda_2(s)\} = 0$$

$$A(s)\lambda_1^\rho(s)\{1 - \lambda_1(s)\} + B(s)\lambda_2^\rho(s)\{1 - \lambda_2(s)\} = 0.$$

Conversely, if these two equations hold for some value of s, then (3.2) represents a solution of the linear system (3.1) and this solution is identically zero only when $\lambda_1(s) = \lambda_2(s)$. Our problem is therefore to find the

---

[8] Part of what follows is a repetition of the theory of chapter XIV. Our quadratic equation occurs there as (4.7); the quantities $\lambda_1(s)$ and $\lambda_2(s)$ of the text were given in (4.8), and the general solution (3.3) appears in chapter XIV as (4.9). The two methods are related, but in many cases the computational details will differ radically.

values of s for which

$$(3.5) \qquad \lambda_1^\rho(s) = \lambda_2^\rho(s) \qquad but \qquad \lambda_1(s) \neq \lambda_2(s).$$

Since $\lambda_1(s)\lambda_2(s) = q/p$ the first relation implies that $\lambda_1(s)\sqrt{p/q}$ must be a (2ρ)th root of unity, that is, we must have

$$(3.6) \qquad \lambda_1(s) = \sqrt{q/p}\, e^{i\pi r/\rho}$$

where r is an integer such that $0 \leq r < 2\rho$. From the definition (3.2) it follows easily that (3.6) holds only when $s = s_r$ where

$$(3.7) \qquad s_r^{-1} = 2\sqrt{pq} \cdot \cos \pi r/\rho.$$

The value $s = s_\rho$ violates the second condition in (3.5); furthermore $s_r = s_{2\rho-r}$, and so ρ distinct characteristic values are given by (3.7) with $r = 0, 1, \ldots, \rho - 1$.

Solving (3.4) with $s = s_r$ and substituting into (3.3) we get

$$(3.8) \qquad x_j^{(r)} = \left(\frac{q}{p}\right)^{j/2} \sin \frac{\pi r j}{\rho} - \left(\frac{q}{p}\right)^{(j+1)/2} \sin \frac{\pi r(j-1)}{\rho}$$

for $r = 1, \ldots, \rho - 1$ whereas for $r = 0$

$$(3.9) \qquad x_j^{(0)} = 1.$$

The adjoint system (1.10) reduces to

$$(3.10) \qquad \begin{aligned} y_1 &= sq(y_1 + y_2), \\ y_k &= s(py_{k-1} + qy_{k+1}), \qquad (k = 2, \ldots, \rho - 1) \\ y_\rho &= sp(y_{\rho-1} + y_\rho). \end{aligned}$$

The middle equation is the same as (3.1) with p and q interchanged, and its general solution is therefore obtained from (3.3) by interchanging p and q. The first and the last equations can be satisfied if $s = s_r$, and a simple calculation shows that for $r = 1, 2, \ldots, \rho - 1$ the solution of (3.10) is

$$(3.11) \qquad y_k^{(r)} = \left(\frac{p}{q}\right)^{k/2} \sin \frac{\pi r k}{\rho} - \left(\frac{p}{q}\right)^{(k-1)/2} \sin \frac{\pi r(k-1)}{\rho}.$$

For $s_0 = 1$ we get similarly

$$(3.12) \qquad y_k^{(0)} = (p/q)^k.$$

It remains to find the coefficients $c^{(r)}$ defined by

$$(3.13) \qquad c^{(r)} \sum_{k=0}^{\rho-1} x_k^{(r)} y_k^{(r)} = 1.$$

When $r = 0$ the kth term of the sum equals $(p/q)^k$ and so

$$(3.14) \qquad c^{(0)} = \frac{q}{p} \cdot \frac{(p/q) - 1}{(p/q)^\rho - 1},$$

except when $p = q$, in which case $c_0 = 1/\rho$. When $r \geq 1$ an elementary, if tedious, calculation[9] leads to

$$(3.15) \qquad c^{(r)} = \frac{2p}{\rho} \left\{ 1 - 2\sqrt{pq} \cos \frac{\pi r}{\rho} \right\}^{-1}.$$

Accordingly, the general representation (1.15) for the higher transition probabilities leads to the final result[10]

$$(3.16) \quad p_{jk}^{(n)} = \frac{(p/q) - 1}{(p/q)^\rho - 1} \left(\frac{p}{q} \right)^{k-1} + \frac{2p}{\rho} \sum_{r=1}^{\rho-1} \frac{x_j^{(r)} y_k^{(r)} [2\sqrt{pq} \cos \pi r/\rho]^n}{1 - 2\sqrt{pq} \cos \pi r/\rho}$$

with $x_j^{(r)}$ and $y_k^{(r)}$ defined by (3.8) and (3.11). When $p = q$ the first term on the right is to be interpreted as $1/\rho$.

4. TRANSIENT STATES; ABSORPTION PROBABILITIES

The theorem of section 1 was derived under the assumption that the roots $t_1, t_2, \ldots$ are distinct. The presence of multiple roots does not require essential modifications, but we shall discuss only a particular

---

[9] The calculations simplify considerably in complex notation using the fact that $\sin v = [e^{iv} - e^{-iv}]/(2i)$. The sum in (3.13) reduces to a linear combination (with complex coefficients) of sums of the form

$$\sum_{j=0}^{\rho-1} e^{2j\pi im/\rho}$$

where $m = 0$ or $m = \pm 1$. In the first case the sum equals ρ, in the second 0, and (3.15) follows trivially.

[10] For analogous formulas in the case of one reflecting and one absorbing barrier see M. Kac, *Random walk and the theory of Brownian motion*, Amer. Math. Monthly, vol. 54 (1947), pp. 369–391. The definition of the reflecting barrier is there modified so that the particle may reach 0; whenever this occurs, the next step takes it to 1. The explicit formulas are then more complicated. Kac's paper contains also formulas for $p_{jk}^{(n)}$ in the Ehrenfest model [example XV, (2.e)].

case of special importance. The root $t_1 = 1$ is multiple whenever the chain contains two or more closed subchains, and this is a frequent situation in problems connected with absorption probabilities. It is easy to adapt the method of section 1 to this case. For conciseness and clarity, we shall explain the procedure by means of examples which will reveal the main features of the general case.

Examples. (*a*) Consider the matrix of transition probabilities

$$(4.1) \qquad P = \begin{bmatrix} \frac{1}{3} & \frac{2}{3} & 0 & 0 & 0 & 0 \\ \frac{2}{3} & \frac{1}{3} & 0 & 0 & 0 & 0 \\ 0 & 0 & \frac{1}{4} & \frac{3}{4} & 0 & 0 \\ 0 & 0 & \frac{1}{5} & \frac{4}{5} & 0 & 0 \\ \frac{1}{4} & 0 & \frac{1}{4} & 0 & \frac{1}{4} & \frac{1}{4} \\ \frac{1}{6} & \frac{1}{6} & \frac{1}{6} & \frac{1}{6} & \frac{1}{6} & \frac{1}{6} \end{bmatrix}.$$

It is clear that E_1 and E_2 form a closed set (that is, no transition is possible to any of the remaining four states; compare XV, 4). Similarly E_3 and E_4 form another closed set. Finally, E_5 and E_6 are transient states. After finitely many steps the system passes into one of the two closed sets and remains there.

The matrix P has the form of a partitioned matrix

$$(4.2) \qquad P = \begin{bmatrix} A & 0 & 0 \\ 0 & B & 0 \\ U & V & T \end{bmatrix}$$

where each letter stands for a 2 by 2 matrix and each zero for a matrix with four zeros. For example, A has the rows $(\frac{1}{3}, \frac{2}{3})$ and $(\frac{2}{3}, \frac{1}{3})$; this is the matrix of transition probabilities corresponding to the chain formed by the two states E_1 and E_2. This matrix can be studied by itself, and the powers A^n can be obtained from example (2.*a*) with $p = \alpha = \frac{2}{3}$. When the powers $P^2, P^3, \ldots$ are calculated, it will be found that the first two rows are in no way affected by the remaining four rows. More precisely, P^n has the form

$$(4.3) \qquad P^n = \begin{bmatrix} A^n & 0 & 0 \\ 0 & B^n & 0 \\ U_n & V_n & T^n \end{bmatrix}$$

where A^n, B^n, T^n are the nth powers of A, B, and T, respectively, and can be calculated[11] by the method of section 1 [cf. example (2.a) where all calculations are performed]. Instead of six equations with six unknowns we are confronted only with systems of two equations with two unknowns each.

It should be noted that the matrices U_n and V_n in (4.3) are not powers of U and V and cannot be obtained in the same simple way as A^n, B^n, and T^n. However, in the calculation of $P^2, P^3, \ldots$ the third and fourth columns never affect the remaining four columns. In other words, if in P^n the rows and columns corresponding to E_3 and E_4 are deleted, we get the matrix

$$(4.4) \qquad \begin{pmatrix} A^n & 0 \\ U_n & T^n \end{pmatrix}$$

which is the nth power of the corresponding submatrix in P, that is, of

$$(4.5) \qquad \begin{pmatrix} A & 0 \\ U & T \end{pmatrix} = \begin{bmatrix} \frac{1}{3} & \frac{2}{3} & 0 & 0 \\ \frac{2}{3} & \frac{1}{3} & 0 & 0 \\ \frac{1}{4} & 0 & \frac{1}{4} & \frac{1}{4} \\ \frac{1}{6} & \frac{1}{6} & \frac{1}{6} & \frac{1}{6} \end{bmatrix}.$$

Therefore matrix (4.4) can be calculated by the method of section 1, which in the present case simplifies considerably. The matrix V_n can be obtained in a similar way.

Usually the explicit forms of U_n and V_n are of interest only inasmuch as they are connected with *absorption probabilities*. If the system starts from, say, E_5, what is the *probability* λ *that it will eventually pass into the closed set formed by* E_1 *and* E_2 (and not into the other closed set)? What is the *probability* λ_n *that this will occur exactly at the nth step*? Clearly $p_{51}^{(n)} + p_{52}^{(n)}$ is the probability that the considered event occurs at the nth step or before, that is,

$$p_{51}^{(n)} + p_{52}^{(n)} = \lambda_1 + \lambda_2 + \cdots + \lambda_n.$$

Letting $n \to \infty$, we get λ. A preferable way to calculate λ_n is as follows. The $(n-1)$st step must take the system to a state other than E_1 and E_2, that is, to either E_5 or E_6 (since from E_3 or E_4 no transition to E_1 and E_2 is possible). The nth step then takes the system to E_1 or E_2.

---

[11] In T the rows do not add to unity so that T is not a stochastic matrix. The matrix is substochastic in the sense of the definition in XV, 8. The method of section 1 applies without change, except that $t = 1$ is no longer a root (so that $T^n \to 0$).

Hence

$$\lambda_n = p_{55}^{(n-1)}(p_{51}+p_{52}) + p_{56}^{(n-1)}(p_{61}+p_{62}) = \tfrac{1}{4}p_{55}^{(n-1)} + \tfrac{1}{3}p_{56}^{(n-1)}.$$

It will be noted that λ_n is completely determined by the elements of T^{n-1}, and this matrix is easily calculated. In the present case

$$p_{55}^{(n)} = p_{56}^{(n)} = \tfrac{1}{4}(\tfrac{5}{12})^{n-1} \quad \text{and hence} \quad \lambda_n = \tfrac{7}{48}(\tfrac{5}{12})^{n-2}.$$

(b) *Brother-sister mating.* We conclude by a numerical treatment of the chain of example XV, (2.j). The main point of the following discussion is to show that the canonical representation

$$(4.6) \qquad\qquad p_{jk}^{(n)} = \sum_{r=1}^{6} t_r^n c^{(r)} x_j^{(r)} y_k^{(r)}$$

remains valid even though $t = 1$ is a *double root* of the characteristic equation.

The system (1.9) of linear equations takes on the form

$$(4.7) \qquad x_1 = tx_1, \quad \tfrac{1}{4}x_1 + \tfrac{1}{2}x_2 + \tfrac{1}{4}x_3 = tx_2,$$

$$\tfrac{1}{16}x_1 + \tfrac{1}{4}x_2 + \tfrac{1}{4}x_3 + \tfrac{1}{4}x_4 + \tfrac{1}{16}x_5 + \tfrac{1}{8}x_6 = tx_3$$

$$\tfrac{1}{4}x_3 + \tfrac{1}{2}x_4 + \tfrac{1}{4}x_5 = tx_4, \quad x_5 = tx_5, \quad x_3 = tx_6,$$

and these equations exhibit the form of the given matrix. From the first and fifth equations it is clear that $x_1 = x_5 = 0$ unless $t = 1$. For $t \neq 1$, therefore, the equations reduce effectively to four equations for four unknowns and the standard elimination of variables leads to a fourth-degree equation for t as a condition for the compatibility of the four equations. Since there are six characteristic roots in all it follows that $t = 1$ is a double root. It is not difficult to verify that the six characteristic roots are[12]

$$(4.8) \quad t_1 = t_2 = 1, \quad t_3 = \tfrac{1}{2}, \quad t_4 = \tfrac{1}{4}, \quad t_5 = \tfrac{1}{4} + \tfrac{1}{4}\sqrt{5}, \quad t_6 = \tfrac{1}{4} - \tfrac{1}{4}\sqrt{5}.$$

The corresponding solutions $(x_1^{(r)}, \ldots, x_6^{(r)})$ of (4.7) can be chosen as follows:

$$(4.9) \quad (1, \tfrac{3}{4}, \tfrac{1}{2}, \tfrac{1}{4}, 0, \tfrac{1}{2}), \quad (0, \tfrac{1}{4}, \tfrac{1}{2}, \tfrac{3}{4}, 1, \tfrac{1}{2}), \quad (0, 1, 0, -1, 0, 0)$$

$$(0, 1, -1, 1, 0, -4), \quad (0, 1, -1+\sqrt{5}, 1, 0, 6-2\sqrt{5}),$$

$$(0, 1, -1-\sqrt{5}, 1, 0, \ \ 6+2\sqrt{5}).$$

---

[12] The root $t_3 = \tfrac{1}{2}$ can be found by inspection since it corresponds to the simple solution $x_2 = -x_4 = 1$ and $x_1 = x_3 = x_5 = x_6 = 0$. The cubic equation for the other roots is of a simple character.

The next problem is to find the corresponding solutions $(y_1^{(r)}, \ldots, y_6^{(r)})$ of the system obtained from (4.7) by interchanging rows and columns. For $r \geq 3$ this solution is determined up to a multiplicative constant, but corresponding to the double root $t_1 = t_2 = 1$ we have to choose among infinitely many solutions of the form $(a, 0, 0, 0, b, 0)$. The appropriate choice becomes obvious from the form of the desired representation (4.6). Indeed, a glance at (4.9) shows that $x_1^{(r)} = 0$ except for $r = 1$, and hence (4.6) yields $p_{1k}^{(n)} = c^{(1)} y_k^{(1)}$ for all k and n. But E_1 is an absorbing state and it is obvious that $p_{1k}^{(n)} = 0$ for all $k \neq 1$. It follows that for $r = 1$ we must choose a solution of the form $(a, 0, 0, 0, 0, 0)$, and for the same reason a solution corresponding to $r = 2$ is $(0, 0, 0, 0, b, 0)$. The solutions corresponding to the remaining characteristic values are easily found. (Those chosen in our calculations are exhibited by the second rows of the matrices below.) The norming constants $c^{(r)}$ are then determined by (1.14), and in this way we get all the qualities entering the representation formula (4.6).

In the display of the final result the matrices corresponding to $r = 1$ and $r = 2$ have been combined into one. Furthermore, the elements $c^{(r)} x_j^{(r)} y_k^{(r)}$ corresponding to $r = 5$ and $r = 6$ are of the form $a \pm b\sqrt{5}$. For typographical convenience and clarity it was necessary to regroup their contributions in the form $a[t_5^n + t_6^n]$ and $b\sqrt{5}[t_5^n - t_6^n]$.

$$
P^n =
\begin{vmatrix}
1 & 0 & 0 & 0 & 0 & 0 \\
\frac{3}{4} & 0 & 0 & 0 & \frac{1}{4} & 0 \\
\frac{1}{2} & 0 & 0 & 0 & \frac{1}{2} & 0 \\
\frac{1}{4} & 0 & 0 & 0 & \frac{3}{4} & 0 \\
0 & 0 & 0 & 0 & 1 & 0 \\
\frac{1}{2} & 0 & 0 & 0 & \frac{1}{2} & 0
\end{vmatrix}
+ \frac{2^{-n}}{4}
\begin{vmatrix}
0 & 0 & 0 & 0 & 0 & 0 \\
-1 & 2 & 0 & -2 & 1 & 0 \\
0 & 0 & 0 & 0 & 0 & 0 \\
1 & -2 & 0 & 2 & -1 & 0 \\
0 & 0 & 0 & 0 & 0 & 0 \\
0 & 0 & 0 & 0 & 0 & 0
\end{vmatrix}
$$

$$
+ \frac{4^{-n}}{20}
\begin{vmatrix}
0 & 0 & 0 & 0 & 0 & 0 \\
-1 & 4 & -4 & 4 & -1 & -2 \\
1 & -4 & 4 & -4 & 1 & 2 \\
-1 & 4 & -4 & 4 & -1 & -2 \\
0 & 0 & 0 & 0 & 0 & 0 \\
4 & -16 & 16 & -16 & 4 & 8
\end{vmatrix}
+ \frac{t_5^n + t_6^n}{40}
\begin{vmatrix}
0 & 0 & 0 & 0 & 0 & 0 \\
-9 & 6 & 4 & 6 & -9 & 2 \\
-11 & 4 & 16 & 4 & -11 & -2 \\
-9 & 6 & 4 & 6 & -9 & 2 \\
0 & 0 & 0 & 0 & 0 & 0 \\
-14 & 16 & -16 & 16 & -14 & 12
\end{vmatrix}
$$

$$
+ \frac{t_5^n - t_6^n}{40}\sqrt{5}
\begin{vmatrix}
0 & 0 & 0 & 0 & 0 & 0 \\
-4 & 2 & 4 & 2 & -4 & 0 \\
-5 & 4 & 0 & 4 & -5 & 2 \\
-4 & 2 & 4 & 2 & -4 & 0 \\
0 & 0 & 0 & 0 & 0 & 0 \\
-6 & 0 & 16 & 0 & -6 & -4
\end{vmatrix}.
$$

It is easily verified that this formula is valid for $n = 0$. On the other hand, from the structure of the right side in (4.6) it is clear that if (4.6) holds for some n then it is valid also for $n + 1$. In this way the validity of (4.6) can be established without recourse to the general theory of section 1.

5. APPLICATION TO RECURRENCE TIMES

In problem 19 of XIII,12 it is shown how the mean μ and the variance σ^2 of the recurrence time of a recurrent event $\mathcal{E}$ can be calculated in terms of the probabilities u_n that $\mathcal{E}$ occurs at the nth trial. If $\mathcal{E}$ is not periodic, then

$$(5.1) \qquad u_n \to \frac{1}{\mu} \quad \text{and} \quad \sum_{n=0}^{\infty} \left(u_n - \frac{1}{\mu} \right) = \frac{\sigma^2 - \mu + \mu^2}{2\mu^2},$$

provided that σ^2 is finite.

If we identify $\mathcal{E}$ with a persistent state E_j, then $u_n = p_{jj}^{(n)}$ (and $u_0 = 1$). In a finite Markov chain all recurrence times have finite variance (cf. problem 19 of XV, 14), so that (5.1) applies. Suppose that E_j is not periodic and that formula (1.5) applies. Then $t_1 = 1$ and $|t_r| < 1$ for $r = 2, 3, \ldots$, so that $p_{jj}^{(n)} \to p_{jj}^{(1)} = \mu_j^{-1}$. To the term $u_n - \mu^{-1}$ of (5.1) there corresponds

$$(5.2) \qquad p_{jj}^{(n)} - \frac{1}{\mu_j} = \sum_{r=2}^{\rho} p_{jj}^{(r)} t_r^n.$$

This formula is valid for $n \geq 1$; summing the geometric series with ratio t_r, we find

$$(5.3) \qquad \sum_{n=1}^{\infty} \left(p_{jj}^{(n)} - \frac{1}{\mu_j} \right) = \sum_{r=2}^{\rho} \frac{p_{jj}^{(r)} t_r}{1 - t_r}.$$

Introducing this into (5.1), we find that if E_j is a *non-periodic persistent state, then its mean recurrence time is given by* $\mu_j = 1/p_{jj}^{(1)}$, *and the variance of its recurrence time is*

$$(5.4) \qquad \sigma_j^2 = \mu_j - \mu_j^2 + 2\mu_j^2 \sum_{r=2}^{\rho} \frac{p_{jj}^{(r)} t_r}{1 - t_r}$$

provided, of course, that formula (1.3) is applicable and $t_1 = 1$. The case of periodic states and the occurrence of double roots require only obvious modifications.

CHAPTER XVII

The Simplest Time-Dependent
Stochastic Processes[1]

1. GENERAL ORIENTATION. MARKOV
PROCESSES

The Markov chains of the preceding chapters may be described very roughly as stochastic processes in which the future development depends only on the present state, but not on the past history of the process or the manner in which the present state was reached. These processes involve only countably many states $E_1, E_2, \ldots$ and depend on a discrete time parameter, that is, changes occur only at fixed epochs[2] $t = 0, 1, \ldots$. In the present chapter we shall consider phenomena such as telephone calls, radioactive disintegrations, and chromosome breakages, where changes may occur at any time. Mathematically speaking, we shall be concerned with stochastic processes involving only countably many states but depending on a continuous time parameter. A complete description of such processes is not possible within the framework of discrete probabilities and, in fact, we are not in a position to delineate formally the class of Markov processes in which we are interested. Indeed, to describe the past history of the process we must specify the epochs at which changes have occurred, and this involves probabilities in a continuum. Saying that the future development is independent of the past history has an obvious intuitive meaning (at least by analogy with discrete Markov chains), but a formal definition involves conditional probabilities which are beyond the scope of this book. However, many problems connected with such

---

[1] This chapter is almost independent of chapters X–XVI. For the use of the term stochastic process see footnote 28 in XV, 13.

[2] As in the preceding chapters, when dealing with stochastic processes we use the term *epoch* to denote points on the time axis. In formal discussions the word *time* will refer to durations.

processes can be treated separately by quite elementary methods provided it is taken for granted that the processes actually exist. We shall now proceed in this manner.

To the transition probability $p_{jk}^{(n)}$ of discrete Markov chains there corresponds now the transition probability $P_{jk}(t)$, namely the conditional probability of the state E_k at epoch $t+s$ given that at epoch $s < t+s$ the system was in state E_j. As the notation indicates, it is supposed that this probability depends only on the duration t of the time interval, but not on its position on the time axis. Such transition probabilities are called *stationary* or time-homogeneous. (However, inhomogeneous processes will be treated in section 9.) The analogue to the basic relations XV,(3.5) is *the Chapman-Kolmogorov identity*

$$(1.1) \qquad P_{ik}(\tau+t) = \sum_j P_{ij}(\tau) P_{jk}(t),$$

which is based on the following reasoning. Suppose that at epoch 0 the system is in state E_i. The jth term on the right then represents the probability of the compound event of finding the system at epoch τ in state E_j, and at the later epoch $\tau+t$ in state E_k. But a transition from E_i at epoch 0 to E_k at epoch $\tau+t$ necessarily occurs through some intermediary state E_j, and summing over all possible E_j we see that (1.1) must hold for arbitrary (fixed) $\tau > 0$ and $t > 0$.

In this chapter we shall study solutions of the basic identity (1.1). It will be shown that simple postulates adapted to concrete situations lead to systems of differential equations for the $P_{jk}(t)$, and interesting results can be obtained from these differential equations even without solving them. These results are meaningful because our solutions are actually the transition probabilities of a Markov process which is uniquely determined by them and the initial state at epoch 0. This intuitively obvious fact[3] will be taken for granted without proof.

For fixed j and t the transition probabilities $P_{jk}(t)$ define an ordinary discrete probability distribution. It depends on the continuous parameter t, but we have encountered many families of distributions involving continuous parameters. Technically the considerations of the following sections remain within the framework of discrete probabilities, but this artificial limitation is too rigid for many purposes. The Poisson distribution $\{e^{-\lambda t}(\lambda t)^n/n!\}$ may illustrate this point. Its zero term $e^{-\lambda t}$ may be

---

[3] It is noteworthy, however, that there may exist (rather pathological) non-Markovian processes with the same transition probabilities. This point was discussed at length in XII, 2.*a*, in connection with processes with independent increments (which are a special class of Markov processes). See also the discussion in section 9, in particular footnote 18.

interpreted as probability that no telephone call arrives within a time interval of fixed length t. But then $e^{-\lambda t}$ is also the probability that the waiting time for the first call exceeds t, and so we are indirectly concerned with a continuous probability distribution on the time axis. We shall return to this point in section 6.

2. THE POISSON PROCESS

The basic Poisson process may be viewed from various angles, and here we shall consider it as the prototype for the processes of this chapter. The following derivation of the Poisson distribution lends itself best for our generalizations, but it is by no means the best in other contexts. It should be compared with the elementary derivation in VI, 6 and the treatment of the Poisson process in XII, (2.a) as the simplest process with independent increments.

For an empirical background take random events such as disintegrations of particles, incoming telephone calls, and chromosome breakages under harmful irradiation. All occurrences are assumed to be of the same kind, and we are concerned with the total number $\mathbf{Z}(t)$ of occurrences in an arbitrary time interval of length t. Each occurrence is represented by a point on the time axis, and hence we are really concerned with certain random placements of points on a line. The underlying physical assumption is that the forces and influences governing the process remain constant so that the probability of any particular event is the same for all time intervals of duration t, and is independent of the past development of the process. In mathematical terms this means that the process is a time-homogeneous Markov process in the sense described in the preceding section. As stated before, we do not aim at a full theory of such processes, but shall be content with deriving the basic probabilities

$$(2.1) \qquad P_n(t) = \mathbf{P}\{\mathbf{Z}(t) = n\}.$$

These can be derived rigorously from simple postulates without appeal to deeper theories.

To introduce notations appropriate for the other processes in this chapter we choose an origin of time measurement and say that *at epoch* $t > 0$ *the system is in state* E_n if exactly n jumps occurred between 0 and t. Then $P_n(t)$ equals the probability of the state E_n at epoch t, but $P_n(t)$ may be described also as the transition probability from an arbitrary state E_j at an arbitrary epoch s to the state E_{j+n} at epoch $s + t$. We now translate our informal description of the process into properties of the probabilities $P_n(t)$.

Let us partition a time interval of unit length into N subintervals of length $h = N^{-1}$. The probability of a jump within any one among these subintervals equals $1 - P_0(h)$, and so the expected number of subintervals containing a jump equals $h^{-1}[1-P_0(h)]$. One feels intuitively that as $h \to 0$ this number will converge to the expected number of jumps within any time interval of unit length, and it is therefore natural to assume[4] that there exists a number $\lambda > 0$ such that

(2.2) $$h^{-1}[1-P_0(h)] \to \lambda.$$

The physical picture of the process requires also that a jump always leads from a state E_j to the neighboring state E_{j+1}, and this implies that the expected number of subintervals (of length h) containing more than one jump should tend to 0. Accordingly, we shall assume that as $h \to 0$

(2.3) $$h^{-1}[1-P_0(h)-P_1(h)] \to 0.$$

For the final formulation of the postulates we write (2.2) in the form $P_0(h) = 1 - \lambda h + o(h)$ where (as usual) $o(h)$ denotes a quantity of smaller order of magnitude than h. (More precisely, $o(h)$ stands for a quantity such that $h^{-1}o(h) \to 0$ as $h \to 0$.) With this notation (2.3) is equivalent to $P_1(h) = \lambda h + o(h)$. We now formulate the

Postulates for the Poisson process. *The process starts at epoch* 0 *from the state* E_0. (i) *Direct transitions from a state* E_j *are possible only to* E_{j+1}. (ii) *Whatever the state* E_j *at epoch* t, *the probability of a jump within an ensuing short time interval between* t *and* $t+h$ *equals* $\lambda h + o(h)$, *while the probability of more than one jump is* $o(h)$.

As explained in the preceding section, these conditions are weaker than our starting notion that the past history of the process in no way influences the future development. On the other hand, our postulates are of a purely analytic character, and they suffice to show that we must have

(2.4) $$P_n(t) = \frac{(\lambda t)^n}{n!} e^{-\lambda t}.$$

To prove this assume first $n \geq 1$ and consider the event that at epoch $t+h$ the system is in state E_n. The probability of this event equals $P_n(t+h)$, and the event can occur in three mutually exclusive ways. First, at epoch t the system may be in state E_n and no jump occurs between t and $t+h$. The probability of this contingency is

$$P_n(t)P_0(h) = P_n(t)[1-\lambda h] + o(h).$$

---

[4] The assumption (2.2) is introduced primarily because of its easy generalization to other processes. In the present case it would be more natural to observe that $P_0(t)$ must satisfy the functional equation $P_0(t+\tau) = P_0(t)P_0(\tau)$, which implies (2.2). (See section 6.)

The second possibility is that at epoch t the system is in state E_{n-1} and exactly one jump occurs between t and $t+h$. The probability for this is $P_{n-1}(t) \cdot \lambda h + o(h)$. Any other state at epoch t requires more than one jump between t and $t+h$, and the probability of such an event is $o(h)$. Accordingly we must have

$$(2.5) \qquad P_n(t+h) = P_n(t)(1-\lambda h) + P_{n-1}(t)\lambda h + o(h)$$

and this relation may be rewritten in the form

$$(2.6) \qquad \frac{P_n(t+h) - P_n(t)}{h} = -\lambda P_n(t) + \lambda P_{n-1}(t) + \frac{o(h)}{h} \, .$$

As $h \to 0$, the last term tends to zero; hence the limit[5] of the left side exists and

$$(2.7) \qquad P'_n(t) = -\lambda P_n(t) + \lambda P_{n-1}(t) \qquad\qquad (n \ge 1).$$

For $n = 0$ the second and third contingencies mentioned above do not arise, and therefore (2.7) is to be replaced by

$$(2.8) \qquad P_0(t+h) = P_0(t)(1-\lambda h) + o(h),$$

which leads to

$$(2.9) \qquad P'_0(t) = -\lambda P_0(t).$$

From this and $P_0(0) = 1$ we get $P_0(t) = e^{-\lambda t}$. Substituting this $P_0(t)$ into (2.7) with $n = 1$, we get an ordinary differential equation for $P_1(t)$. Since $P_1(0) = 0$, we find easily that $P_1(t) = \lambda t e^{-\lambda t}$, in agreement with (2.4). Proceeding in the same way, we find successively all terms of (2.4).

3. THE PURE BIRTH PROCESS

The simplest generalization of the Poisson process is obtained by permitting the probabilities of jumps to depend on the actual state of the system. This leads us to the following

Postulates. (i) *Direct transitions from a state E_j are possible only to E_{j+1}.* (ii) *If at epoch t the system is in state E_n the probability of a jump*

---

[5] Since we restricted h to positive values, $P'_n(t)$ in (2.7) should be interpreted as a right-hand derivative. It is really an ordinary two-sided derivative. In fact, the term $o(h)$ in (2.5) does not depend on t and therefore remains unchanged when t is replaced by $t - h$. Thus (2.5) implies continuity, and (2.6) implies differentiability in the ordinary sense. This remark applies throughout the chapter and will not be repeated.

within an ensuing short time interval between t *and* $t+h$ *equals* $\lambda_n h + o(h)$, *while the probability of more than one jump within this interval is* $o(h)$.

The salient feature of this assumption is that the time which the system spends in any particular state plays no role; there are sudden changes of state but no aging as long as the system remains within a single state.

Again let $P_n(t)$ be the probability that at epoch t the system is in state E_n. The functions $P_n(t)$ satisfy a system of differential equations which can be derived by the argument of the preceding section, with the only change that (2.5) is replaced by

$$(3.1) \qquad P_n(t+h) = P_n(t)(1 - \lambda_n h) + P_{n-1}(t)\lambda_{n-1}h + o(h).$$

In this way we get the *basic system of differential equations*

$$(3.2) \qquad \begin{aligned} P_n'(t) &= -\lambda_n P_n(t) + \lambda_{n-1}P_{n-1}(t) \qquad\qquad (n \geq 1), \\ P_0'(t) &= -\lambda_0 P_0(t). \end{aligned}$$

In the Poisson process it was natural to assume that the system starts from the initial state E_0 at epoch 0. We may now assume more generally that the system starts from an arbitrary initial state E_i. This implies that[6]

$$(3.3) \qquad\qquad P_i(0) = 1, \qquad P_n(0) = 0 \qquad\qquad for \ \ n \neq i.$$

These *initial conditions* uniquely determine the solution $\{P_n(t)\}$ of (3.2). [In particular, $P_0(t) = P_1(t) = \cdots = P_{i-1}(t) = 0.$] Explicit formulas for $P_n(t)$ have been derived independently by many authors but are of no interest to us. It is easily verified that for arbitrarily prescribed λ_n the system $\{P_n(t)\}$ has all required properties, except that under certain conditions $\sum P_n(t) < 1$. This phenomenon will be discussed in section 4.

Examples. (a) *Radioactive transmutations.* A radioactive atom, say uranium, may by emission of particles or γ-rays change to an atom of a different kind. Each kind represents a possible state of the system, and as the process continues, we get a succession of transitions $E_0 \rightarrow E_1 \rightarrow E_2 \rightarrow \rightarrow \cdots \rightarrow E_m$. According to accepted physical theories, the probability of a transition $E_n \rightarrow E_{n+1}$ remains unchanged as long as the atom is in state E_n, and this hypothesis is expressed by our starting supposition. The differential equations (3.2) therefore describe the process (a fact well known to physicists). If E_m is the terminal state from which no further

---

[6] It will be noticed that $P_n(t)$ is the same as the transition probability $P_{in}(t)$ of section 1.

transitions are possible, then $\lambda_m = 0$ and the system (3.2) terminates with $n = m$. [For $n > m$ we get automatically $P_n(t) = 0$.]

(b) *The Yule process.* Consider a population of members which can (by splitting or otherwise) give birth to new members but cannot die. Assume that during any short time interval of length h each member has probability $\lambda h + o(h)$ to create a new one; the constant λ determines the rate of increase of the population. If there is no interaction among the members and at epoch t the population size is n, then the probability that an increase takes place at some time between t and $t+h$ equals $n\lambda h + o(h)$. The probability $P_n(t)$ that the population numbers exactly n elements therefore satisfies (3.2) with $\lambda_n = n\lambda$, that is,

$$(3.4) \qquad P_n'(t) = -n\lambda P_n(t) + (n-1)\lambda P_{n-1}(t) \qquad (n \geq 1).$$

$$P_0'(t) = 0.$$

Denote the initial population size by i. The initial conditions (3.3) apply and it is easily verified that for $n \geq i > 0$

$$(3.5) \qquad P_n(t) = \binom{n-1}{n-i} e^{-i\lambda t}(1-e^{-\lambda t})^{n-i}$$

and, of course, $P_n(t) = 0$ for $n < i$ and all t. Using the notation VI,(8.1) for the negative binomial distribution we may rewrite (3.5) as $P_n(t) = f(n - i; i, e^{-\lambda t})$. It follows [cf. example IX,(3.c)] that the population size at epoch t is the sum of i independent random variables each having the distribution obtained from (3.5) on replacing i by 1. These i variables represent the progenies of the i original members of our population.

This type of process was first studied by Yule[7] in connection with the mathematical theory of evolution. The population consists of the species within a genus, and the creation of a new element is due to mutations.

---

[7] G. Udny Yule, *A mathematical theory of evolution, based on the conclusions of Dr. J. C. Willis, F.R.S.,* Philosophical Transactions of the Royal Society, London, Series B, vol. 213 (1924), pp. 21–87. Yule does not introduce the differential equations (3.4) but derives $P_n(t)$ by a limiting process similar to the one used in VI,5, for the Poisson process. Much more general, and more flexible, models of the same type were devised and applied to epidemics and population growth in an unpretentious and highly interesting paper by Lieutenant Colonel A. G. M'Kendrick, *Applications of mathematics to medical problems,* Proceedings Edinburgh Mathematical Society, vol. 44 (1925), pp. 1–34. It is unfortunate that this remarkable paper passed practically unnoticed. In particular, it was unknown to the present author when he introduced various stochastic models for population growth in *Die Grundlagen der Volterraschen Theorie des Kampfes ums Dasein in wahrscheinlichkeitstheoretischer Behandlung,* Acta Biotheoretica, vol. 5 (1939), pp. 11–40.

The assumption that each species has the same probability of throwing out a new species neglects the difference in species sizes. Since we have also neglected the possibility that a species may die out, (3.5) can be expected to give only a crude approximation.

Furry[8] used the same model to describe a process connected with cosmic rays, but again the approximation is rather crude. The differential equations (3.4) apply strictly to a population of particles which can split into exact replicas of themselves, provided, of course, that there is no interaction among particles. ▶

*4. DIVERGENT BIRTH PROCESSES

The solution $\{P_n(t)\}$ of the infinite system of differential equations (3.2) subject to initial conditions (3.3) can be calculated inductively, starting from $P_i(t) = e^{-\lambda_i t}$. The distribution $\{P_n(t)\}$ is therefore uniquely determined. From the familiar formulas for solving linear differential equations it follows also that $P_n(t) \geq 0$. The only question left open is whether $\{P_n(t)\}$ is an honest probability distribution, that is, whether or not

$$(4.1) \qquad \sum P_n(t) = 1$$

for all t. We shall see that this is not always so: With rapidly increasing coefficients λ_n it may happen that

$$(4.2) \qquad \sum P_n(t) < 1.$$

When this possibility was discovered it appeared disturbing, but it finds a ready explanation. The left side in (4.2) may be interpreted as the probability that during a time interval of duration t only a *finite number* of jumps takes place. Accordingly, the difference between the two sides in (4.2) accounts for the possibility of infinitely many jumps, or a sort of explosion. For a better understanding of this phenomenon let us compare our probabilistic model of growth with the familiar deterministic approach.

The quantity λ_n in (3.2) could be called the average rate of growth of a population of size n. For example, in the special case (3.4) we have $\lambda_n = n\lambda$, so that the average rate of growth is proportional to the actual population size. If growth is not subject to chance fluctuations and has a rate of increase proportional to the instantaneous population size $x(t)$,

---

* This section treats a special topic and may be omitted.
[8] *On fluctuation phenomena in the passage of high-energy electrons through lead,* Physical Reviews, vol. 52 (1937), p. 569.

the latter varies in accordance with the deterministic differential equation

$$(4.3) \qquad \frac{dx(t)}{dt} = \lambda x(t).$$

It implies that

$$(4.4) \qquad x(t) = ie^{\lambda t},$$

where $i = x(0)$ is the initial population size. It is readily seen that the expectation $\sum n P_n(t)$ of the distribution (3.5) coincides with $x(t)$, and thus $x(t)$ describes not only a deterministic growth process, but also the expected population size in example (3.b).

Let us now consider a deterministic growth process where the rate of growth increases faster than the population size. To a rate of growth proportional to $x^2(t)$ there corresponds the differential equation

$$(4.5) \qquad \frac{dx(t)}{dt} = \lambda x^2(t)$$

whose solution is

$$(4.6) \qquad x(t) = \frac{i}{1 - \lambda it}.$$

Note that $x(t)$ increases beyond all bounds as $t \to 1/\lambda i$. In other words, the assumption that the rate of growth increases as the square of the population size implies an infinite growth within a finite time interval. Similarly, if in (3.4) the λ_n increase too fast, there is a finite probability that infinitely many changes take place in a finite time interval. A precise answer about the conditions when such a divergent growth occurs is given by the

Theorem. *In order that* $\sum P_n(t) = 1$ *for all t it is necessary and sufficient that the series* $\sum \lambda_n^{-1}$ *diverges.*[9]

Proof. Put

$$(4.7) \qquad S_k(t) = P_0(t) + \cdots + P_k(t).$$

Because of the obvious monotonicity the limit

$$(4.8) \qquad \mu(t) = \lim_{k \to \infty} [1 - S_k(t)]$$

exists. Summing the differential equations (3.2) over $n = 0, \ldots, k$ we get

$$(4.9) \qquad S_k'(t) = -\lambda_k P_k(t).$$

---

[9] It is not difficult to see that the inequality $\sum P_n(t) < 1$ holds either for all $t > 0$, or else for no $t > 0$. See problem 22.

In view of the initial conditions (3.3) this implies for $k \geq i$

$$(4.10) \qquad\qquad 1 - S_k(t) = \lambda_k \int_0^t P_k(\tau) \, d\tau$$

and hence

$$(4.11) \qquad\qquad \lambda_k^{-1} \mu(t) \leq \int_0^t P_k(s) \, ds \leq \lambda_k^{-1}.$$

Summing for $k = i, \ldots, n$ we get for $n \geq i$

$$(4.12) \quad \mu(t)[\lambda_i^{-1} + \cdots + \lambda_n^{-1}] \leq \int_0^t S_n(s) \, ds \leq \lambda_i^{-1} + \cdots + \lambda_n^{-1}.$$

When $\sum \lambda_n^{-1} < \infty$ the rightmost member remains bounded as $n \to \infty$, and hence it is impossible that the integrand tends to 1 for all t. Conversely, if $\sum \lambda_n^{-1} = \infty$ we conclude from the first inequality that $\mu(t) = 0$ for all t, and in view of (4.8) this implies that $S_n(t) \to 1$, as asserted. ▶

The criterion becomes plausible when interpreted probabilistically. The system spends some time at the initial state E_0, moves from there to E_1, stays for a while there, moves on to E_2, etc. The probability $P_0(t)$ that the sojourn time in E_0 exceeds t is obtained from (3.2) as $P_0(t) = e^{-\lambda_0 t}$. This sojourn time, $\mathbf{T}_0$, is a random variable, but its range is the positive t-axis and therefore formally out of bounds for this book. However, the step from a geometric distribution to an exponential being trivial, we may with impunity trespass a trifle. An approximation to $\mathbf{T}_0$ by a discrete random variable with a geometric distribution shows that it is natural to define the expected sojourn time at E_0 by

$$(4.13) \qquad\qquad \mathbf{E}(\mathbf{T}_0) = \int_0^\infty t e^{-\lambda_0 t} \, dt = \lambda_0^{-1}.$$

At the epoch when the system enters E_j, the state E_j takes over the role of the initial state and the same conclusion applies to the sojourn time $\mathbf{T}_j$ at E_j: The *expected sojourn time at E_j is* $\mathbf{E}(\mathbf{T}_j) = \lambda_j^{-1}$. It follows that $\lambda_0^{-1} + \lambda_1^{-1} + \cdots + \lambda_n^{-1}$ is the expected duration of the time it takes the system to pass through $E_0, E_1, \ldots, E_n$, and we can restate the criterion of section 4 as follows:

In order that $\sum P_n(t) = 1$ for all t it is necessary and sufficient that

$$(4.14) \qquad\qquad \sum \mathbf{E}(\mathbf{T}_j) = \sum \lambda_j^{-1} = \infty;$$

that is, the total expected duration of the time spent at $E_0, E_1, E_2, \ldots$ must be infinite. Of course, $L_0(t) = 1 - \sum P_n(t)$ is the probability that the system has gone through *all* states before epoch t.

With this interpretation the possibility of the inequality (4.2) becomes understandable. If the expected sojourn time at E_j is 2^{-j}, the probability that the system has passed through all states within time $1 + 2^{-1} + 2^{-2} + \cdots = 2$ must be positive. Similarly, a particle moving along the x-axis at an exponentially increasing velocity traverses the entire axis in a finite time.

[We shall return to divergent birth process in example (9.b).]

5. THE BIRTH-AND-DEATH PROCESS

The pure birth process of section 3 provides a satisfactory description of radioactive transmutations, but it cannot serve as a realistic model for changes in the size of populations whose members can die (or drop out). This suggests generalizing the model by permitting transitions from the state E_n not only to the next higher state E_{n+1} but also to the next lower state E_{n-1}. (More general processes will be defined in section 9.) Accordingly we start from the following

Postulates. *The system changes only through transitions from states to their nearest neighbors (from E_n to E_{n+1} or E_{n-1} if $n \geq 1$, but from E_0 to E_1 only). If at epoch t the system is in state E_n, the probability that between t and $t+h$ the transition $E_n \to E_{n+1}$ occurs equals $\lambda_n h + o(h)$, and the probability of $E_n \to E_{n-1}$ (if $n \geq 1$) equals $\mu_n h + o(h)$. The probability that during $(t, t+h)$ more than one change occurs is $o(h)$.*

It is easy to adapt the method of section 2 to derive differential equations for the probabilities $P_n(t)$ of finding the system in state E_n. To calculate $P_n(t+h)$, note that the state E_n at epoch $t+h$ is possible only under one of the following conditions: (1) At epoch t the system is in E_n and between t and $t+h$ no change occurs; (2) at epoch t the system is in E_{n-1} and a transition to E_n occurs; (3) at epoch t the system is in E_{n+1} and a transition to E_n occurs; (4) between t and $t+h$ there occur two or more transitions. By assumption, the probability of the last event is $o(h)$. The first three contingencies are mutually exclusive and their probabilities add. Therefore

$$(5.1) \quad P_n(t+h) = P_n(t)\{1 - \lambda_n h - \mu_n h\} + $$
$$+ \lambda_{n-1} h P_{n-1}(t) + \mu_{n+1} h P_{n+1}(t) + o(h).$$

Transposing the term $P_n(t)$ and dividing the equation by h we get on the left the difference ratio of $P_n(t)$, and in the limit as $h \to 0$

$$(5.2) \qquad P_n'(t) = -(\lambda_n + \mu_n) P_n(t) + \lambda_{n-1} P_{n-1}(t) + \mu_{n+1} P_{n+1}(t).$$

This equation holds for $n \geq 1$. For $n = 0$ in the same way

$$(5.3) \qquad\qquad P_0'(t) = -\lambda_0 P_0(t) + \mu_1 P_1(t).$$

If the initial state is E_i, the *initial conditions* are

$$(5.4) \qquad\qquad P_i(0) = 1, \qquad P_n(0) = 0 \qquad\qquad for \ \ n \neq i.$$

The birth-and-death process is thus seen to depend on the infinite system of differential equations (5.2)–(5.3) together with the initial condition (5.4). The question of existence and of uniqueness of solutions is in this case by no means trivial. In a pure birth process the system (3.2) of differential equations was also infinite, but it had the form of recurrence relations; $P_0(t)$ was determined by the first equation and $P_n(t)$ could be calculated from $P_{n-1}(t)$. The new system (5.2) is not of this form, and all $P_n(t)$ must be found simultaneously. We shall here (and elsewhere in this chapter) state properties of the solutions without proof.[10]

For arbitrarily prescribed coefficients $\lambda_n \geq 0$, $\mu_n \geq 0$ *there always exists a positive solution* $\{P_n(t)\}$ *of* (5.2)–(5.4) *such that* $\sum P_n(t) \leq 1$. *If the coefficients are bounded* (*or increase sufficiently slowly*), *this solution is unique and satisfies the regularity condition* $\sum P_n(t) = 1$. However, it is possible to choose the coefficients in such a way that $\sum P_n(t) < 1$ and that there exist infinitely many solutions. In the latter case we encounter a phenomenon analogous to that studied in the preceding section for the pure birth process. This situation is of considerable theoretical interest, but the reader may safely assume that in all cases of practical significance the conditions of uniqueness are satisfied; in this case automatically $\sum P_n(t) = 1$ (see section 9).

When $\lambda_0 = 0$ the transition $E_0 \to E_1$ is impossible. In the terminology of Markov chains E_0 is an *absorbing state* from which no exit is possible; once the system is in E_0 it stays there. From (5.3) it follows that in this case $P_0'(t) \geq 0$, so that $P_0(t)$ increases monotonically. The limit $P_0(\infty)$ is the probability of *ultimate absorption*.

It can be shown (either from the explicit form of the solutions or from the general ergodic theorems for Markov processes) that under any circumstance *the limits*

(5.5) $$\lim_{t \to \infty} P_n(t) = p_n$$

exist and are independent of the initial conditions (5.4); they satisfy the system of linear equations obtained from (5.2)–(5.3) on replacing the derivatives on the left by zero.

The relations (5.5) resemble the limit theorems derived in XV,7 for ordinary Markov chains, and the resemblance is more than formal. Intuitively (5.5) becomes almost obvious by a comparison of our process

---

[10] The simplest existence proof and uniqueness criterion are obtained by specialization from the general theory developed by the author (see section 9). Solutions of the birth-and-death process such that $\sum P_n(t) < 1$ have recently attracted wide attention. For explicit treatments see W. Lederman and G. E. Reuter, *Spectral theory for the differential equations of simple birth and death processes*. Philosophical Transactions of the Royal Society, London, Series A, vol. 246 (1954), pp. 387–391; S. Karlin and J. L. McGregor, *The differential equations of birth-and-death processes and the Stieltjes moment problem*, Trans. Amer. Math. Soc., vol. 85 (1957), pp. 489–546, and *The classification of birth and death processes*, ibid. vol. 86 (1957), pp. 366–400. See also W. Feller, *The birth and death processes as diffusion processes*, Journal de Mathématiques Pures at Appliquées, vol. 38 (1959), pp. 301–345.

with a simple Markov chain with transition probabilities

$$(5.6) \qquad p_{n,n+1} = \frac{\lambda_n}{\lambda_n + \mu_n}, \qquad p_{n,n-1} = \frac{\mu_n}{\lambda_n + \mu_n}.$$

In this chain the only direct transitions are $E_n \to E_{n+1}$ and $E_n \to E_{n-1}$, and they have the same conditional probabilities as in our process; the difference between the chain and our process lies in the fact that, with the latter, changes can occur at arbitrary times, so that the number of transitions during a time interval of length t is a random variable. However, for large t this number is certain to be large, and hence it is plausible that for $t \to \infty$ the probabilities $P_n(t)$ behave as the corresponding probabilities of the simple chain.

If the simple chain with transition probabilities (5.6) is transient we have $p_n = 0$ for all n; if the chain is ergodic the p_n define a stationary probability distribution. In this case (5.5) is usually interpreted as a "tendency toward the steady state condition" and this suggestive name has caused much confusion. It must be understood that, except when E_0 is an absorbing state, the chance fluctuations continue forever unabated and (5.5) shows only that in the long run the influence of the initial condition disappears. The remarks made in XV, 7 concerning the statistical equilibria apply here without change.

The principal field of applications of the birth-and-death process is to problems of waiting times, trunking, etc.; see sections 6 and 7.

Examples. (*a*) *Linear growth.* Suppose that a population consists of elements which can split or die. During any short time interval of length h the probability for any living element to split into two is $\lambda h + o(h)$, whereas the corresponding probability of dying is $\mu h + o(h)$. Here λ and μ are two constants characteristic of the population. If there is no interaction among the elements, we are led to a birth and death process with $\lambda_n = n\lambda$, $\mu_n = n\mu$. The basic differential equations take on the form

$$(5.7) \quad \begin{aligned} & P_0'(t) = \mu P_1(t), \\ & P_n'(t) = -(\lambda+\mu)nP_n(t) + \lambda(n-1)P_{n-1}(t) + \mu(n+1)P_{n+1}(t). \end{aligned}$$

Explicit solutions can be found[11] (cf. problems 11–14), but we shall not

---

[11] A systematic way consists in deriving a partial differential equation for the generating function $\sum P_n(t)s^n$. A more general process where the coefficients λ and μ in (5.7) are permitted to depend on time is discussed in detail in David G. Kendall, *The generalized "birth and death" process*, Ann. Math. Statist., vol. 19 (1948), pp. 1–15. See also the same author's *Stochastic processes and population growth*, Journal of the Royal Statistical Society, B, vol. 11 (1949), pp. 230–265 where the theory is generalized to take account of the age distribution in biological populations.

discuss this aspect. The limits (5.5) exist and satisfy (5.7) with $P'_n(t) = 0$. From the first equation we find $p_1 = 0$, and we see by induction from the second equation that $p_n = 0$ for all $n \geq 1$. If $p_0 = 1$, we may say that the probability of ultimate extinction is 1. If $p_0 < 1$, the relations $p_1 = p_2 \cdots = 0$ imply that with probability $1 - p_0$ the population increases over all bounds; ultimately the population must either die out or increase indefinitely. To find the probability p_0 of extinction we compare the process to the related Markov chain. In our case the transition probabilities (5.6) are independent of n, and we have therefore an ordinary random walk in which the steps to the right and left have probabilities $p = \lambda/(\lambda+\mu)$ and $q = \mu/(\lambda+\mu)$, respectively. The state E_0 is absorbing. We know from the classical ruin problem (see XIV, 2) that the probability of extinction is 1 if $p \leq q$ and $(q/p)^i$ if $q < p$ and i is the initial state. We conclude that *in our process the probability* $p_0 = \lim P_0(t)$ *of ultimate extinction is* 1 *if* $\lambda \leq \mu$, *and* $(\mu/\lambda)^i$ *if* $\lambda > \mu$. (This is easily verified from the explicit solution; see problems 11–14.)

As in many similar cases, the explicit solution of (5.7) is rather complicated, and it is desirable to calculate the mean and the variance of the distribution $\{P_n(t)\}$ directly from the differential equations. We have for the mean

$$(5.8) \qquad M(t) = \sum_{n=1}^{\infty} n P_n(t).$$

We shall omit a formal proof that $M(t)$ is finite and that the following formal operations are justified (again both points follow readily from the solution given in problem 12). Multiplying the second equation in (5.7) by n and adding over $n = 1, 2, \ldots$, we find that the terms containing n^2 cancel, and we get

$$(5.9) \qquad M'(t) = \lambda \sum (n-1)P_{n-1}(t) - \mu \sum (n+1)P_{n+1}(t) =$$

$$= (\lambda-\mu)M(t).$$

This is a differential equation for $M(t)$. The initial population size is i, and hence $M(0) = i$. Therefore

$$(5.10) \qquad M(t) = ie^{(\lambda-\mu)t}.$$

We see that the mean tends to 0 or infinity, according as $\lambda < \mu$ or $\lambda > \mu$. The variance of $\{P_n(t)\}$ can be calculated in a similar way (cf. problem 14).

(b) *Waiting lines for a single channel.* In the simplest case of constant coefficients $\lambda_n = \lambda$, $\mu_n = \mu$ the birth-and-death process reduces to a special case of the waiting line example (7.b) when $a = 1$.

6. EXPONENTIAL HOLDING TIMES

The principal field of applications of the pure birth-and-death process is connected with trunking in telephone engineering and various types of waiting lines for telephones, counters, or machines. This type of problem can be treated with various degrees of mathematical sophistication. The method of the birth-and-death process offers the easiest approach, but this model is based on a mathematical simplification known as the *assumption of exponential holding times.* We begin with a discussion of this basic assumption.

For concreteness of language let us consider a telephone conversation, and let us assume that its length is necessarily an integral number of seconds. We treat the length of the conversation as a random variable X and assume its probability distribution $p_n = P\{X = n\}$ known. The telephone line then represents a physical system with two possible states, "busy" (E_0) and "free" (E_1). When the line is busy, the probability of a change in state during the next second depends on how long the conversation has been going on. In other words, the past has an influence on the future, and our process is therefore not a Markov process (see XV,13). This circumstance is the source of difficulties, but fortunately there exists a simple exceptional case discussed at length in XIII,9.

Imagine that the decision whether or not the conversation is to be continued is made each second at random by means of a skew coin. In other words, a sequence of Bernoulli trials with probability p of success is performed at a rate of one per second and continued until the first success. The conversation ends when this first success occurs. In this case the total length of the conversation, the "holding time," has the geometric distribution $p_n = q^{n-1}p$. Whenever the line is busy, the probability that it will remain busy for more than one second is q, and the probability of the transition $E_0 \to E_1$ at the next step is p. These probabilities are now independent of how long the line was busy.

When it is undesirable to use a discrete time parameter it becomes necessary to work with continuous random variables. The role of the geometric distribution for waiting times is then taken over by the *exponential distribution.* It is the only distribution having a Markovian character, that is, endowed with complete lack of memory. In other words, the probability that a conversation which goes on at epoch x continues beyond $x + h$ is independent of the past duration of the conversation if, and only if, the probability that the conversation lasts for longer than t time units is given by an exponential $e^{-\lambda t}$. We have encountered this "exponential holding time distribution" as the zero term in the Poisson distribution (2.4), that is, as the waiting time up to the occurrence of the first change.

The method of the birth-and-death process is applicable only if the transition probabilities in question do not depend on the past; for trunking and waiting line problems this means that all holding times must be exponential. From a practical point of view this assumption may at first sight appear rather artificial, but experience shows that it reasonably describes actual phenomena. In particular, many measurements have shown that telephone conversations within a city[12] follow the exponential law to a surprising degree of accuracy. The same situation prevails for other holding times (e.g., the duration of machine repairs).

It remains to characterize the so-called incoming traffic (arriving calls, machine breakdowns, etc.). We shall assume that during any time interval of length h the probability of an incoming call is λh plus negligible terms, and that the probability of more than one call is in the limit negligible. According to the results of section 2, this means that the number of incoming calls has a Poisson distribution with mean λt. We shall describe this situation by saying that *the incoming traffic is of the Poisson type with intensity λ.*

It is easy to verify the described property of exponential holding times. Denote by $u(t)$ the probability that a conversation lasts for at least t time units. The probability $u(t+s)$ that a conversation starting at 0 lasts beyond $t + s$ equals the probability that it lasts longer than t units multiplied by the conditional probability that a conversation lasts additional s units, given that its length exceeds t. If the past duration has no influence, the last conditional probability must equal $u(s)$; that is, we must have

$$(6.1) \qquad u(t+s) = u(t)\,u(s).$$

To prove the asserted characterization of exponential holding times it would suffice to show that *monotone* solutions of this functional equation are necessarily of the form $e^{-\lambda t}$. We prove a slightly stronger result which is of interest in itself.[13]

Theorem. *Let u be a solution of (6.1) defined for $t > 0$ and bounded in some interval. Then either $u(t) = 0$ for all t, or else $u(t) = e^{-\lambda t}$ for some constant λ.*

Proof. Clearly

$$(6.2) \qquad u(a) = u^2(\tfrac{1}{2}a).$$

Suppose first that $u(a) = 0$ for some value a. From (6.2) we conclude by induction that $u(2^{-n}a) = 0$ for all integers n, and from (6.1) it is clear that $u(s) = 0$ implies

---

[12] Long distance conversations are usually counted in units of three minutes and the holding times are therefore frequently multiples of three minutes. Under such circumstances the exponential distribution does not apply.

[13] (6.1) is only a notational variant of the famous Hamel equation $f(t+s) = f(t) + f(s)$. We prove that its solutions are either of the form at or else unbounded in *every* interval. (It is known that no such solution is a Baire function, that is, no such solution can be obtained by series expansions or other limiting processes starting from continuous functions.)

$u(t) = 0$ for all $t > s$. Thus $u(a) = 0$ implies that u vanishes identically. Since (6.2) obviously excludes negative values of u it remains only to consider strictly positive solutions of (6.1).

Put $e^{-\lambda} = u(1)$ and $v(t) = e^{\lambda t}u(t)$. Then

$$(6.3) \qquad v(t+s) = v(t)v(s) \quad and \quad v(1) = 1.$$

We have to prove that this implies $v(t) = 1$ for all t. Obviously for arbitrary positive integers m and n

$$(6.4) \qquad v\left(\frac{m}{n}\right) = v^m\left(\frac{1}{n}\right) = \sqrt[n]{v^m(1)} = 1$$

and hence $v(s) = 1$ for all rational s. Furthermore, if $v(a) = c$ then $v(a^n) = c^n$ for any positive or negative integer n. It follows that if u assumes some value $c \neq 1$ then it assumes also arbitrarily large values. But using (6.1) with $t + s = \tau$ it is seen that $v(\tau - s) = v(\tau)$ for all rational s. Accordingly, if a value A is assumed at some point τ, the same value is assumed in every interval, however small. The boundedness of u in any given interval therefore precludes the possibility of any values $\neq 1$.   ▶

7. WAITING LINE AND SERVICING PROBLEMS

(a) *The simplest trunking problem.*[14] Suppose that infinitely many trunks or channels are available, and that the probability of a conversation ending between t and $t+h$ is $\mu h + o(h)$ (exponential holding time). The incoming calls constitute a traffic of the Poisson type with parameter λ. The system is in state E_n if n lines are busy.

It is, of course, assumed that the durations of the conversations are mutually independent. If n lines are busy, the probability that one of them will be freed within time h is then $n\mu h + o(h)$. The probability that within this time two or more conversations terminate is obviously of the order of magnitude h^2 and therefore negligible. The probability of a new call arriving is $\lambda h + o(h)$. The probability of a combination of several calls, or of a call arriving and a conversating ending, is again $o(h)$. Thus, in the

---

[14] C. Palm, *Intensitätsschwankungen im Fernsprechverkehr*, Ericsson Technics (Stockholm), no. 44 (1943), pp. 1–189, in particular p. 57. Waiting line and trunking problems for telephone exchanges were studied long before the theory of stochastic processes was available and had a stimulating influence on the development of the theory. In particular, Palm's impressive work over many years has proved useful. The earliest worker in the field was A. K. Erlang (1878–1929). See E. Brockmeyer, H. L. Halström, and Arne Jensen, *The life and works of A. K. Erlang*, Transactions of the Danish Academy Technical Sciences, No. 2, Copenhagen, 1948. Independently valuable pioneer work has been done by T. C. Fry whose book, *Probability and its engineering uses*, New York (Van Nostrand), 1928, did much for the development of engineering applications of probability.

notation of section 5

(7.1) $$\lambda_n = \lambda, \qquad \mu_n = n\mu.$$

The basic differential equations (5.2)–(5.3) take the form

(7.2)
$$P_0'(t) = -\lambda P_0(t) + \mu P_1(t)$$
$$P_n'(t) = -(\lambda+n\mu)P_n(t) + \lambda P_{n-1}(t) + (n+1)\mu P_{n+1}(t)$$

where $n \geq 1$. Explicit solutions can be obtained by deriving a partial differential equation for the generating function (cf. problem 15). We shall only determine the quantities $p_n = \lim P_n(t)$ of (5.5). They satisfy the equations

(7.3)
$$\lambda p_0 = \mu p_1$$
$$(\lambda+n\mu)p_n = \lambda p_{n-1} + (n+1)\mu p_{n+1}.$$

We find by induction that $p_n = p_0(\lambda/\mu)^n/n!$, and hence

(7.4) $$p_n = e^{-\lambda/\mu}\frac{(\lambda/\mu)^n}{n!}.$$

Thus, *the limiting distribution is a Poisson distribution with parameter* λ/μ. *It is independent of the initial state.*

It is easy to find the mean $M(t) = \sum nP_n(t)$. Multiplying the nth equation of (7.2) by n and adding, we get, taking into account that the $P_n(t)$ add to unity,

(7.5) $$M'(t) = \lambda - \mu M(t).$$

When the initial state is E_i, then $M(0) = i$, and

(7.6) $$M(t) = \frac{\lambda}{\mu}(1-e^{-\mu t}) + ie^{-\mu t}.$$

The reader may verify that in the special case $i = 0$ the $P_n(t)$ are given exactly by the Poisson distribution with mean $M(t)$.

(b) *Waiting lines for a finite number of channels.*[15] We now modify the last example to obtain a more realistic model. The assumptions are the same, except that *the number a of trunklines or channels is finite. If all a channels are busy, each new call joins a waiting line and waits until a channel is freed.* This means that all trunklines have a *common* waiting line.

The word "trunk" may be replaced by *counter* at a postoffice and "conversation" by *service*. We are actually treating the general waiting

---

[15] A. Kolmogoroff, *Sur le problème d'attente*, Recueil Mathématique [Sbornik], vol. 38 (1931), pp. 101–106. For related processes see problems 6–8 and 20.

line problem for the case where a person has to wait only if all a channels are busy.

We say that *the system is in state E_n if there are exactly n persons either being served or in the waiting line.* Such a line exists only when $n > a$, and then there are $n - a$ persons in it.

As long as at least one channel is free, the situation is the same as in the preceding example. However, if the system is in a state E_n with $n > a$, only a conversations are going on, and hence $\mu_n = a\mu$, for $n \geq a$. The basic system of differential equations is therefore given by (7.2) for $n < a$, but for $n \geq a$ by

$$(7.7) \qquad P'_n(t) = -(\lambda+a\mu)P_n(t) + \lambda P_{n-1}(t) + a\mu P_{n+1}(t).$$

In the special case of a single channel $(a = 1)$ these equations reduce to those of a birth-and-death process with coefficients independent of n. The limits $p_n = \lim p_n(t)$ satisfy (7.3) for $n < a$, and

$$(7.8) \qquad (\lambda+a\mu)p_n = \lambda p_{n-1} + a\mu p_{n+1}$$

for $n \geq a$. By recursion we find that

$$(7.9) \qquad p_n = p_0 \frac{(\lambda/\mu)^n}{n!}, \qquad\qquad n \leq a$$

$$(7.10) \qquad p_n = \frac{(\lambda/\mu)^n}{a!\, a^{n-a}} p_0, \qquad\qquad n \geq a.$$

The series $\sum (p_n/p_0)$ converges only if

$$(7.11) \qquad \lambda/\mu < a.$$

Hence a limiting distribution $\{p_k\}$ cannot exist when $\lambda \geq a\mu$. *In this case $p_n = 0$ for all n, which means that gradually the waiting line grows over all bounds.* On the other hand, if (7.11) holds, then we can determine p_0 so that $\sum p_n = 1$. From the explicit expressions for $P_n(t)$ it can be shown that the p_n thus obtained really represent the *limiting distribution* of the $P_n(t)$. Table 1 gives a numerical illustration for $a = 3$, $\lambda/\mu = 2$.

(c) *Servicing of machines.*[16] For orientation we begin with the simplest case and generalize it in the next example. The problem is as follows.

We consider automatic machines which normally require no human care except that they may break down and call for service. The time required

---

[16] Examples (c) and (d), including the numerical illustrations, are taken from an article by C. Palm, *The distribution of repairmen in servicing automatic machines* (in Swedish), Industritidningen Norden, vol. 75 (1947), pp. 75–80, 90–94, 119–123. Palm gives tables and graphs for the most economical number of repairmen.

for servicing the machine is again taken as a random variable with an exponential distribution. In other words, the machine is characterized by two constants λ and μ with the following properties. If at epoch t the machine is in working state, the probability that it will call for service before epoch $t+h$ equals λh plus terms which are negligible in the limit $h \to 0$. Conversely, when the machine is being serviced, the probability that the servicing time terminates before $t+h$ and the machine reverts to the working state equals $\mu h + o(h)$. For an efficient machine λ should be relatively small and μ relatively large. The ratio λ/μ is called the *servicing factor*.

We suppose that *m machines with the same parameters λ and μ and working independently are serviced by a single repairman*. A machine which

TABLE 1

LIMITING PROBABILITIES IN THE CASE OF $a = 3$
CHANNELS AND $\lambda/\mu = 2$

n	0	1	2	3	4	5	6	7
Lines busy	0	1	2	3	3	3	3	3
People waiting	0	0	0	0	1	2	3	4
p_n	0.1111	0.2222	0.2222	0.1481	0.9888	0.0658	0.0439	0.0293

breaks down is serviced immediately unless the repairman is servicing another machine, in which case a waiting line is formed. We say that *the system is in state E_n if n machines are not working*. For $1 \leq n \leq m$ this means that one machine is being serviced and $n - 1$ are in the waiting line; in the state E_0 all machines work and the repairman is idle.

A transition $E_n \to E_{n+1}$ is caused by a breakdown of one among the $m - n$ working machines, whereas a transition $E_n \to E_{n-1}$ occurs if the machine being serviced reverts to the working state. Hence we have a birth-and-death process with coefficients

$$(7.12) \qquad \lambda_n = (m-n)\lambda, \qquad \mu_0 = 0, \qquad \mu_1 = \mu_2 = \cdots = \mu_m = \mu.$$

For $1 \leq n \leq m - 1$ the basic differential equations (5.2) become

$$(7.13) \quad P'_n(t) = -\{(m-n)\lambda+\mu\}P_n(t) + (m-n+1)\lambda P_{n-1}(t) + \mu P_{n+1}(t),$$

while for the limiting states $n = 0$ and $n = m$

$$(7.13a) \qquad \begin{aligned} P'_0(t) &= -m\lambda P_0(t) + \mu P_1(t), \\ P'_m(t) &= -\mu P_m(t) + \lambda P_{m-1}(t). \end{aligned}$$

This is finite system of differential equations and can be solved by standard methods. The limits $p_n = \lim P_n(t)$ are determined by

$$m\lambda p_0 = \mu p_1,$$

(7.14) $$\{(m-n)\lambda + \mu\}p_n = (m-n+1)\lambda p_{n-1} + \mu p_{n+1},$$

$$\mu p_m = \lambda p_{m-1}.$$

TABLE 2

ERLANG'S LOSS FORMULA
PROBABILITIES p_n FOR THE CASE $\lambda/\mu = 0.1$,
$m = 6$

n	Machines in Waiting Line	p_n
0	0	0.4845
1	0	0.2907
2	1	0.1454
3	2	0.0582
4	3	0.0175
5	4	0.0035
6	5	0.0003

From these equations we get the recursion formula

(7.15) $$(m-n)\lambda p_n = \mu p_{n+1}.$$

Substituting successively $n = m - 1, m - 2, \ldots, 1, 0$, we find

$$p_{m-k} = \frac{1}{k!}\left(\frac{\mu}{\lambda}\right)^k \cdot p_m.$$

The remaining unknown constant p_m can be obtained from the condition that the p_j add to unity. The result is known as *Erlang's loss formula*:

(7.16) $$p_m = \left\{1 + \frac{1}{1!}\left(\frac{\mu}{\lambda}\right)^1 + \cdots + \frac{1}{m!}\left(\frac{\mu}{\lambda}\right)^m\right\}^{-1}.$$

Typical numerical values are exhibited in table 2.

The probability p_0 may be interpreted as the probability of the repairman's being idle (in the example of table 2 he should be idle about half the time). The *expected number of machines in the waiting line is*

$$(7.17) \qquad w = \sum_{k=1}^{m}(k-1)p_k = \sum_{k=1}^{m}kp_k - (1-p_0).$$

This quantity can be calculated by adding the relations (7.15) for $n = 0, 1, \ldots, m$. Using the fact that the p_n add to unity, we get

$$m\lambda - \lambda w - \lambda(1-p_0) = \mu(1-p_0)$$

or

$$(7.18) \qquad w = m - \frac{\lambda + \mu}{\lambda}(1-p_0).$$

In the example of table 2 we have $w = 6 \cdot (0.0549)$. Thus 0.0549 is the average contribution of a machine to the waiting line.

(d) *Continuation: several repairmen.* We shall not change the basic assumptions of the preceding problem, except that the *m machines are now serviced by r repairmen* ($r < m$). Thus for $n \le r$ the state E_n means that $r - n$ repairmen are idle, n machines are being serviced, and no machine is in the waiting line for repairs. For $n > r$ the state E_n signifies that r machines are being serviced and $n - r$ machines are in the waiting line. We can use the setup of the preceding example except that (7.12) is obviously to be replaced by

$$(7.19) \qquad \begin{aligned} \lambda_0 &= m\lambda, & \mu_0 &= 0, \\ \lambda_n &= (m-n)\lambda, & \mu_n &= n\mu & (1 \le n \le r), \\ \lambda_n &= (m-n)\lambda, & \mu_n &= r\mu & (r \le n \le m). \end{aligned}$$

We shall not write down the basic system of differential equations but only the equations for the limiting probabilities p_n. For $1 \le n < r$

$$(7.20a) \qquad \{(m-n)\lambda + n\mu\}p_n = (m-n+1)\lambda p_{n-1} + (n+1)\mu p_{n+1}$$

while for $r \le n \le m$

$$(7.20b) \qquad \{(m-n)\lambda + r\mu\}p_n = (m-n+1)\lambda p_{n-1} + r\mu p_{n+1}.$$

For $n = 0$ obviously $m\lambda p_0 = \mu p_1$. This relation determines the ratio p_1/p_0, and from (7.20a) we see by induction that for $n < r$

$$(7.21) \qquad (n+1)\mu p_{n+1} = (m-n)\lambda p_n;$$

finally, for $n \ge r$ we get from (7.20b)

$$(7.22) \qquad r\mu p_{n+1} = (m-n)\lambda p_n.$$

These equations permit calculating successively the ratios p_n/p_0. Finally, p_0 follows from the condition $\sum p_k = 1$. The values in table 3 are obtained in this way.

A comparison of tables 2 and 3 reveals surprising facts. They refer to the same machines ($\lambda/\mu = 0.1$), but in the second case we have $m = 20$ machines and $r = 3$ repairmen. The number of machines per repairman

TABLE 3

PROBABILITIES p_n FOR THE CASE $\lambda/\mu = 0.1$, $m = 20$, $r = 3$

n	Machines Serviced	Machines Waiting	Repairment Idle	p_n
0	0	0	3	0.13625
1	1	0	2	0.27250
2	2	0	1	0.25888
3	3	0	0	0.15533
4	3	1	0	0.08802
5	3	2	0	0.04694
6	3	3	0	0.02347
7	3	4	0	0.01095
8	3	5	0	0.00475
9	3	6	0	0.00190
10	3	7	0	0.00070
11	3	8	0	0.00023
12	3	9	0	0.00007

has increased from 6 to $6\frac{2}{3}$, and yet the machines are serviced more efficiently. Let us define a *coefficient of loss for machines* by

$$(7.23) \qquad \frac{w}{m} = \frac{\text{average number of machines in waiting line}}{\text{number of machines}}$$

and a coefficient of loss for repairmen by

$$(7.24) \qquad \frac{\rho}{r} = \frac{\text{average number of repairmen idle}}{\text{number of repairmen}}.$$

For practical purposes we may identify the probabilities $P_n(t)$ with their limits p_n. In table 3 we have then $w = p_4 + 2p_5 + 3p_6 + \cdots + 17p_{20}$ and $\rho = 3p_0 + 2p_1 + p_2$. Table 4 proves conclusively that for our particular machines (with $\lambda/\mu = 0.1$) *three repairmen per twenty machines are much more economical than one repairman per six machines.*

(e) *A power-supply problem.*[17]   One electric circuit supplies a welders
who use the current only intermittently. If at epoch t a welder uses
current, the probability that he ceases using before epoch $t+h$ is $\mu h + o(h)$; if at epoch t he requires no current, the probability that he calls
for current before $t+h$ is $\lambda h + o(h)$. The welders work independently
of each other.

We say that the system is in state E_n if n welders are using current.
Thus we have only finitely many states $E_0, \ldots, E_a$.

TABLE 4

COMPARISON OF EFFICIENCIES OF TWO SYSTEMS DISCUSSED
IN EXAMPLES (c) AND (d)

	(c)	(d)
Number of machines	6	20
Number of repairmen	1	3
Machines per repairman	6	$6\frac{2}{3}$
Coefficient of loss for repairmen	0.4845	0.4042
Coefficient of loss for machines	0.0549	0.01694

If the system is in state E_n, then $a - n$ welders are not using current
and the probability for a new call for current within a time interval of
duration h is $(a-n)\lambda h + o(h)$; on the other hand, the probability that
one of the n welders ceases using current is $n\mu h + o(h)$. Hence we have a
birth-and-death process with

$$(7.25) \qquad \lambda_n = (a-n)\lambda, \qquad \mu_n = n\mu, \qquad 0 \le n \le a.$$

The basic differential equations become

$$
\begin{aligned}
P_0'(t) &= -a\lambda P_0(t) + \mu P_1(t), \\
P_n'(t) &= -\{n\mu+(a-n)\lambda\}P_n(t) + (n+1)\mu P_{n+1}(t) + \\
&\qquad + (a-n+1)\lambda P_{n-1}(t), \\
P_a'(t) &= -a\mu P_a(t) + \lambda P_{a-1}(t).
\end{aligned}
$$

(7.26)

---

[17] This example was suggested by the problem treated (inadequately) by H. A. Adler
and K. W. Miller, *A new approach to probability problems in electrical engineering*,
Transactions of the American Institute of Electrical Engineers, vol. 65 (1946), pp.
630–632.

(Here $1 \leq n \leq a - 1$.) It is easily verified that *the limiting probabilities are given by the binomial distribution*

$$(7.27) \qquad p_n = \binom{a}{n} \left(\frac{\lambda}{\lambda + \mu} \right)^n \left(\frac{\mu}{\lambda + \mu} \right)^{a-n},$$

a result which could have been anticipated on intuitive grounds. (Explicit representations for the $P_n(t)$ are given in problem 17.)

8. THE BACKWARD (RETROSPECTIVE) EQUATIONS

In the preceding sections we were studying the probabilities $P_n(t)$ of finding the system at epoch t in state E_n. This notation is convenient but misleading, inasmuch as it omits mentioning the initial state E_i of the system at time zero. For the further development of the theory it is preferable to revert to the notations of section 1 and to the use of *transition probabilities*. Accordingly we denote by $P_{in}(t)$ the (conditional) probability of the state E_n at epoch $t + s$ given that at epoch s the system was in state E_i. We continue to denote by $P_n(t)$ the (absolute) probability of E_n at epoch t. When the initial state E_i is given, the absolute probability $P_n(t)$ coincides with $P_{in}(t)$, but when the initial state is chosen in accordance with a probability distribution $\{a_i\}$ we have

$$(8.1) \qquad P_n(t) = \sum_i a_i P_{in}(t).$$

For the special processes considered so far we have shown that for fixed i the transition probabilities $P_{in}(t)$ *satisfy the basic differential equations* (3.2) *and* (5.2). The subscript i appears only in the initial conditions, namely

$$(8.2) \qquad P_{in}(0) = \begin{cases} 1 & \text{for} \quad n = i \\ 0 & \text{otherwise.} \end{cases}$$

As a preparation for the theory of more general processes we now proceed to show that the same transition probabilities satisfy also a second system of differential equations. To fix ideas, let us start with the pure birth process of section 3. The differential equations (3.2) were derived by prolonging the time interval $(0, t)$ to $(0, t+h)$ and considering the possible changes during the short time $(t, t+h)$. We could as well have prolonged the interval $(0, t)$ in the direction of the past and considered the changes during $(-h, 0)$. In this way we get a new system of differential equations in which n (instead of i) remains fixed. Indeed, a transition from E_i at epoch $-h$ to E_n at epoch t can occur in three mutually exclusive ways: (1) No jump occurs between $-h$ and 0, and the system passes from the state E_i at epoch 0 to E_n. (2) Exactly one jump occurs between $-h$ and 0, and the system passes from the state E_{i+1} at epoch 0 to E_n at epoch t; (3) more than one jump occurs between $-h$ and 0. The probability of the first contingency is $1 - \lambda_i h + o(h)$, that of the second $\lambda_i h + o(h)$, while the third contingency has probability $o(h)$. As in sections 2 and 3 we conclude that

$$(8.3) \qquad P_{in}(t+h) = P_{in}(t)(1-\lambda_i h) + P_{i+1,n}(t)\lambda_i h + o(h).$$

Hence for $i \geq 0$ the new basic system now takes the form

$$(8.4) \qquad P'_{in}(t) = -\lambda_i P_{in}(t) + \lambda_i P_{i+1,n}(t).$$

These equations are called the *backward equations*, and, for distinction, equations (3.2) are called the *forward equations*. The initial conditions are (8.2). [Intuitively one should expect that

$$(8.5) \qquad P_{in}(t) = 0 \qquad \text{if} \quad n < i,$$

but pathological exceptions exist; see section 9.]

In the case of the birth-and-death process the basic *forward equations* (for fixed i) are represented by (5.2)–(5.3). The argument that lead to (8.4) now leads to the corresponding *backward equations*

$$(8.6) \qquad P'_{in}(t) = -(\lambda_i + \mu_i)P_{i,n}(t) + \lambda_i P_{i+1,n}(t) + \mu_i P_{i-1,n}(t).$$

It should be clear that the forward and backward equations are not independent of each other; the solution of the backward equations with the initial conditions (8.2) automatically satisfies the forward equations, except in the rare situations where the solution is not unique.

Example. *The Poisson process.* In section 2 we have interpreted the Poisson expression (1.1) as the probability that exactly n calls arrive during any time interval of length t. Let us say that at epoch t the system is in state E_n if exactly n calls arrive within the time interval from 0 to t. A transition from E_i at t_1 to E_n at t_2 means that $n - i$ calls arrived between t_1 and t_2. This is possible only if $n \geq i$, and hence we have for the transition probabilities of the Poisson process

$$(8.7) \qquad \begin{aligned} P_{in}(t) &= e^{-\lambda t}\frac{(\lambda t)^{n-i}}{(n-i)!} \qquad \text{if} \quad n \geq i, \\ P_{in}(0) &= 0 \qquad\qquad\qquad \text{if} \quad n < i. \end{aligned}$$

They satisfy the forward equations

$$(8.8) \qquad P'_{in}(t) = -\lambda P_{in}(t) + \lambda P_{i,n-1}(t)$$

as well as the backward equations

$$(8.9) \qquad P'_{in}(t) = -\lambda \bar{P}_{in}(t) + \lambda P_{i+1,n}(t). \qquad \blacktriangleright$$

9. GENERAL PROCESSES

So far the theory has been restricted to processes in which direct transitions from a state E_n are possible only to the neighboring states E_{n+1} and E_{n-1}. Moreover, the processes have been time-homogeneous, that is to say, the transition probabilities $P_{in}(t)$ have been the same for all time intervals of length t. We now consider more general processes in which both assumptions are dropped.

As in the theory of ordinary Markov chains, we shall permit direct transitions from any state E_i to any state E_n. The transition probabilities are permitted to vary in time. This necessitates specifying the two endpoints of any time interval instead of specifying just its length. Accordingly, we shall write $P_{in}(\tau, t)$ *for the conditional probability of finding the system at epoch* t *in state* E_n, *given that at a previous epoch* τ *the state was* E_i. The symbol $P_{in}(\tau, t)$ is meaningless unless $\tau < t$. If the process is homogeneous in time, then $P_{in}(\tau, t)$ depends only on the difference $t - \tau$, and we can write $P_{in}(t)$ instead of $P_{in}(\tau, \tau+t)$ (which is then independent of τ).

We saw in section 1 that the transition probabilities of time-homogeneous Markov processes satisfy the *Chapman-Kolmogorov equation*

$$(9.1a) \qquad P_{in}(s+t) = \sum_{\nu} P_{i\nu}(s) P_{\nu n}(t).$$

The analogous identity for non-homogeneous processes reads

$$(9.1b) \qquad P_{in}(\tau, t) = \sum_{\nu} P_{i\nu}(\tau, s) P_{\nu n}(s, t)$$

and is valid for $\tau < s < t$. This relation expresses the fact that a transition from the state E_i at epoch τ to E_n at epoch t occurs via some state E_ν at the intermediate epoch s, and for Markov processes the probability $P_{\nu n}(s, t)$ of the transition from E_ν to E_n is independent of the previous state E_i. The transition probabilities of Markov processes with countably many states are therefore solutions of the Chapman-Kolmogorov identity (9.1b) satisfying the side conditions

$$(9.2) \qquad P_{ik}(\tau, t) \geq 0, \qquad \sum_{k} P_{ik}(\tau, t) = 1.$$

We shall take it for granted without proof that, conversely, such solution represents the transition probabilities of a Markov process.[18] It follows that a basic problem of the theory of Markov processes consists in finding all solutions of the Chapman-Kolmogorov identity satisfying the side conditions (9.2).

The main purpose of the present section is to show that the postulates of the birth-and-death processes admit of a natural generalization permitting arbitrary direct transitions $E_i \to E_j$. From these postulates we shall derive two systems of ordinary differential equations, to be called forward and backward equations, respectively. Under ordinary circumstances each of the two systems uniquely determines the transition probabilities. The forward equations are probabilistically more natural but, curiously enough, their derivation requires stronger and less intuitive assumptions.

In the time-homogeneous birth-and-death process of section 5 the starting postulates referred to the behavior of the transition probabilities $P_{jk}(h)$ for small h; in essence it was required that the derivatives P'_{jk} exist at the origin. For inhomogeneous processes we shall impose the same condition on $P_{jk}(t, t+x)$ considered as functions of x. The derivatives will have an analogous probabilistic interpretation, but they will be functions of t.

Assumption 1.   *To every state E_n there corresponds a continuous function $c_n(t) \geq 0$ such that as $h \to 0$*

$$(9.3) \qquad \frac{1 - P_{nn}(t, t+h)}{h} \to c_n(t).$$

Assumption 2.   *To every pair of states E_j, E_k with $j \neq k$ there correspond transition probabilities $p_{jk}(t)$ (depending on time) such that as $h \to 0$*

$$(9.4) \qquad \frac{P_{jk}(t, t+h)}{h} \to c_j(t) p_{jk}(t) \qquad\qquad (j \neq k).$$

---

[18] The notion of a Markov process requires that, given the state E_v at epoch s, the development of the process prior to epoch s has no influence on the future development. As was pointed out in section 1, the Chapman-Kolomogorov identity expresses this requirement only partially because it involves only one epoch $\tau < s$ and one epoch $t > s$. The long-outstanding problem whether there exist non-Markovian processes whose transition probabilities satisfy (9.1) has now been solved in the affirmative; the simplest known such process is time-homogeneous and involves only three states E_j [See W. Feller, Ann. Math. Statist., vol. 30 (1959), pp. 1252–1253.] Such processes are rather pathological, however, and their existence does not contradict the assertion that *every* solution of the Chapman-Kolomogorov equation satisfying (9.2) corresponds (in a unique manner) to a Markov process.

The $p_{jk}(t)$ are continuous in t, and for every fixed t, j

$$(9.5) \qquad \sum_k p_{jk}(t) = 1, \qquad\qquad p_{jj}(t) = 0.$$

The probabilistic interpretation of (9.3) is obvious; if at epoch t the system is in state E_n, the probability that between t and $t+h$ a change occurs is $c_n(t)h + o(h)$. The coefficient $p_{jk}(t)$ can be interpreted as the conditional probability that, *if* a change from E_j occurs between t and $t+h$, this change takes the system from E_j to E_k. In the birth-and-death process $c_n(t) = \lambda_n + \mu_n$,

$$(9.6) \qquad p_{j,j+1}(t) = \frac{\lambda_j}{\lambda_j + \mu_j}, \qquad p_{j,j-1}(t) = \frac{\mu_j}{\lambda_j + \mu_j},$$

and $p_{jk}(t) = 0$ for all other combinations of j and k. For every fixed t the $p_{jk}(t)$ can be interpreted as transition probabilities of a Markov chain.

The two assumptions suffice to derive a system of backward equations for the $P_{jk}(\tau, t)$, but for the forward equations we require in addition

Assumption 3. *For fixed k the passage to the limit in (9.4) is uniform with respect to j.*

The necessity of this assumption is of considerable theoretical interest and will be discussed presently.

We proceed to derive differential equations for the $P_{ik}(\tau, t)$ as functions of t and k (forward equations). From (9.1) we have

$$(9.7) \qquad P_{ik}(\tau, t+h) = \sum_j P_{ij}(\tau, t) P_{jk}(t, t+h).$$

Expressing the term $P_{kk}(t, t+h)$ on the right in accordance with (9.3), we get

$$(9.8) \quad \frac{P_{ik}(\tau, t+h) - P_{ik}(\tau, t)}{h} =$$
$$= -c_k(t) P_{ik}(\tau, t) + h^{-1} \sum_{j \neq k} P_{ij}(\tau, t) P_{jk}(t, t+h) + \cdots$$

where the neglected terms tend to 0 with h, and the sum extends over all j except $j = k$. We now apply (9.4) to the terms of the sum. Since (by assumption 3) the passage to the limit is uniform in j, the right side has a limit. Hence also the left side has a limit, which means that $P_{ik}(\tau, t)$ has a partial derivative with respect to t, and

$$(9.9) \qquad \frac{\partial P_{ik}(\tau, t)}{\partial t} = -c_k(t) P_{ik}(\tau, t) + \sum_j P_{ij}(\tau, t) c_j(t) p_{jk}(t).$$

This is the basic system of forward differential equations. Here i and τ are fixed so that we have (despite the formal appearance of a partial derivative) a system of *ordinary differential equations*[19] for the functions $P_{ik}(\tau, t)$. The parameters i and τ appear only in the initial *condition*

$$(9.10) \qquad\qquad P_{ik}(\tau, \tau) = \begin{array}{ll} 1 & \text{for} \quad k = i. \\ 0 & \text{otherwise.} \end{array}$$

We now turn to the backward equations. In them k and t are kept constant so that the transition probabilities $P_{ik}(\tau, t)$ are considered as functions of the initial data E_i and τ. In the formulation of our starting assumptions the initial variable was kept fixed, but for the derivation of the backward equations it is preferable to formulate the same conditions with reference to a time interval from $t-h$ to t. In other words, it is more natural to start from the following *alternative form for the conditions* (9.3) *and* (9.4):

$$(9.3a) \qquad\qquad \frac{1 - P_{nn}(t-h, t)}{h} \to c_n(t)$$

$$(9.4a) \qquad\qquad \frac{P_{jk}(t-h, t)}{h} \to c_j(t)p_{jk}(t) \qquad\qquad (j \neq k).$$

It is not difficult to prove the equivalence of the two sets of conditions (or to express them in a unified form), but we shall be content to start from the alternative form. The remarkable feature of the following derivation is that no analogue to assumption 3 is necessary.

By the Chapman-Kolmogorov identity (9.1b)

$$(9.11) \qquad\qquad P_{ik}(\tau-h, t) = \sum_{v} P_{iv}(\tau-h, \tau)P_{vk}(\tau, t),$$

and using (9.3a) with $n = i$, we get

$$(9.12) \quad \frac{P_{ik}(\tau-h, t) - P_{ik}(\tau, t)}{h} =$$

$$= -c_i(\tau)P_{ik}(\tau, t) + h^{-1}\sum_{v \neq i} P_{iv}(\tau-h, \tau)P_{vk}(\tau, t) + \cdots.$$

---

[19] The standard form would be

$$x'_k(t) = -c_k(t)x_k(t) + \sum_{j} x_j(t)c_j(t)p_{jk}(t).$$

Here $h^{-1}P_{iv}(\tau-h, \tau) \to c_i(\tau)p_{iv}(\tau)$ and the passage to the limit in the sum to the right in (9.12) is always uniform. In fact, if $N > i$ we have

$$(9.13) \quad 0 \le h^{-1} \sum_{v=N+1}^{\infty} P_{iv}(\tau-h, \tau)P_{vk}(\tau, t) \le h^{-1} \sum_{v=N+1}^{\infty} P_{iv}(\tau-h, \tau) \le$$

$$\le h^{-1}\left\{1 - \sum_{v=0}^{N} P_{iv}(\tau-h, \tau)\right\} \to c_i(\tau)\left\{1 - \sum_{v=0}^{N} p_{iv}(\tau)\right\}.$$

In view of condition (9.5) the right side can be made arbitrarily small by choosing N sufficiently large. It follows that a termwise passage to the limit in (9.12) is permitted and we obtain

$$(9.14) \qquad \frac{\partial P_{ik}(\tau, t)}{\partial \tau} = c_i(\tau)P_{ik}(\tau, t) - c_i(\tau) \sum_{v} p_{iv}(\tau)P_{vk}(\tau, t).$$

These are the basic *backward differential equations*. Here k and t appear as fixed parameters and so (9.14) represents a system of *ordinary* differential equations. The parameters k and t appear only in the *initial conditions*

$$(9.15) \qquad P_{ik}(t, t) = \begin{array}{ll} 1 & \text{for} \quad i = k \\ 0 & \text{otherwise.} \end{array}$$

Example. (*a*) *Generalized Poisson process.* Consider the case where *all* $c_i(t)$ *equal the same constant,* $c_i(t) = \lambda$, *and the* p_{jk} *are independent of* t. In this case the p_{jk} are the transition probabilities of an ordinary Markov chain and (as in chapter XV) we denote its higher transition probabilities by $p_{jk}^{(n)}$.

From $c_i(t) = \lambda$, it follows that the probability of a transition occurring between t and $t + h$ is independent of the state of the system and equals $\lambda h + o(h)$. This implies that the number of transitions between τ and t has a Poisson distribution with parameter $\lambda(t-\tau)$. Given that exactly n transitions occurred, the (conditional) probability of a passage from j to k is $p_{jk}^{(n)}$. Hence

$$(9.16) \qquad P_{ik}(\tau, t) = e^{-\lambda(t-\tau)} \sum_{n=0}^{\infty} \frac{\lambda^n(t-\tau)^n}{n!} p_{ik}^{(n)}$$

(where, as usual, $p_{jj}^{(0)} = 1$ and $p_{jk}^{(0)} = 0$ for $j \neq k$). It is easily verified that (9.16) is in fact a solution of the two systems (9.9) and (9.14) of differential equations satisfying the boundary conditions.

In particular, if

$$(9.17) \qquad p_{jk} = 0 \quad \text{for} \quad k < j, \qquad p_{jk} = f_{k-j} \quad \text{for} \quad k \ge j$$

(9.16) reduces to the *compound Poisson distribution* of XII,2.   ▶

Our two systems of differential equations were first derived by A. Kolmogorov in an important paper developing the foundations of the theory of Markov processes.[20] Assuming that the sequence of coefficients $c_n(t)$ remains bounded for each t it was then shown by W. Feller that there exists a unique solution $\{P_{jk}(\tau, t)\}$ common to both systems, and that this solution satisfies the Chapman-Kolmogorov identity (9.1b) as well as the side conditions (9.2). Furthermore, in this case neither system of differential equations possesses any other solutions, and hence the two systems are essentially equivalent. However, concrete problems soon lead to equations with unbounded sequences $\{c_n\}$ and, as shown in section 4, in such cases we sometimes encounter unexpected solutions for which

$$(9.18) \qquad \sum_k P_{jk}(\tau, t) \leq 1$$

holds with the strict inequality. It has been shown[21] [without any restrictions on the coefficients $c_n(t)$] that there always exists a *minimal solution* $\{P_{jk}(\tau, t)\}$ satisfying both systems of differential equations as well as the Chapman-Kolmogorov identity (9.1b) and (9.18). This solution is called minimal because

$$(9.19) \qquad \bar{P}_{jk}(\tau, t) \geq P_{jk}(\tau, t)$$

whenever the left sides satisfy either the backward or the forward differential equations (together with the trite initial conditions (9.10)]. When the minimal solution satisfies (9.18) with the equality sign for all t, this implies that neither the backward nor the forward equations can have any probabilistically meaningful solutions besides $P_{jk}(\tau, t)$. In other words, when the minimal solution is not defective, the process is uniquely determined by either system of equations. As stated before, this is so when the coefficients $c_n(t)$ remain bounded for each fixed t.

The situation is entirely different when the minimal solution is defective, that is, when in (9.18) the inequality sign holds for some (and hence for all) t. In this case there exist infinitely many honest transition probabilities

[20] A. Kolmogoroff, *Über die analytischen Methoden in der Wahrscheinlichkeitsrechnung*, Mathematische Annalen, vol. 104 (1931), pp. 415–458.

[21] W. Feller, *On the integro-differential equations of purely discontinuous Markoff processes*, Trans. Amer. Math. Soc., vol. 48 (1940), pp. 488–515. This paper treats more general state spaces, but countable state spaces are mentioned as special case of greatest interest. This was overlooked by subsequent authors who gave more complicated and less complete derivations. The minimal solution in the time-homogeneous case is derived in XIV, 7 of volume 2 by the use of Laplace transforms. For a more complete treatment see W. Feller, *On boundaries and lateral conditions for the Kolmogorov differential equations*, Ann. Math., vol. 65 (1957), pp. 527–570.

satisfying the backward equations and the Chapman-Kolmogorov identity, and hence there exist infinitely many Markovian processes satisfying the basic assumptions 1 and 2 underlying the backward equations. Some of these may satisfy also the forward equations, but in other cases the solution of the forward equations is unique.[22]

Example. (b) *Birth processes.* The differential equations (3.2) for the time-homogeneous birth process were of the form

$$(9.20) \qquad x_0'(t) = -\lambda_0 x_0(t), \qquad x_k'(t) = -\lambda_k x_k(t) + \lambda_{k-1} x_{k-1}(t).$$

These are the forward equations. Since they form a recursive system the solution is uniquely determined by its initial values for $t = 0$. For the transition probabilities we get therefore successively $P_{ik}(t) = 0$ for all $k < i$,

$$(9.21) \qquad P_{ii}(t) = e^{-\lambda_i t}, \qquad P_{i,i+1}(t) = \frac{\lambda_i}{\lambda_i - \lambda_{i+1}} (e^{-\lambda_{i+1} t} - e^{-\lambda_i t}),$$

and finally for $k > i$

$$(9.22) \qquad P_{ik}(t) = \lambda_{k-1} \int_0^t e^{-\lambda_k s} P_{i,k-1}(t-s) \, ds.$$

To see that these transition probabilities satisfy the Chapman-Kolmogorov identity (9.1a) it suffices to notice that for fixed i and s both sides of the identity represent solutions of the differential equations (9.20) assuming the same initial values.

The backward equations were derived in (8.4) and are of the form

$$(9.23) \qquad y_i'(t) = -\lambda_i y_i(t) + \lambda_i y_{i+1}(t).$$

We have to show that this equation is satisfied by $P_{ik}(t)$ when k is kept fixed. This is trivially true when $k < i$ because in this case all three terms in (9.23) vanish. Using (9.21) it is seen that the assertion is true also when $k - i = 0$ and $k - i = 1$. We can now proceed by induction using the fact that for $k > i + 1$

$$(9.24) \qquad P_{ik}'(t) = \lambda_{k-1} \int_0^t e^{-\lambda_k s} \cdot P_{i,k-1}'(t-s) \, ds.$$

---

[22] It will be recalled that only assumptions 1 and 2 are probabilistically meaningful whereas assumption 3 is of a purely analytic character and was introduced only for convenience. It is unnatural in the sense that not even all solutions of the forward equations satisfy the imposed uniformity condition. Thus the backward equations express probabilistically meaningful conditions and lead to interesting processes, but the same cannot be said of the forward equations. This explains why the whole theory of Markov processes must be based on the backward equations (or abstractly, on semi-groups of transformations of functions rather than probability measures).

Assume that the $P_{ik}(t)$ satisfy (9.23) if $k - i \leq n$. For $k = i + 1 + n$ we can then express the integrand in (9.24) using the right side in (9.23) with the result that (9.23) holds also for $k - i = n + 1$.

We have thus proved that a system of transition probabilities $P_{ik}(t)$ is uniquely determined by the forward equations, and that these probabilities satisfy the backward equations as well as the Chapman-Kolmogorov identity.

The backward equations (9.23) may have other solutions. The asserted minimality property (9.19) of our transition probabilities may be restated as follows. For arbitrary non-negative solutions of (9.23)

$$(9.25) \qquad if \quad y_i(0) = P_{ik}(0) \qquad then \quad y_i(t) \geq P_{ik}(t)$$

for all $t > 0$. Here k is arbitrary, but fixed. This assertion is trivial for $k < i$ since in this case the right sides vanish. Given y_{i+1} the solution y_i of (9.23) can be represented explicitly by an integral analogous to (9.22), and the truth of (9.25) now follows recursively for $i = k, k - 1, \ldots$.

Suppose now that $\sum \lambda_k^{-1} < \infty$. It was shown in section 4 that in this case the quantities

$$(9.26) \qquad L_i(t) = 1 - \sum_{k=0}^{\infty} P_{ik}(t)$$

do not vanish identically. Clearly $L_i(t)$ may be interpreted as the probability that, starting from E_i, "infinity" is reached before epoch t. It is also obvious that the L_i are solutions of the differential equations (9.23) with the initial values $L_i(0) = 0$. Consider then arbitrary non-negative functions A_k and define

$$(9.27) \qquad \bar{P}_{ik}(t) = P_{ik}(t) + \int_0^t L_i(t-s)A_k(s)\, ds.$$

It is easily verified that for fixed k *the $\bar{P}_{ik}(t)$ satisfy the backward differential equations* and $\bar{P}_{ik}(0) = P_{ik}(0)$. The question arises whether the $A_k(t)$ can be defined in such a way that the $\bar{P}_{ik}(t)$ become transition probabilities satisfying the Chapman-Kolmogorov equation. The answer is in the affirmative. We refrain from proving this assertion but shall give a probabilistic interpretation.

The $P_{ik}(t)$ define the so-called *absorbing boundary process*: *When the system reaches infinity, the process terminates.* Doob[23] was the first to study a *return process* in which, on reaching infinity, the system instantaneously returns to E_0 (or some other prescribed state) and the process starts from scratch. In such a process the system may pass from E_0 to E_5 either in

[23] J. L. Doob, *Markoff chains—denumerable case*, Trans. Amer. Math. Soc., vol. 58 (1945), pp. 455–473.

five steps or in infinitely many, having completed one or several complete runs from E_0 to "infinity." The transition probabilities of this process are of the form (9.27). They *satisfy the backward equations* (9.23) *but not the forward equations* (9.24). ▶

This explains why in the derivation of the forward equations we were forced to introduce the strange-looking assumption 3 which was unnecessary for the backward equations: The probabilistically and intuitively simple assumptions 1–2 are compatible with return processes, for which the forward equations (9.24) do not hold. In other words, if we start from the assumptions 1–2 then *Kolmogorov's backward equations are satisfied, but to the forward equations another term must be added.*[24]

The pure birth process is admittedly too trite to be really interesting, but the conditions as described are typical for the most general case of the Kolmogorov equations. Two essentially new phenomena occur, however. First, the birth process involves only one escape route out to "infinity" or, in abstract terminology, a single *boundary* point. By contrast, the general process may involve boundaries of a complicated topological structure. Second, in the birth process the motion is directed toward the boundary because only transitions $E_n \to E_{n+1}$ are possible. Processes of a different type can be constructed; for example, the direction may be reversed to obtain a process in which only transitions $E_{n+1} \to E_n$ are possible. Such a process can *originate* at the boundary instead of ending there. In the birth-and-death process, transitions are possible in both directions just as in one-dimensional diffusion. It turns out that in this case there exist processes analogous to the elastic and reflecting barrier processes of diffusion theory, but their description would lead beyond the scope of this book.

10. PROBLEMS FOR SOLUTION

1. In the pure birth process defined by (3.2) let $\lambda_n > 0$ for all n. Prove that for every fixed $n \geq 1$ the function $P_n(t)$ first increases, then decreases to 0. If t_n is the place of the maximum, then $t_1 < t_2 < t_3 < \ldots$. *Hint:* Use induction; differentiate (3.2).

2. *Continuation.* If $\sum \lambda_n^{-1} = \infty$ show that $t_n \to \infty$. *Hint:* If $t_n \to \tau$, then for fixed $t > \tau$ the sequence $\lambda_n P_n(t)$ increases. Use (4.10).

3. *The Yule process.* Derive the mean and the variance of the distribution defined by (3.4). [Use only the differential equations, not the explicit form (3.5).]

4. *Pure death process.* Find the differential equations of a process of the Yule type with transitions only from E_n to E_{n-1}. Find the distribution $P_n(t)$, its mean, and its variance, assuming that the initial state is E_i.

---

[24] For further details see XIV,8 of volume 2.

5. *Parking lots.* In a parking lot with N spaces the incoming traffic is of the Poisson type with intensity λ, but only as long as empty spaces are available. The occupancy times have an exponential distribution (just as the holding times in section 7). Find the appropriate differential equations for the probabilities $P_n(t)$ of finding exactly n spaces occupied.

6. *Various queue disciplines.* We consider the waiting line at a single channel subject to the rules given in example (7.*b*). This time we consider the process entirely from the point of view of Mr. Smith whose call arrives at epoch 0. His waiting time depends on the queue discipline, namely the order in which waiting calls are cleared. The following disciplines are of greatest interest:

(*a*) *Last come last served*, that is, calls are cleared in the order of arrival.

(*b*) *Random order*, that is, the members of the waiting line have equal probabilities to be served next.

(*c*) *Last come first served*, that is, calls are cleared in the inverse order of arrival.[25]

It is convenient to number the states starting with -1. During Mr. Smith's actual servicetime the system is said to be in state E_0, and at the expiration of this servicetime it passes into E_{-1} where it stays forever. For $n \geq 1$ the system is in state E_n if Mr. Smith's call is still in the waiting line together with $n-1$ other calls that will, or may, be served before Mr. Smith. (The call being served is not included in the waiting line.) Denote by $P_n(t)$ the probability of E_n at epoch t. Prove that

$$P'_{-1}(t) = \mu P_0(t)$$

in all three cases. Furthermore

(*a*) Under *last come last served discipline*

$$P'_n(t) = -\mu P_n(t) + \mu P_{n-1}(t), \qquad n \geq 0.$$

(*b*) *under random order discipline* when $n \geq 2$

$$P'_n(t) = -(\lambda+\mu)P_n(t) + \frac{n\mu}{n+1} P_{n+1}(t) + \lambda P_{n-1}(t),$$

$$P'_1(t) = -(\lambda+\mu)P_1(t) + \tfrac{1}{2}\mu P_2(t)$$

$$P'_0 = -\mu P_0(t) + \mu P_1(t) + \tfrac{1}{2}\mu P_2(t) + \tfrac{1}{3}\mu P_3(t) + \cdots.$$

(*c*) Under *last come first served discipline* for $n \geq 2$

$$P'_n(t) = -(\lambda+\mu)P_n(t) + \mu P_{n+1}(t) + \lambda P_{n-1}(t)$$

$$P'_1(t) = -(\lambda+\mu)P_1(t) + \mu P_2(t)$$

$$P'_0(t) = -\mu P_0(t) + \mu P_1(t).$$

(See also problem 20.)

---

[25] This discipline is meaningful in information-processing machines when the latest information (or observation) carries greatest weight. The treatment was suggested by E. Vaulot, *Delais d'attente des appels téléphoniques dans l'ordre inverse de leur arrivée*, Comptes Rendues, Académie des Sciences, Paris, vol. 238 (1954), pp. 1188–1189.

7. *Continuation.* Suppose that the queue discipline is last come last served (case *a*) and that $P_r(0) = 1$. Show that

$$P_{r-k}(t) = \frac{(\mu t)^{r-k}}{(r-k)!} e^{-\mu t}, \qquad 0 \leq k \leq r.$$

8. *Continuation.* Generalize problem 6 to the case of *a* channels.

9. *The Polya process.*[26] This is a non-stationary pure birth process with λ_n depending on time:

(10.1) $$\lambda_n(t) = \frac{1 + an}{1 + at}.$$

Show that the solution with initial condition $P_0(0) = 1$ is

$$P_0(t) = (1 + at)^{-1/a}$$

(10.2)

$$P_n(t) = \frac{(1+a)(1+2a) \cdots \{1+(n-1)a\}}{n!} t^n (1+at)^{-n-1/a}.$$

Show from the differential equations that the mean and variance are t and $t(1+at)$, respectively.

10. *Continuation.* The Polya process can be obtained by a passage to the limit from the Polya urn scheme, example V, (2.c). If the state of the system is defined as the number of red balls, then the transition probability $E_k \to E_{k+1}$ at the $(n+1)$st drawing is

(10.3) $$p_{k,n} = \frac{r + kc}{r + b + nc} = \frac{p + k\gamma}{1 + n\gamma}$$

where $p = r/(r+b)$, $\gamma = c/(r+b)$.

As in the passage from Bernoulli trials to the Poisson distribution, let drawings be made at the rate of one in h time units and let $h \to 0$, $n \to \infty$ so that $np \to t$, $n\gamma \to at$. Show that in the limit (10.3) leads to (10.1). Show also that the Polya distribution V, (2.3) passes into (10.2).

11. *Linear growth.* If in the process defined by (5.7) $\lambda = \mu$, and $P_1(0) = 1$, then

(10.4) $$P_0(t) = \frac{\lambda t}{1 + \lambda t}, \qquad P_n(t) = \frac{(\lambda t)^{n-1}}{(1+\lambda t)^{n+1}}.$$

The probability of ultimate extinction is 1.

12. *Continuation.* Assuming a trial solution to (5.7) of the form $P_n(t) = A(t)B^n(t)$, prove that the solution with $P_1(0) = 1$ is

(10.5) $$P_0(t) = \mu B(t), \qquad P_n(t) = \{1 - \lambda B(t)\}\{1 - \mu B(t)\}\{\lambda B(t)\}^{n-1}$$

---

[26] O. Lundberg, *On random processes and their applications to sickness and accident statistics*, Uppsala, 1940.

with

(10.6) $$B(t) = \frac{1 - e^{(\lambda-\mu)t}}{\mu - \lambda e^{(\lambda-\mu)t}}.$$

13. *Continuation.* The generating function $P(s, t) = \sum P_n(t)s^n$ satisfies the partial differential equation

(10.7) $$\frac{\partial P}{\partial t} = \{\mu - (\lambda+\mu)s + \lambda s^2\} \frac{\partial P}{\partial s}.$$

14. *Continuation.* Let $M_2(t) = \sum n^2 P_n(t)$ and $M(t) = \sum n P_n(t)$ (as in section 5). Show that

(10.8) $$M_2'(t) = 2(\lambda-\mu)M_2(t) + (\lambda+\mu)M(t).$$

Deduce that when $\lambda > \mu$ the *variance* of $\{P_n(t)\}$ is given by

(10.9) $$e^{2(\lambda-\mu)t}\{1 - e^{(\mu-\lambda)t}\}(\lambda+\mu)/(\lambda-\mu).$$

15. For the process (7.2) the generating function $P(s, t) = \sum P_n(t) s^n$ satisfies the partial differential equation

(10.10) $$\frac{\partial P}{\partial t} = (1-s)\left(-\lambda P + \mu \frac{\partial P}{\partial s} \right).$$

Its solution is

$$P(s, t) = e^{-\lambda(1-s)(1-e^{-\mu t})/\mu}\{1-(1-s)e^{-\mu t}\}^i.$$

For $i = 0$ this is a Poisson distribution with parameter $\lambda(1 - e^{-\mu t})/\mu$. *As* $t \to \infty$, *the distribution* $\{P_n(t)\}$ *tends to a Poisson distribution with parameter* λ/μ.

16. For the process defined by (7.26) the generating function for the steady state $P(s) = \sum p_n s^n$ satisfies the partial differential equation

(10.11) $$(\mu+\lambda s)\frac{\partial P}{\partial s} = a\lambda P,$$

with the solution $P = \{(\mu+\lambda s)/(\lambda+\mu)\}^n$.

17. For the differential equations (7.26) assume a trial solution of the form

$$P_n(t) = \binom{a}{n} A^n(1 - A)^{a-n}.$$

Prove that this is a solution if, and only if,

$$A = \frac{\lambda}{\lambda + \mu} (1 - e^{-(\lambda+\mu)t})$$

18. In the "simplest trunking problem," example (7.*a*), let $Q_n(t)$ be the probability that starting from E_n the system will reach E_0 before epoch t.

Prove the validity of the differential equations

$$Q'_n(t) = -(\lambda+n\mu)Q_n(t) + \lambda Q_{n+1}(t) + n\mu Q_{n-1}(t), \qquad (n \geq 2)$$

(10.12)

$$Q'_1(t) = -(\lambda+\mu)Q_1(t) + \lambda Q_2(t) + \mu$$

with the initial conditions $Q_n(0) = 0$.

19. *Continuation.* Consider the same problem for a process defined by an arbitrary system of forward equations. Show that the $Q_n(t)$ satisfy the corresponding *backward equations* (for fixed k) with $P_{0k}(t)$ replaced by 1.

20. Show that the differential equations of problem 6 are essentially the same as the forward equations for the transition probabilities. Derive the corresponding backward equations.

21. Assume that the solution of at least one of the two systems of (forward and backward) equations is unique. Prove that the transition probabilities satisfying this system satisfy the Chapman-Kolmogorov equation (1.1).

Hint: Show that both sides satisfy the same system of differential equations with the same initial conditions.

22. Let $P_{ik}(t)$ satisfy the Chapman-Komogorov equation (1.1). Supposing that $P_{ik}(t) > 0$ and that $S_i(t) = \sum_k P_{ik}(t) \leq 1$, prove that either $S_i(t) = 1$ for all t or $S_i(t) < 1$ for all t.

23. *Ergodic properties.* Consider a stationary process with finitely many states; that is, suppose that the system of differential equations (9.9) is finite and that the coefficients c_j and p_{jk} are constants. Prove that the solutions are linear combinations of exponential terms $e^{\lambda(t-\tau)}$ where the real part of λ is negative unless $\lambda = 0$. Conclude that the asymptotic behavior of the transition probabilities is the same as in the case of *finite* Markov chains except that the periodic case is impossible.

Answers to Problems

1. (a) $\frac{3}{5}$; (b) $\frac{3}{5}$; (c) $\frac{3}{10}$.

2. The events S_1, S_2, $S_1 \cup S_2$, and $S_1 S_2$ contain, respectively, 12, 12, 18, and 6 points.

4. The space contains the two points HH and TT with probability $\frac{1}{4}$; the two points HTT and THH with probability $\frac{1}{8}$; and generally two points with probability 2^{-n} when $n \geq 2$. These probabilities add to 1, so that there is no necessity to consider the possibility of an unending sequence of tosses. The required probabilities are $\frac{15}{16}$ and $\frac{2}{3}$, respectively.

9. $P\{AB\} = \frac{1}{6}$, $P\{A \cup B\} = \frac{23}{36}$, $P\{AB'\} = \frac{1}{3}$.

12. $x = 0$ in the events (a), (b), and (g).
$x = 1$ in the events (e) and (f).
$x = 2$ in the event (d).
$x = 4$ in the event (c).

15. (a) A; (b) AB; (c) $B \cup (AC)$.

16. Correct are (c), (d), (e), (f), (h), (i), (k), (l). The statement (a) is meaningless unless $C \subset B$. It is in general false even in this case, but is correct in the special case $C \subset B$, $AC = 0$. The statement (b) is correct if $C \supset AB$. The statement (g) should read $(A \cup B) - A = A'B$. Finally (k) is the correct version of (j).

17. (a) $AB'C'$; (b) ABC'; (c) ABC; (d) $A \cup B \cup C$;
(e) $AB \cup AC \cup BC$; (f) $AB'C' \cup A'BC' \cup A'B'C$;
(g) $ABC' \cup AB'C \cup A'BC = (AB \cup AC \cup BC) - ABC$;
(h) $A'B'C'$; (i) $(ABC)'$.

18. $A \cup B \cup C = A \cup (B-AB) \cup \{C-C(A \cup B)\} = A \cup BA' \cup CA'B'$.

1. (a) 26^3; (b) $26^2 + 26^3 = 18{,}252$; (c) $26^2 + 26^3 + 26^4$. In a city with 20,000 inhabitants either some people have the same set of initials or at least 1748 people have more than three initials.

2. $2(2^{10}-1) = 2046$.

3. $\binom{n}{2} + n = \dfrac{n(n+1)}{2}$.   **4.** (a) $\dfrac{1}{n}$; (b) $\dfrac{1}{n(n-1)}$.

5. $q_A = (\frac{5}{6})^6$, $\quad q_B = (\frac{5}{6})^{12} + 12(\frac{5}{6})^{11} \cdot \frac{1}{6}$.

6. (a) $p_1 = 0.01$, $p_2 = 0.27$, $p_3 = 0.72$.
(b) $p_1 = 0.001$, $p_2 = 0.063$, $p_3 = 0.432$, $p_4 = 0.504$.

7. $p_r = (10)_r 10^{-r}$. For example, $p_3 = 0.72$, $p_{10} = 0.00036288$. Stirling's formula gives $p_{10} = 0.0003598 \ldots$.

8. (a) $(\frac{9}{10})^k$; (b) $(\frac{9}{10})^k$; $(\frac{8}{10})^k$; (d) $2(\frac{9}{10})^k - (\frac{8}{10})^k$; (a) AB and $A \cup B$.

9. $\binom{n}{2} n! \, n^{-n}$. **10.** $9 \Big/ \binom{12}{8} = \frac{1}{55}$.

11. The probability of exactly r trials is $(n-1)_{r-1}/(n)_r = n^{-1}$.

12. (a) $[1 \cdot 3 \cdot 5 \cdots (2n-1)]^{-1} = 2^n n!/(2n)!$;

(b) $n! \, [1 \cdot 3 \cdots (2n-1)]^{-1} = 2^n \Big/ \binom{2n}{n}$.

13. On the assumption of randomness the probability that all of twelve tickets come either on Tuesdays or Thursdays is $(\frac{2}{7})^{12} = 0.0000003 \ldots$. There are only $\binom{7}{2} = 21$ pairs of days, so that the probability remains extremely small even for any two days. Hence it is reasonable to assume that the police have a system.

14. Assuming randomness, the probability of the event is $(\frac{6}{7})^{12} = \frac{1}{6}$ appr. No safe conclusion is possible.

15. $(90)_{10}/(100)_{10} = 0.330476 \ldots$.

16. $25! \, (5!)^{-5} 5^{-25} = 0.00209 \ldots$.

17. $\dfrac{2(n-2)_r (n-r-1)!}{n!} = \dfrac{2(n-r-1)}{n(n-1)}$.

18. (a) $\frac{1}{216}$; (b) $\frac{83}{3888}$.

19. The probabilities are $1 - (\frac{5}{6})^4 = 0.517747 \ldots$ and $1 - (\frac{35}{36})^{24} = 0.491404 \ldots$.

20. (a) $(n-N)_r/(n)_r$. (b) $(1-N/n)^r$. For $r = N = 3$ the probabilities are (a) $0.911812 \ldots$; (b) $0.912673 \ldots$. For $r = N = 10$ they are (a) 0.330476; (b) $0.348678 \ldots$.

21. (a) $(1-N/n)^{r-1}$. (b) $(n)_{Nr}/((n)_N)^r$.

22. $(1-2/n)^{2r-2}$; for the median $2^{r+1} = 0.7n$, approximately.

23. On the assumption of randomness, the probabilities that three or four breakages are caused (a) by one girl, (b) by the youngest girl are, respectively, $\frac{13}{64} \approx 0.2$ and $\frac{13}{256} \approx 0.05$.

24. (a) $12!/12^{12} = 0.000054$. (b) $\binom{12}{2}(2^6 - 2)12^{-6} = 0.00137 \ldots$.

25. $\dfrac{30!}{2^6 6^6} \binom{12}{6} 12^{-30} \approx 0.00035 \ldots$.

26. (a) $\dbinom{n}{2r} 2^{2r} \Big/ \dbinom{2n}{2r}$; (b) $n \dbinom{n-1}{2r-2} 2^{2r-2} \Big/ \dbinom{2n}{2r}$;

(c) $\dbinom{n}{2} \dbinom{n-2}{2r-4} 2^{2r-4} \Big/ \dbinom{2n}{2r}$.

27. $\dbinom{N-3}{r-1} \Big/ \dbinom{N-1}{r-1}$.

28. $p = \dbinom{2N}{N}^2 \Big/ \dbinom{4N}{2N} \approx \sqrt{2/(N\pi)}$.

29. $p = \dfrac{\dbinom{4}{k}\dbinom{48}{13-k}\dbinom{39}{13}\dbinom{26}{13}}{\dbinom{52}{13}\dbinom{39}{13}\dbinom{26}{13}} = \dfrac{\dbinom{4}{k}\dbinom{48}{13-k}}{\dbinom{52}{13}}$.

30. Cf. problem 29. The probability is

$$\dbinom{13}{m}\dbinom{39}{13-m}\dbinom{13-m}{n}\dbinom{26+m}{13-n} \Big/ \dbinom{52}{13}\dbinom{39}{13}.$$

31. $\dbinom{4}{k}\dbinom{48}{26-k} \Big/ \dbinom{52}{26}$.

32. $\dfrac{\dbinom{13}{a}\dbinom{39}{13-a}\dbinom{13-a}{b}\dbinom{26+a}{13-b}\dbinom{13-a-b}{c}\dbinom{13+a+b}{13-c}}{\dbinom{52}{13}\dbinom{39}{13}\dbinom{26}{13}}$.

33. (a) $24p(5, 4, 3, 1)$; (b) $4p(4, 4, 4, 1)$; (c) $12p(4, 4, 3, 2)$.

34. $\dfrac{\dbinom{13}{a}\dbinom{13}{b}\dbinom{13}{c}\dbinom{13}{d}}{\dbinom{52}{13}}$. (Cf. problem 33 for the probability that the

hand contains a cards of some suit, b of another, etc.)

35. $p_0(r) = (52-r)_4/(52)_4$; $p_1(r) = 4r(52-r)_3/(52)_4$;
$p_2(r) = 6r(r-1)(52-r)_2/(52)_4$;
$p_3(r) = 4r(r-1)(r-2)(52-r)/(52)_4$; $p_4(r) = r_4/(52)_4$.

36. The probabilities that the waiting times for the first, $\ldots$, fourth ace *exceed* r are

$$w_1(r) = p_0(r); \quad w_2(r) = p_0(r) + p_1(r);$$

$$w_3(r) = p_0(r) + p_1(r) + p_2(r);$$

$$w_4(r) = 1 - p_4(r).$$

Next $f_i(r) = w_i(r-1) - w_i(r)$. The medians are 8, 20, 32, 44.

37. (a) $\dbinom{4}{k}\dbinom{4-k}{k}\dbinom{48}{r-k}\dbinom{48-r+k}{r-k} \Big/ \dbinom{52}{r}\dbinom{52-r}{r}$,　　　　with $k \leq 2$;

(b) $\left\{\dbinom{4}{k}\dbinom{48}{r-k}\Big/\dbinom{52}{r}\right\}^2$, with $k \leq 4$.

39. $\dbinom{r_1+n-1}{r_1}\dbinom{r_2+n-1}{r_2}$.　　　**40.** $\dbinom{r_1+5}{5}(r_2+1)$.

41. $\dfrac{(r_1+r_2+r_3)!}{r_1!\,r_2!\,r_3!}$.　　　**42.** $(49)_4/(52)_4$.

43. $\mathbf{P}\{(7)\}$　　　　　$= 10 \cdot 10^{-7}$　　　　　$= 0.000\,001$.

$\mathbf{P}\{(6, 1)\}$　　　$= \dfrac{10!}{8!\,1!\,1!} \cdot \dfrac{7!}{1!\,6!} \cdot 10^{-7}$　　　$= 0.000\,063$.

$\mathbf{P}\{(5, 2)\}$　　　$= \dfrac{10!}{8!\,1!\,1!} \cdot \dfrac{7!}{2!\,5!} \cdot 10^{-7}$　　　$= 0.000\,189$.

$\mathbf{P}\{(5, 1, 1)\}$　　　$= \dfrac{10!}{7!\,2!\,1!} \cdot \dfrac{7!}{1!\,1!\,5!} \cdot 10^{-7}$　　　$= 0.001\,512$.

$\mathbf{P}\{(4, 3)\}$　　　$= \dfrac{10!}{8!\,1!\,1!} \cdot \dfrac{7!}{3!\,4!} \cdot 10^{-7}$　　　$= 0.000\,315$.

$\mathbf{P}\{(4, 2, 1)\}$　　　$= \dfrac{10!}{7!\,1!\,1!} \cdot \dfrac{7!}{1!\,2!\,4!} \cdot 10^{-7}$　　　$= 0.007\,560$.

$\mathbf{P}\{(4, 1, 1, 1)\}$　　　$= \dfrac{10!}{6!\,3!\,1!} \cdot \dfrac{7!}{1!\,1!\,1!\,4!} \cdot 10^{-7}$　　$= 0.017\,640$.

$\mathbf{P}\{(3, 3, 1)\}$　　　$= \dfrac{10!}{7!\,2!\,1!} \cdot \dfrac{7!}{1!\,3!\,3!} \cdot 10^{-7}$　　　$= 0.005\,040$.

$\mathbf{P}\{(3, 2, 2)\}$　　　$= \dfrac{10!}{7!\,2!\,1!} \cdot \dfrac{7!}{2!\,2!\,3!} \cdot 10^{-7}$　　　$= 0.007\,560$.

$\mathbf{P}\{(3, 2, 1, 1)\}$　　　$= \dfrac{10!}{6!\,2!\,1!\,1!} \cdot \dfrac{7!}{1!\,1!\,2!\,3!} \cdot 10^{-7} = 0.105\,840$.

$\mathbf{P}\{(3, 1, 1, 1, 1)\}$　　　$= \dfrac{10!}{5!\,4!\,1!} \cdot \dfrac{7!}{1!\,1!\,1!\,1!\,3!} \cdot 10^{-7} = 0.105\,840$.

$\mathbf{P}\{(2, 2, 2, 1)\}$　　　$= \dfrac{10!}{6!\,3!\,1!} \cdot \dfrac{7!}{1!\,2!\,2!\,2!} \cdot 10^{-7}$　　$= 0.052\,920$.

$\mathbf{P}\{(2, 2, 1, 1, 1)\}$　　　$= \dfrac{10!}{5!\,3!\,2!} \cdot \dfrac{7!}{1!\,1!\,1!\,2!\,2!} \cdot 10^{-7} = 0.317\,520$.

$\mathbf{P}\{(2, 1, 1, 1, 1, 1)\}$　　$= \dfrac{10!}{4!\,5!\,1!} \cdot \dfrac{7!}{1!\,1!\,1!\,1!\,1!\,2!} \cdot 10^{-7} = 0.317\,520$.

$\mathbf{P}\{(1, 1, 1, 1, 1, 1, 1,)\}$　$= \dfrac{10!}{3!\,7!} \cdot 7! \cdot 10^{-7}$　　　　$= 0.060\,480$.

44. Letting S, D, T, Q stand for simple, double, triple, and quadruple, respectively, we have

$$P\{22S\} = \frac{365!}{343!} \cdot 365^{-22} = 0.524\ 30.$$

$$P\{20S + 1D\} = \frac{365!}{1!\ 344!} \cdot \frac{22!}{20!\ 2!} \cdot 365^{-22} = 0.352\ 08.$$

$$P\{18S + 2D\} = \frac{365!}{2!\ 345!} \cdot \frac{22!}{18!\ 2!\ 2!} \cdot 365^{-22} = 0.096\ 95.$$

$$P\{16S + 3D\} = \frac{365!}{3!\ 346!} \cdot \frac{22!}{16!\ 2!\ 2!\ 2!} \cdot 365^{-22} = 0.014\ 29.$$

$$P\{19S + 1T\} = \frac{365!}{345!} \cdot \frac{22!}{19!\ 3!} \cdot 365^{-22} = 0.006\ 80.$$

$$P\{17S + 1D + 1T\} = \frac{365!}{346!} \cdot \frac{22!}{17!\ 2!\ 3!} \cdot 365^{-22} = 0.003\ 36.$$

$$P\{14S + 4D\} = \frac{365!}{347!} \cdot \frac{22!}{14!\ 2!\ 2!\ 2!\ 2!} \cdot 365^{-22} = 0.001\ 24.$$

$$P\{15S + 2D + 1T\} = \frac{365!}{347!} \cdot \frac{22!}{15!\ 2!\ 2!\ 3!} \cdot 365^{-22} = 0.000\ 66.$$

$$P\{(18S + 1Q\} = \frac{365!}{346!} \cdot \frac{22!}{18!\ 4!} \cdot 365^{-22} = 0.000\ 09.$$

45. Let $q = \binom{52}{5} = 2{,}598{,}960.$ The probabilities are:

(a) $4/q;$ (b) $13 \cdot 12 \cdot 4 \cdot q^{-1} = \frac{1}{4165};$ (c) $13 \cdot 12 \cdot 4 \cdot 6 \cdot q^{-1} = \frac{6}{4165};$

(d) $9 \cdot 4^5 \cdot q^{-1} = \frac{768}{216580};$ (e) $13 \cdot \binom{12}{2} 4 \cdot 4^2 \cdot q^{-1} = \frac{88}{4165};$

(f) $\binom{13}{2} \cdot 11 \cdot 6 \cdot 6 \cdot 4 \cdot q^{-1} = \frac{198}{4165};$ (g) $13 \cdot \binom{12}{3} \cdot 6 \cdot 4^3 \cdot q^{-1} = \frac{1760}{4165}.$

CHAPTER IV

1. 99/323. **2.** 0.21 .... **3.** 1/4. **4.** $7/2^6.$

5. $1/81$ and $31/6^6.$

6. If A_k is the event that (k, k) does not appear, then from 1(.5)

$$1 - p_r = 6\left(\frac{35}{36}\right)^r - \binom{6}{2}\left(\frac{34}{36}\right)^r + \binom{6}{3}\left(\frac{33}{36}\right)^r - \binom{6}{4}\left(\frac{32}{36}\right)^r + 6\left(\frac{31}{36}\right)^r - \left(\frac{30}{36}\right)^r.$$

7. Put $p^{-1} = \binom{52}{13}.$ Then $S_1 = 13\binom{48}{9}p;$ $S_2 = \binom{13}{2}\binom{44}{5}p;$

$S_3 = 40\binom{13}{3}p.$ Numerically, $P_{[0]} = 0.09658;$ $P_{[1]} = 0.0341;$ $P_{[2]} = 0.0001,$ approximately.

8. $u_r = \sum_{k=0}^{N} (-1)^k \binom{N}{k} \left(1 - \frac{k}{n}\right)^r$.

9. $p_r = \sum_{k=0}^{N} (-1)^k \binom{N}{k} \frac{(n-k)_r}{(n)_r}$. See II, (12.18) for a proof that the two results agree.

10. The general term is $a_{1k_1} a_{2k_2} \cdots a_{Nk_N}$, where $(k_1, k_2, \ldots, k_N)$ is a permutation of $(1, 2, \ldots, N)$. For a diagonal element $k_v = v$.

12. $u_r = \sum_{k=0}^{n} (-1)^k \binom{n}{k} \frac{(ns - ks)_r}{(ns)_r}$.

14. Note that, by definition, $u_r = 0$ for $r < n$ and $u_n = n! \, s^n/(ns)_n$.

15. $u_r - u_{r-1} = \sum_{k=1}^{n} (-1)^{k-1} \binom{n-1}{k-1} \frac{(ns-ks)_{r-1}}{(ns-1)_{r-1}}$.

The limit equals $\sum_{k=0}^{n-1} (-1)^k \binom{n-1}{k} \left(1 - \frac{k+1}{n}\right)^{r-1}$.

16. $\binom{N}{2}^{-r} \binom{N}{m} \sum_{k=2}^{m} (-1)^{m-k} \binom{m}{k} \binom{k}{2}^r$.

17. Use $\binom{52}{5} S_k = \binom{4}{k} \binom{52 - 13k}{5}$.

$P_{[0]} = 0.264$, $P_{[1]} = 0.588$, $P_{[2]} = 0.146$, $P_{[3]} = 0.002$, approximately.

18. Use $\binom{52}{13} S_k = \binom{4}{k} \binom{52-2k}{13-2k}$.

$$P_{[0]} = 0.780217, \qquad P_{[1]} = 0.204606, \qquad P_{[2]} = 0.014845,$$

$$P_{[3]} = 0.000330, \qquad P_{[4]} = 0.000002, \text{ approximately.}$$

19. $m! \, N! \, u_m = \sum_{k=0}^{N-m} (-1)^k (N-m-k)!/k!$.

20. Cf. the following formula with $r = 2$.

21. $(rN)! \, x =$

$$= \binom{N}{2} r^2 (rN-2)! - \binom{N}{3} r^3 (rN-3)! + - \cdots + (-1)^N r^N (rN-N)!.$$

24. $P_{[m]} = \dfrac{\binom{n}{m}}{\binom{n+r-1}{r}} \sum_{k=0}^{n-m} (-1)^k \binom{n-m}{k} \binom{n-m+r-1-k}{r}$.

25. Use II, (12.16) and (12.4).

26. Put $U_N = A_1 \cup \cdots \cup A_N$ and note that $U_{N+1} = U_N \cup A_{N+1}$ and $U_N A_{N+1} = (A_1 A_{N+1} \cup \cdots \cup (A_N A_{N+1})$.

CHAPTER V

1. $1 - \dfrac{(5)_3}{(6)_3} = \dfrac{1}{2}$.   **2.** $p = 1 - \dfrac{10 \cdot 5^9}{6^{10} - 5^{10}} = 0.61 \ldots$.

3. (a) $\dbinom{35}{13} \Big/ \dbinom{39}{13} = 0.182 \ldots$.   The probability of exactly one ace is

$4 \dbinom{35}{12} \Big/ \dbinom{39}{13} = 0.411 \ldots$.   (b) $1 - 0.182 - 0.411 = 0.407$, approximately.

4. (a) $2 \dfrac{\dbinom{23}{10}}{\dbinom{26}{13}} = \dfrac{11}{50}$;   (b) $2 \dfrac{\dbinom{23}{12}}{\dbinom{26}{13}} = \dfrac{13}{50}$.

6. $\frac{125}{345}$; $\frac{140}{345}$; $\frac{80}{345}$.   **7.** $\frac{20}{21}$.   **9.** $(\frac{5}{6})^2$.   **10.** $1 - (\frac{5}{6})^2$.

12. $\dfrac{p}{2 - p}$.   **13.** (b) $\frac{3}{5}$; (c) $2^n (1 + 2^n)^{-1}$.

14. (d) Put $a_n = x_n - \frac{4}{7}$, $b_n = y_n - \frac{1}{7}$, $c_n = z_n - \frac{2}{7}$. Then

$$|a_n| + |b_n| + |c_n| = \tfrac{1}{2}\{|a_{n+1}| + |b_{n+1}| + |c_{n+1}|\}.$$

Hence $|a_n| + |b_n| + |c_n|$ increases geometrically.

15. $p = (1 - p_1)(1 - p_2) \cdots (1 - p_n)$.

16. Use $1 - x < e^{-x}$ for $0 < x < 1$ or Taylor's series for $\log (1 - x)$; cf. II, (12.26).

18. $\dfrac{b + c}{b + c + r}$.

19. Suppose the assertion to be true for the nth drawing regardless of b, r, and c. Considering the two possibilities at the *first* drawing we find then that the probability of black at the $(n+1)$st trial equals

$$\frac{b}{b + r} \cdot \frac{b + c}{b + r + c} + \frac{r}{b + r} \cdot \frac{b}{b + r + c} = \frac{b}{b + r}.$$

20. The preceding problem states that the assertion is true for $m = 1$ and all n. For induction, consider the two possibilities at the first trial.

23. Use II, (12.9).

24. The binomial coefficient on the right is the limit of the first factor in the numerator in (8.2). Note that

$$\binom{-1/\gamma}{n} \sim \binom{-1/\gamma}{n_2} (1 + \rho)^{n_1}.$$

26. $2v = 2p(1 - p) \le \frac{1}{2}$ in consequence of (5.2).

28. (a) u^2;   (b) $u^2 + uv + v^2/4$;   (c) $u^2 + (25uv + 9v^2 + vw + 2uw)/16$.

33. $p_{11} = p_{32} = 2p_{21} = p$, $p_{12} = p_{33} = 2p_{23} = q$, $p_{13} = p_{31} = 0$, $p_{22} = \frac{1}{2}$.

CHAPTER VI

1. $\frac{5}{16}$.   **2.** The probability is $0.02804 \ldots$.   **3.** $(9.9)^x \leq 0.1$, $x \geq 22$.

4. $q^x \leq \frac{1}{2}$ and $(1 - 4p)^x \leq \frac{1}{2}$ with $p = \binom{48}{9} \Big/ \binom{52}{13}$. Hence $x \geq 263$ and $x \geq 66$, respectively.

5. $1 - (0.8)^{10} - 2(0.8)^9 = 0.6242 \ldots$.

6. $\{1 - (0.8)^{10} - 2(0.8)^9\}/\{1 - (0.8)^{10}\} = 0.6993 \ldots$.

7. $\binom{26}{2}\binom{26}{11} \Big/ \binom{52}{13} = 0.003954 \ldots$, and $\binom{13}{2}\frac{1}{2^{13}} = 0.00952 \ldots$.

8. $\binom{12}{2}\{6^{-6} - 2 \cdot 12^{-6}\}$.

9. True values: $0.6651 \ldots, 0.40187 \ldots$, and $0.2009 \ldots$,; Poisson approximations: $1 - e^{-1} = 0.6321 \ldots, 0.3679 \ldots$, and $0.1839 \ldots$.

10. $e^{-2} \sum_4^\infty 2^k/k! = 0.143 \ldots$.   **11.** $e^{-1} \sum_3^\infty 1/k! = 0.080 \ldots$.

12. $e^{-x/100} \leq 0.05$ or $x \geq 300$.

13. $e^{-1} = 0.3679 \ldots$, $1 - 2 \cdot e^{-1} = 0.264 \ldots$.

14. $e^{-x} \leq 0.01$, $x \geq 5$.   **15.** $1/p = 649{,}740$.

16. $1 - p^n$ where $p = p(0; \lambda) + \cdots + p(k; \lambda)$.

18. q^3 for $k = 0$; pq^3 for $k = 1, 2, 3$;   and $pq^3 - pq^6$ for $k = 4$.

19. $\sum_{k=0}^n \binom{n}{k}^2 2^{-2n} = \binom{2n}{n} 2^{-2n} \approx 1/\sqrt{\pi n}$ for large n.

20. $\sum_{k=a}^{a+b-1} \binom{a+b-1}{k} p^k q^{a-b-1-k}$. This can be written in the alternative form

$p^a \sum_{k=0}^{b-1} \binom{a+k-1}{k} q^k$, where the kth term equals the probability that the ath

success occurs directly after $k \leq b - 1$ failures.

21. $x_r = \binom{2N-1-r}{N-1} \cdot 2^{-2N+r+1}$.

22. (a) $x = \sum_{r=1}^N x_r 2^{-r-1} = 2^{-2N} \sum_{r=1}^N \binom{2N-1-r}{N-1}$;   (b) Use II, (12.6).

23. $k_i \approx np_i$, $k_{12} \approx np_{12}$ whence $n \approx k_1 k_2/k_{12}$.

24. $\binom{n}{n_1} \cdot \binom{n-s_1}{n_2} \cdots \binom{n-s_{r-1}}{n_r} \cdot q^{s_r} p^{(rn-s_1-\cdots-s_r)}$

where $s_i = n_1 + \cdots + n_i$.

25. $p = p_1 q_2 (p_1 q_2 + p_2 q_1)^{-1}$.

31. By the Taylor expansion for the logarithm

$$b(0; n, p) = q^n = (1 - \lambda/n)^n < e^{-\lambda} = p(0; \lambda).$$

The terms of each distribution add to unity, and therefore it is impossible that *all* terms of one distribution should be greater than the corresponding terms of the other.

32. There are only finitely many terms of the Poisson distribution which are greater than ϵ, and the remaining ones dominate the corresponding terms of the binomial distribution.

CHAPTER VII

1. Proceed as in section 1.   **2.** Use (1.7).   **3.** $\mathfrak{N}(-\frac{32}{30}) = 0.143\ldots$.

4. 0.99.   **5.** 511.   **6.** 66,400.

7. Most certainly. The inequalities of chapter VI suffice to show that an excess of more than eight deviations is exceedingly improbable.

8. $(2\pi n)^{-1}\{p_1 p_2(1-p_1-p_2)\}^{-\frac{1}{2}}$.

CHAPTER VIII

1. $\beta = 21$.

2. $x = pu + qv + rw$, where u, v, w are solutions of

$$u = p^{\alpha-1} + (qv+rw)\frac{1-p^{\alpha-1}}{1-p}, \qquad v = (pu+rw)\frac{1-q^{\beta-1}}{1-q}$$

$$w = pu + qv + rw = x.$$

3. $u = p^{\alpha-1} + (qv+rw)\dfrac{1-p^{\alpha-1}}{1-p}$,

$$v = (pu+rw)\frac{1-q^{\beta-1}}{1-q}, \qquad w = (pu+qv)\frac{1-r^{\gamma-1}}{1-r}.$$

4. Note that $\mathbf{P}\{A_n\} < (2p)^n$, but

$$\mathbf{P}\{A_n\} > 1 - (1-p^n)^{2^n/2n} > 1 - e^{(-2p)^n/2n}.$$

If $p = \frac{1}{2}$, the last quantity is $\sim \frac{1}{2}n$; if $p > 1$, then $\mathbf{P}\{A_n\}$ does not even tend to zero.

CHAPTER IX

1. The possible combinations are $(0,0), (0,1), (0,2), (1,0), (1,1), (2,0), (2,1), (3,0)$. Their probabilities are 0.047539, 0.108883, 0.017850, 0.156364, 0.214197, 0.321295, 0.026775, 0.107098.

2. (*a*) The joint distribution takes on the form of a 6-by-6 matrix. The main diagonal contains the elements $q, 2q, \ldots, 6q$ where $q = \frac{1}{36}$. On one side of the main diagonal all elements are 0, on the other q. (*b*) $E(X) = \frac{7}{2}$, Var $(X) = \frac{35}{12}$, $E(Y) = \frac{161}{36}$, Var $(Y) = \frac{2555}{1296}$, Cov $(X, Y) = \frac{105}{72}$.

3. In the joint distribution of **X, Y** the rows are 32^{-1} times $(1, 0, 0, 0, 0, 0)$, $(0, 5, 4, 3, 2, 1,)$ $(0, 0, 6, 6, 3, 0)$, $(0, 0, 0, 1, 0, 0)$; of **X, Z**: $(1, 0, 0, 0, 0, 0)$, $(0, 5, 6, 1, 0, 0)$, $(0, 0, 4, 6, 1, 0)$, $(0, 0, 0, 3, 2, 0)$, $(0, 0, 0, 0, 2, 0)$, $(0, 0, 0, 0, 0, 1)$; **Y, Z**: $(1, 0, 0, 0)$, $(0, 5, 6, 1)$, $(0, 4, 7, 0)$, $(0, 3, 2, 0)$, $(0, 2, 0, 0)$, $(0, 1, 0, 0)$. Distribution of **X** + **Y**: $(1, 0, 5, 4, 9, 8, 5)$ all divided by 32, and the values of **X** + **Y** ranging from 0 to 6; of **XY**: $(1, 5, 4, 3, 8, 1, 6, 0, 3, 1)$ all divided by 32, the values ranging from 0 to 9.

$E(X) = \frac{5}{2}$, $E(Y) = \frac{3}{2}$, $E(Z) = \frac{31}{16}$, Var $(X) = \frac{5}{4}$, Var $(Y) = \frac{3}{8}$, Var $(Z) = \frac{303}{256}$.

4. (*a*) $p/(1 + q)$; (*b*) $1/(1 + q + q^2)$; (*c*) $1/(1 + q)$.

8. The distribution of $\mathbf{V}_n$ is given by (3.5), th^2 of $\mathbf{U}_n$ follows by symmetry.

9. (*a*) $P\{X \le r, Y \ge s\} = N^{-n}(r-s+1)^n \qquad$ for $r \ge s$;

$$P\{X = r, Y = s\} = N^{-n}\{(r-s+1)^n - 2(r-s)^n + (r-s-1)^n\},$$

if $r > s$, and $= N^{-n}$ if $r = s$.

(*b*) $x = \dfrac{r^{n-2} - (r-1)^{n-2}}{r^n - (r-1)^n} \qquad$ if $\quad j < r$ and $k < r$.

$x = \dfrac{r^{n-2}}{r^n - (r-1)^n} \qquad$ if $j \le r$ and $k = r$, or $j = r$ and $k \le r$.

$x = 0 \qquad\qquad\qquad$ if $j > r$ or $k > r$.

(*c*) $\sigma^2 \approx \dfrac{nN^2}{(n+1)^2(n+2)}$.

10. Probability for n double throws $2pq(p^2+q^2)^{n-1}$. Expectation $1/(2pq)$.

12. $P\{N = n, K = k\} = \dbinom{n}{k} p^{n-k}(qq')^k \cdot qp'$.

$P\{N = n\} = (1-qp')^n qp'$.

$P\{K = k\} = (qq')^k qp' \sum \dbinom{-k-1}{\nu} (-p)^\nu = p'q'^k$.

13. $P\left(\dfrac{K}{N+1}\right) = \Sigma k p_{k,n}/(n+1) = q^2 p'q' \sum_{n=1}^{\infty}\left(1 - \dfrac{1}{n+1}\right)(p+qq')^{n-1} =$

$= \dfrac{qq'}{1 - qp'} - \dfrac{q^2p'q'}{(1-qp')^2} \log\dfrac{1}{qp'}$.

$E(K) = \dfrac{q'}{p'}$; $E(N) = \dfrac{(1-qp')}{qp'}$; Cov $(K, N) = \dfrac{q'}{qp'^2}$.

$\rho(K, N) = \sqrt{q'/(1-qp')}$.

14. (a) $p_k = p^k q + q^k p$; $E(X) = pq^{-1} + qp^{-1}$;

$$\text{Var}(X) = pq^{-2} + qp^{-2} - 2.$$

(b) $q_k = p^2 q^{k-1} + q^2 p^{k-1}$; $P\{X = m, Y = n\} = p^{m+1}q^n + q^{m+1}q^n$ with m, $n \geq 1$; $E(Y) = 2$; $\sigma^2 = 2(pq^{-1} + qp^{-1} - 1)$.

17. $\binom{n}{k} 364^{n-k} 365^{1-n}$.

18. (a) $365\{1 - 364^n \cdot 365^{-n} - n364^{n-1} \cdot 365^{-n}\}$; (b) $n \geq 28$.

19. (a) $\mu = n$, $\sigma^2 = (n-1)n$; (b) $\mu = (n+1)/2$, $\sigma^2 = (n^2-1)/12$.

20. $E(X) = np_1$; $\text{Var}(X) = np_1(1-p_1)$; $\text{Cov}(X, Y) = -np_1p_2$.

21. $-n/36$. This is a special case of problem 20.

25. $E(Y_r) = \sum_{k=1}^{r} \dfrac{N}{r - k + 1}$; $\text{Var}(Y_r) = \sum_{k=1}^{r} \dfrac{N(N-r+k-1)}{(r-k+1)^2}$.

26. (a) $1 - q^k$; (b) $E(X) = N\{1 - q^k + k^{-1}\}$; (c) $\dfrac{dE(X)}{dk} = 0$.

27. $\Sigma(1-p_j)^n$. Put $X_j = 1$ or 0 according as the jth class is not or is presented.

28. $E(X) = \dfrac{r_1(r_2+1)}{r_1 + r_2}$; $\text{Var}(X) = \dfrac{r_1 r_2(r_1-1)(r_2+1)}{(r_1+r_2-1)(r_1+r_2)^2}$.

30. $E(S_n) = \dfrac{nb}{b + r}$; $\text{Var}(S_n) = \dfrac{nbr\{b+r+nc\}}{(b+r)^2(b+r+c)}$.

33. $E\left(\dfrac{X}{r}\right) = r\sum_{r=k}^{\infty} k^{-1}\binom{k-1}{r-1} p^r q^{k-r} =$

$$= \sum_{k=1}^{r-1}(-1)^{k-1}\dfrac{r}{r-k}\left(\dfrac{p}{q}\right)^k + \left(\dfrac{-p}{q}\right)^r r\log p.$$

To derive the last formula from the first, put $f(q) = r\sum k^{-1}\binom{k-1}{r-1}q^k$. Using II, (12.4), we find that $f'(q) = rq^{r-1}(1-q)^{-r}$. The assertion now follows by repeated integrations by part.

CHAPTER XI

1. $sP(s)$ and $P(s^2)$.

2. (a) $(1-s)^{-1}P(s)$; (b) $(1-s)^{-1}sP(s)$; (c) $\{1-sP(s)\}/(1-s)$; (d) $p_0 s^{-1} + \{1-s^{-1}P(s)\}/(1-s)$; (e) $\frac{1}{2}\{P(\sqrt{s}) + P(-\sqrt{s})\}$.

3. $U(s) = pqs^2/(1-ps)(1-qs)$. Expectation $= 1/pq$, $\text{Var} = (1-3pq)/p^2q^2$.

6. The generating function satisfies the quadratic equation $A(s) = A^2(s) + s$. Hence $A(s) = \frac{1}{2} - \frac{1}{2}\sqrt{1-4s}$ and $a_n = n^{-1}\binom{2n-2}{n-1}$.

10. (a) $\Phi^r(s)F^k(s)|p - q|$
(b) $\Phi^r(s)[1+F(s) + \cdots + F^k(s)]|p - q|$.

11. (a) $(q/p)^r\Phi^{2r}(s)$.
(b) $(q/p)^r\Phi^{2r}(s)U(s)$.

12. Using the generating function for the geometric distribution of $\mathbf{X}_v$ we have without computation

$$P_r(s) = s^r\left(\frac{N-1}{N-s}\right)\left(\frac{N-2}{N-2s}\right) \cdots \left(\frac{N-r+1}{N-(r-1)s}\right).$$

13. $P_r(s)\{N - (r-1)s\} = P_{r-1}(s)(N-r-1)s$.

14. $P_r(s) = \dfrac{s}{N-(N-1)s} \cdot \dfrac{2s}{N-(N-2)s} \cdots \dfrac{rs}{N-(N-r)s}$.

15. S_r is the sum of r independent variables with a common geometric distribution. Hence

$$P_r(s) = \left(\frac{q}{1-ps}\right)^r, \qquad p_{r,k} = q^r p^k\binom{r+k-1}{k}.$$

16. (a) $\mathbf{P}\{\mathbf{R} = r\} = \displaystyle\sum_{k=0}^{v-1}\mathbf{P}\{\mathbf{S}_{r-1} = k\}\mathbf{P}\{\mathbf{X}_r \geq v - k\} =$

$$= \sum_{k=0}^{v-1} q^{r-1}p^k\binom{r+k-2}{k}p^{v-k} = p^v q^{r-1}\binom{r+v-2}{v-1}.$$

$$E(\mathbf{R}) = 1 + \frac{qv}{p}, \qquad \text{Var}(\mathbf{R}) = \frac{vq}{p^2}.$$

(b) $(p_1p_2)^N \displaystyle\sum_{v=1}^{\infty}\binom{N+v-2}{v-1}^2 (q_1q_2)^{v-1}$.

17. Note that

$$1 + s + \cdots + s^{ab-1} = (1 + s + \cdots + s^{a-1})(1 + s^a + s^{2a} + \cdots + s^{(b-1)a}).$$

21. $u_n = q^n + \displaystyle\sum_{k=3}^{n}\binom{k-1}{2}p^3q^{k-3}u_{n-k}$ with $u_0 = 1$, $u_1 = q$, $u_2 = q^2$, $u_3 = p^3 + q^3$. Using the fact that this recurrence relation is of the convolution type,

$$U(s) = \frac{1}{1-qs} + \frac{(ps)^3}{(1-qs)^3} U(s).$$

22. $u_n = pw_{n-1} + qu_{n-1}$, $v_n = pu_{n-1} + qv_{n-1}$, $w_n = pv_{n-1} + qw_{n-1}$. Hence $U(s) - 1 = psW(s) + qsU(s)$; $V(s) = psU(s) + qs \cdot V(s)$; $W(s) = psV(s) + qsW(s)$.

CHAPTER XIII

1. It suffices to show that for all roots $s \neq 1$ of $F(s) = 1$ we have $|s| \geq 1$, and that $|s| = 1$ is possible only in the periodic case.

2. $u_{2n} = \left\{\binom{2n}{n} 2^{-2n}\right\}^r \sim 1/\sqrt{(\pi n)^r}$. Hence $\mathcal{E}$ is persistent only for $r = 2$.
For $r = 3$ the tangent rule for numerical integration gives

$$\sum_{n=1}^{\infty} u_{2n} \approx \frac{1}{\sqrt[3]{\pi}} \int_{\frac{1}{2}}^{\infty} \frac{1}{\sqrt[3]{x}} dx = \sqrt[3]{\frac{2}{\pi}} \approx \frac{1}{2}.$$

3. u_{6n} is comparable to $n^{-\frac{1}{6}}$, and $f \approx 0.022$.

5. $2F(s) = 1 - \sqrt{1 - 4p^2 q s^3}$.

6. From $\sum f_i + \mathbf{P}\{\mathbf{X}_1 > 0\} \leq 1$ conclude that $f < 1$ unless $\mathbf{P}\{\mathbf{X}_1 > 0\} = 0$. In this case all $\mathbf{X}_i < 0$ and $\mathcal{E}$ occurs at the first trial or never.

7. $\mathbf{Z}_n$ = smallest integer $\geq (\mathbf{N}_n - n)/r$. Furthermore $\mathbf{E}(\mathbf{Z}_n) \sim np/(q + pr)$, Var $(\mathbf{Z}_n) \sim npq(q + pr)^{-3}$.

8. $G(s) = \dfrac{(1 - qs)q^r s^r}{1 - s + pq^r s^{r+1}}$,

$\quad F(s) = qs + psG(s), \qquad \mu = q^{-r}$.

9. $G(s) = \dfrac{(1 - qs)B(qs)}{1 - s + psB(qs)}$,

and $F(s)$ as in problem 8.

11. $\mathbf{N}_n^* \approx (\mathbf{N}_n - 714.3)/22.75$; $\mathfrak{N}(\frac{2}{3}) - \mathfrak{N}(-\frac{2}{3}) \approx \frac{1}{2}$.

12. $r_n = r_{n-1} - \frac{1}{4}r_{n-2} + \frac{1}{8}r_{n-3}$ with $r_0 = r_1 = r_2 = 1$; $R(s) = (8 + 2s^2)(8 - 8s + 2s^2 - s^3)^{-1}$; $r_n \sim 1.444248(1.139680)^{-n-1}$.

14. If a_n is the probability that an A-run of length r occurs at the nth trial, then $A(s)$ is given by (7.5) with p replaced by α and q by $1 - \alpha$. Let $B(s)$ and $C(s)$ be the corresponding functions for B- and C-runs. The required generating functions are $F(s) = 1 - U^{-1}(s)$, where in case (a) $U(s) = A(s)$; in (b) $U(s) = A(s) + B(s) - 1$; in (c) $U(s) = A(s) + B(s) + C(s) - 2$.

15. Use a straightforward combination of the method in example (8.b) and problem 14.

16. Expected number for age k equals Npq^k.

18. $w_k(n) = v_{n-k}r_k$ when $n > k$ and $w_k(n) = \beta_{k-n}r_k/r_{k-n}$ when $n \leq k$.

19. Note that $1 - F(s) = (1 - s)Q(s)$ and $\mu - Q(s) = (1 - s)R(s)$, whence $Q(1) = \mu$, $2R(1) = \sigma^2 - \mu + \mu^2$. The power series for $Q^{-1}(s) = \sum (u_n - u_{n-1})s^n$ converges for $s = 1$.

CHAPTER XIV

1. $\dfrac{(q/p)^b - 1}{(q/p)^{a+b} - 1}$ if $p \neq q$, and $\dfrac{b}{a + b}$ if $p = q$.

3. When $q < p$, the number of visits is a defective variable.

4. The expected number of visits equals $p(1 - q_1)/qq_{a-1} = (p/q)^a$.

5. The probability of ruin is still given by (2.4) with $p = \alpha(1 - \gamma)^{-1}$, $q = \beta(1 - \gamma)^{-1}$. The expected duration of the game is $D_z(1 - \gamma)^{-1}$ with D_z given by (3.4) or (3.5).

6. The boundary conditions (2.2) are replaced by $q_0 - \delta q_1 = 1 - \delta$, $q_a = 0$. To (2.4) there corresponds the solution

$$q_z = \frac{\{(q/p)^a - (q/p)^z\}(1-\delta)}{(q/p)^a(1-\delta) + \delta q/p - 1}.$$

The boundary conditions (3.2) become $D_0 = \delta D_1$, $D_a = 0$.

7. To (2.1) there corresponds $q_2 = pq_{z+2} + qq_{z-1}$, and $q_z = y^z$ is a particular solution if $\lambda = p\lambda^3 + q$, that is, if $\lambda = 1$ or $\lambda^2 + \lambda = qp^{-1}$. The probability of ruin is

$$q_z = \begin{cases} 1 & \text{if } q \geq 2p \\ \left\{\sqrt{\dfrac{1}{4} + \dfrac{q}{p}} - \dfrac{1}{2}\right\}^z & \text{if } q \leq 2p. \end{cases}$$

10. $w_{z,n+1}(x) = pw_{z+1,n}(x) + qw_{z-1,n}(x)$ with the boundary conditions (1) $w_{0,n}(x) = w_{a,n}(x) = 0$ for $n \geq 1$; (2) $w_{z,0}(x) = 0$ for $z \neq x$ and $w_{x,0}(x) = 1$.

11. Replace (1) by $w_{0,n}(x) = w_{1,n}(x)$ and $w_{a,n}(x) = w_{a-1,n}(x)$.

12. Boundary condition: $u_{a,n} = u_{a-1,n}$. Generating function:

$$\frac{\lambda_1^z(s)\lambda_2^{a-\frac{1}{2}}(s) + \lambda_2^z(s)\lambda_1^{a-\frac{1}{2}}(s)}{\lambda_1^{a-\frac{1}{2}}(s) + \lambda_2^{a-\frac{1}{2}}(s)}.$$

18. $\mathbf{P}\{\mathbf{M}_n < z\} = \sum_{x=1}^{\infty} (v_{x-z,n} - v_{x+z,n})$

$\mathbf{P}\{\mathbf{M}_n = z\} = \mathbf{P}\{\mathbf{M}_n < z + 1\} - \mathbf{P}\{\mathbf{M}_n < z\}$.

19. The first passage through x must have occurred at $k \leq n$, and the particle returned from x in the following $n - k$ steps.

31. The relation (8.2) is replaced by

$$U_z(s) = s\sum_{x=1}^{a-1} U_x(s)p_{x-z} + sr_z.$$

The characteristic equation is $s \sum p_k \sigma^k = 1$.

CHAPTER XV

1. P has rows $(p, q, 0, 0)$, $(0, 0, p, q)$, $(p, q, 0, 0)$, and $(0, 0, p, q)$. For $n > 1$ the rows are (p^2, pq, pq, q^2).

2. (a) The chain is irreducible and ergodic; $p_{jk}^{(n)} \to \frac{1}{3}$ for all j, k. (Note that P is doubly stochastic.)

(b) The chain has period 3, with G_1 containing E_1 and E_2; the state E_4 forms G_2, and E_3 forms G_3. We have $u_1 = u_2 = \frac{1}{2}$, $u_3 = u_4 = 1$.

(c) The states E_1 and E_3 form a closed set S_1, and E_4, E_5 another closed set S_2, whereas E_2 is transient. The matrices corresponding to the closed sets are 2-by-2 matrices with elements $\frac{1}{2}$. Hence $p_{jk}^{(n)} \to \frac{1}{2}$ if E_j and E_k belong to the same S_r; $p_{j2}^{(n)} \to 0$; finally $p_{2k}^{(n)} \to \frac{1}{2}$ if $k = 1, 3$, and $p_{2k}^{(n)} \to 0$ if $k = 2, 4, 5$.

(d) The chain has period 3. Putting $a = (0, 0, 0, \frac{1}{3}, \frac{1}{3}, \frac{1}{3})$, $b = (1, 0, 0, 0, 0, 0)$, $c = (0, \frac{1}{2}, \frac{1}{2}, 0, 0, 0)$, we find that the rows of $P^2 = P^5 = \cdots$ are a, b, b, c, c, c, those of $P^3 = P^6 = \cdots$ are b, c, c, a, a, a, those of $P = P^4 = \cdots$ are c, a, a, b, b, b.

3. $p_{jj}^{(n)} = (j/6)^n$, $p_{jk}^{(n)} = (k/6)^n - ((k-1)/6)^n$ if $k > j$, and $p_{jk}^{(n)} = 0$ if $k < j$.

4. $x_k = (\frac{3}{4}, \frac{1}{2}, \frac{1}{4}, \frac{1}{2})$, $y_k = (\frac{1}{4}, \frac{1}{2}, \frac{3}{4}, \frac{1}{2})$.

6. For $n \geq j$

$$f_{j0}^{(n)} = \binom{n-1}{j-1} p^{n-j}q^j = \binom{-j}{n-j}(-p)^j q^j.$$

Generating function $(qs)^j(1 - ps)^{-j}$. Expectation $\mu_j = j/q$.

7. $f_{jj}^{(n)} = \sum_{k=1}^{n-1} v_k \binom{n-2}{k-1} p^{n-1-k}q^k.$

8. The even-numbered states form an irreducible closed set. The probability of a return to E_0 at or before the nth step equals

$$1 - v_0 + v_0(1-v_2) + v_0v_2(1-v_4) + \cdots + v_0v_2 \cdots v_{2n-2}(1-v_{2n}) =$$

$$= 1 - v_0v_2v_4 \cdots v_{2n}$$

Thus the even states are persistent if, and only if, the last product tends to 0. The probability that starting from E_{2r+1} the system remains forever among the odd (transient) states equals $v_{2r+1}v_{2r+3} \cdots$.

9. $u_r = [1 - p/q](p/q)^{r-1}[1 - (p/q)^p]^{-1}.$

10. Possible states $E_0, \ldots, E_w$. For $j > 0$

$$p_{j,j-1} = j(\rho - w + j)\rho^{-2}, \qquad p_{j,j+1} = (\rho - j)(w - j)\rho^{-2},$$

$$p_{jj} = j(w - j)\rho^{-2} + (\rho - j)(\rho - w + j)\rho^{-2}$$

$$u_k = \binom{w}{k}\binom{b}{\rho - k} \bigg/ \binom{2\rho}{\rho}.$$

13.
$$P = \begin{bmatrix} q & p & & & & 0 & 0 \\ 0 & 0 & 1 & & \cdots & 0 & 0 \\ 0 & 0 & 0 & 1 & \cdots & 0 & 0 \\ & & \cdots & \cdots & \cdots & & \\ 0 & 0 & 0 & 0 & \cdots & 0 & 1 \\ q & p & 0 & 0 & \cdots & 0 & 0 \end{bmatrix}.$$

14. Note that the matrix is doubly stochastic; use example (7.h).

15. Put $p_{k,k+1} = 1$ for $k = 1, \ldots, N - 1$, and $p_{Nk} = p_k$.

16. $\Sigma u_j p_{jk} = u_k$, then $U(s) = u_0(1-s)\{P(s) - s\}^{-1}$. For ergodicity it is necessary and sufficient that $P'(1) < 1$.

25. If $N \geq m - 2$, the variables $X^{(m)}$ and $X^{(n)}$ are independent, and hence the three rows of the matrix $p\,_{jk}^{(m,n)}$ are identical with the distribution of $\mathbf{X}^{(n)}$, namely $(\frac{1}{4}, \frac{1}{2}, \frac{1}{4})$. For $n = m + 1$ the three rows are $(\frac{1}{2}, \frac{1}{2}, 0)$, $(\frac{1}{4}, \frac{1}{2}, \frac{1}{4})$, $(0, \frac{1}{2}, \frac{1}{2})$.

CHAPTER XVII

3. $E(X) = ie^{\lambda t}$; $\quad \text{Var}(X) = ie^{\lambda t}(e^{\lambda t} - 1)$.

4. $P'_n = -\lambda n P_n + \lambda(n+1)P_{n+1}$.

$$P_n(t) = \binom{i}{n} e^{-i\lambda t}(e^{\lambda t} - 1)^{i-nt} \qquad (n \leq i).$$

$$E(X) = ie^{-\lambda t}; \qquad \text{Var}(X) = ie^{-\lambda t}(1 - e^{-\lambda t}).$$

5. $P'_n(t) = -(\lambda + n\mu)P_n(t) + \lambda P_{n-1}(t) + (n+1)\mu P_{n+1}(t)$ for $n \leq N - 1$ and $P'_N(t) = -N\mu P_N(t) + \lambda P_{N-1}(t)$.

19. The standard method of solving linear differential equations leads to a system of linear equations.

Index